Switching
Power Supply
Design

Other McGraw-Hill Books of Interest

Handbooks

AVALLONE AND BAUMEISTER • *Standard Handbook for Mechanical Engineers*

BENSON • *Audio Engineering Handbook*

BENSON • *Television Engineering Handbook*

BILLINGS • *Switchmode Power Supply Handbook*

COOMBS • *Printed Circuits Handbook*

DI GIACOMO • *VLSI Handbook*

FINK AND BEATY • *Standard Handbook for Electrical Engineers*

FINK AND CHRISTIANSEN • *Electronics Engineers' Handbook*

FLANAGAN • *Handbook of Transformer Applications*

HARPER • *Handbook of Electronic Packaging and Interconnection*

INGLIS • *Electronic Communications Handbook*

JOHNSON AND JASIK • *Antenna Engineering Handbook*

JURAN • *Quality Control Handbook*

KAUFMAN AND SEIDMAN • *Handbook of Electronics Calculations*

KAUFMAN AND SEIDMAN • *Handbook for Electronics Engineering Technicians*

STOUT AND KAUFMAN • *Handbook of Operational Amplifier Circuit Design*

WILLIAMS AND TAYLOR • *Electronic Filter Design Handbook*

Encyclopedias

CONCISE ENCYCLOPEDIA OF SCIENCE AND TECHNOLOGY

ENCYCLOPEDIA OF ELECTRONICS AND COMPUTERS

ENCYCLOPEDIA OF ENGINEERING

Dictionaries

DICTIONARY OF SCIENTIFIC AND TECHNICAL TERMS

DICTIONARY OF ELECTRICAL AND ELECTRONIC ENGINEERING

DICTIONARY OF ENGINEERING

Other

ANTOGNETTI • *Power Integrated Circuits*

CHRYSSIS • *High-Frequency Switching Power Supplies*

GROSSNER • *Transformers in Electronic Circuits*

MITCHELL • *DC/DC Switching Regulator Analysis*

ROMBAUT • *Power Electronic Converters: AC/AC Conversion*

SEGUIER • *Power Electronic Converters: AC/DC Conversion*

Switching Power Supply Design

Abraham I. Pressman
President, Switchtronix Power, Inc.
Waban, Massachusetts

McGraw-Hill, Inc.
New York   San Francisco   Washington, D.C.   Auckland   Bogotá
Caracas   Lisbon   London   Madrid   Mexico City   Milan
Montreal   New Delhi   San Juan   Singapore
Sydney   Tokyo   Toronto

Library of Congress Cataloging-in-Publication Data

Pressman, Abraham I.
    Switching power supply design / Abraham I. Pressman.
        p.   cm.
    Includes bibliographical references and index.
    ISBN 0-07-050806-2
    1. Electronic apparatus and appliances—Power supply.
    2. Microelectronics—Power supply.   3. Electric current converters.
    I. Title.
    TK7868.P6P75   1991
    621.381'044—dc20   91-3261
                                                                  CIP

    3 4 5 6 7 8 9 0   DOC/DOC 9 7 6 5 4 3

ISBN   0-07-050806-2

*The sponsoring editor for this book was Daniel A. Gonneau, the
editing supervisor was Joseph Bertuna, and the production supervisor
was Pamela A. Pelton. It was set in Century Schoolbook by
McGraw-Hill's Professional Book Group composition unit.*

Printed and bound by R. R. Donnelley & Sons Company.

To my wife Annie

Contents

Part 2   Magnetics and Circuits Designs

Part 3   Typical Switching Power Supply Waveforms

Preface

Much has changed in the power conversion field since the author's previous book on switching power supply design (*Switching and Linear Power Supply, Power Converter Design*, 1978).

The main goal of these changes has been to make the power supply smaller. As integrated circuits packed more features in a smaller volume, it became essential also to decrease the size of a system's power supply. Switching power supply packing density currently ranges from 2 to 6 load watts per cubic inch (W/in^3) as compared to about 1 W/in^3 a decade ago. Newer resonant converter techniques offer a possibility of 20 to 40 W/in^3.

Higher switching frequencies, made possible by power MOSFET transistors, newer topologies, and integrated-circuit pulse-width-modulating chips, which pack more control and supervisory features in a smaller volume, have contributed to making present-day power supplies smaller. All these new technologies are covered in this book.

It has been the author's experience, in teaching a course on modern switching power supply design to all levels of engineers from most of the major American electronics companies, that those who have a good understanding of the fundamental principles can easily solve their day-to-day design problems as well as assess and adapt to new technologies.

Thus, this book covers the new technologies in a tutorial way so that the reader can understand the fundamental reasons for various effects. Explanations for various significant waveshapes and explanations for alternative design decisions are given. Care has been taken to avoid offering "handy-dandy" design equations without showing how they were derived. All equations that effect a design decision are derived from fundamental relations.

Magnetics design is emphasized; for, the majority of power supply designers are primarily circuits-oriented. They appreciate and can analyze problems when they can see DC voltage levels, voltage spikes, and waveshapes on an oscilloscope. But the locus of operation on a *BH* loop cannot be seen on an oscilloscope. Thus, circuits designers too often shy away from or do not fully understand magnetics design. They leave that to a magnetics specialist who may not appreciate how circuits characteristics effect magnetics design decisions. It is hoped the emphasis on magnetics herein may help correct that problem.

Throughout this text and throughout the literature, idealized voltage-current waveforms are often shown. But I feel it is very valuable from a tutorial viewpoint to view actual Polaroid waveforms taken at critical points on working circuits. Seeing an actual photographed waveform with its spikes, rings, and oddities conveys a great deal more information and confidence about a circuit than does an idealized, hand-drawn waveform. Such photographed waveforms are presented at critical points at various frequencies on some of the most commonly used topologies.

This book is directed primarily to design engineers and engineering students at the undergraduate and graduate level. It may also be of significant value to people who are not directly involved in start-from-scratch designs, and whose main interest is power supply design analysis, design review, test, and debugging.

The material contained herein is a consolidation and, hopefully, a simpler, clearer explanation and logical reorganization of the highpoints of all the proven and practical aspects of modern switching power supply technology. As such, credit for the material belongs to the innumerable engineers, designers in industry, and universities that have brought switching power supply technology to its present advanced state.

Abraham I. Pressman

Topologies

Fundamental Switching Regulators—Buck, Boost, and Inverter Topologies

1.1 Introduction

There are about 14 basic topologies (basic block diagrams) commonly used to implement a switching power supply. Each topology has unique properties which make it best suited for certain applications.

Some are best used for AC/DC off-line converters at low (<200 W) output power, some at higher output power. Some are a better choice for high AC input voltages (≥220 V AC); some are better for an AC input of 120 V or less. Some have advantages for higher DC output voltages (> ~ 200 V) or in applications where there are more than four or five different output voltages. Some have a lower parts count than do others for the same output power or offer a better tradeoff in parts count versus reliability. Lesser input or output ripple and noise is a frequent factor in a topology selection.

Similarly, some topologies are better used for DC/DC converters—again with high and low output power, high or low output voltages, and minimum parts count as significant selection criteria. Further, some topologies have inherent design drawbacks which require additional circuitry or more complex circuitry, not completely analyzable in various worst-case situations.

Thus to make the best choice of a topology, it is essential to be familiar with the merits, drawbacks, and areas of usage of all topologies. A poor choice of a topology can doom a new power supply design at the very outset.

In this chapter, the schematics of the fundamental and earliest topologies—the buck, boost, and polarity inverter—are described. Their basic operation is described; critical waveforms are shown and explained; and merits, drawbacks, and application areas are discussed. Peak transistor current and voltage stresses versus output power and input voltage and their tolerances are discussed. The dependence of input current on output power and input voltage is shown. Efficiency and DC and AC switching losses are discussed.

To show the origin and need for switching regulators, the discussion starts with what preceded them—linear or *series-pass* regulators.

1.2   Linear Regulators—Switching Regulator Ancestors

1.2.1   Basic operation—merits and drawbacks

The basic circuit is shown in Fig. l.la. It consists of an electrically variable resistance in the form of a transistor (operating in the linear mode) in series with the output load. An error amplifier senses the DC output voltage via a sampling resistor network $R1$, $R2$ and compares it with a reference voltage V_{ref}. The error amplifier output voltage drives the base of the series-pass power transistor via a current amplifier.

The phasing is such that if the DC output voltage goes up (as a result of either an increase in input voltage or a decrease in output load

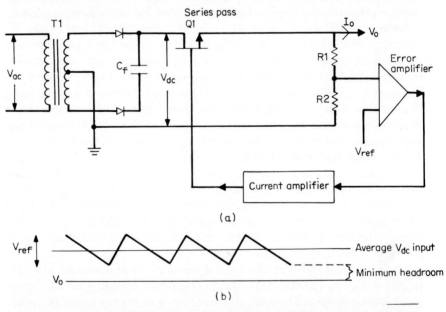

(a)

(b)

Figure 1.1   (*a*) Linear regulator $Q1$ in series with output load is an electrically variable resistance. The negative-feedback loop alters its resistance to keep V_o constant. (*b*) Headroom in linear regulator. With an NPN series pass transistor, a minimum input-output differential or headroom of 2.5 V between V_o and the bottom of the input ripple triangle must exist at minimum V_{ac} input.

current), the base of the series-pass transistor (assuming an NPN transistor) goes down. This increases the resistance of the series-pass element and hence brings the output voltage back down so that sampled output equals the reference voltage. This negative-feedback loop works in a similar fashion for decreases in output voltage due to a drop in input voltage or an increase in output load current. In that case, the error output voltage moves the series-pass base slightly more positive, decreases its collector-to-emitter resistance, and raises the DC output voltage so that the sampled output again equals the reference.

Essentially, any change in input voltage—due to either AC input line voltage ripple, steady-state changes in the input over its tolerance band, or dynamic changes resulting from rapid load changes—is absorbed across the series-pass element leaving the output voltage constant to an extent determined by the gain in the open-loop feedback amplifier.

The feedback loop is entirely DC-coupled. There are no elements switching on and off and within the loop; all DC voltage levels are predictable and calculable. There are no transformers within the loop and no fast-rise-time voltage or current spikes to cause RFI noise output. With no transistors switching on and off, there are no AC switching losses due to momentary overlap of falling current and rising voltage across the transistors. All power losses are due to DC currents in and DC voltages across the various elements, and these are easily calculable.

1.2.2 Linear regulator drawbacks

This simple, DC-coupled series pass regulator was the basis for a multi-billion-dollar power supply industry until the early 1960s or so. It could produce only lower voltage from a higher one; its output voltage always had one end DC common with the input voltage, yet frequently DC isolation between input and output was required.

The raw DC input voltage (V_{dc} in Fig.1.1a) was usually derived from the rectified secondary of a 60-Hz transformer whose weight and volume was often a serious system constraint.

1.2.3 Power dissipation in the series-pass transistor

The major drawback of a linear regulator is mainly the excessive dissipation in the series-pass element. Since all the load current must pass through the pass transistor, its dissipation is $(V_{dc} - V_o)(I_o)$. The minimum differential ($V_{dc} - V_o$), which is often referred to as "headroom," in most cases is 2.5 V for NPN pass transistors.

Now when the raw DC input comes from the rectified secondary of a 60-Hz transformer, the secondary turns can always be chosen so that the rectified secondary voltage is V_o + 2.5 V (assume for the moment that the filter capacitor is large enough to yield insignificant ripple) when the input AC is at its low tolerance limit. But when the input AC voltage is at its high tolerance limit, the headroom will be much greater, series-pass element dissipation will be greater, and the power supply efficiency will be significantly lower. This effect of very poor efficiency at high tolerance limit input voltage when the raw DC input has been chosen for a minimum 2.5 V headroom at lowest DC input is much more pronounced at lower output voltages.

This can be seen dramatically in the following three examples of linear regulators: the first with an output of 5 V at 10 A, the second with an output of 15 V at 10 A, and a third at 30 V at 10 A.

Assume a large secondary filter capacitor so that ripple input to the regulator is negligible. The rectified secondary voltage DC voltage tolerances will be identical to the AC input tolerances, which are assumed to be ±15 percent. The transformer secondary voltages will be chosen to yield V_o + 2.5 V when the AC input is at its low tolerance limit of − 15 percent. Then the maximum DC input is 1.30 (V_o + 2.5) V when the AC input is at its maximum tolerance limit of +15 percent. Thus

V_o	I_o, A	$V_{dc(min)}$, V	$V_{dc(max)}$, V	Head-room, max, V	$P_{in(max)}$, W	$P_{o(max)}$, W	Dissi-pation $Q1_{max}$	Effi-ciency, % $P_o/P_{in(max)}$
5.0	10	7.5	9.75	4.75	97.5	50.0	47.5	51.25
15.0	10	17.5	22.8	7.75	228	150	78.0	65.9
30.0	10	32.5	42.25	12.25	423	300	123	71.0

It thus can be seen that at higher DC output voltages, the efficiency is significantly higher than at lower voltages. When realistic input line ripple voltages are assumed, efficiency for 5-V output for input line tolerances of ±15 percent are in the range 32 to 35 percent.

1.2.4   Linear regulator efficiency versus output voltage

When ripple is taken into account, the minimum headroom of 2.5 V must be guaranteed at the bottom of the ripple triangle at the low tolerance limit of the input AC voltage as shown in Fig. 1.1b. Regulator efficiency is then calculated as follows for various assumed input AC tolerances and output voltages.

Assume an input voltage tolerance of ±T percent about its nominal. Transformer secondary turns will be selected so that the voltage at the bottom of the ripple triangle will be 2.5 V above the desired output voltage (2.5 V minimum headroom) when the AC input is at its low tolerance limit. For a peak-to-peak ripple voltage of V_r volts, the average or DC voltage at the input to the pass transistor is $(V_o + 2.5 + V_r/2)$ volts when the input AC is at its low tolerance limit as can be seen in Fig. 1.1b. But when the AC input is at its high tolerance limit, the DC voltage at the input to the series-pass element is

$$V_{dc(max)} = \frac{1 + 0.01T}{1 - 0.01T}(V_o + 2.5 + V_r/2)$$

The maximum achievable efficiency, which occurs at maximum input voltage and hence maximum input power, is

$$\text{Efficiency}_{max} = \frac{P_o}{P_{in(max)}} = \frac{V_o I_o}{V_{dc(max)} I_o} = \frac{V_o}{V_{dc(max)}} \qquad (1.1)$$

$$= \frac{1 - 0.01T}{1 + 0.01T}\left(\frac{V_o}{V_o + 2.5 + V_r/2}\right) \qquad (1.2)$$

This is plotted in Fig. 1.2 for an assumed peak-to-peak (p/p) ripple voltage of 8 V (it will later be shown that in a 60-Hz full-wave recti-

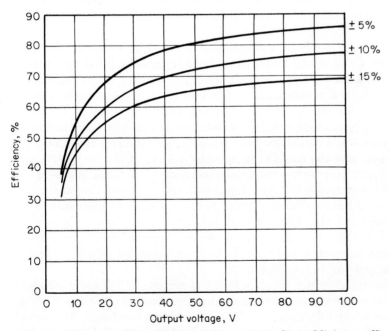

Figure 1.2 Linear regulator efficiency versus output voltage. Minimum efficiency at maximum V_{ac} input assuming 2.5 V headroom at bottom of ripple triangle at minimum V_{ac} input. Assumes 8 V peak-to-peak ripple at top of filter capacitor. (*From Eq. 1.2*)

fier, the p/p ripple voltage is 8 V if the filter capacitor is chosen at the rate of 1000 microfarads per ampere of DC load current).

It can be seen in Fig. 1.2 that even for 10-V outputs, efficiency is under 50 percent for reasonable AC line tolerance of ± 10 percent. It is this poor efficiency and the weight and size of the 60-Hz input transformer which led to the revolution of switching power supplies.

Nevertheless, if a preregulated (to ± 5 percent or so) raw DC input is available (as frequently is the case in some of the later configurations to be shown), a linear regulator is a reasonable choice if still better regulation is required. Complete integrated-circuit linear regulators are available up to 1.5 A output in single plastic packages at prices in the 50¢ range. They are also available at 3 to 5 A in metal-case integrated-circuit packages at higher prices, but the dissipation across the internal series-pass transistor becomes a serious problem, especially at the 5-A output level and higher.

1.2.5   Linear regulators with PNP series-pass transistors for lesser required headroom

Linear regulators using PNP transistors as the series-pass element can operate with a minimum headroom down to 1 or even 0.5 V and hence achieve better efficiency. The reason for this can be seen in Fig. 1.3.

With an NPN series-pass element as in Fig. 1.3a, base current must be inward directed and hence must come from some point at a potential higher than $V_o + V_{be}$ or roughly ($V_o + 1$) volts. If the base drive comes through a resistor, the input end of that resistor must come from a point higher than $V_o + 1$ to force current through it. The least expensive scheme is to supply the base current resistor from the same point which feeds the series-pass collector, i.e., the raw DC input.

However, now the raw DC input—the bottom of the ripple triangle at low input tolerance—cannot be permitted to come too close to $V_o + 1$ V—nominally the base input voltage. For then, the base resistor R_b would have to be very small to allow sufficient base current at high output current. Then at high input tolerance, when $V_{dc} - V_o$ is much greater, R_b would deliver an excessive current to the base and a significant amount would have to be diverted away into the current amplifier, adding to its dissipation.

It is this effect which dictates that the minimum voltage at the bottom of the ripple triangle not be required to come to less than 2.5 V at minimum input tolerance, i.e., 2.5-V minimum headroom. It renders R_b more of a constant-current resistor and results in relatively constant current through R_b over the range of input voltage tolerances.

With a PNP series-pass transistor (as in Fig. 1.3b), however, this problem does not exist. For drive current is outward-directed (sinked)

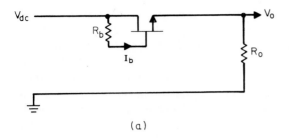

(a)

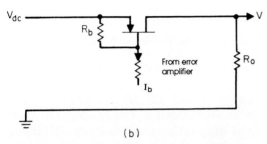

(b)

Figure 1.3 (a) Linear regulator with an NPN series pass transistor. If base drive is taken from V_{dc} via a resistor R_b, a minimum voltage or headroom must exist across R_b to supply inward-directed base current at the bottom of the input ripple triangle. (b) Linear regulator with a PNP series pass transistor. With a PNP series pass transistor, the required base current does not come from V_{dc} but flows outward from the base to the current amplifier; V_{dc} is no longer restricted to a minimum of 2.5 V above V_o. Headroom of 1.0 to 0.5 V is possible.

from the base and is supplied from the current amplifier. Nothing dictates how close V_{dc} may get to V_o except the knee of the I_c versus V_{ce} characteristic of the pass transistor. Minimum headroom with a PNP pass transistor thus can be as low as 1.0 or 0.5 V and low dissipation and higher efficiency results.

Integrated-circuit linear regulators with PNP for transistors are now available but are considerably more expensive. In the fabrication technique of integrated circuits, it is more difficult to make a high-current PNP transistor on the same chip as the lower-current NPN control transistors.

1.3 "Buck" Switching Regulator Topology

1.3.1 Basic operation

The high dissipation across the series-pass transistor in a linear regulator made the use of the linear regulator prohibitive for output currents over 5 A or so. The high dissipation required large-volume heat sinks. This and the large volume and weight of the input 60-Hz transformer rendered the power supply disproportionately large as integrated circuits made the rest of an electronic system smaller. Linear regulators, with their large input transformer and heat sinks, could achieve output load power densities of only 0.2 to 0.3 W/in^3, and this was not good enough for the smaller systems made possible by integrated circuits.

Alternatives to linear regulators started being widely used in the early 1960s. These so-called switching regulators used a fast-operating transistor switch to switch a DC input voltage through to the output at an adjustable duty cycle. By varying the duty cycle, the average DC voltage delivered to the output could be controlled. Such "average" voltage consisted of rectangular voltage pulses of adjustable width whose average value was the required DC output voltage (Fig. 1.4*b*).

With the use of appropriately chosen *LC* filters, however, the square-wave modulation could be eliminated and ripple-free DC voltages equal to the average of the duty-cycle-modulated raw DC input resulted. By sensing the DC output and controlling the switch duty cycle in a negative-feedback loop, the DC output could be regulated against input line and output load changes.

Such switching regulators are currently achieving 1 to 4 load watts per cubic inch and are capable of generating a multiplicity of output voltages from a single input—all DC isolated from the input. They require no input 50/60-Hz power transformers. Some DC/DC converter designers are claiming load power densities of 40 to 50 W/in^3.

The earliest of these switching regulators, the "buck" regulator, is shown in Fig. 1.4. There, a single-pole single-throw switch in the form of a transistor $Q1$, is in series with the DC input V_{dc}. It is closed for a time T_{on} out of the switching period T. When it is on, the voltage at $V1$ is V_{dc} (assuming for the moment the "on" drop across $Q1$ is zero). When it is open, the voltage at $V1$ falls very rapidly to ground and would have gone dangerously negative had it not been caught and held at ground by the so-called free-wheeling or clamp diode $D1$.

Assume for the moment that the "on" drop of diode $D1$ is zero also. Then the voltage at $V1$ (Fig. 1.4*b*) is rectangular, ranging between V_{dc} and ground with a "high" time of T_{on}. The average or DC value of this voltage is $V_{dc}T_{on}/T$. The L_oC_o filter is added in series between $V1$ and V_o and yields a clean, ripple-free DC voltage at V_o whose magnitude is $V_{dc}T_{on}/T$.

Now V_o is sensed by sampling resistors $R1$, $R2$ and compared to a reference voltage V_{ref} in the error amplifier (EA). The amplified DC

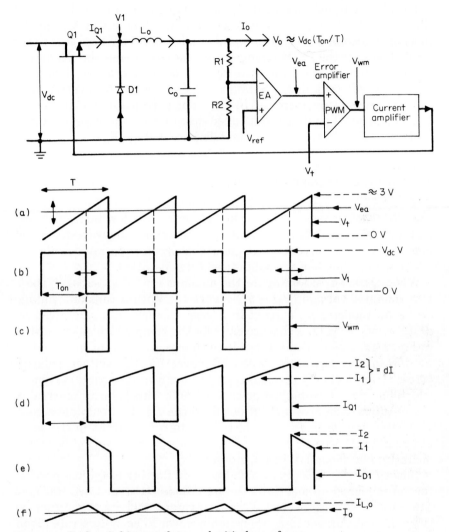

Figure 1.4   Buck switching regulator and critical waveforms.

error voltage V_{ea} is fed to a pulse-width-modulator (PWM) which is essentially a voltage comparator. Another input to the PWM is a sawtooth (Fig. 1.4a) of period T and usually 3 V in amplitude (V_t). The PWM voltage comparator generates a rectangular waveform (V_{wm}, Fig. 1.4c) which goes high at the start of the triangle and low at the instant the triangle crosses the DC voltage level of the error-amplifier output. The PWM output pulse width T_{on} is thus proportional to the EA amplifier output DC voltage level.

The PWM output pulse is fed to a current amplifier and used to control the "on" time of switch transistor $Q1$ in a negative-feedback loop. The phasing is such that if V_{dc} goes slightly high, the EA DC level goes closer to the botom of the PWM triangle, the triangle crosses the EA output level earlier in time and the $Q1$ on time decreases, bringing $V_o (= V_{dc}T_{on}/T)$ back down. Similarly, if V_{dc} goes low by a certain percentage, the on time increases by the same percentage to maintain V_o constant. The $Q1$ on time is controlled so as to make the sampled output $V_o R_2/(R_1 + R_2)$ always equal to the reference voltage V_{ref}.

1.3.2 Significant current waveforms in buck regulator

The major advantage of the buck regulator is its low internal losses and high efficiency. It is necessary to understand the waveshape and magnitude of the currents throughout the circuit to permit calculating efficiency and some of the subtleties of its operation.

When $Q1$ is on, assuming for the moment zero drop across it, there is a constant voltage $(V_{dc} - V_o)$ across L_o. With a constant voltage across an inductor L_o, current in it rises linearly at a rate given by $dI/dT = (V_{dc} - V_o)/L_o$. This accounts for the ramp which sits on a step in Fig. 1.4d. Now it is not possible to change the current in an inductor instantaneously. Thus when $Q1$ turns off, the voltage polarity across L_o immediately reverses trying to maintain the same current I_2 which had been flowing just prior to turnoff. This polarity reversal is the so-called inductive kick. If not for diode $D1$, V_1 would have gone very far negative in an attempt to maintain L_o current in the same direction. But diode $D1$ latches in and holds the front end of L_o at one diode drop or about 1 V below ground.

Now the same current I_2 which had been flowing in $Q1$ just prior to turnoff is picked up and flows through diode $D1$ (Fig. 1.4e). But now the voltage polarity across L_o has reversed and its magnitude is $(V_o + 1)$. The current in L_o then ramps down linearly at a rate given by $dI/dT = (V_o + 1)/L_o$. This is the downward-going ramp which sits on a step in Fig. 1.4e. At the end of the $Q1$ off time, the L_o current has fallen to I_1 and is still flowing through $D1$. Now $Q1$ turns on again and starts supplying current into the cathode of $D1$, displacing its forward current. When $Q1$ current has risen to I_1, all the forward $D1$ current has been displaced and V_1 rises to within about 1 V below V_{dc} back-biasing $D1$.

The current in L_o is then the sum of the $Q1$ current when it is on (Fig. 1.4d) and the $D1$ current when $Q1$ is off. This is the current $I(L_o)$ in Fig. 1.4f. It is seen to ramp an amount $(I_2 - I_1)$ around the DC output current I_o. Thus the value of the current at the center of the ramp in Fig. 1.4d and 1.4e is simply the DC output current I_o. As the DC output current I_o is varied, the center of the ramps in either Fig. 1.4d or e moves, but the slope of the ramps remain parallel to their original value. During the $Q1$ on time the ramp rate in L_o is still $(V_{dc} - V_o)/L_o$, and during the $Q1$ off time it is $(V_o + 1)/L_o$.

It will be seen shortly that when the DC current I_o is reduced to the point where I_1 in Fig. 1.4d and 1.4e just reaches zero, a drastic change occurs; but this will be discussed shortly.

1.3.3 Buck regulator efficiency neglecting AC switching losses

With the currents in the switch transistor $Q1$ and free-wheeling diode $D1$ (Fig. 1.4d and 1.4e), losses and efficiency can be calculated. If the preceding currents flowed through $Q1$ and $D1$ at zero voltage drop, total losses would be zero and efficiency would be 100 percent. When $Q1$ is off, it operates at a maximum voltage of V_{dc} but at zero current and hence dissipates no power. When $Q1$ is on, $D1$ operates at a reverse voltage of V_{dc} and draws negligible current and also dissipates no power.

Thus the only losses in the circuit are the DC conduction losses in $Q1$ and $D1$ plus the AC switching losses in $Q1$. There is an AC switching loss in $Q1$ during the turnon transition as a result of the momentary overlap of rising current and falling voltage across it. Also at the turnoff transition, there is an AC switching loss in $Q1$ due to the momentary overlap of falling current and rising voltage across it.

It can be seen in Fig. 1.4d and 1.4e that the average currents in $Q1$ and $D1$ during their conduction times of T_{on} and T_{off} are the values at the center of the ramps or I_o, the DC output current. These currents flow at a forward voltage of about 1 V over a very large range of currents. Thus conduction losses are

$$P_{dc} = L(Q1) + L(D1) = 1I_o \frac{T_{on}}{T} + 1I_o \frac{T_{off}}{T} = 1I_o$$

Thus if AC switching losses could be neglected, efficiency would be

$$\text{Efficiency} = \frac{P_o}{P_o + \text{losses}} = \frac{V_o I_o}{V_o I_o + 1I_o} = \frac{V_o}{V_o + 1} \qquad (1.3)$$

1.3.4 Buck regulator efficiency including AC switching losses

Alternating-current switching or voltage/current overlap loss calculations depend on the scenario assumed in the relative timing and slopes of the rising current and falling voltage. A best-case scenario—which rarely exists in actual cases—is shown in Fig. 1.5a.

Here in the best-case scenario, at turnon, voltage and current start moving simultaneously and reach their endpoints simultaneously. Current goes from 0 to I_o and voltage across $Q1$ goes from a maximum of V_{dc} to zero. The average power during this switching time is $P(T_{on}) = \int_0^{T_{on}} IV\, dt = I_o V_{dc}/6$ and the power averaged over one complete period is $(I_o V_{dc}/6)(T_{on}/T)$.

Assuming the same scenario of simultaneous starting and ending points of the current fall and voltage rise waveforms at the turnoff transition, voltage/current overlap dissipation at this transition is given by $P(T_{off}) = \int_0^{T_{off}} IV\, dt = I_o V_{dc}/6$, and this power averaged over one complete cycle is $(I_o V_{dc}/6)(T_{off}/T)$.

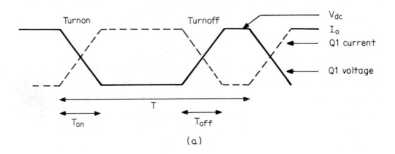

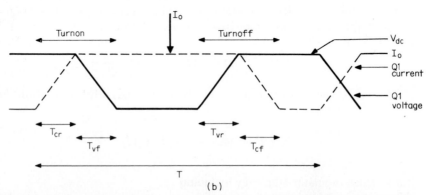

Figure 1.5 (a) Transistor switching—best-case scenario. Voltage and current transitions start and end simultaneously. (b) Transistor switching—worst-case scenario. At turnon, voltage remains constant at $V_{dc(max)}$ until current reaches its maximum. At turnoff, current remains constant at I_o until $Q1$ voltage reaches its maximum of V_{dc}.

Assuming $T_{on} = T_{off} = T_s$, total switching losses (the sum of turnoff and turnon losses) are $P_{ac} = (V_{dc}I_oT_s)/3T$ and efficiency is

$$\text{Efficiency} = \frac{P_o}{P_o + \text{DC losses} + \text{AC losses}}$$

$$= \frac{V_oI_o}{V_oI_o + 1I_o + V_{dc}I_oT_s/3T} \qquad (1.4)$$

$$= \frac{V_o}{V_o + 1 + V_{dc}T_s/3T}$$

It is of interest to calculate the efficiency of a buck regulator and compare it to that of a linear regulator. Assume bucking down from 48 to 5 V, 50-kHz switching frequency ($T = 20$ μs).

If there were no AC switching losses and a switching time T_s of 0.3 μs were assumed, Eq. 1.3 would give

$$\text{Efficiency} = \frac{5}{5+1} = 83.3\%$$

If switching losses and the best-case scenario as shown in Fig. 1.5a were assumed, Eq. 1.4 would give for $T_s = 0.3$ μs and $T = 20$ μs:

$$\text{Efficiency} = \frac{5}{5 + 1 + 48 \times 0.3/3 \times 20}$$

$$= \frac{5}{5 + 1 + 0.24} = \frac{5}{5 + 1.24}$$

$$= 80.1\%$$

If a worst-case scenario—as shown in Fig. 1.5b, which is closer to reality—is assumed, efficiencies are lower. In Fig. 1.5b, it is assumed that at turnon, the voltage across the transistor remains at its maximum value (V_{dc}) until the on-turning current reaches its maximum value of I_o. Then voltage starts falling, and to a close approximation, current rise time T_{cr} will equal voltage fall time. Turnon switching losses will then be

$$P(T_{on}) = \frac{V_{dc}I_o}{2}\frac{T_{cr}}{T} + \frac{I_oV_{dc}}{2}\frac{T_{vf}}{T}$$

and for $T_{cr} = T_{vf} = T_s$, $P(T_{on}) = V_{dc}I_o(T_s/T)$.

At turnoff as seen in Fig. 1.5b, it is assumed that current hangs on at its maximum value I_o until the voltage has risen to its maximum value of V_{dc} in a time T_{vr}. Then current starts falling and reaches zero in a time T_{cf}. Total turnoff dissipation is then

$$P(T_{\text{off}}) = \frac{I_o V_{\text{dc}}}{2} \frac{T_{\text{vr}}}{T} + \frac{V_{\text{dc}} I_o}{2} \frac{T_{\text{cf}}}{T}$$

and for $T_{\text{vr}} = T_{\text{cf}} = T_s$, $P(T_{\text{off}}) = V_{\text{dc}} I_o (T_s/T)$. Total AC losses (the sum of turnon plus turnoff losses) are then

$$P_{\text{ac}} = 2 V_{\text{dc}} I_o \frac{T_s}{T} \qquad (1.5)$$

Total losses (the sum of DC plus AC losses) are

$$P_t = P_{\text{dc}} + P_{\text{ac}} = 1 I_o + 2 V_{\text{dc}} I_o \frac{T_s}{T} \qquad (1.6)$$

and efficiency is

$$\text{Efficiency} = \frac{P_o}{P_o + P_t} = \frac{V_o I_o}{V_o I_o + 1 I_o + 2 V_{\text{dc}} I_o T_s/T}$$

$$= \frac{V_o}{V_o + 1 + 2 V_{\text{dc}} T_s/T} \qquad (1.7)$$

For the same 50-kHz, 48- to 5-V buck regulator as above with $T_s = 0.3$ μs, efficiency from Eq. 1.7 is

$$\text{Efficiency} = \frac{5}{5 + 1 + 2 \times 48 \times 0.3/20} = \frac{5}{5 + 1 + 1.44}$$

$$= \frac{5}{5 + 2.44}$$

$$= 67.2\%$$

If a linear regulator were used to bring 48 V down to 5 V, its efficiency which is $V_o/V_{\text{dc(max)}}$, would be unacceptably lower at 5/48 = 10.4 percent (from Eq. 1.1).

1.3.5 Optimum switching frequency in buck regulator

The output voltage of the buck regulator is $V_o = V_{\text{dc}} T_{\text{on}}/T$ independent of whatever the period T is. The question arises as to whether there is an optimum period and on what basis the period is selected. At first thought it might seem best to minimize the size of the filter components L_o, C_o by going to as high a frequency as possible.

However, going to higher frequencies does not necessarily minimize the overall size of the regulator when all factors are considered. This can be appreciated by examining the expression for the AC losses in the circuit seen in Eq. 1.5, where the AC losses are inversely proportional to the switching period T. Decreasing T results in increased losses and possibly necessitates the use of a larger-volume heat sink to keep the switching transistor temperature within desired limits.

Further, Eq. 1.5 gives losses in the switching transistor alone and neglects losses in the free-wheeling diode $D1$ due to its finite reverse recovery time. This time is the time required for the diode to cease drawing reverse leakage current measured from the instant it has been subjected to reverse voltage. Free-wheeling diodes as $D1$ should be specified as ultra-fast recovery types which have recovery times as low as 35 to 50 ns. But even such types can dissipate significant power which is inversely proportional to the switching period. Thus increasing switching frequency (decreasing switching period) does decrease size of the filter elements L_oC_o but adds to the total losses and contributes to the requirement for a larger heat sink.

In general, then, between 25 and 50 kHz, overall volume of the buck regulator is lower at a higher frequency. But going to frequencies above 50 kHz offers only marginal advantages because of the increased AC switching losses and possibly larger heat sink.

1.3.6 Design relations—output filter inductor selection

Current waveform of the output inductor is shown in Fig. 1.4d and its characteristic "ramp-on-a-step" shape is defined in Sec. 1.3.2, where it was noted that the current at the center of the ramp is equal to the DC output current I_o. As the DC output current decreases, the slope of the ramp remains constant as the voltage across L_o remains constant. But the current at the center of the ramp decreases. At a DC current of $I_o = (I_2 - I_1)/2$ or half the magnitude of the ramp slope dI, the front end of the ramp reaches zero. At this point, the inductor is said to "run dry" or enter into the "discontinuous" operating mode and a drastic change occurs in the current and voltage waveforms.

The effect of operation in the discontinuous mode can be seen in Fig. 1.6a. These are the inductor or switch transistor on time current waveforms of a 20- to 5-V buck regulator operating at 25 kHz designed for a nominal output current of 5 A and a minimum current of 1 A. The top two waveforms have the characteristic ramp-on-a-step waveshape with the step smaller in amplitude at the lower current and the DC current level at the center of the ramp very closely equal to the DC output current.

In the third waveform in Fig. 1.6a at $I_o = 0.95$ A, the step has just disappeared and the front end of the ramp starts at zero current. This is the start of the discontinuous or "run-dry" mode for the inductor. It can be seen in the first three waveforms, the $Q1$ on time is constant

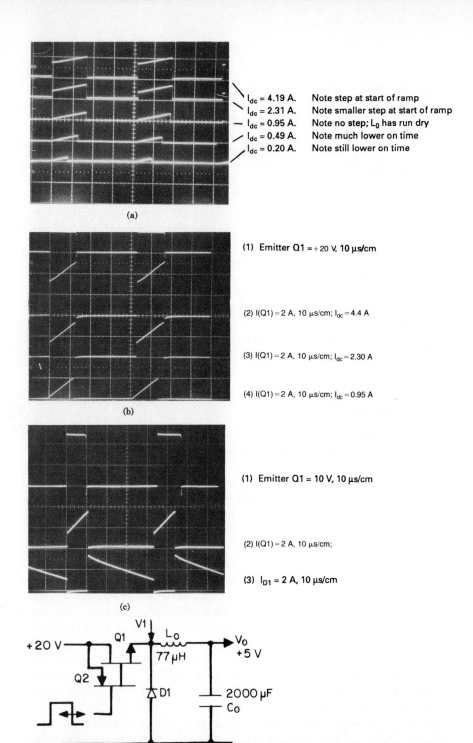

(a)

I_{dc} = 4.19 A.   Note step at start of ramp
I_{dc} = 2.31 A.   Note smaller step at start of ramp
I_{dc} = 0.95 A.   Note no step; L_0 has run dry
I_{dc} = 0.49 A.   Note much lower on time
I_{dc} = 0.20 A.   Note still lower on time

(1) Emitter Q1 = +20 V, 10 µs/cm

(2) I(Q1) = 2 A, 10 µs/cm; I_{dc} = 4.4 A

(3) I(Q1) = 2 A, 10 µs/cm; I_{dc} = 2.30 A

(4) I(Q1) = 2 A, 10 µs/cm; I_{dc} = 0.95 A

(b)

(1) Emitter Q1 = 10 V, 10 µs/cm

(2) I(Q1) = 2 A, 10 µs/cm;

(3) I_{D1} = 2 A, 10 µs/cm

(c)

Figure 1.6 A 25-kHz buck regulator, showing the effect of the output inductor L_o running dry or moving from the continuous mode to the discontinuous mode. In panel (a), note that on time remains constant only so long as inductor is in the continuous mode.

but decreases drastically after operation has become discontinuous. Yet the DC output voltage remains constant to within 5 mV even after the inductor has gone discontinuous.

It would seem then that there is no drawback in permitting the inductor to go discontinuous. There actually is no drawback for a buck regulator. Up to the start of the discontinuous mode, the DC output voltage is given by $V_o = V_1 T_{on}/T$. The on time decreases just a very small amount as I_o decreases because the forward drop across $Q1$ decreases slightly with decreasing current. This increases $V1$ slightly, requiring a small decrease in T_{on}.

After going into the discontinuous mode, however, the relation $V_o = V_1 T_{on}/T$ no longer holds, as can be seen in the bottom two waveforms of Fig. 1.6a, where the $Q1$ on time has markedly decreased and depends mainly DC output current. Before the start of the discontinuous mode, the circuit coped with DC output current changes by changing the amplitude of the step part of the ramp-on-step waveforms in the $Q1$ and $D1$ waveforms of Figs. 1.4d and 1.4e. It could do this at relatively constant $Q1$ on time.

Now the average of the sum of the $Q1$ and $D1$ currents [Fig. 1.6c(2) and 1.6c(3)] is the DC output current. Once the inductor has gone discontinuous and the step part of the latter waveforms has gone to zero, the only way the average of their sum can decrease further is to decrease the $Q1$ on time. The negative-feedback loop automatically sets the $Q1$ on time so that the average of the sum of $Q1$ and $D1$ currents is equal to the DC output current at the correct output voltage as fixed by the error amplifier, the sampling resistors, and the reference voltage of Fig. 1.4.

The loss of the step in the $Q1$ and $D1$ currents between nominal and the start of the discontinuous mode can be seen more clearly in Fig. 1.7a,b. When the inductor has gone discontinuous, the $D1$ current has fallen to zero before the next $Q1$ turn on as seen in Fig. 1.7b(2). This causes a decaying "ring" at the $Q1$ emitter at a frequency determined by L_o and the capacitance looking into the $D1$ cathode and $Q1$ emitter [Fig. 1.7b(1)]. This causes no problem; the $Q1$ on time simply is readjusted by the feedback loop so that the average voltage at the emitter of $Q1$ is equal to the commanded, DC output voltage. The ring in Fig. 1.7b(1) is no problem; it is easily eliminated by the $L_o C_o$ filter.

So though operating in the discontinuous mode is no problem in the buck regulator, it is in later topologies with buck-type output $L_o C_o$ filters. Hence in all such output filters, the inductor will be chosen so that it does not go discontinuous until the DC output current falls to its specified minimum value, which in most cases is one-tenth the nominal value or 0.1 (I_{on}). Since the onset of the discontinuous mode occurs at a DC current equal to half the amplitude of the inductor cur-

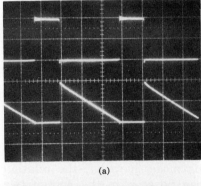

(1) Emitter Q1 = 10 V, 10μs/cm

(2) I_{D1} = 1A, 10 μs/cm
Note L0 has just barely gone discontinuous
as evidenced by D1 current just falling to
zero at instant of next turn-on; I_{dc} = 1.0 A

(a)

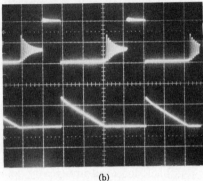

(1) Emitter (Q1) = 10 V, 10 μs/cm;
Note ringing at instant inductor current has
fallen to zero; despite ringing, feedback loop
corrects main on time and supply still
regulates

(2) I_{D1} = 1A, 10 μs/cm
Inductor has gone discontinuous or fallen to
zero current before next turn-on; this occurs
because DC current is less than half the
peak-to-peak ramp amplitude in the photo;
I_{dc} = 0.45 A

(b)

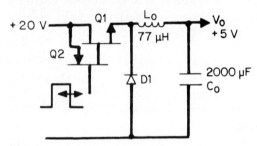

Figure 1.7 A 25-kHz buck regulator, showing $Q1$ emitter waveforms for the case of L_o at the brink of going into the discontinuous mode and also beyond that point.

rent ramp [$(I_2 - I_1)$ of Fig. 1.4d], then $I_{o(min)}$ = 0.1I_{on} = $(I_2 - I_1)/2$ or $(I_2 - I_1)$ = dI = 0.2I_{on}. But dI, the slope ramp amplitude, is $dI = V_L T_{on}/L = (V_1 - V_o)T_{on}/L$, where V_1 is voltage at the input end of I_o and is very closely equal to V_{dc}. Then

$$L = \frac{(V_{dc} - V_o)T_{on}}{dI} = \frac{(V_{dc} - V_o)T_{on}}{0.2I_{on}}$$

)

But $T_{\text{on}} = V_oT/V_{\text{dc}}$; then

$$L = \frac{5(V_{\text{dcn}} - V_o)V_oT}{V_{\text{dcn}}I_{\text{on}}} \tag{1.8}$$

where V_{dcn} and I_{on} are their nominal values.

Thus if L is selected from Eq. 1.8, $(I_2 - I_1) = 0.2I_{\text{on}}$ and I_{on} is the inductor current at the center of the ramp at nominal DC output current, the inductor current swings ± 10 percent around its value at the center. If the inductor remains constant in value up to $I_2 = 1.1I_{\text{on}}$, the ramp will be linear. Thus the inductor must be designed so that it does not saturate or significantly saturate at DC current bias of $1.1I_{\text{on}}$.

Such inductors, which remain relatively constant in value under DC bias conditions, can be built with gapped ferrite cores or powdered iron or powdered Permalloy (a magnetic alloy of nickel and iron). Such powdered cores have an effective distributed air gap as they are made from a sludge of powdered magnetic particles embedded in a resin which forms the uniformly distributed air gap. Design of such inductors will be discussed in a later chapter.

The inductor selected from Eq. 1.8 can tolerate higher DC output currents than the specified I_{on} if it is designed not to saturate at these higher currents. The only restriction on maximum current in the buck regulator is the increased DC and AC losses given by Eq. 1.6. The minimum current restriction on the inductor chosen from Eq. 1.8 is that below I_{on} it will go discontinuous and load regulation will slightly degrade.

If the inductor is chosen half the value given by Eq. 1.8, it will go discontinuous at one-fifth rather than one-tenth the nominal DC output current. This will slightly degrade the load regulation commencing at the higher minimum current. But since it is a smaller inductor, the buck regulator will respond more quickly and with a smaller transient output spike to dynamic load changes.

1.3.7 Design relations—output filter capacitor selection

The filter capacitor of Fig. 1.4 is chosen to meet the output ripple specifications. It is not an ideal capacitor, as shown in the figure. It has a resistance R_o and inductance L_o in series with it as shown in Fig. 1.8. These are referred to as the *equivalent series resistance* (ESR) and equivalent series inductance or (ESL). Below about 300 or 500 kHz, L_o can be neglected and output ripple is determined by R_o and C_o.

There are two ripple components, due to R_o and C_o. They are not in phase as that due to R_o is proportional to $I_2 - I_1$, the peak-to-peak inductor ramp current of Fig. 1.4f, and that due to C_o is proportional to

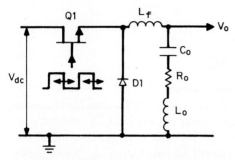

Figure 1.8 Output ripple in the buck regulator. For a given inductor current ripple amplitude, output ripple is determined by the value of the output filter capacitor, C_o, its equivalent series resistance (ESR) R_o, and its equivalent series inductance (ESL) L_o. Below about 500 kHz, L_o can be neglected. In most cases, the ripple component contributed by C_o is small compared to that contributed by R_o. Under 500 kHz, output ripple is closely equal to the AC ripple current in L_o times R_o.

the integral of that current. For a worst-case comparison, however, it can be assumed that they are in phase.

To assess these ripple components and permit a capacitor selection, it is necessary to know the values of R_o, which are seldom given by capacitor manufacturers. But examination of a number of manufacturers' catalogs shows that for the most frequently used types (aluminum electrolytic) over a large range of voltage ratings and capacitance values, R_oC_o tends to be constant. It ranges from 50 to 80 $\times$ 10^{-6} F.

It is instructive to calculate the capacitive and resistive ripple components for a typical buck regulator. Assume a 20- to 5-V regulator with I_{on} = 5 A operating at 25 kHz. Assume $I_{o(\text{min})}$ = $0.1I_{on}$ = 0.5 A and choose L from Eq. 1.8:

$$L = \frac{5(V_{\text{dcn}} - V_o)V_oT}{V_{\text{dcn}}I_{on}} = \frac{5(20 - 5)5 \times 40 \times 10^{-6}}{20 \times 5} = 150 \quad \mu\text{H}$$

and $I2 - I1$, the peak-to-peak ramp amplitude, is $0.2I_{on}$ = 1 A.

Assume to start, a resistive ripple component V_{rr}, of 0.05 V peak-to-peak. Then $0.05 = (I2 - I1)R_o = 1R_o$ or $R_o = 0.05$ Ω and for R_oC_o = 50×10^{-6}, $C_o = 50 \times 10^{-6}/0.05 = 1000$ μF.

Now calculate the capacitive ripple voltage V_{cr} from Fig. 1.4d. There it is seen that the ripple current is positive from the center of the offtime to the center of the on time or for one-half of a period or 20 μs. The average value of this triangle of current is $(I_2 - I_1)/$

4 = 0.25 A. Then this average current produces across C_o a ripple voltage:

$$V_{cr} = \frac{It}{C_o} = \frac{0.25 \times 20 \times 10 \times 10^{-6}}{1000 \times 10^{-6}} = 0.005 \quad V$$

The ripple current below the I_o line in Fig. 1.4f yields another 0.005-V ripple for a total peak-to-peak capacitive ripple voltage of 0.01 V. Thus in this particular case, the ripple due to the capacitance is small compared to that due to the ESR resistor R_o and may be ignored. The filter capacitor is then chosen to yield the desired peak-to-peak ripple voltage output by choosing R_o from

$$R_o = \frac{V_{or}}{I_2 - I_1} = \frac{V_{or}}{0.2I_{on}} \tag{1.9}$$

and selecting C_o from the average value of the R_oC_o product, which is closely 65×10^{-6} or

$$C_o = \frac{65 \times 10^{-6}}{R_o} = (65 \times 10^{-6}) \frac{0.2I_{on}}{V_{or}} \tag{1.10}$$

The preceding result—that the output ripple is determined mainly by the ESR of the filter capacitor R_o—has been demonstrated more generally in a paper by K. V. Kantak.[1] There the author shows that if R_oC_o is is larger than half the transistor on time and half the transistor off time—which is the usual case—the output ripple is determined by the ESR resistor itself as demonstrated above for a particular case.

1.3.8 DC-isolated, regulated voltage from a buck regulator

The return end of the regulated output voltage is DC-common with the return end of the raw DC input as can be seen in Fig. 1.4. It is frequently necessary to have a second regulated DC output voltage which is DC-isolated from the main regulated output voltage. This can be done with negligibly fewer additional components as shown in Fig. 1.9 if output variations of about 2 to 3 percent in this second voltage are acceptable.

In Fig. 1.9, a second winding with $N2$ turns is added to the output filter choke. Its output is peak-rectified with diode $D2$ and capacitor $C2$. The polarity of the $N1$, $N2$ windings are shown by the dots. When $Q1$ turns off, the no-dot end of $N1$ goes negative and is caught at one diode drop below ground by free-wheeling diode $D1$. Since V_o is regulated against line and load changes, the voltage across $N1$ is constant as long as the current in free-wheeling diode $D1$ remains constant.

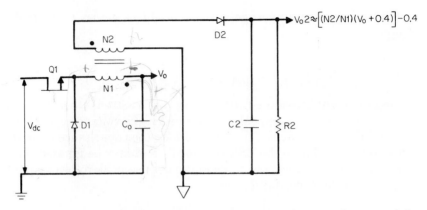

Figure 1.9 Deriving a second output from a buck regulator by using the output choke as a transformer. The second output is DC-isolated from input ground and is regulated to within about 2 to 3 percent as its primary is powered from the regulated V_o and the cathode of $D1$ when $Q1$ turns off.

With $D1$ a low-forward-drop Schottky diode, its forward drop remains constant at about 0.4 V over a large change in DC output current.

Thus when $Q1$ turns off, the voltage across $N2$ is relatively constant at $N_2/N_1(V_o + 0.4)$ volts with its dot end positive. This is peak-rectified by $D2$ and $C2$ to yield $V_o2 = N_2/N_1(V_o + 0.4) - 0.4$ if $D2$ is also a Schottky diode. This output is independent of V_{dc} as $D2$ is reverse-biased when $Q1$ turns on. Capacitor $C2$ should be selected large enough so that its output does not droop for the maximum $Q1$ on time. The 2 to 3 percent variation in V_o2 is due to changes in $D1$ forward drop as I_o changes. Since $N2$ and $N1$ are DC-isolated from one another, this auxiliary regulated output voltage can be referenced to any desired DC voltage level.

1.4   Boost Switching Regulator Topology

1.4.1   Basic operation

The switching technique of Fig. 1.4 can only produce a lower voltage from a higher voltage. Figure 1.10 shows how switching techniques can produce a higher regulated voltage from a lower unregulated voltage. The circuit is called a "boost regulator" or a "ringing choke" converter. It works as follows. An inductor $L1$ is placed in series with V_{dc} and a switching transistor $Q1$. The bottom end of $L1$ feeds the output capacitor C_o and load resistor through rectifying diode $D1$.

The output voltage V_o is higher than the DC input V_{dc}, as can be seen qualitatively thus: When $Q1$ is on for a time t_{on}, $D1$ is reverse-

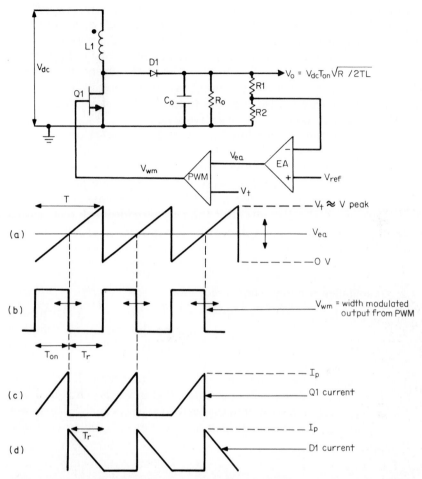

Figure 1.10 Boost regulator and critical waveforms. Energy stored in $L1$ during the $Q1$ on time is delivered to the output via $D1$ at a higher output voltage when $Q1$ turns off and the polarity across $L1$ reverses.

biased and current ramps up linearly in $L1$ to a peak value $I_p = V_{dc}t_{on}/L1$. This represents an amount of stored energy:

$$E = \frac{1}{2L_1(I_p)^2} = 0.5\,L_1 I_p^2 \tag{1.11}$$

where E is in joules, L_1 is in henries, and I_p is in amperes.

During the $Q1$ on time, the output current is supplied entirely from C_o, which is chosen large enough to supply the load current for the time t_{on} with the minimum specified droop.

When $Q1$ turns off, since the current in an inductor cannot change instantaneously, the current in $L1$ reverses in an attempt to maintain the current constant. Now the no-dot end of $L1$ is positive with respect to the dot end, and since the dot end is at V_{dc}, $L1$ delivers its stored energy to C_o and charges it up via $D1$ to a higher voltage (a boosted-up voltage) than V_{dc}. This energy supplies the load current and replenishes the charge drained away from C_o when it alone was supplying load current. Energy is also supplied to the load from V_{dc} during the $Q1$ off time as will be seen quantitatively below.

The output voltage is regulated by controlling the $Q1$ on time in a negative-feedback loop. If DC load current increases, the on time is automatically increased to deliver the greater required energy to the load. If V_{dc} decreases, and if t_{on} were not changed, the peak current and hence also the energy stored in $L1$ would decrease and the DC output voltage would decrease. But the negative-feedback loop senses a slightly decreased output voltage and increases t_{on} to maintain output voltage constant.

1.4.2   Quantitative relations—boost regulator

If the current through $D1$ has fallen to zero before the next $Q1$ turnon, all the energy stored in $L1$ (Eq. 1.11) during the last $Q1$ on time has been delivered to the output load and the circuit is said to be operating in the "discontinuous" mode.

An amount of energy E delivered to a load in a time T represents power. With E in joules and T in seconds, P is in watts. Thus if all the joules of Eq. 1.11 are delivered to the load once per period T, the power to the load from $L1$ alone (assuming for the moment 100 percent efficiency) is

$$P_L = \frac{\frac{1}{2}L(I_p)^2}{T} \quad W \tag{1.12}$$

During the time the current in $L1$ is ramping down to zero (T_r in Fig. 1.10d), however, that same current is flowing through V_{dc} and is also delivering to the load an amount of power P_{dc} equal to the average current during T_r multiplied by its duty cycle and V_{dc}:

$$P_{dc} = V_{dc}\frac{I_p}{2}\frac{T_r}{T} \tag{1.13}$$

The total power delivered to the load is then

$$P_t = P_L + P_{dc} = \frac{\frac{1}{2}L_1(I_p)^2}{T} + V_{dc}\frac{I_p}{2}\frac{T_r}{T} \tag{1.14}$$

But $I_p = V_{dc}T_{on}/L_1$. Then

$$P_t = \frac{(\frac{1}{2}L_1)(V_{dc}T_{on}/L_1)^2}{T} + V_{dc}\frac{V_{dc}T_{on}}{2L_1}\frac{T_r}{T}$$

$$= \frac{V_{dc}^2 T_{on}}{2TL_1}(T_{on} + T_r) \qquad (1.15)$$

Now to make sure that the current in $L1$ has ramped down to zero before the next $Q1$ turnon, set $(T_{on} + T_r) = kT$, where k is fraction less than 1. Then $P_t = (V_{dc}^2 T_{on}/2TL_1)(kT)$.

But for an output voltage V_o and output load resistor R_o

$$P_t = \frac{V_{dc}^2 T_{on}}{2TL_1}(kT) = \frac{V_o^2}{R_o}$$

or
$$V_o = V_{dc}\sqrt{\frac{kR_oT_{on}}{2L1}} \qquad (1.16)$$

Thus the negative-feedback loop keeps the output constant against input voltage changes and output load R_o changes in accordance with Eq. 1.16. As V_{dc} and R_o go down or up, the loop will increase or decrease T_{on} so as to keep V_o constant.

1.4.3 Discontinuous and continuous modes in boost regulator

It was mentioned in the previous section that if the $D1$ current (Fig. 1.10d) fell to zero before the next turnon, the circuit is said to operate in the discontinuous mode. If the current has not fallen to zero at the end of the off time, the $Q1$ current at the next turnon will have a front-end step as the current in an inductor cannot change instantaneously. Currents in $Q1$ and $D1$ will have a characteristic ramp-on-a-step waveshape as in Fig. 1.11. The circuit is now said to be operating in the continuous mode.

If the feedback loop had been successfully stabilized for operation in the discontinuous mode, as R_o or V_{dc} decreases, the feedback loop increases T_{on} to maintain the output voltage constant. As R_o or V_{dc} continues to decrease, a point is reached such that T_{on} is so large that the decaying current through $D1$ has not yet fallen to zero before the next turnon (Figs. 1.10, 1.11) and the circuit is in the continuous mode.

Now the error-amplifier circuit, which had successfully stabilized the loop while it was operating in the discontinuous mode, is not able to keep the loop stable in the continuous mode and begins to oscillate. In the jargon of feedback-loop analysis, the continuous-mode boost

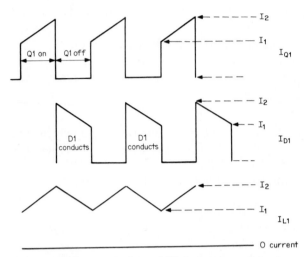

Figure 1.11 Current in $Q1$ and $D1$ for boost regulator in continuous mode. Inductor $L1$ has not had enough time to release all its current to the load before the next $Q1$ turnon.

regulator has a *right-half-plane zero*. The only way to stabilize a loop with a right-half-plane zero is to drastically reduce the error-amplifier bandwidth. Right-half-plane zeros will be discussed in more detail in the chapter on feedback stabilization.

1.4.4 Discontinuous-mode boost regulator design relations

In Fig. 1.10d, the decaying $D1$ current is seen to just come down to zero at the start of the next turnon. That was the very end of discontinuous-mode operation. It is seen from Eq. (1.16) to occur at certain combinations of V_{dc}, T_{on}, R_o, and $L1$ for a given operating period T.

If certain combinations of these result in $D1$ current falling to zero just immediately prior to the next $Q1$ turnon as shown in Fig. 1.10d, any further decrease in V_{dc} or R_o (increase in load current) will force the circuit into the continuous mode and oscillation will occur if the error amplifier has not been designed for this mode. This can be seen from Eq. (1.16). If the circuit is just at the end of discontinuous-mode operation, any further decrease in V_{dc} or R_o will cause the error amplifier to increase T_{on} in order to keep V_o constant. Then $D1$ starts ramping down later in time (and from a higher current as T_{on} has increased). Now at the start of the next $Q1$ on time, the $D1$ current has not yet fallen to zero and the circuit has entered the continuous mode.

To avoid this problem (see Eq. 1.16) T_{on} must be selected so that when it is a maximum (which is when V_{dc} and R_o are at their minimum specified values), and then when the current in $D1$ has fallen back to zero, there is an arbitrarily selected dead-time margin (T_{dt}) before $Q1$ turns on again. In the time the current in $D1$ returns to zero, the $L1$ core must be restored or "reset" to its starting place on its hysteresis loop.

Now to understand how the core may fail to be reset to its starting place and to comprehend the basic concept of the core moving up (being set) or moving down (being reset) on its hysteresis loop, the most fundamental law in magnetics—Faraday's law—must be appreciated. Faraday's law states

$$E = NA_e \,(dB/dt) \times 10^{-8} \qquad (1.17)$$

where E = voltage across a core (inductor or transformer winding) volts
N = number of turns on the winding
A_e = iron area of core (cm^2)
dB = core flux change (gauss) (which has a plus or minus direction depending on polarity of the voltage across the winding)
dt = time for that flux change (seconds)

Now if a voltage E is applied across a winding of N turns for a time dt, it produces from Faraday's law a flux change of

$$dB = \frac{E \, dt \times 10^{+8}}{NA_e} \qquad \text{(gauss)} \qquad (1.18)$$

Thus, as shown in Fig. 1.12, if a core is subjected to a positive flux change of $dB = B2 - B1$, when, say, the dot end of the winding had been positive, the core must be restored exactly to B_1 by a reversed voltage polarity before original polarity voltage may be applied. If not,

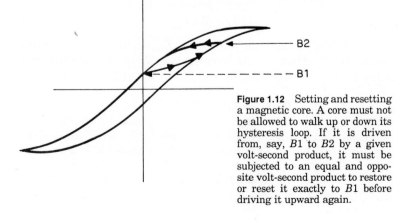

Figure 1.12 Setting and resetting a magnetic core. A core must not be allowed to walk up or down its hysteresis loop. If it is driven from, say, $B1$ to $B2$ by a given volt-second product, it must be subjected to an equal and opposite volt-second product to restore or reset it exactly to $B1$ before driving it upward again.

if a core moves from, say, $B1$ to $B2$ and with a reverse polarity voltage is restored to only a few percent above $B1$, then after many such cycles, it will drift up its hysteresis loop and saturate the core. Since a saturated core cannot sustain voltage, the voltage at the transistor collector will suddenly move up to the supply voltage and the transistor will be destroyed.

From Eq. (1.18), the flux change dB caused by a voltage E applied for a time dt is proportional to the volt-second product $E\,dt$. Thus if a core is moved up or "set" by a given volt-second product, it must be "reset" by an opposite polarity and exactly equal the volt-second product.

Now in Fig. 1.10, during the transistor on time T_{on}, the dot end of $L1$ will be positive and the core will be set or moved—say, upward—on the hysteresis loop by the volt-second product $V_{dc}T_{on}$ (assuming negligible on drop across $Q1$). When $Q1$ turns off, polarity across $L1$ reverses, the no-dot end of $L1$ is now positive, and the core is reset in a time T_r to its exact starting point on the hysteresis loop. During the reset time, the voltage across $L1$ (assuming here also negligible drop across $D1$) is $(V_o - V_{dc})$. To ensure that the core is always reset to its initial starting point and does not drift either way on the hysteresis loop, the on or set volt-second product must be equal to the off or reset volt-second product.

Now to ensure that the circuit remains in the discontinuous mode, a dead-time T_{dt} of 20 percent of a full period will be established such that the sum of the maximum on time, the core reset time, and the dead time will equal a full period as in Fig. 1.13. This ensures that the stored current in $L1$ has fallen to zero 20 percent of a full period before the next $Q1$ turnon.

Now hereafter, a line appearing below a term will indicate the minimum permitted or specified or required value of that term, and a line appearing over a term will indicate the maximum value of that term. Then $\overline{T_{on}} + T_r + T_{dt} = T$, $\overline{T_{on}} + T_r + 0.2T = T$, or

$$\overline{T_{on}} + T_r = 0.8T \tag{1.19}$$

From Eq. (1.16), maximum on time $\overline{T_{on}}$ occurs at minimum V_{dc} and minimum R_o. Then for the on or set volt-second product to equal the off or reset volt-second product at minimum V_{dc} and minimum $\underline{R_o}$:

$$V_{dc}\overline{T_{on}} = (V_o - V_{dc})T_r \tag{1.20}$$

Now in Eqs. (1.19) and (1.20) there are only two unknowns, $\overline{T_{on}}$ and T_r, and thus both are determined; $\overline{T_{on}}$ is then

$$\overline{T_{on}} = \frac{0.8T(V_o - V_{dc})}{V_o} \tag{1.21}$$

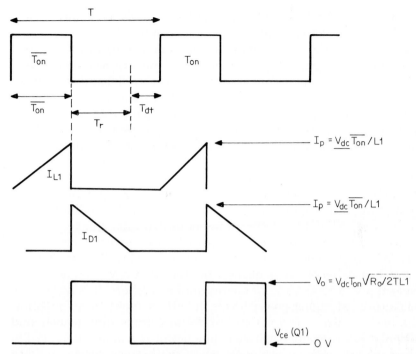

Figure 1.13 Ensuring discontinuous-mode operation in a boost regulator. For discontinuous-mode operation, the current in $D1$ (Fig. 1.10) must have decayed to zero before the next turnon. To ensure this, with a minimum input voltage, a maximum on time, and a maximum output current at the desired output voltage, the inductor $L1$ is chosen such that $T_{on(max)} + T_r = 0.8T$, leaving a dead time T_{dt} of $0.2T$.

Now in Eq. 1.16, with V_{dc} and R_o (maximum load current) specified, $\overline{T_{on}}$ calculated from Eq. $\overline{1.21}$ and $\overline{k}$ [= $(\overline{T_{on}} + T_r)/T)$] = 0.8 as set from Eq. 1.19, inductor $L1$ is fixed and the circuit is guaranteed not to enter the continuous mode. If output load current is inadvertently increased beyond its specified maximum value (R_o decreased below its specified minimum) or V_{dc} is decreased below its specified minimum, the feedback loop will attempt to increase T_{on} in order to keep V_o constant. This will eat into the dead time T_{dt} and move the circuit closer to the continuous mode. To avoid this, a clamp to limit maximum on time or maximum peak current must be introduced.

With $L1$ determined as above from Eq. 1.16, V_{dc} specified and $\overline{T_{on}}$ calculated from Eq. 1.21, the peak current in $Q1$ can be calculated from Eq. 1.14 and a transistor selected to have adequate gain at I_p.

1.4.5 Boost regulator applications and flyback comparison

The boost regulator is not as widely used as the buck simply because there are fewer instances where a higher from a lower voltage is required. In those instances where the higher voltage is required, there are alternative and preferable ways to obtain it.

Nevertheless, the boost regulator has been treated in rather great detail because by replacing the inductor $L1$ by a transformer, a very similar, valuable, and widely used topology—the "flyback" is realized. As for the boost, the flyback stores energy in its magnetics in one part of the switching period and, in a subsequent part, transfers it to the output load. Because of the transformer, output return is DC-isolated from input return. Also by using multiple secondaries, a multi-output-voltage power supply is possible with outputs at a higher or lower voltage than the input.

The problems of discontinuous or continuous operation and the design relationships and procedures for the flyback are similar to those of the boost and will be discussed in detail in a later chapter.

The boost regulator is most frequently used at low power levels (<10 W). Its greatest usage at such low power levels is on printed-circuit boards where it is desired to step up a 5-V computer logic level supply to 12 or 15 V for operational amplifiers. It is frequently encountered at higher power levels in battery input power supplies. As a battery discharges, its output voltage drops significantly and suddenly. Many systems whose prime power is a nominal 12- or 28-V battery will present problems when the battery voltage falls to about 9 or 22 V, respectively. Boost regulators are frequently used in such applications to boost the voltages back up to the 12- and 28-V level. Power level in such applications can be in the 50- to 200-W level.

1.5   Polarity Inverting Switching Regulator Topology

1.5.1   Basic operation

Polarity inverting switching regulator topology is shown in Fig. 1.14. It uses the same basic principle of energy storage in an inductor in one part of the operating period and then transferring it to the output load in the latter part of the period.

Comparing Figs. 1.14 and 1.10, it is seen that the transistor and inductor have changed places. In the polarity inverter, the transistor is above the inductor rather than below it as in the boost. Also the orientation of the rectifying diode has been reversed.

In Fig. 1.14, when $Q1$ turns on, diode $D1$ is reverse-biased as its cathode is at V_{dc} (assuming to a close approximation that the on drop across $Q1$ is zero) and assuming for the moment that C_o has charged down to some negative voltage. With a fixed voltage V_{dc}

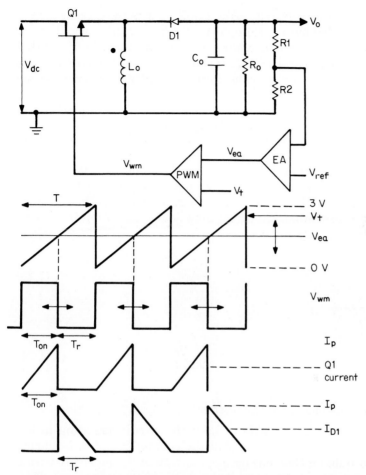

Figure 1.14   Polarity inverter and critical waveforms. When $Q1$ is on, current ramps up linearly in L_o and stores current I_p in L_o. When $Q1$ turns off, polarity across L_o reverses. Current I_p now decays linearly through C_o and D1, charging the top end of C_o negatively. If all the current I_p stored in L_o during the $Q1$ on time has decayed to zero before the next $Q1$ turnon, power delivered to the load is $P_o = \frac{1}{2}L_o(I_p)^2/T$.

across L_o, current in it ramps up linearly at a rate $di/dt = V_{dc}/L_o$. After an on time T_{on}, current in L_o has reached $I_p = V_{dc}t_{on}/L_o$ and represents a stored energy (in joules) of $E = \frac{1}{2}L_oI_p^2$. When $Q1$ turns off, polarity across L_o reverses in an attempt to maintain its current unchanged. Thus at the instant of turnoff, the same I_p which flowed through $Q1$ before it turned off now flows through C_o and D1. This current flowing upward through C_o charges the top end of it to a negative voltage as assumed.

After a number of cycles, the error amplifier sets the $Q1$ on time T_{on} so that the sampled output voltage $[V_o R2/(R1 + R2)]$ is equal to the reference voltage V_{ref}. Further, if all the energy stored in L_o is delivered to the load before the next $Q1$ turnon (by I_{D1} having fallen to zero before turnon), the circuit operates in the discontinuous mode and the power delivered to the load is

$$P_t = \frac{\tfrac{1}{2}L_o I_p^{\,2}}{T} \tag{1.22}$$

It should be noted that unlike the case of the boost regulator, when $Q1$ turns off, the stored current does not flow through the supply source (see Eq. 1.13). Hence the only power to the load is that given by Eq. 1.22. Thus assuming 100 percent efficiency, and a minimum output resistance R_o, output power is

$$P_o = \frac{V_o^{\,2}}{R_o} = \frac{\tfrac{1}{2}L_o I_p^{\,2}}{T} \tag{1.23}$$

and for $I_p = V_{\text{dc}} T_{\text{on}}/L_o$

$$V_o = V_{\text{dc}} T_{\text{on}} \sqrt{\frac{R_o}{2TL_o}} \tag{1.24}$$

1.5.2   Design relations in polarity inverter

As in the boost, it is desirable to keep the circuit operating in the discontinuous mode by ensuring that the current stored in L_o during the $Q1$ maximum on time has decayed to zero at the end of T_r with a dead time T_{dt} margin of $0.2T$ before the next $Q1$ turnon. Thus $\overline{T_{\text{on}}} + T_r + T_{\text{dt}} = T$, and for $T_{\text{dt}} = 0.2T$, we obtain

$$\overline{T_{\text{on}}} + T_r = 0.8T \tag{1.25}$$

In addition, as in the boost regulator, the on volt-second product must equal the reset volt-second product to prevent the core from drifting up or down its hysteresis loop. Since maximum T_{on} occurs for minimum V_{dc} and minimum R_o (as can be seen from Eq. 1.24) it follows that

$$V_{\text{dc}} \overline{T_{\text{on}}} = V_o T_r \tag{1.26}$$

Thus in both Eqs. 1.25 and 1.26 there are two unknowns: $\overline{T_{\text{on}}}$ and T_r. This fixes $\overline{T_{\text{on}}}$ at

$$\overline{T}_{\text{on}} = \frac{0.8 V_o T}{V_{\text{dc}} + V_o} \qquad (1.27)$$

Now, with $\overline{T}_{\text{on}}$ calculated from Eq. 1.27, V_{dc}, R_o, V_o, and T specified, Eq. 1.24 fixes L_o. This fixes $I_p = V_{\text{dc}} \overline{T}_{\text{on}}/L_o$ and transistor $Q1$ can be selected to have adequate gain at $\overline{I}_p$.

Reference

1. K. V. Kantak, "Output Voltage Ripple in Switching Power Converters," *Power Electronics Conference Proceedings*, Boxborough, Mass., pp. 35–44, April 1987.

Push-Pull and Forward Converter Topologies

2.1 Introduction

The three earliest switching regulator topologies discussed in the previous chapter had the significant drawbacks that the output returns were DC-common with the input returns and that multiple outputs were not possible (except for the restricted case discussed in Sec. 1.3.8).

In this chapter, the most widely used switching regulator topologies are discussed. These topologies—the push-pull, single-ended forward converter, and two modifications of the latter, the double-ended and interleaved forward converter—have sufficient similarity to consider them as a family. All these topologies deliver their power to the loads via a transformer; hence output voltage returns are DC-isolated from input returns, and with multiple transformer secondaries, multiple DC output voltages are possible.

2.2 Push-Pull Topology

2.2.1 Basic operation—master/slave outputs

Push-pull topology is shown in Fig. 2.1. It consists of a transformer $T1$ with multiple secondaries. Each secondary supplies a pair of 180° out-of-phase square-wave power pulses whose amplitude is fixed by the number of secondary turns. Pulse widths at all secondaries are, of course, identical and are determined by the control circuit in the negative-feedback loop around a main secondary V_m. That control circuit is basically much like that for the buck and boost regulators of Figs. 1.4 and 1.10 except that two equal and adjustable-width, 180°

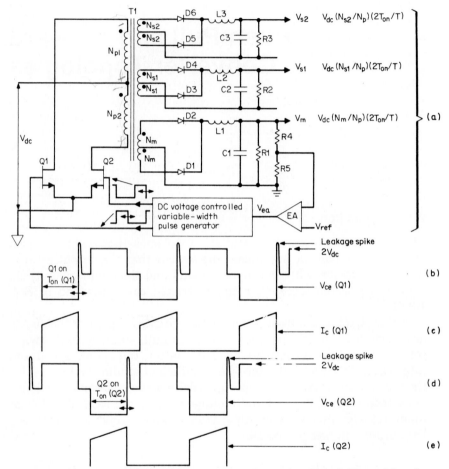

Figure 2.1 Push-pull width-modulated converter. Transistors $Q1$ and $Q2$ are driven by 180 out-of-phase width-modulated signals. Outputs are one master (V_{sm}) and two slaves (V_{s1} and V_{s2}). Feedback loop is closed around V_{sm} and T_{on} is controlled to regulate it against line and load changes. Slaves are regulated against line but only partially against load.

out-of-phase pulses are supplied to drive the bases of $Q1$, $Q2$. Secondaries N_{s1}, N_{s2} are referred to as "slaves."

Transistor base drives at turnon are sufficient to bring the bottom end of each half primary down to the $V_{ce(sat)}$ level of about 1 V for the transistors over the full specified current range. Hence when either transistor turns on, it applies to its half primary a square voltage pulse of magnitude $V_{dc} - 1$.

Then for output rectifier forward drops of V_d, outputs at the rectifier cathodes will be flat-topped square waves of amplitude $(V_{dc} - 1)(N_s/N_p) - V_d$ and of duration T_{on}. Here, V_d, the rectifier diode forward drop, will be taken as 1 V for a conventional fast-recovery diode and 0.5 V for a Schottky diode (usually used for 5-V high-current outputs as V_m). These output pulses at the rectifier cathodes have a duty cycle of $2T_{on}/T$ as there is one such pulse of duration T_{on} per half period $T/2$.

Thus the waveform at the input to the LC filters in Fig. 2.1 is very much like that at the input to the buck regulating LC filter of Fig. 1.4. It has a unique flat-topped amplitude and adjustable width. The LC filters of Fig. 2.1 serve the same purpose as that in Fig. 1.4. They provide a DC output which is the average of the square wave at their inputs and filter out the square-wave ripple. The analysis of the inductor and capacitor functions proceeds exactly as for the buck regulator, and the relations for calculating their magnitudes are exactly as for the buck.

Thus the DC or average voltage at the V_m output in Fig. 2.2 (assuming $D1$, $D2$ are 0.5-V forward-drop Schottky diodes) is

$$V_m = \left[(V_{dc} - 1)\left(\frac{N_m}{N_p}\right) - 0.5\right]\frac{2T_{on}}{T} \qquad (2.1)$$

Waveforms at the V_m output rectifiers are shown in Fig. 2.2. Now, if a negative-feedback loop is closed around V_m as in Fig. 2.1 to control

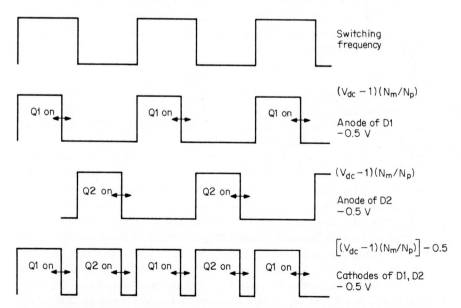

Figure 2.2 Voltages at main (N_m) secondary winding. Output LC filter is an averaging filter. It yields DC out voltage = $V_m = [(V_{dc} - 1)(N_m/N_p) - 0.5](2T_{on}/T)$. As V_{dc} varies, the negative-feedback loop corrects T_{on} in such a direction as to keep V_m constant.

T_{on}, V_m will be regulated against DC input voltage and load current output changes. Although load current does not appear in Eq. 2.1, whatever causes V_m to change, that change will be sensed by the error amplifier and T_{on} will be altered in such a direction as to correct that change. So long as $L1$ (Fig. 2.1) does not go discontinuous, changes in T_{on} will be small and the absolute value of T_{on} will be given by Eq. 2.1 for any turns ratio N_m/N_p, V_{dc}, and period T.

Now the voltage at the cathodes of the slave rectifying diodes is fixed by the number of slave secondary turns, and the duration of the square waves is the same T_{on} as was fixed by the master (V_m) feedback loop. Thus the slave outputs (assuming non-Schottky rectifier diodes) are

$$V_{s1} = \left[(V_{dc} - 1)\frac{N_{s1}}{N_p} - 1\right]\frac{2T_{on}}{T} \tag{2.2}$$

$$V_{s2} = \left[(V_{dc} - 1)\frac{N_{s2}}{N_p} - 1\right]\frac{2T_{on}}{T} \tag{2.3}$$

2.2.2 Slave line-load regulation

It can now be seen from Eqs. 2.1, 2.2, and 2.3 that the slaves are regulated against V_{dc} input changes by the negative-feedback loop which keeps V_m constant. As V_{dc} changes, the loop changes T_{on} so that $(V_{dc} - 1)T_{on}$ is kept constant to maintain V_m constant in accordance with Eq. 2.1. But the same product $(V_{dc} - 1)T_{on}$ also appears in Eqs. 2.2 and 2.3, and thus V_{s1}, V_{s2} are also kept constant as V_{dc} changes.

But if load current in the master (V_m) changes, forward drop across its rectifying diodes will change slightly, decreasing the peak voltage at their cathodes slightly. The forward drop across a Schottky rectifying diode was assumed as 0.5 V as a simplifying approximation. That drop can change by ±0.1 V with large load changes. Thus the negative-feedback loop to correct for V_m load changes, will alter T_{on} to keep V_m constant as dictated by Eq. 2.1.

Then in Eqs. 2.2 and 2.3, T_{on} will change without corresponding changes in V_{dc} and changes in V_{s1}, V_{s2} will result. Such changes in the slave output voltages due to changes in the master output current is referred to as *cross regulation*. Slave output voltages will also change as a result of changes in their own output currents. Slave current changes will cause forward voltage drop changes in their rectifying diodes, lowering the peak voltage slightly at the input to their voltage-averaging LC filter. These, of course, are not corrected by the main feedback loop, which senses only V_m. But so long as the slave output inductors, $L2$, $L3$ and especially main inductor $L1$ do not go discontinuous, slave output voltages can be depended on to remain constant to about ±5 to ±8 percent.

2.2.3 Slave absolute output voltage levels

Although slave output voltage changes are relatively small, their absolute values are not accurately adjustable. As seen in Eqs. 2.2 and 2.3, they are fixed by T_{on} and their corresponding secondary turns N_{s1}, N_{s2}. But T_{on} is fixed by the feedback loop in keeping the master constant. Also, since the number of slave secondary turns can be changed only by integral numbers, the absolute value of slave output voltages is not finely settable. The change in secondary voltage for a single turn change in N_s is given by Faraday's law (Eq. 1.17). From that relation, the secondary volts per turn is

$$\frac{E}{N} = A_e \, (dB/dt) \times 10^{-8} \qquad (2.4)$$

Here A_e is the core iron area in cm^2 and dB is the flux change in gauss in a time $dt(= T_{on})$ in seconds. Since T_{on} is some fraction of a half period (see Fig. 2.1), the volts per turn E/N is directly proportional to the switching frequency. In practice, the volts per turn ranges from about 2 V at a switching frequency of 25 kHz to 5 or 6 V at 100 kHz. In Eq. 2.4, since E/N is also proportional to dB, at 100 kHz it is less than four times its value at 25 kHz. This is so because, as will be seen in the chapter on magnetics, higher core losses at the higher frequency force a lower permissible dB at the high frequency.

In most cases, the absolute value of slave output voltages is not too important. Slaves usually drive operational amplifiers or motors, and these most often can tolerate DC voltage levels within about 2 V of a desired value. If absolute magnitude of a slave output is important, it is usually designed higher than required and brought back down to a desired exact value with a linear regulator or buck regulator. Because a slave output is semiregulated (against line changes only), it is not too inefficient to use a linear regulator. In such cases, the slave absolute voltage level is designed to be at about the minimum headroom (2.5 to 3 V) above the desired exact output voltage when DC input voltage is at its minimum.

2.2.4 Master output inductor minimum current limitations

The selection of the output inductor for a buck regulator was discussed in Sec. 1.3.6. It was mentioned that at a DC current level when the step at the front end of the inductor current waveform has fallen to zero (Figs 1.6a and 1.6b), the inductor is said to run dry or go discontinuous. Up to this point and beyond, the feedback loop maintains the buck regulator's output voltage constant, but with somewhat poorer load regulation after the inductor has gone discontinuous.

In Fig. 1.6a, however, it can be seen that before going discontinuous the on time is very nearly constant over large output current changes.

After run-dry, the on time changes drastically. In the buck regulator, this does not matter at all as only the one voltage is involved and the feedback loop keeps the output voltage constant. But in the push-pull width-modulated converter with a master and some slaves, the slave output voltages are directly proportional to the master's on time as shown by Eqs. 2.2 and 2.3.

It is thus very important when slaves are involved that the master output inductor not be permitted to go discontinuous until it reaches its minimum specified output current level. If the master's minimum output current is specified at one-tenth its nominal value, an output inductor selected from Eq. 1.8 will prevent the discontinuous mode condition until the master output current has fallen to its minimum value. Up to this point, the slave output voltages will remain constant to within about 5 percent. After the master inductor has gone discontinuous—below its minimum DC current specification—T_{on} will decrease significantly, and so will slave output voltages. But the feedback loop will keep the master output voltage constant.

Slave outputs, of course, must not be permitted to go discontinuous until they reach their own specified minimum current limits. Slave output inductors should also be selected from Eq. 1.8 if their minimum currents are as low as one-tenth their nominal value. If minimum currents are only one-fifth their nominal value, inductors can be half the Eq. 1.8 value before the discontinuous mode situation occurs.

2.2.5 Flux imbalance in push-pull topology

The push-pull converter is one of the oldest topologies and a still valuable one. It has multiple outputs whose returns are DC-isolated from input ground and from one another. Output voltages can be higher or lower than DC input voltages. The master is regulated against line and load variations. The slaves are equally well regulated against line changes and to within about 5 percent for load changes as long as output inductors are not permitted to go discontinuous.

The topology was widely used and, in very large numbers, performed successfully in the field. Yet occasionally and in greater numbers as output powers increased, power transistor failures started occurring in the field for unknown reasons. Waveforms prior to shipping looked normal and field performance prior to the failures showed no problems. Generally, no obvious design flaw would be found and after just simple replacement of the power transistors, the supplies would continue to work well for months until another unexplained transistor failure would occur.

Eventually, a rather subtle reason for these failures became obvious and widely known throughout the industry. It led to less frequent use

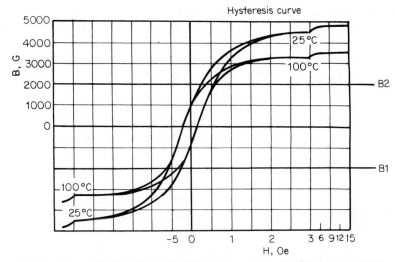

Figure 2.3   Hysteresis loop of a typical ferrite core material (Ferroxcube 3C8). Flux excursions are generally limited to ±2000 G up to about 30 kHz by requirement to stay on the linear part of the loop. At frequencies of 100 to 300 kHz, peak flux excursions must be reduced to about ±1200 or ±800 G because of core losses at these higher frequencies.

of the push-pull topology or to applications where simple and inexpensive "fixes" could avoid the problem.

This subtle failure mode in push-pull converters is known as *flux imbalance*. It can be understood by examination of the hysteresis loop (Fig. 2.3)* of a typical ferrite core material used in the power transformer.

In normal operation, the core's flux excursion is between levels such as B_1 and B_2 gauss in Fig. 2.3. It is desirable to stay on the linear part of the hysteresis loop below ±2000 G. At frequencies of up to 25 kHz, core losses are low and it may be permitted to move between plus and minus 2000 G. Yet other considerations discussed in Sec. 2.2.9.4 dictate that in a conservative design, excursions between ±1600 G are preferable even though losses at ±2000 G are easily acceptable. But core losses go up rapidly with frequency, and above 100 kHz they may limit peak flux density to 1200 or even 800 G.

Now (see Fig. 2.1) when $Q1$ is on, the no-dot end of N_{p1} is positive with respect to the dot end and the core moves up the hysteresis loop— say, from B_1 toward B_2. The actual amount it moves up is proportional to the product of the voltage across N_{p1} and the $Q1$ on time (from

---

*Hysteresis loop of 3C8, a typical ferrite from Ferroxcube Corporation. Other materials from the same or other manufacturers are very similar. Other materials differ mainly in core losses and Curie temperature.

Faraday's law; Eq. 1.18). When $Q1$ turns off and $Q2$ turns on, the dot end of N_{p2} is positive with respect to the no-dot end and the core moves back down from B_2 toward B_1. The actual amount it moves down is now proportional to the voltage across N_{p2} and the $Q2$ on time.

Further, if the volt-second product across N_{p1} when $Q1$ is on is equal to the volt-second product across N_{p2} when $Q2$ is on, after one complete period, the core will have moved up from B_1 to B_2 and returned exactly to B_1. But if those volt-second products differ by only a few percent and the core has not returned to its exact starting point in one period, after a number of periods, the core will "walk" or drift off center of the hysteresis loop into saturation. In saturation, of course, the core cannot sustain voltage and the next time the appropriate transistor turns on, it is subjected to high current and high voltage and is destroyed.

Now there are a number of factors which cause the on or set volt-second product to be different from the off or reset volt-second product. The $Q1$ and $Q2$ collector voltage on times are not exactly equal even if their base voltage on times are equal. Base voltage on times are very closely equal as the usual integrated-circuit control chip which generates them makes them so.

But if $Q1$, $Q2$ are bipolar transistors, they have "storage" times which keep the collector on for a longer time than does the base on voltage time. Storage times can range from 0.3 to 6 μs and have large production spread. They also are very temperature-dependent, increasing significantly as temperature increases; and even if, fortunately, $Q1$ and $Q2$ have equal storage times at the same temperature, they may be very unequal if located far apart on a heat sink and operate at different temperatures.

Further, if one transistor has a slightly larger volt second product than the other, it will start the core drifting slightly off center toward saturation. This will cause that transistor to draw slightly more current than the other as the core moves onto the curved part of the hysteresis loop (Fig. 2.3) and the core's magnetizing current on that half period starts to become a significant part of the load current. Now the transistor which draws more current will run slightly warmer, increasing its storage time. With a longer storage time in that transistor, the volt-second product it applies to the core in its on half period increases, the current in that half period increases, storage time in that transistor increases still further. Thus a runaway condition arises which quickly drives the core into saturation and destroys the transistor.

The on volt-second product between $Q1$ and $Q2$ can also differ because of their initially unequal "on" or $V_{ce(sat)}$ voltages, which have a significant production spread. As described above, with bipolar transistors, any initial difference in on voltage is magnified because the on voltage with bipolars decreases as temperature decreases.

If $Q1$, $Q2$ are MOSFET transistors, the flux imbalance problem is much less serious. To start with, MOSFETs have no storage time and with equal input on (gate) times, output (drain) times are equal—and, importantly, the on voltage of a MOSFET transistor increases as temperature increases. Thus the runaway condition described above cannot occur.

To the contrary, the fact that MOSFET on voltage increases with temperature provides negative feedback, which tends to correct any tendency to flux imbalance. If there were any initial inequality in volt-second product, in the half period in which it was larger, transistor current would be greater as the core started moving up the curved part of the hysteresis loop. That transistor with the larger current would run warmer, and its on voltage would increase and rob voltage from its half primary. This would decrease the volt-second product in that half period and bring the transistor current back down.

2.2.6 Indications of flux imbalance

A push-pull converter can continue to operate for some time with a certain amount of flux imbalance without immediately saturating its core and destroying its transistors. The mechanism described above may imply a slight imbalance in volt-second product between each half cycle causes certain failure. But failure is not certain.

Obviously, unless there was an inherent corrective mechanism, core saturation and transistor failure would always occur. It would simply take more switching cycles with a small volt-second imbalance. Thus if there were an initial volt-second imbalance of 0.01 percent (which would be practically impossible to achieve), it would take only 10,000 cycles before the core would move from a lowermost starting point of B_1 (Fig. 2.3) to a starting point of B_2, and the transistors would be destroyed considerably before that.

The corrective mechanism which permits the converter to survive and operate with no external indications of possible imminent failure is simply the primary wiring resistance. If there is an initial volt-second imbalance in the half period with the larger product, the transistor will commence taking more current as the core commences walking up the curved part of its hysteresis loop. But as that side takes more current, it produces a larger voltage drop across its half primary resistance. That voltage drop robs volt-seconds from the winding and restores the volt-second balance.

The converter can then remain in the unbalanced state without immediately going into run away and completely saturating the core. An indication of where the core is on the hysteresis loop and how close to disaster the converter is can be obtained by placing a current probe in transformer center tap as shown in Fig. 2.4*d*.

The waveform indicating a volt-second balance is shown in Fig. 2.4*a*, where alternate current peaks are equal. Primary load current

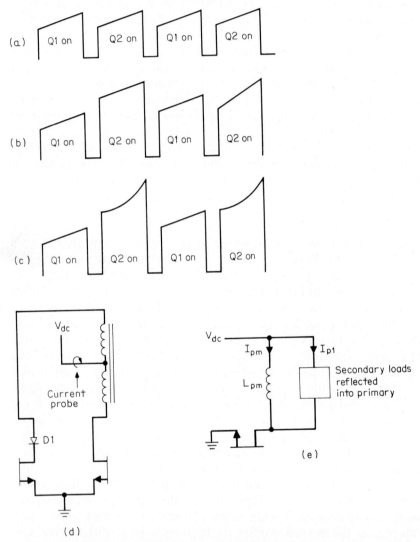

Figure 2.4 (*a*) Current in transformer center tap. Equal volt-second product on both halves of transformer primary. (*b*) Transformer center tap current. Unequal volt-second product on both halves of transformer primary. Core is not yet on curved part of hysteresis loop. (*c*) Transformer center tap current. Unequal volt-second product. Upward concavity indicates dangerous situation. Core is far up on curved part of hysteresis loop. (*d*) Adding a diode in series with one side of primary to test how serious a volt-second inequality exists. (*e*) Total primary current is the sum of the ramp-on-a-step reflected secondary load currents plus the linear ramp of magnetizing current.

pulses have the characteristic shape of a ramp on a step just as for the buck regulator in Fig. 1.4d. They have this shape because all the secondaries have output LC filters which generate such waveshapes as described in Sec. 1.3.2.

Now the primary load current waveshape is the sum of all the secondary ramps on a step reflected into the primary by their respective turns ratios.

However, the total primary current is the sum of these secondary currents reflected into the primary plus the so-called magnetizing current. This magnetizing current is the current drawn by the *magnetizing inductance,* which is the inductance seen looking into the primary with all secondaries open-circuited. This inductance is always present in a loaded transformer and is effectively in parallel with the secondary currents reflected into the primary as in Fig. 2.4e.

The waveshape of the total primary current is then the sum of the ramp-on-a-step reflected load currents and the magnetizing current. But the magnetizing current is a linear ramp starting from zero current level. When a transistor turns on, it applies a step of voltage of approximately $V_{dc} - 1$ across the magnetizing inductance L_m. Magnetizing current then ramps up linearly at a rate $dI/dt = (V_{dc} - 1)/L_m$ and for the transistor on time of T_{on} reaches a peak of

$$I_{pm} = \frac{(V_{dc} - 1)(T_{on})}{L_{pm}} \qquad (2.5)$$

This I_{pm} is kept small compared to the sum of the load currents reflected into the primary by ensuring that L_m in Eq. (2.5) is large. Maximum permissible peak magnetizing current should be no greater than 10 percent of the primary load current.

Since the ramp of magnetizing current is small, added to the ramp on a step of load current, it simply increases the slope of the latter slightly and is not noticeable. Also, if volt-seconds are equal on alternate half cycles, peak currents will also be equal on each half cycle as in Fig. 2.4a as operation is centered around the zero-oersted (0-Oe) origin of the hysteresis loop of Fig. 2.3.

However, if volt-second products on alternate half cycles are unequal, core operation is not centered around the origin of the hysteresis loop. Since oersteds are proportional to magnetizing current, this shows up as a DC current bias as in Fig. 2.4b, making alternate current pulses unequal in amplitude.

As long as the DC bias does not drive the core appreciably up the hysteresis loop, the slope of the ramp still remains linear (Fig. 2.4b) and operation is still safe. Primary wiring resistance keeps the core from moving further up into saturation.

But if there is a large inequality in volt-seconds on alternate half cycles, the core is biased closer toward saturation and enters the curved part of the hysteresis loop. Now, magnetizing inductance, which is proportional to the slope of the hysteresis loop, decreases and magnetizing current increases significantly. This shows up as an upward concavity in the current slope as in Fig. 2.4c.

This is a dangerous and imminent failure situation. Now small temperature increases can bring on the runaway scenario described above. The core will be driven hard into saturation and destroy the power transistor. A push-pull converter design should certainly not be considered safe if current pulses in the primary center tap show any upward concavity in their ramps. Even linear ramps as in Fig. 2.4b with anything greater than 20 percent inequality in peak currents are unsafe and should not be accepted.

2.2.7 Testing for flux imbalance

A simple test to determine how close to a dangerous flux imbalance situation a push-pull converter may be is shown in Fig. 2.4d. Here a silicon diode with about 1 V forward drop is placed in series with the end of either half of the transformer. Now in the on state, that half with the diode in series has 1 V less voltage across it than the other half and there is an artificially produced volt-second unbalance. The center tap waveform will then look like either Fig. 2.4b or 2.4c. The current ramp corresponding to the side which does not have the diode will have the larger volt-second product and the larger peak current. By switching the diode to the other side, the larger peak current will be seen to switch to the opposite transformer half primary.

Now it can be determined how close to the upward concave situation of Fig. 2.4c the circuit is. If one series diode can make a current ramp go concave, the circuit is too close to imminent failure. Going to two series diodes on one side will give an indication of how much margin there is.

It should be noted that primary magnetizing current contributes no power to the secondaries. It will not be reflected by any turns ratio into the secondaries. It simply swings the magnetic core across the hysteresis loop of Fig. 2.3 and is related to the driving force in oersteds in that figure by the fundamental magnetic relation

$$H = \frac{0.4\pi N_p I_m}{L_m} \tag{2.6}$$

where H is in oersteds
  N_p is in turns
  I_m is in amperes
  L_m is in henries

2.2.8 Coping with flux imbalance

The flux imbalance problem has caused the push-pull topology to fall out of favor in recent years. There are a number of ways to circumvent the problem, but they all more or less have drawbacks in terms of increased cost or components. Some schemes to combat flux imbalance are described in the following subsections.

2.2.8.1 Gapping the core. Flux imbalance becomes serious when the core moves out onto the curved part of the hysteresis loop (Fig. 2.3) and magnetizing current starts increasing exponentially as in Fig. 2.4c. This can be avoided by moving the curved part of the hysteresis loop out to greater oersted levels. The core can then tolerate a larger DC current bias or volt-second product inequality.

An air gap introduced in series with the magnetic flux lines has the effect shown in Fig. 2.5. It tilts the slope of the hysteresis loop, keeping the point where it crosses the zero-gauss (0-G) level (the so-called coercive force H_c) fixed. An air gap of 2 to 4 mils brings the curved portion of the loop far out in oersteds so that the core can accept a reasonably large volt-second product inequality for cores used in the 10- to 500-W power level.

The air gap for a prototype EE or cup core is usually done with plastic shims in the center and outer legs. Since the flux passes through the center leg and returns through the outer legs, the total gap is twice the shim thickness. In a production transformer, it is not very much more expensive to have the center leg ground down to twice the

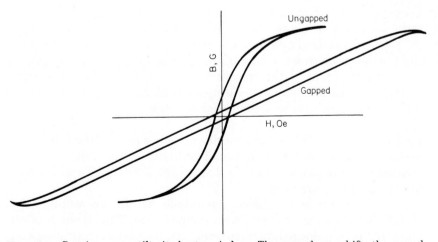

Figure 2.5 Gapping a core tilts its hysteresis loop. The gapped core shifts the curved part of the hysteresis loop out to higher oersted region and permits operation with a greater flux imbalance or DC current bias without saturation.

shim thickness. This will achieve pretty much the same effect as shims in the center and outer legs but is preferable as the gap remains more constant over time and results in less RFI interference.

2.2.8.2 Adding primary resistance. It was pointed out in Sec. 2.2.6 that primary wiring resistance keeps the core from rapidly being driven into saturation if there is a volt-second inequality. If there is such an inequality, the half primary with the larger volt-second product draws a larger peak current. That larger current causes a larger voltage drop across the wiring resistance and robs volt-seconds from that half primary, restoring the current balance.

This effect can be augmented by adding additional resistance in series with both primary halves. The added resistors can be located in either the collectors or emitters of the power transistors. They are best determined empirically by observing the current pulses in the transformer center tap. The resistors are usually under 0.25 Ω.

2.2.8.3 Matching power transistors. Since a volt-second inequality arises mainly from an inequality in storage time or on voltage in the power transistors, if those parameters are matched, it adds confidence that together with the above two "fixes" there will be no problem with flux imbalance.

This is not a certain or inexpensive fix. It is quite expensive to match transistors in two parameters. It requires a specialized test set up to do the matching and this is not available if field replacements become necessary.

It also must be ascertained that if the matching is done at certain load currents and room temperature, the matching still holds when these vary. Further, a storage time match is difficult to make credible as it depends strongly on forward and reverse base input currents in the bipolar transistors. Generally, any matching is usually done by matching V_{ce} and V_{be} (the on collector-to-emitter and base-to-emitter voltages) at the maximum operating current. Matching is not a viable solution for high-volume commercial supplies.

2.2.8.4 Using MOSFET power transistors. Since most of the volt-second inequality arises from storage time inequality between the two power transistors, this problem largely disappears if MOSFETs which have no storage times are used.

Further, there is an added advantage as the on voltage of a MOSFET transistor increases with temperature. Thus if one half primary tends to take a larger current, its transistor runs somewhat warmer and its on voltage increases and steals voltage from the winding. This reduces the volt-second product on that side and tends to restore balance. This, of course, is qualitatively in the right direction but cannot be depended on quantitatively and with certainty to solve the flux-imbalance problem at all power levels and with a worst-case combination of the two power transistors.

Yet with power MOSFETs, at power levels under 100 W and with a gapped core, push-pull converters can be built with a high degree of confidence that there will be no flux imbalance problem.

2.2.8.5 Using current-mode topology. The best solution to the flux-imbalance problem is not to use the push-pull topology at all but a modified two-transistor push-pull version of it. This version—*current-mode topology*—has all the advantages of the conventional push-pull, solves the flux-imbalance problem with certainty, and has significant advantages of its own.

In conventional push-pull, there is always a residual fear that despite all the fixes, a flux-imbalance problem will arise in some worst-case situations. One transistor will start drawing more current as its half primary moves into saturation, and the transistor will be destroyed. Current-mode topology solves this problem by monitoring the current in each of the push-pull transistors on a pulse-by-pulse basis and forcing alternate current pulses to have equal amplitude.

Details of current-mode topology will be discussed in a later chapter.

2.2.9 Power transformer design relations

2.2.9.1 Core selection. Design of the transformer starts with an initial decision on the selection of a core for the desired total output power. The available output power from a core depends on operating frequency, peak operating flux density (B_1 and B_2 in Fig. 2.3), the core's iron area A_e and bobbin area A_b, and the current density in each winding.

Decisions on each of these parameters are interrelated, and choices are made to minimize the transformer size and its temperature rise. In Chap. 7 on magnetics, an equation will be derived showing the maximum available output power from a given core as a function of the parameters mentioned above.

The equation can be used in a set of iterative calculations, first making a tentative selection of a specific core, peak flux density, and operating frequency and calculating the available output power. Then if the available power is insufficient, a larger-sized core is selected and the calculations repeated until a core with the required output power is found.

This is a long and cumbersome procedure, and instead, the equation is turned into a set of charts which permit a core and operating frequency to be selected at a glance for any desired output power. Such equations and charts will be presented for most of the commonly used topologies in the chapter on magnetics.

But for the present, it will be assumed that these charts will be used to select a core and its iron area A_e is known. The rest of the transformer design involves calculation of the number of turns on the primary and secondaries, selection of wire sizes, and calculation of core and copper losses and transformer temperature rise.

Optimum sequencing of the various layers of wire on the core bobbin is important in improving coupling between the windings and reducing copper losses due to "skin" and "proximity" effects. Sequencing and skin and proximity effects will be discussed in Chap. 7. For the present, the design will proceed from the known value of the core iron area A_e for the core chosen from the selection charts described above.

2.2.9.2 Maximum power transistor on-time selection. Equation 2.1 shows that the converter keeps output voltage V_m constant by increasing T_{on} as V_{dc} decreases. Thus the maximum on time T_{on} occurs at the minimum specified DC input voltage V_{dc}. But the maximum on time must not exceed half the switching period. For if it did, the reset volt-second product would be less than the set volt-second product (Sec. 2.2.5) and after a very few cycles, the core would drift into saturation and destroy the power transistor.

Moreover, because of storage time in bipolar transistors, the base drive on time cannot be as large as a full half period. For storage time would cause the collector voltage on time to overlap with the on time of the opposite transistor on time. With simultaneous conduction in the two power transistors, the two half primaries could not support voltage. For (see Fig. 2.1) the dot end of N_{p1} would be trying to go negative and the no-dot end of N_{p2} would be trying to go negative also. Consequently, there would be no dB/dT in the core and from Faraday's law, there could be no voltage across the windings. Thus each transistor would take large currents at the full supply voltage and would immediately be destroyed.

Thus, to ensure that the core will always be reset within one period and there is never any possibility of simultaneous conduction, whenever the DC input voltage is at its minimum V_{dc} and the feedback loop is trying to increase T_{on} to maintain V_m constant, the on time will be constrained by some kind of a clamp to never be more than 80 percent of a half period. Then in Eq. 2.1, for specified V_{dc}, T and for $\overline{T_{on}} = 0.8T/2$, the ratio N_m/N_p will be fixed to yield the desired output V_m.

2.2.9.3 Primary turns selection. The number of primary turns is determined by Faraday's law (Eq. 1.17). From it N_p is fixed by the minimum voltage across the primary ($V_{dc} - 1$) and the maximum on time, which as above, is to be no more than $0.8T/2$. Then

$$N_p = \frac{(V_{dc} - 1)(0.8T/2) \times 10^{+8}}{A_e\,dB} \tag{2.7}$$

Since A_e in Eq. 2.7 is fixed by the selected core, V_{dc} and T are specified and the number of primary turns is fixed as soon as dB (the desired flux change in $0.8T/2$) is decided on. This decision is made as follows.

2.2.9.4 Maximum flux change selection. From Eq. 2.7, it is seen that the number of primary turns is inversely proportional to dB, the flux swing. It would seem desirable to maximize dB so as to minimize N_p, for fewer turns would mean that larger wire size could be used, resulting in higher permissible currents and more output from a given core. Also, fewer turns would result in a less expensive transformer and lower stray parasitic capacities.

From the hysteresis loop of Fig. 2.3, however, it is seen that in ferrite cores, the loop enters the curved portion above ± 2000 G. It is desirable to stay below that point as there the magnetizing current starts increasing exponentially. It might seem, then, that a good choice is ± 2000 G if that is not limited by core losses.

Now ferrite core losses increase at about the 2.7th power of the peak flux density and at about the 1.6th power of the operating frequency. Up to about 50 kHz, core losses do not prohibit operation to ± 2000 G and it would seem desirable at least up to that frequency to operate at that high peak flux level.

However, for a not easily evident reason, it is preferable to restrict operation to ± 1600 G even at frequencies where core losses are not prohibitive. The explanation is as follows. Faraday's law solved for the flux change dB is

$$dB = \frac{(V_{dc} - 1)(T_{on}) \times 10^{+8}}{N_p A_e} \tag{2.8}$$

Now Eq. 2.8 says that if N_p is chosen for a given dB—say, from -2000 to $+2000$ G or a dB of 4000 G, as long as the product of $(V_{dc} - 1)(T_{on})$ is constant, dB will be constant at 4000 G. Further, if the feedback loop is working and keeping the output voltage V_m constant, Eq. 2.1 says that $(V_{dc} - 1)(T_{on})$ is constant and dB will truly remain constant. That is, the feedback loop always ensures that whenever V_{dc} is a minimum, T_{on} is a maximum and there can never be a situation when T_{on} is a maximum and V_{dc} is simultaneously a maximum.

Now in some transient or fault condition even if for a single or possibly a few cycles, if T_{on} had been a maximum and V_{dc} had a transient step to 50 percent above its normal value and the feedback loop failed to reduce the on time in accordance with Eq. 2.1, the condition of maximum V_{dc} and maximum T_{on} could exist. Equation 2.8 then says that dB would be 1.5(4000) or 6000 G.

Then if the core had started from the -2000-G point, at the end of that on time the core would have been driven 6000 G above that or to $+4000$ G. Also, the hysteresis loop (Fig. 2.3) shows that at temperatures somewhat above 25°C, it would be deep in saturation and could not support the applied voltage. The transistor would be subject to high current and high voltage and would immediately fail.

This situation could arise as can be seen from the circuit in Fig. 2.1 if there were a delay in the response of the error amplifier. The error amplifier shown in that figure will always eventually correct the on time so as to keep the product $(V_{dc} - 1)(T_{on})$ constant in accordance with Eq. 2.1, for that is how the circuit regulates. But as will be seen in the chapter on feedback analysis, the error amplifier has a delay in its response time as its bandwidth is limited to stabilize the feedback loop.

Thus if even for a single cycle, if the core is subjected to maximum input voltage and maximum on time as a result of error-amplifier delay, it will saturate and destroy the transistor.

However, if N_p in Eq. 2.8 is chosen to yield dB of 3200 G at $\overline{V_{dc}}$ and $\overline{T_{on}}$ the design is safer and can tolerate a 50 percent transient step in input voltage. With dB = 3200 G, if the error amplifier is too slow to correct the on time, the transient dB will be 1.5(3200) or 4800 G; and if the core started from its normal location of -1600 G, it will be driven up to only $-1600 + 4800$ or $+3200$ G. The hysteresis loop of Fig. 2.3 shows that the core can tolerate that even at 100°C.

Thus the number of primary turns is selected from Eq. 2.7 for dB = 3200 G even at frequencies where larger flux changes would not yield excessive core losses. Above 50 kHz, increasing core losses force a decrease in peak flux density. At 100 to 200 kHz, peak flux density may have to be limited to 1200 or possibly to 800 G, respectively, to achieve an acceptably low core temperature rise.

2.2.9.5 Secondary turns selection. Secondary turns for the main and slave output voltages are selected from Eqs. 2.1, 2.2, and 2.3. In those equations all parameters have already been specified, arbitrarily set, or calculated. Output voltages, $\underline{V_{dc}}$ and T have been specified. The maximum on time $\overline{T_{\text{on}}}$ has been arbitrarily set at $0.8T/2$ and N_p has been calculated from Faraday's law (Eq. 2.7) for the known A_e from the selected core. Flux change dB has been set at 3200 G for frequencies under 50 kHz and to minimize core losses, at lower values at higher frequencies as discussed above.

2.2.10 Primary, secondary peak and rms currents

Selection of wire sizes for all the windings requires knowledge of the rms currents they carry. For wire sizes will be selected on the basis of a conservative value of their operating current density in terms of circular mils[*] of area per rms ampere.

2.2.10.1 Primary peak current calculation.

Current drawn from the DC input source V_{dc} may be monitored in the transformer center tap and has the waveshape shown in Fig. 2.1b and 2.1d. The pulses have the characteristic ramp-on-a-step waveshape because the secondaries all have output LC filters as discussed in Sec. 1.3.2. The primary current is simply the sum of all the secondary ramp-on-a-step currents reflected by their turns ratios into the primary plus the magnetizing current.

As discussed in Sec. 2.2.9.2, at minimum DC input voltage V_{dc}, transistor on times will be 80 percent of a half period and since there is one pulse for each half period, the duty cycle of the pulses in Fig. 2.1 is 0.8 at V_{dc}. To simplify calculation, the pulses in the figure are assumed to have an equivalent flat-topped waveshape whose amplitude I_{pft} is the value of the current at the center of the ramp.

Then the input power at V_{dc} is that voltage times the average current, which is $0.8I_{\text{pft}}$, and assuming 80 percent efficiency (which is usually achievable up to 200 kHz), $P_o = 0.8P_{\text{in}}$ or

$$P_{\text{in}} = 1.25P_o = \underline{V_{\text{dc}}\,0.8I_{\text{pft}}}$$

Then $\qquad\qquad I_{\text{pft}} = 1.56\dfrac{P_o}{V_{\text{dc}}}$ $\qquad(2.9)$

This is a useful relation, as it gives the equivalent flat-topped primary current pulse amplitude in terms of what is known—the output power and the specified minimum DC input voltage. It permits select-

---

[*]A circular mil is the area of a circle 1 mil in diameter. Thus, area in square inches $= (\pi/4)10^{-6}$ (area in circular mils).

ing a transistor with an adequate current rating and choosing primary wire size from the corresponding primary rms current.

2.2.10.2 Primary rms current calculation and wire size selection. Each half primary carries only one of the I_{pft} pulses per period and hence its duty cycle is $(0.8T/2)/T$ or 0.4. It is well known that the rms value of a flat-topped pulse of amplitude I_{pft} at a duty cycle D is

$$I_{rms} = I_{pft}\sqrt{D} = I_{pft}\sqrt{0.4}$$

or

$$I_{rms} = 0.632 I_{pft} \tag{2.10}$$

and from Eq. 2.9

$$I_{rms} = 0.632 \frac{1.56 P_o}{V_{dc}} = \frac{0.986 P_o}{V_{dc}} \tag{2.11}$$

This again gives the rms current in each half primary in terms of what is known: output power and the specified minimum DC input voltage.

Now conservative practice in transformer design is to operate the windings at a current density of 500 circular mils per rms ampere. There is nothing absolute about this; current densities of 300 circular mils per rms ampere are frequently used for windings with few turns. As a general rule, however, densities greater than 300 circular mils per rms ampere should be avoided as that will cause excessive copper losses and temperature rise.

Thus at 500 circular mils per rms ampere, the required number of circular mils for the half primaries is

$$\text{Primary circular mil requirement} = 500 \frac{0.986 P_o}{V_{dc}}$$

$$= 493 \frac{P_o}{V_{dc}} \tag{2.12}$$

This, too, is in terms of known values—output power and specified minimum DC input voltage. Proper wire size can then be chosen from wire tables at the circular mils given by Eq. 2.12.

2.2.10.3 Secondary peak, rms current, and wire size calculation. Currents in each half secondary are shown in Fig. 2.6. Note the ledge at the end of the transistor on time. This ledge of current exists because there is no free-wheeling diode $D1$ at the input to the filter inductor as

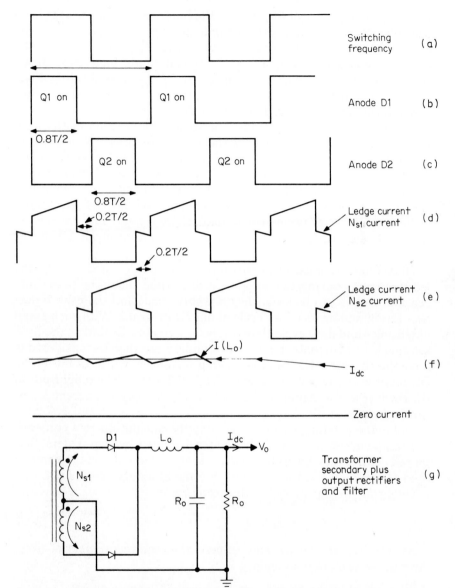

Figure 2.6 Output rectifiers serve as free-wheeling diodes in a push-pull circuit. Secondaries carry the normal free-wheeling "ledge" current during the 20 percent dead time. This should be considered in estimating secondary copper losses.

in the buck regulator of Fig. 1.4. In the buck, the free-wheeling diode was essential as a return path for inductor current when the transistor turned off. When the transistor turned off, the polarity across the output inductor reversed and its front end would have gone disastrously negative if it had not been caught by the free-wheeling diode at about 1 V below ground. Inductor current then continued to flow through the free-wheeling diode $D1$ of Fig. 1.4e.

In the push-pull output stages, however, the function of the free-wheeling diode is performed by the output rectifiers. When either transistor turns off, the front end of the inductor tries to go negative. As soon as it goes about one diode drop below ground, both rectifiers latch in, each drawing roughly half the total current the inductor had been drawing just prior to turnoff (Fig. 2.6d and 2.6e). Since the impedance of each half secondary is small, there is negligible drop across them and the rectifier diode cathodes are caught at about 1 V below ground.

Thus if half-secondary rms currents are to be calculated exactly, the ledge currents during the 20 percent dead time should be taken into account. But as can be seen, they are only about half the peak inductor current and have a duty cycle of $(0.4T/2)/T$ or 0.2. With such small amplitudes and duty cycle they can be ignored in calculating the half-secondary rms currents. Each half secondary can then be considered to have the characteristic ramp-on-a-step waveform, which at minimum DC input comes at a duty cycle of $(0.8T/2)/T$ or 0.4. The magnitude of the current at the center of the ramp is the DC output current I_{dc}, as can be seen from Fig. 2.6f.

As for the primary currents, to simplify calculating rms currents, the ramp-on-a-step pulses will be approximated by "equivalent flat-topped" pulses I_{sft} whose amplitude is that at the center of the ramp or the DC output current I_{dc} and which come at a duty cycle of 0.4.

Thus rms current in each half secondary is

$$I_{s(rms)} = I_{dc}\sqrt{D} = I_{dc}\sqrt{0.4} = 0.632I_{dc} \qquad (2.13)$$

At 500 circular mils per rms ampere, the required number of circular mils for each half secondary is

$$\text{Secondary circular mil requirement} = 500(0.632)I_{dc}$$

$$= 316I_{dc} \qquad (2.14)$$

2.2.11 Transistor voltage stress and leakage inductance spikes

It can be seen from the transformer dots in Fig. 2.1 that when either transistor is on, the opposite transistor's collector is subject to at least twice the DC supply voltage since both half primaries have an equal number of turns.

However, the maximum stress is somewhat more than twice the maximum DC input voltage. The added contribution comes from the so-called leakage inductance spikes shown in Fig. 2.1a and 2.1c. These come about because there is an effective small inductance (leakage inductance L_l) in series with each half primary as shown in Fig. 2.7a.

At the instant of turnoff, current in the transistor falls rapidly at a rate dI/dT causing a positive-going spike of amplitude $E_{ls} = L_l \, dI/dT$ at the bottom end of the leakage inductance. Conservative design practice is to assume the leakage inductance spike may be as much as

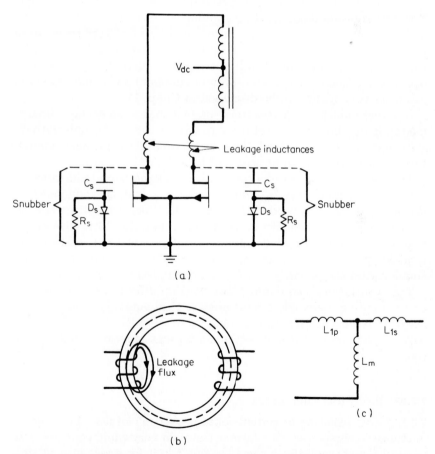

(a)

(b)

(c)

Figure 2.7 (a) Leakage inductances cause the spikes of Fig. 2.1a. (b) Leakage inductance stems from the fact that some of the magnetic flux lines return through a local air path rather than linking the secondary through the core. (c) Low-frequency equivalent circuit of a transformer showing magnetizing inductance L_m and primary and secondary leakage inductances L_{1p} and L_{1s}.

30 percent more than twice the maximum DC input voltage. The transistors should then be chosen so that they can tolerate with some safety margin, a maximum voltage stress (V_{ms}) of

$$V_{ms} = 1.3(2\overline{V_{dc}}) \tag{2.15}$$

Magnitude of the leakage inductance is not easily calculable. It can be minimized by use of a transformer core with a long center leg and sandwiching the secondary windings (especially the higher current ones) in between halves of the primary. A good transformer should have leakage inductance no more than 2 to 4 percent of its magnetizing inductance.

Leakage inductance spikes can be minimized by addition of a capacitor, resistor, and diode (CRD) combination to the transistor collector as shown in Fig. 2.7a. Such CRD configurations (referred to as "snubbers") also serve the important function of reducing AC switching losses due to the overlap of falling transistor current and rising voltage at the collector. Detailed design of snubbers and some associated penalties they incur will be discussed in Chap. 11.

Leakage inductance arises from the fact that some of the primary's magnetic flux lines do not return through the core and couple with the secondary windings. Instead, they return around the primary winding through a local air path as seen in Fig. 2.7b.

The equivalent circuit of a core with its magnetizing inductance L_m (Sec. 2.2.6) and primary L_{1p} and secondary L_{1s} leakage inductances is shown in Fig. 2.7c. Secondary leakage inductance arises from the fact that some of the secondary current's magnetic flux lines also do not couple with the primary but instead link the secondary windings via a local air path. But in most cases, the number of secondary turns is smaller than the primary and L_{1s} can be neglected.

The transformer's equivalent circuit (Fig. 2.7c) is very valuable in understanding many odd circuit effects. That equivalent circuit is an accurate representation up to about 300 or 500 kHz, where shunt parasitic capacitors across and between windings must be taken into account.

2.2.12   Power transistor losses

2.2.12.1   AC switching or current-voltage "overlap" losses.   Leakage inductance in the power transformer causes a very rapid collector voltage fall time because for a short time at $T = 0$, for a fast current step, an inductor is an infinite impedance. Since the current cannot change instantaneously through an inductor, current rises slowly through it.

Thus there is very little overlap of falling voltage and rising current at turnon and negligible switching losses.

At turnoff, however, there is significant overlap and a worst-case scenario such as that for the buck regulator of Fig. 1.5b is assumed. The exact situation is shown in Fig. 2.8, where it is assumed that the current hangs on at its equivalent flat-topped peak value I_{pft} (Sec. 2.2.10.1) for the time it takes the voltage to rise T_{vr} to its maximum value of $2\overline{V_{dc}}$. Then the voltage remains at $2\overline{V_{dc}}$ during the time it takes the current to fall from I_{pft} to zero T_{cf}. Assuming $T_{vr} = T_{cf} = T_s$ and a switching period T, the total switching dissipation per transistor per period $P_{t(ac)}$ is

$$P_{t(ac)} = I_{pft}\frac{2\overline{V_{dc}}}{2}\frac{T_s}{T} + 2V_{dc}\frac{I_{pft}}{2}\frac{T_s}{T}$$

$$= 2(I_{pft})(\overline{V_{dc}})\frac{T_s}{T}$$

and from Eq. 2.9, $I_{pft} = 1.56(P_o/V_{dc})$:

$$P_{t(ac)} = 3.12\frac{P_o}{V_{dc}}\overline{V_{dc}}\frac{T_s}{T} \qquad (2.16)$$

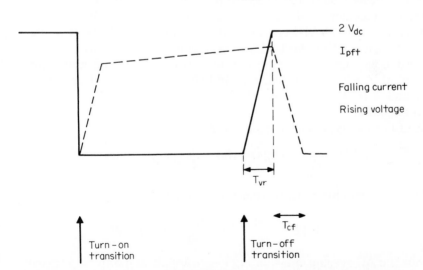

Figure 2.8 AC or "overlap" switching losses in push-pull transistor. There are negligible switching losses at turnon because transformer leakage inductance causes a very fast voltage fall down and a slow current rise time. This results in very little overlap of falling voltage and rising current. Worst-case scenario is assumed at turnoff. Current remains constant at its peak I_{pft} until voltage rises to $2\overline{V_{dc}}$. The voltage remains at $2\overline{V_{dc}}$ for the duration of the current fall time T_{cf}.

2.2.12.2 DC conduction losses. Maximum DC losses per transistor are simply the on voltage times the on current times the on duty cycle per transistor, or

$$P_{dc} = I_{pft} V_{on} \frac{0.8T/2}{T} = 0.4 I_{pft} V_{on}$$

It will be seen in Chap. 8 on bipolar base drives that a technique called *Baker clamping* will be used to reduce transistor storage times. This forces the collector on potential to be about 1 V over a large range of current. Then for I_{pft} from Eq. 2.9 we obtain

$$P_{dc} = 0.4 \frac{1.56 P_o}{V_{dc}} = \frac{0.624 P_o}{V_{dc}} \tag{2.17}$$

and total losses per transistor are

$$P_{total} = P_{t(ac)} + P_{dc}$$

$$= 3.12 \frac{P_o}{V_{dc}} \overline{V_{dc}} \frac{T_s}{T} + \frac{0.624 P_o}{V_{dc}} \tag{2.18}$$

2.2.12.3 Typical losses: 150-W, 50 kHz push-pull converter. It is instructive to get a feel for the dissipation per transistor in a 150-W push-pull converter at, say, 50 kHz operating from a standard telephone industry power source. Standard telephone industry power sources provide a nominal voltage of 48 V, minimum (V_{dc}) of 38 V and maximum $(\overline{V_{dc}})$ of 60 V. It is assumed that at 50 kHz, bipolar transistors will be used and a reasonable value of the switching time $(T_s$ as defined above) is 0.3 μs.

The DC conduction losses from Eq. 2.17 are

$$P_{dc} = \frac{0.624 \times 150}{38} = 2.46 \quad \text{W}$$

and the AC switching losses from Eq. 2.16 are

$$P_{t(ac)} = 3.12 \times \frac{150}{38} \times 60 \times \frac{0.3}{20} = 11.08 \quad \text{W}$$

Thus the AC overlap or switching losses are about 4.5 times as great as the DC conduction losses. If MOSFET transistors with switching times T_s of about 0.05 μs, are used, the falling current and rising voltage intersect so low down on the current waveform that switching losses are negligible.

2.2.13 Output power and input voltage
limitations in push-pull topology

Aside from the flux-imbalance problem in the push-pull topology (which does not exist in its close cousin, viz., current-mode topology), its area of usage in output power is limited by Eq. 2.9 and in input voltage by Eq. 2.15.

Equation 2.9 gives the peak current required of the transistor for a desired output power, and Eq. 2.15 gives the maximum voltage stress on the transistor in terms of the maximum DC input voltage. Both these relations limit the push-pull to about 300 W. Above that level, it is difficult to find a bipolar transistor which can meet the peak current and voltage stresses and be fast enough with adequate gain and low on voltage.

The faster MOSFET transistor with adequately high voltage and current ratings and sufficiently low on voltage may be too expensive for commercial applications.

Thus consider a 400-W push-pull converter operating from telephone industry prime voltage source which is 48 V (nominal), 38 V (minimum), and 60 V (maximum).

Equation 2.9 gives the peak current requirement as $I_{\text{pft}} = 1.56 P_o / V_{\text{dc}} = 1.56(400)/38 = 16.4$ A, and Eq. 2.15 gives the maximum off voltage stress as $V_{\text{ms}} = 2.6 V_{\text{dc}} = 2.6 \times 60 = 156$ V. To provide a margin of safety, a transistor with at least a 200-V rating would be sought.

A potential bipolar transistor candidate for the above supply is possibly the MJ13330. It has a 20-A peak current rating, V_{ceo} rating of 200 V, and V_{cev} (the voltage it can sustain if, at the instant of turnoff, it has a negative bias of -1 to -5 V) rating of 400 V. It can thus meet the peak voltage and current stresses.

At the 16-A level, it has a maximum on potential of about 3 V, a minimum gain of about 5, and a storage time of about 1.3 to 4 μs. With these limitations, it would have high DC and AC switching losses, have difficulty with flux imbalance (unless the current-mode equivalent version of push-pull were used) and would have difficulty operating above 40 kHz because of the long storage times.

A potential MOSFET transistor for such an application might be a MTH30N20. This is a 30-A, 200-V device which at 16 A would have 1.3 V of on drop and hence half the DC conduction losses of the preceding bipolar transistor. With its rapid current fall time, it would have negligible AC switching losses. But at $11.50 in quantities above 100, it would be too expensive for commercial applications. The 15-A, 200-V device (MTH15N200) could be used and would cost only $4.10 in quantities above 100. But it would have twice the on drop and twice the DC conduction losses.

For off-line converters the push-pull topology is almost always ruled out by the maximum off voltage stress of $2.6V_{dc}$ (Eq. 2.15). Thus for a 120-V-AC line input with ±10 percent tolerance, peak rectified DC voltage is $1.41 \times 1.1 \times 120 = 186$ V. At the top of the leakage spike, Eq. 2.15 gives peak off stress as $2.6 \times 186 = 484$ V.

Transients above the maximum steady-state value must also be considered. Transients seldom are specified for commercial power supplies, in which case conservative design practice is to assume that they are 15 percent above the maximum steady-state value. This would bring the above maximum stress to 1.15×484 or 557 V.

Input voltage transients in special cases can be greater than 15 percent above maximum steady-state value. Thus AC input voltage specifications on military aircraft are given by Military Standard 704. That specification gives the nominal voltage as 113 V AC but with a 10-ms transient to 180 V AC. At 180 V AC, the peak off stress from Eq. 1.42 is $180 \times 1.41 \times 2.6$ or 660 V.

There are many fast bipolar transistors, which can safely sustain voltages as high as 850 V if they have a reverse input bias of −1 to −5 V at turnoff (V_{cev} rating). But it is unnecessarily dangerous to use a topology which subjects the off transistor to twice the maximum DC input plus a 30 percent leakage spike. There are topologies to be described below which subject the off transistor to only the maximum DC input voltage with no leakage spike. These are a better choice— not only because of the lesser voltage stress but also because the smaller voltage excursion at turnoff produces less electromagnetic interference (EMI).

2.2.14   Output filter design relations

2.2.14.1   Output inductor design.   It was pointed out in Sec. 2.2.4 that in both master and slave outputs the output inductors should not be permitted to go discontinuous. Recall that the discontinuous mode situation commences when the front end of the inductor current ramp of Fig. 1.6b has dropped to zero and that this occurs when the DC current has dropped to half the ramp amplitude dI (Sec. 1.3.6). Then (see Fig. 2.9)

$$dI = 2I_{dc} = V_L \frac{T_{on}}{L_o} = (V_1 - V_o) \frac{T_{on}}{L_o} \tag{2.19}$$

But $V_o = V_1(2T_{on}/T)$. Then

$$T_{on} = \frac{V_o T}{2V_1}$$

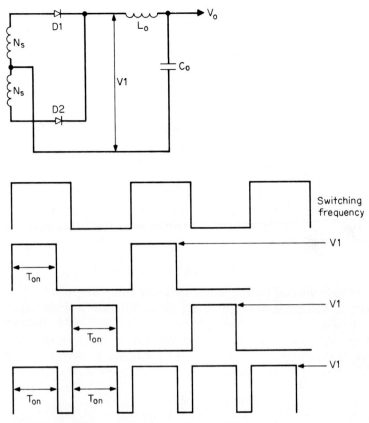

Figure 2.9 Output circuit for calculation and L_o, C_o. When V_{dc} at its minimum, N_s will be chosen so that as $V1$ is at its minimum, T_{on} will not have to be greater than $0.8T/2$ to yield the specified value of V_o.

But N_s will be chosen so that T_{on} will be $0.8T/2$ when V_{dc} and consequently V_1 are at their minima. Then

$$\overline{T_{on}} = \frac{0.8T}{2} = \frac{V_o T}{2V_1} \quad \text{or} \quad \underline{V_1 = 1.25V_o}$$

and

$$dI = \frac{(1.25V_o - V_o)(0.8T/2)}{L_o} = 2I_{dc} \quad \text{and} \quad L_o = \frac{0.05V_o T}{I_{dc}}$$

Then if the minimum current I_{dc} is specified as one-tenth the nominal current I_{on} (the usual case)

$$L_o = \frac{0.5 V_o T}{I_{\text{on}}} \tag{2.20}$$

where L_o is in henries
$\quad V_o$ is in volts
$\quad T$ is in seconds
$\quad I_{\text{dc}}$ is minimum output current in amperes
$\quad I_{\text{on}}$ is nominal output current in amperes

2.2.14.2 Output capacitor design. The output capacitor C_o is selected to meet the maximum output ripple voltage specification. In Sec. 1.3.7 it was shown that the output ripple is determined almost completely by the magnitude of the ESR (equivalent series resistance, R_o) in the filter capacitor and not by the magnitude of the capacitor itself. The peak-to-peak ripple voltage V_r is very closely equal to

$$V_r = R_o \, dI \tag{2.21}$$

where dI is the selected peak-to-peak inductor ramp amplitude.

However, it was pointed out that (for aluminum electrolytic capacitors) the product $R_o C_o$ has been observed to be relatively constant over a large range of capacitor magnitudes and voltage ratings. For aluminum electrolytics, the product $R_o C_o$ ranges between 50 and 80×10^{-6}. Then C_o is selected as

$$C_o = \frac{80 \times 10^{-6}}{R_o} = \frac{80 \times 10^{-6}}{V_r / dI}$$

$$= \frac{(80 \times 10^{-6})(dI)}{V_r} \tag{2.22}$$

where C_o is in farads for dI in amperes (Eq. 2.19) and V_r is in volts.

2.3   Forward Converter Topology

2.3.1   Basic operation

Forward converter topology is shown in Fig. 2.10. It is probably the most widely used topology for output powers under 150 to 200 W when maximum DC input voltage is in the range of 60 to 200 V. Below a maximum of 60 V, for the associated minimum input voltage, the required primary input current becomes uncomfortably large. Above a maximum DC input voltage of about 250 V, the maximum voltage stress on the transistor becomes too large. Above a required output power of 200 W, at any DC input voltage, the required primary input current becomes too large. Mathematical explanations for these limitations will be shown in the discussions to follow.

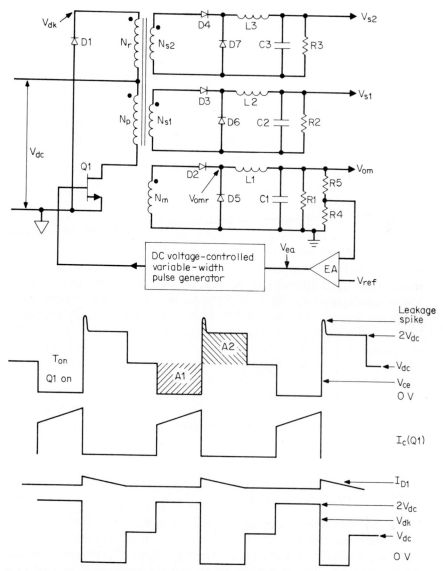

Figure 2.10 Forward converter topology. Showing feedback loop closed around one master N_{om} which is regulated against line and load changes. Also two semiregulated slaves (V_{s1} and V_{s2}) which are regulated against line changes only.

The topology is an outgrowth of the push-pull circuit of Fig. 2.1 but does not suffer from the latter's major shortcoming of flux imbalance. Since it has one rather than two transistors, compared to the push-pull, it is more economical in dollars and required space.

As for the push-pull, Fig. 2.10 shows a master output V_{om} and two slaves, V_{s1} and V_{s2}. A negative-feedback loop is closed around the master and controls the $Q1$ on time so as to keep V_{om} constant against line and load changes. With an on time fixed by the master feedback loop, the slave outputs V_{s1}, V_{s2} are kept constant against input voltage changes but only partly (to about 5 to 8 percent) against load changes either in themselves or in the master. The circuit works as follows.

In the forward converter, one of the transistors of the push-pull of Fig. 2.1 has been replaced by the diode $D1$. When $Q1$ is turned on, the dot end of the primary power winding N_p and of all secondaries go positive with respect to their no dot ends. Current and power flows into the dot end of N_p. All rectifier diodes $D2$ to $D4$ are forward-biased and current and power flows out of the dot ends of all secondaries to the LC filters and the loads.

Note that power flows to the loads when the power transistor $Q1$ is turned on—thus the term *forward converter*. The push-pull and buck regulator also deliver power to the loads when the power transistors are on and are also forward types. In contrast, the boost regulator, the polarity inverter of Figs. 1.10 and 1.14, and the flyback type (to be discussed in a later chapter) store energy in an inductor or transformer primary when the power transistor is on and deliver it to the load when the transistor turns off. Such energy storage topologies can operate in either the discontinuous or continuous mode. They are fundamentally different from forward topologies, are discussed in Secs. 1.4.2 and 1.4.3, and will be taken up again in Chap. 4 on flyback topology.

Now, for a $Q1$ on time of T_{on}, the voltage at the master rectifier cathode (Fig. 2.10b) is at a high level for T_{on}. Assuming a 1-V on voltage for $Q1$ and a rectifier on forward drop of V_{D2}, that high-level voltage V_{omr} is

$$V_{omr} = \left[(V_{dc} - 1) \frac{N_m}{N_p} \right] - V_{D2} \tag{2.23}$$

The circuitry after the rectifier diode cathodes is exactly like that of the buck regulator of Fig. 1.4. Diodes $D5$ to $D7$ act like the freewheeling diode $D1$ of that figure. When $Q1$ turns off, current stored in the magnetizing inductance of $T1$ (recall the equivalent circuit of a transformer as in Fig. 2.7c) reverses the polarity of the voltage across N_p. Now all the dot ends of primary and secondary windings go negative with respect to their no-dot ends. If not for "catch" diode $D1$, the dot end of N_r would go very far negative and since N_p and N_r have equal turns (usually), the no-dot end of N_p would go sufficiently positive to avalanche $Q1$ and destroy it.

However, catch diode $D1$ catches the dot end of N_r at one diode drop below ground. If there were no leakage inductance in $T1$ (recall again

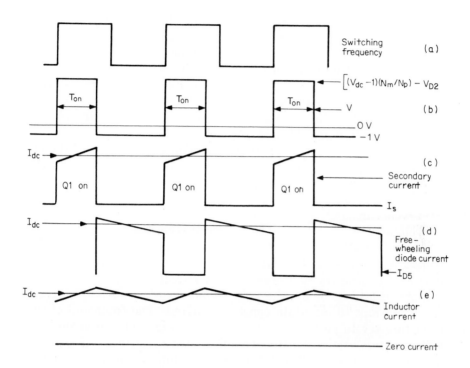

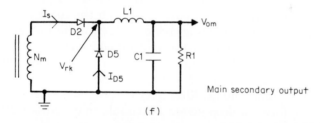

Figure 2.11 Critical secondary currents in forward converter. Each secondary has the characteristic ramp-on-a-step waveshape because of the fixed voltage across the output inductor and its constant inductance. Inductor current is the sum of the secondary plus the free-wheeling diode current. It ramps up and down about the DC output current. Primary current is the sum of all the ramp-on-a-step secondary currents reflected by their turns ratios into the primary. Primary current is then also at ramp-on-a-step waveform.

the equivalent circuit of a transformer as in Fig. 2.7c), the voltage across N_p would equal that across N_r. Assuming that the 1-V forward drop across $D1$ can be neglected, the voltage across N_r and N_p is V_{dc} and the voltage at the no-dot end of N_p and at the $Q1$ collector is then $2V_{dc}$.

Recall, now, that within one cycle, if a core has moved in one direction on its hysteresis loop, it must be restored to exactly its original position on the loop before it moves in the same direction again in the next cycle. For otherwise, after many cycles, the core will be pushed in one direction or another into saturation. It will not be able to support the applied voltage and the transistor will be destroyed.

In Fig. 2.10, it is seen that when $Q1$ is on for a time T_{on}, N_p is subjected to volt-second product $V_{dc}T_{on}$ with its dot end positive. That volt-second product is the area $A1$ in Fig. 2.10. By Faraday's law (Eq. 1.17), that volt-second product causes—say, a positive—flux change $dB = (V_{dc}T_{on}/N_pA_e)10^{-8}$ gauss.

At turnoff, when the magnetizing inductance has reversed the polarity across N_p and kept its no dot-end at $2V_{dc}$ long enough for the volt-second area product $A2$ in Fig. 2.10 to equal area $A1$, the core has been restored to its original position on the hysteresis loop and the next cycle can safely start. In the common jargon expression, the "reset volt-seconds" has equaled the "set volt-seconds."

Now when $Q1$ has turned off, the dot ends of all secondaries go negative with respect to their no-dot ends. Current in all output inductors $L1$ to $L3$ try to decrease. Since current in inductors cannot change instantaneously, the polarity across all inductors reverses in an attempt to maintain constant current. The front end of the inductors try to go far negative but are caught at one diode drop below output ground by free-wheeling diodes $D5$ to $D7$ (Fig. 2.10) and rectifier diodes $D2$ to $D4$ are reverse-biased. Inductor current now continues to flow in the same direction through its output end, returning through the load, partly through the filter capacitor, and up through the free-wheeling diode back into the inductor.

Voltage at the cathode of the main diode rectifier $D2$ is then as shown in Fig. 2.11b. It is high at a level of $[(V_{dc} - 1)(N_m/N_p)] - V_{D2}$ for time T_{on}, and for a time $T - T_{on}$ it is one free-wheeling diode($D5$) drop below ground. The LC filter averages this waveform, and assuming that the forward drop across $D5$ equals that across $D2(=V_d)$, the DC output voltage at V_{om} is

$$V_{om} = \left[\left((V_{dc} - 1)\frac{N_m}{N_p}\right) - V_d\right]\frac{T_{on}}{T} \qquad (2.24)$$

2.3.2 Design relations: output/input voltage, on time, turns ratios

The negative-feedback loop senses a fraction of V_{om}, compares it to a reference voltage V_{ref}, and varies T_{on} so as to keep V_{om} constant for any changes in V_{dc} or load current.

From Eq. 2.24, it can be seen that as V_{dc} changes, the feedback loop keeps the output constant by keeping the product $V_{dc}T_{on}$ constant.

Thus maximum $T_{on}(\overline{T_{on}})$ will occur at minimum specified $V_{dc}(\overline{V_{dc}})$ and Eq. 2.24 can be rewritten for minimum DC input voltage as

$$V_{om} = \left[\left((\underline{V_{dc}} - 1)\frac{N_m}{N_p}\right) - V_d\right]\frac{\overline{T_{on}}}{T} \tag{2.25}$$

In relation 2.25, a number of design decisions must be made in the proper sequence. First, the minimum DC input voltage V_{dc} is specified. Then the maximum permitted on time T_{on} which occurs at $\underline{V_{dc}}$ (minimum V_{dc}) will be set at 80 percent of a half period.

This is done to ensure (Fig. 2.10) that the area $A2$ can equal $A1$. For if on time were permitted to go to a full half period, $A2$ would just barely equal $A1$ at the start of the next full cycle. Now small increases in on time due to storage time changes with temperature or production spreads in storage time would not permit $A2$ to equal $A1$. The core would not be completely reset to its starting point on the hysteresis loop, it would drift up into saturation after some cycles and destroy the transistor.

Next the number of primary turns N_p will be established from Faraday's law (Eq. 1.17) for V_{dc} and a certain specified flux change dB in the time T_{on}. Limits on that flux change are similar to those described for the push-pull topology in Sec. 1.5.9 and will also be discussed below.

Thus in Eq. 2.25, $\underline{V_{dc}}$, $\overline{T_{on}}$, T, and V_d are specified and N_p is calculated from Faraday's law. That fixes the number of main secondary turns N_m to achieve the required main output voltage V_{om}.

2.3.3 Slave output voltages

The slave output filters $L2$, $C2$ and $L3$, $C3$ average the width-modulated rectangular waveforms at their respective rectifier cathodes. The waveform upper levels are $[(V_{dc} - 1)(N_{s1}/N_p)] - V_{d3}$ and $[V_{dc} - 1)(N_{s2}/N_p)] - V_{d4}$, respectively. At their lower level, voltages are one diode drop below ground. They are at their high level for the same maximum T_{on} as the main secondary when the input DC input voltage is at its specified minimum V_{dc}. Then again assuming that the forward rectifier and free-wheeling diode drops are equal V_d, the slave output voltages at low line V_{dc} are

$$V_{s1} = \left[\left((\underline{V_{dc}} - 1)\frac{N_{s1}}{N_p}\right) - .V_d\right]\frac{\overline{T_{on}}}{T} \tag{2.26}$$

$$V_{s2} = \left[\left((\underline{V_{dc}} - 1)\frac{N_{s2}}{N_p}\right) - V_d\right]\frac{\overline{T_{on}}}{T} \tag{2.27}$$

Now in regulating V_{om}, the feedback loop keeps $V_{dc}T_{on}$ constant. But that same product appears in Eqs. 2.26 and 2.27 and hence the slave outputs remain constant as V_{dc} varies.

It can be seen from Eq. 2.24 and Fig. 2.14 that the negative-feedback loop keeps the main output constant for either line or load changes by appropriately controlling T_{on} so that the sampled output is equal to the reference voltage V_{ref}. This is not obvious for load changes as load current does not appear directly in Eq. 2.24. But it does appear indirectly. For load changes will change the on drop of $Q1$ (assumed as 1 V heretofore) and the forward drop in the rectifier diode. These, though small, will cause small changes in the output voltage, be sensed by the error amplifier, and be corrected for by a small change in T_{on}.

Moreover, as can be seen in Eqs. 2.26 and 2.27, changes in T_{on} without corresponding changes in V_{dc} will cause changes in the slave output voltages. Slave output voltages also change with changes in their own load currents. As those currents change, the rectifier forward drops change, causing a change in the peak voltage at the input to the LC averaging filter. Slave output voltages will change as peak voltages to the averaging filter change without a corresponding change in T_{on}.

Such changes in the slave outputs for load changes in the master and slave can be kept to within 5 to 8 percent. But as discussed in Sec. 2.2.4, neither master nor slave output inductors must be permitted to go discontinuous at their minimum load currents. This is done by choosing the output inductors appropriately large, as will be described below.

The number of slave secondary turns N_{s1}, N_{s2} is calculated from Eqs. 2.26 and 2.27 as all parameters there are either specified or calculated from specified values. The parameters V_{dc}, T, and V_d are all specified and $\overline{T_{on}}$ is set at $0.8T/2$ as discussed above; N_p is calculated from Faraday's law (Eq. 1.17) as described above.

2.3.4 Secondary load, free-wheeling diode, and inductor currents

Knowledge about the amplitude and waveshape of the various output currents is needed to select secondary and output inductor wire sizes and current ratings of the rectifier and free-wheeling diodes.

As described for the buck regulator in Sec. 1.3.2, secondary current during the $Q1$ on time has the shape of an upward-sloping ramp sitting on a step (Fig, 2.11c) because of the constant voltage across the inductor with its input end positive with respect to the output end.

Now when $Q1$ turns off, the input end of the inductor is negative with respect to the output end and inductor current ramps downward.

The free-wheeling diode, at the instant of turnoff, picks up exactly the inductor current which had been flowing in it just prior to turnoff. That diode current then ramps downward (Fig. 2.11d) as it is in series with the inductor. Inductor current is the sum of the secondary current when $Q1$ is on plus the free-wheeling diode current when $Q1$ is off and is shown in Fig. 2.11e. Current at the center of the ramp in either of Fig. 2.11c, 2.11d, or 2.11e is equal to the DC output current.

2.3.5 Relations between primary current, output power, and input voltage

Assume an efficiency of 80 percent from the DC input voltage node to the total output power from all secondaries. Then $P_o = 0.8P_{in}$ or $P_{in} = 1.25P_o$. Now calculate P_{in} at minimum DC input voltage V_{dc}. That input power is V_{dc} times the average primary current at minimum DC input.

Now all secondary currents have the waveshape of a ramp sitting on a step as all secondaries have output inductors. These ramp-on-a-step waveforms have a width of $0.8T/2$ at minimum DC input voltage. All these secondary currents reflect into the primary by their turns ratio, and hence the primary current pulse is a single ramp-on-a-step waveform of width $0.8T/2$. There is only one such pulse per period (see Fig. 2.10) as this is a single-transistor circuit. The duty cycle of this primary pulse is then $(0.8T/2)/T$ or 0.4.

Now as for the push-pull topology, approximate this ramp-on-a-step by an equivalent flat-topped pulse I_{pft} of the same width and whose amplitude is that at the center of the ramp. The average value of this current is then $0.4I_{pft}$. Then

$$P_{in} = 1.25P_o = V_{dc}(0.4I_{pft}) \qquad \text{or} \qquad I_{pft} = \frac{3.13P_o}{V_{dc}} \qquad (2.28)$$

This is a valuable relation. It gives the equivalent peak flat-topped primary current pulse amplitude in terms of what is known at the outset—the minimum DC input voltage and the total output power. This permits an immediate selection of a transistor with adequate current rating and gain if it is a bipolar transistor or with sufficiently low on resistance if it is a MOSFET type.

It can be seen that for a forward converter, Eq. 2.28 shows I_{pft} is twice the value required in a push-pull topology (Eq. 2.9) at the same output power and minimum DC input voltage.

This is obvious as in the push-pull there are two pulses of current or power per period as compared to a single pulse in the forward converter. In the forward converter from Eqn. 2.25, if the number of secondary turns is chosen large enough, then the maximum on time at minimum DC input voltage will not need to be greater than 80 percent of a half period. Then, as seen in Fig. 2.10, the area $A2$ can always equal $A1$ before the start of the next period. The core is then always reset to the same point on its hysteresis loop within one cycle and can never walk up into saturation.

But the penalty paid for this guarantee in the forward converter, that flux walking cannot occur is that the primary peak current is twice that for a push-pull at the same output power. In the push-pull, with all the precautions described in Sec. 2.2.8, there is never complete certainty that flux imbalance does not occur under unusual dynamic load or line conditions.

2.3.6 Maximum off-voltage stress in power transistor

In the forward converter, with the number of turns on the reset N_r winding equal to that on the power winding N_p, maximum off-voltage stress on the power transistor is twice the maximum DC input voltage plus a leakage spike. Leakage inductance spikes, and their origin and minimization have been discussed in Sec. 2.2.11. Conservative design, even with all precautions to minimize leakage spikes, should assume they may be 30 percent above twice the maximum DC input voltage. Maximum off-voltage stress is then the same as in the push-pull and is

$$V_{\mathrm{ms}} = 1.3(2\overline{V_{\mathrm{dc}}}) \tag{2.29}$$

2.3.7 Practical input voltage/output power limits

At the outset in Sec. 2.3.1 it was stated the practical maximum output power limit for a forward converter whose maximum DC input voltage is under 60 V is about 150 to 200 W. This is so because the peak primary current as calculated from Eq. 2.28 becomes excessive as there is only a single pulse per period as compared to two in the push-pull topology.

Thus consider a 200-W forward converter for the telephone industry where the specified minimum and maximum input voltages are 38 and 60 V, respectively. Peak primary current from Eq. 2.28 is $I_{\mathrm{pft}} = 3.13 P_o / V_{\mathrm{dc}} = 3.13(200)/38 = 16.5$ A and from Eq. 2.29, maximum off voltage stress is $\overline{V_{\mathrm{ms}}} = 2.6\overline{V_{\mathrm{dc}}} = 2.6 \times 60 = 156$ V.

To provide safety margin, a device with at least a 200-V rating would be used to provide protection against input voltage transients which could drive the DC input above the maximum steady-state value of 60 V.

Transistors with 200-V, 16-A ratings are available, but they all have drawbacks as was discussed in Sec. 2.2.13. Bipolar transistors are slow, and MOSFETs are easily fast enough but expensive. For such a 200-W application, a push-pull version guaranteed to be free from flux imbalance would be preferable; with two pulses of current per period, peak current would be only 8 A. With the lower peak current, noise spikes on ground buses and the radio-frequency interference (RFI) would be considerably less—a very important consideration for a telephone industry power supply. Such a flux imbalance free topology is "current mode," which is discussed later.

The forward converter topology, like the push-pull (discussed in Sec. 2.2.13), has the same difficulty in coping with maximum voltage stress in an off-line converter where the AC input voltage is 120 ±10 percent. At high line, the rectified DC input is $1.1 \times 120 \times 1.41 = 186$ V minus 2 V for the rectifier diode drops or 184 V. From Eq. 2.29 the maximum voltage stress on the transistor in the off state is $\overline{V_{ms}} = 2.6 \times 184 = 478$ V.

At minimum AC input voltage, the rectified DC output is $\overline{V_{dc}} = (0.9 \times 120 \times 1.41) - 2 = 150$ V, and from Eq. 2.28, the peak primary current is $I_{pft} = 3.13 \times 22/150 = 4.17$ A.

Thus, for a 200-W off-line forward converter, the greater problem is more the 478-V maximum voltage stress than the 4.17-A peak primary current stress—for, as was seen in Sec. 2.2.13, when a 15 percent input transient is taken into account, the peak off voltage stress is 550 V. With a bipolar transistor operating under V_{cev} conditions (reverse input bias of -1 to -5 V at the instant of turnoff), a voltage stress of even 550 V is not a serious restriction. There are many devices with 650- to 850-V V_{cev} ratings and which have high gain, low on drop, and high speed at 4.17 A. But, as discussed in Sec. 2.2.13, there are preferable topologies, discussed below, which subject the off transistor to only V_{dc} and not twice V_{dc}.

2.3.8 Forward converter with unequal power and reset winding turns

Heretofore, it has been assumed that the numbers of turns on the power winding N_p and the reset winding N_r are equal. Some advantages result if N_r is made smaller or larger than N_p.

The number of primary power turns N_p is always chosen by Faraday's law and will be discussed in Sec. 2.3.10.2. If N_r is chosen less than N_p, the peak current required for a given output power is less than that calculated from Eq. 2.28, but the maximum $Q1$ off-voltage stress is greater than that calculated from Eq. 2.29. If N_r is chosen larger than N_p, the maximum $Q1$ off-voltage stress is less than that calculated from Eq. 2.29, but the peak primary current for a given output power is greater than that calculated from Eq. 2.29. This can be seen from Fig. 2.12 as follows. When $Q1$ turns off, polarities across N_p and N_r reverse, the dot end of N_r goes negative and is caught at ground by catch diode $D1$. Transformer $T1$ is now an autotransformer. There is a

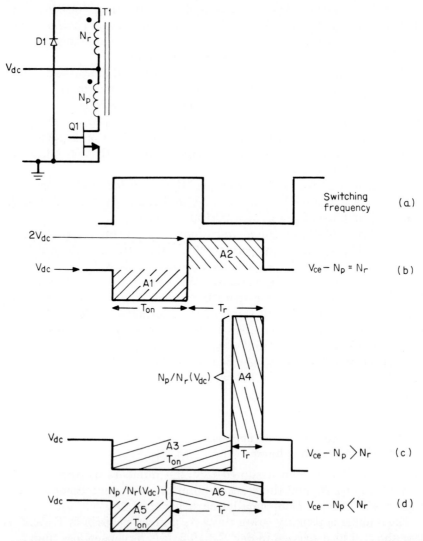

Figure 2.12 Forward converter–collector-to-emitter voltages for $N_p = N_r$. Note in all cases that reset volt-second product equals set volt-second product. (a) Switching frequency; (b) $N_p = N_r$; (c) $N_p > N_r$; (d) $N_p < N_r$.

voltage V_{dc} across N_r and hence a voltage $N_p/N_r(V_{dc})$ across N_p. The core is set by the volt-second product $V_{dc}T_{on}$ during the on time and must be reset to its original place on the hysteresis loop by an equal volt-second product. That reset volt-second product is $N_p/N_r(V_{dc})T_r$.

When N_r equals N_p, the reset voltage equals the set voltage and the reset time is equal to the set time (area $A1$ = area $A2$) as seen in Fig. 2.12b. For $N_r = N_p$, the maximum $Q1$ on time which occurs at minimum DC input voltage is chosen as $0.8T/2$ to ensure that the core is reset before the start of the next period; $T_{on} + T_r$ is then $0.8T$.

Now if N_r is less than N_p, the resetting voltage is larger than V_{dc} and consequently T_r can be smaller (area $A3$ = area $A4$) as shown in Fig. 2.12c. With a shorter T_r, T_{on} can be longer than $0.8T/2$ and $T_{on} + T_r$ can still be $0.8T$ so that the core is reset before the start of the next period. With a longer T_{on}, the peak current is smaller for the same average current and the same average output power. Thus in Fig. 2.12c, as compared to Fig. 2.12b, a smaller peak current stress has been traded for a larger voltage stress,

With N_r greater than N_p, the reset voltage is less than V_{dc}. Then if $T_{on} + T_r$ is still to equal $0.8T$, and the reset volt-seconds is to equal the set volt-seconds (area $A5$ = area $A6$ in Fig. 2.12d), T_r must be longer and T_{on} must be shorter than $0.8T/2$ as the reset voltage is less than the set voltage. With T_{on} less than $0.8T/2$, the peak current must be higher for the same average current. Thus in Fig. 2.12d, a lesser voltage stress has been achieved at the cost of a higher peak current for the same output power as in Fig. 2.12b. This can be seen quantitatively as

$$\text{Set } T_{on} + T_r = 0.8T; \quad \text{reset voltage} = V_r = \frac{N_p}{N_r}V_{dc} \quad (2.30)$$

For on volt-seconds equal to reset volt-seconds

$$V_{dc}T_{on} = \frac{N_p}{N_r}V_{dc}T_r \quad (2.31)$$

Combining Eqs. 2.30 and 2.31

$$\overline{T_{on}} = \frac{0.8T}{1 + N_r/N_p} \quad (2.32)$$

For 80 percent efficiency $P_{in} = 1.25P_o$ and P_{in} at $\overline{V_{dc}} = \overline{V_{dc}(I_{av})} = \overline{V_{dc}}$ $I_{pft}(\overline{T_{on}})/T$ or $I_{pft} = 1.25(P_o/\overline{V_{dc}})(T/T_{on})$. Then from $\overline{\text{Eq. 2.32}}$

$$I_{pft} = 1.56 \left(\frac{P_o}{\underline{V_{dc}}}\right)(1 + N_r/N_p) \quad (2.33)$$

and the maximum $Q1$ off voltage stress $\overline{V_{ms}}$—exclusive of the leakage spike—is the maximum DC input voltage V_{dc} plus the reset voltage (voltage across N_p when the dot end of N_r is at ground). Thus

$$\overline{V_{ms}} = \overline{V_{dc}} + \frac{N_p}{N_r}(\overline{V_{dc}}) = \overline{V_{dc}}(1 + N_p/N_r) \qquad (2.34)$$

Values of I_{pft} and V_{ms} calculated from Eqs. 2.33 and 2.34 are

N_r/N_p	I_{pft} (from Eq. 2.33)	V_{ms} (from Eq. 2.34)
0.6	$2.50(P_o/V_{dc})$	$2.67\overline{V_{dc}}$ + leakage spike
0.8	$2.81(P_o/V_{dc})$	$2.25\overline{V_{dc}}$ + " "
1.0	$3.12(P_o/V_{dc})$	$2.00\overline{V_{dc}}$ + " "
1.2	$3.43(P_o/V_{dc})$	$1.83\overline{V_{dc}}$ + " "
1.4	$3.74(P_o/V_{dc})$	$1.71\overline{V_{dc}}$ + " "
1.6	$4.06(P_o/V_{dc})$	$1.62\overline{V_{dc}}$ + " "

2.3.9 Forward converter magnetics

2.3.9.1 First-quadrant operation only. The transformer core in the forward converter operates in the first quadrant of the hysteresis loop only. This can be seen in Fig. 2.10. When $Q1$ is on, the dot end of $T1$ is positive with respect to the no-dot end and the core is driven, say, in a positive direction on the hysteresis loop and the magnetizing current ramps up linearly in the magnetizing inductance.

When $Q1$ turns off, stored current in the magnetizing inductance reverses the polarity of voltages on all windings. The dot end of N_r goes negative until it is caught one diode drop below ground by catch diode $D1$. Now the magnetizing current which really is stored in the magnetic core continues to flow. It simply transfers from N_p, where it had ramped upward during the $Q1$ on time, into N_r. It flows out of the no-dot end of N_r into the positive end of the supply voltage V_{dc}, out of the negative end of V_{dc}, through the anode, then through the cathode of $D1$, and back into N_r.

During the $Q1$ off time, as the dot end of N_r is positive with respect to its no-dot end, the magnetizing current I_d ramps linearly downward as can be seen in Fig. 2.10. When it has ramped down to zero (at the end of area $A2$ in Fig. 2.10), there is no longer any stored energy in the magnetizing inductance and nothing to hold the dot end of N_r below the $D1$ cathode. The voltage at the dot end of N_r starts rising toward V_{dc}, and that at the no-dot end of N_p ($Q1$ collector) starts falling from $2V_{dc}$ back down toward V_{dc}.

Thus operation on the hysteresis loop is centered about half the peak magnetizing current ($V_{dc}T_{on}/2L_m$). Nothing ever reverses the direction of the magnetizing current—it simply builds up linearly to a peak and relaxes back down linearly to zero.

This first-quadrant operation has some favorable and some unfavorable consequences. First, compared to a push-pull circuit, it halves the available output power from a given core. This can be seen from Faraday's law (Eq. 1.17), which fixes the number of turns on the primary.

Solving Faraday's law for the number of primary turns, $N_p = E \, dt / A_e \, dB \times 10^{-8}$. If dB in the forward converter is limited to an excursion from zero to some B_{max} instead of from $-B_{max}$ to $+B_{max}$ as in a push-pull topology, the number of primary turns for the forward converter will be twice that in each half primary for a push-pull operating from the same V_{dc}. Although the push-pull has two half primaries, each of which must support the same volt-second product as the forward converter, the push-pull offers two power pulses per period as compared to one for the forward converter. The end result is that a core used in a forward converter offers only half the available output power it is capable of in a push-pull configuration.

But the push-pull core at twice the output power will run somewhat warmer as its flux excursion is twice that of the forward converter. Since core losses are proportional to the area of the hysteresis loop traversed, the push-pull core losses are twice that of the forward converter.

Yet total copper losses in both half primaries of a push-pull are no greater than that of the forward converter of half the output power. For the rms current in each push-pull half primary is equal to that in the forward converter of half the output power. But since the number of turns in each push-pull half primary is half that of the forward converter of half the output power, each push-pull half primary has half the resistance of the forward converter. Thus, total copper losses of a forward converter is then equal to the total losses of the two half primaries in a push-pull of twice the output power.

2.3.9.2   Core gapping in a forward converter.   In Fig. 2.3, the hysteresis loop of a ferrite core with no air gap is shown. It is seen that at zero magnetizing force (0 Oe) there is a residual magnetic flux density of about ± 1000 G. This residual flux is referred to as *remanence*.

In a forward converter, if the core started at 0 Oe and hence at 1000 G, the maximum flux change dB possible before the core is driven up into the curved part of the hysteresis loop is about 1000 G. It is desirable to stay off the curved part of the hysteresis loop, and hence the forward converter core with no air gap is restricted to a maximum dB of 1000 G. As shown above, the number of primary turns is inversely proportional to dB. Such a relatively small dB requires a relatively large number of primary turns. A larger number of primary turns requires smaller wire size and hence decreases the current and power available from the transformer.

By introducing an air gap in the core, the hysteresis loop is tilted as shown in Fig. 2.5 and magnetic remanence is reduced significantly.

The hysteresis loop tilts over and still crosses the zero flux density at the same point on the H axis (referred to as *coercive force.* Coercive force for ferrites is seen to be about 0.2 Oe in Fig. 2.3. An air gap of about 2 to 4 mils will reduce remanence to about 200 G for most cores used at a 200- to 500-W output power level. With remanence of 200 G, the permissible dB before the core enters the curved part of the hysteresis loop is now about 1800 G and fewer turns are permissible.

However, there is a penalty paid in introducing an air gap. Figure 2.5 shows the slope of the hysteresis loop tilted over. The slope is dB/dH or the core permeability, which has been decreased by adding the gap. Decreasing permeability has decreased the magnetizing inductance and increased the magnetizing current ($I_m = V_{dc}T_{on}/L_m$). Magnetizing current contributes no output power to the load; it simply moves the core across the hysteresis loop and is wasteful if it exceeds 10 percent of the primary load current.

2.3.9.3 Magnetizing inductance with gapped core.

Magnetizing inductance with a gapped core can be calculated as follows. Voltage across the magnetizing inductance is $L_m \, dI_m/dt$ and from Faraday's law:

$$V_{dc} = \frac{L_m dI_m}{dt} = \frac{N_p A_e \, dB}{dt} 10^{-8} \quad \text{or} \quad L_m = \frac{N_p A_e \, dB}{dI_m} 10^{-8} \qquad (2.35)$$

where L_m = magnetizing inductance, H
$\quad N_p$ = number of primary turns
$\quad A_e$ = core area, cm^2
$\quad dB$ = core flux change, G
$\quad dI_m$ = change in magnetizing current, A

Now a fundamental law in magnetics is Ampere's law:

$$\int H \cdot dl = 0.4\pi NI$$

This states that if a line is drawn encircling a number of ampere turns NI, the dot product $H \cdot dl$ along that line is equal to $0.4\pi NI$. If the line is taken through the core parallel to the magnetic flux lines and across the gap, since H is uniform at a level H_i within the core and uniform at a value H_a across the gap, then

$$H_i l_i + H_a l_a = 0.4\pi NI_m \qquad (2.36)$$

where H_i = magnetic field intensity in iron (ferrite), Oe
$\quad l_i$ = length of iron path, cm
$\quad H_a$ = magnetic field intensity in air gap, Oe
$\quad l_a$ = length of the air gap, cm
$\quad I_m$ = magnetizing current, A

However, $H_i = B_i/u$, where B_i is the magnetic flux density in iron and u is the iron permeability; $H_a = B_a$ as the permeability of air is 1; and $B_a = B_i$(flux density in iron = flux density in air) if there is no fringing flux around the air gap. Then Eq. 2.36 can be written as

$$\frac{B_i}{u} l_i + B_i l_a = 0.4\pi N_p I_m \qquad \text{or} \qquad B_i = \frac{0.4\pi NI_m}{l_a + l_i/u} \qquad (2.37)$$

Then $dB/dI_m = 0.4\pi N/(l_a + l_i/u)$, and substituting this into Eq. 2.35

$$L_m = \frac{0.4\pi (N_p)^2 A_e \times 10^{-9}}{l_a + l_i/u} \qquad (2.38)$$

Thus, introducing an air gap of length l_a to a core of iron path length l_i reduces the magnetizing inductance in the ratio of

$$\frac{L_{m \text{ (with gap)}}}{L_{m \text{ (without gap)}}} = \frac{l_i/u}{l_a + l_i/u} \qquad (2.39)$$

It is instructive to consider a specific example. Take an international standard core such as the Ferroxcube 783E608-3C8. It has a magnetic path length of 9.7 cm and an effective permeability of 2300. Then if a 4-mil (= 0.0102-cm) gap were introduced into the magnetic path, from Eq. 2.39

$$L_{m \text{ (with gap)}} = \frac{9.7/2300}{0.0102 + 9.7/2300} L_{m \text{ (without gap)}}$$

$$= 0.29 L_{m \text{ (without gap)}}$$

A useful way of looking at a gapped core is to examine the denominator in Eq. 2.38. In most cases, u is so high that the term l_i/u is small compared to the air gap l_a and the inductance is determined primarily by the length of the air gap.

2.3.10   Power transformer design relations

2.3.10.1   Core selection.   As discussed in Sec. 2.2.9.1 on core selection for a push-pull transformer, the amount of power available from a core for a forward converter transformer is related to the same parameters—peak flux density, core iron and bobbin areas, frequency, and coil current density in circular mils per rms ampere.

In Chap. 7, an equation will be derived giving the amount of available output power as a function of these parameters. This equation will be converted to a chart which permits selection of core size and operating frequency at a glance.

For the present, it is assumed that a core has been selected and its iron and bobbin area are known.

2.3.10.2 Primary turns calculation. The number of primary turns is calculated from Faraday's law as given in Eq. 2.7. Recall (Sec. 2.3.9.2) that in the forward converter, with a gapped core, flux moves from about 200 G to some higher value B_{max}. As in the push-pull topology, this peak value will be set at 1600 G for ferrites even at low frequencies where core losses are not a limiting factor.

This, as discussed in Sec. 2.2.9.4, is to avoid the problem of a much larger and dangerous flux swing resulting from rapid changes in DC input voltage or load current. Such rapid changes are not immediately corrected for because the limited error-amplifier bandwidth does not permit a rapid correction in the power transistor on time.

During the error-amplifier delay, the peak flux density can, for a number of cycles, go up to as high as 50 percent above the calculated for normal steady-state operation. This can be tolerated if the normal peak flux density in the absence of a line or load transient is set to a low value of 1600 G. As discussed above, the excursion from approximately zero to 1600 G will take place in 80 percent of a half period to ensure that the core can be reset before the start of the next period (Fig. 2.12b).

Thus the number of primary turns is set by Faraday's law at

$$N_p = \frac{(V_{dc} - 1)(0.8T/2) \times 10^{+8}}{A_e \, dB} \tag{2.40}$$

where V_{dc} = minimum DC input, V
$\overline{}T$ = operating period, s
A_e = iron area, cm^2
dB = 1600 G

2.3.10.3 Secondary turns calculation. Secondary turns are calculated from Eqs. 2.25 to 2.27. In those relations, all values except the secondary turns are specified or already calculated. Thus (Fig. 2.10):

V_{dc} = minimum DC input, V
$\overline{}T_{on}$ = maximum on time, s (= 0.8T/2)
N_m, N_{s1}, N_{s2} = numbers of main and slave turns
N_p = number of primary turns
V_d = rectifier forward drop

Usually the main output is a high-current 5-V one for which a Schottky diode of 0.5 V is used. The slaves usually have higher output voltages which require the use of diodes with higher reverse-voltage ratings. Such fast-recovery higher-reverse-voltage diodes have forward drops of 1.0 V over a large range of currents.

2.3.10.4 Primary rms current and wire size selection. Primary equivalent flat-topped current is given by Eq. 2.28. That current flows a maximum of 80 percent of a half period out of each full period, and hence its maximum duty cycle is 0.4. Recalling that the rms value of a flat-topped pulse of amplitude I_p is $I_{rms} = I_p\sqrt{T_{on}/T}$, the rms primary current is

$$I_{rms\,(primary)} = \frac{3.12P_o}{V_{dc}}\sqrt{0.4}$$

$$= \frac{1.97P_o}{V_{dc}} \tag{2.41}$$

If the wire size is chosen on the basis of 500 circular mils per rms ampere, the required number of circular mils is

$$Circular\ mils\ needed = \frac{500 \times 1.97P_o}{V_{dc}}$$

$$= \frac{985P_o}{V_{dc}} \tag{2.42}$$

2.3.10.5 Secondary rms current and wire size selection. It is seen in Fig. 2.11 that the secondary current has the characteristic shape of a ramp on a step. The pulse amplitude at the center of the ramp is equal to the DC output current. Thus the equivalent flat-topped secondary current pulse at V_{dc} (when its width is a maximum) has an amplitude of I_{dc}, a width of $\overline{0.8T/2}$, and a duty cycle of $(0.8T/2)/T$ or 0.4. Then

$$I_{rms\,(secondary)} = I_{dc}\sqrt{0.4}$$

$$= 0.632I_{dc} \tag{2.43}$$

and at 500 circular mils per rms ampere, the required number of circular mils for each secondary is

$$Circular\ mils\ needed = 500 \times 0.632I_{dc}$$

$$= 316I_{dc} \tag{2.44}$$

2.3.10.6 Reset winding rms current and wire size selection. The reset winding carries only magnetizing current, as can be seen by the dots in Fig. 2.10. When $Q1$ is on, diode $D1$ is reverse-biased and no current flows in the reset winding. But magnetizing current builds up linearly in the power winding N_p. When $Q1$ turns off, that magnetizing current must continue to flow. When $Q1$ current ceases, the current in the magnetizing inductance reverses all winding polarities. When the dot end of N_r reaches ground, the magnetizing current transfers from N_p to N_r and continues flowing through the DC input voltage source V_{dc} out from the negative end of V_{dc} through $D1$ and back into N_r. Since the no-dot end of N_r is positive with respect to the dot end, the magnetizing current ramps downward to zero as seen in Fig. 2.10.

The waveshape of this N_r current is the same as that of the magnetizing current which ramped upward when $Q1$ was on, but it is reversed from left to right. Thus the peak of this triangle of current is $I_{p\ (\text{magnetizing})} = V_{dc}T_{on}/L_{mg}$, where L_{mg} is the magnetizing inductance with an air gap as calculated from Eq. 2.39. The inductance without the gap is calculated from the ferrite catalog value of A_l, the inductance per 1000 turns. Since inductance is proportional to the square of the number of turns, inductance for n turns is $L_n = A_l(n/1000)^2$. The duration of this current triangle is $0.8T/2$ (the time required for the core to reset), and it comes at a duty cycle of 0.4.

It is known that the rms value of a repeating triangle (no spacing between successive triangles) of peak amplitude I_p is $I_{rms} = I_p/\sqrt{3}$. But this triangle comes at a duty cycle of 0.4, and hence its rms value is

$$I_{rms} = \frac{V_{dc}T_{on}}{L_{mg}}\frac{\sqrt{0.4}}{\sqrt{3}}$$

$$= 0.365\frac{V_{dc}T_{on}}{L_{mg}}$$

and at 500 circular mils per rms ampere, the required number of circular mils for the reset winding is

$$\text{Circular mils required} = 500 \times 0.365\frac{V_{dc}T_{on}}{L_{mg}} \qquad (2.45)$$

Most frequently, magnetizing current is so small that the reset winding can be done with wire sizes smaller than No. 30 wire (AWG).

2.3.11 Output filter design relations

The output filters $L1C1$, $L2C2$, and $L3C3$ average the peak voltage at the rectifier cathodes. The inductor is selected so as not to go discontinuous (Sec. 1.3.6) at the minimum DC output current. The capacitor is selected to yield a minimum specified output ripple voltage.

2.3.11.1 Output inductor design. It will be recalled from Sec. 1.3.6 that the discontinuous mode condition occurs when the front end of the inductor current ramp drops to zero (Fig. 2.10). Since the DC output current is the value at the center of the ramp, discontinuous mode starts at a minimum current I_{dc} equal to half the ramp amplitude dI as can be seen in Fig. 2.10.

Now referring to Fig. 2.11:

$$dI = 2\overline{I_{dc}} = \frac{(V_{rk} - V_o)\overline{T_{on}}}{L1} \quad \text{or} \quad L1 = \frac{(V_{rk} - V_o)(\overline{T_{on}})}{2\overline{I_{dc}}}$$

But $V_o = V_{rk}\overline{T_{on}}/T$. Then

$$L1 = \left(\frac{V_o T}{T_{on}} - V_o\right)\frac{\overline{T_{on}}}{2\overline{I_{dc}}}$$

$$= \frac{V_o(T/\overline{T_{on}} - 1)\overline{T_{on}}}{2\overline{I_{dc}}}$$

But $\overline{T_{on}} = 0.8T/2$. Then

$$L1 = \frac{0.3 V_o T}{\overline{I_{dc}}} \tag{2.46}$$

and if minimum DC current $\overline{I_{dc}}$ is one-tenth the nominal output current I_{on}, then

$$L1 = \frac{3 V_o T}{I_{on}} \tag{2.47}$$

2.3.11.2 Output capacitor design. It was seen in Sec. 1.3.7 that the output ripple is almost completely determined by the equivalent series resistance R_o of the filter capacitor. The peak-to-peak ripple amplitude V_{or} is $V_{or} = R_o\, dI$, where dI is the peak-to-peak ripple current amplitude chosen by the selection of the ripple inductor as discussed above. Then assuming as in Sec. 1.3.7 that the average value of $R_o C_o$ for aluminum electrolytic capacitors of a large range of voltage and capacitance ratings is given by $R_o C_o = 65 \times 10^{-6}$:

$$C_o = 65 \times 10^{-6}/R_o$$

$$= 65 \times 10^{-6}\frac{dI}{V_{or}} \tag{2.48}$$

where dI is in amperes and V_{or} is in volts for C_o in farads.

2.4 Double-Ended Forward Converter Topology

2.4.1 Basic operation

Double-ended forward converter topology is shown in Fig. 2.13. Although it has two transistors rather than one compared to the single-ended forward converter of Fig. 2.10, it has a very significant advantage. In the off state, both transistors are subjected to only the DC input voltage rather than twice that as in the single-ended converter. Further, at turnoff, there is no leakage inductance spike.

It was pointed out in Sec. 2.3.7 that the off-voltage stress in the single-ended forward converter operating off a nominal 120-V-AC line can be as high as 550 V when there is a 15 percent transient above a 10 percent steady-state high line and a 30 percent leakage spike.

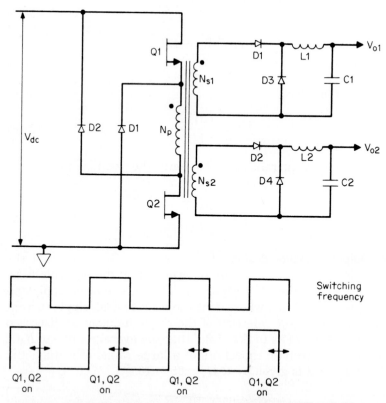

Figure 2.13 Double-ended forward converter. Transistors $Q1$ and $Q2$ are turned on and off simultaneously. Diodes $D1$ and $D2$ keep the maximum off voltage stress on $Q1$, $Q2$ at a maximum of V_{dc} as contrasted with $2V_{dc}$ plus a leakage spike for the single-ended forward converter of Fig. 2.10.

Although there are a number of bipolar transistors with V_{cev} ratings up to 650 and even 850 V which can take that stress, it is a far more reliable design to use the double-ended forward converter with half the off-voltage stress. Reliability is of overriding importance in a power supply design, and in any weighing of reliability versus initial cost, the best and—in the long run—least expensive choice is reliability.

Further, for power supplies to be used in the European market where the AC voltage is 220 V (rectified DC voltage is nominally about 308 V), the single-ended forward converter is not usable at all because of the excessive voltage stress on the off transistor (Eq. 2.29). The double-ended forward converter and the half bridge and the full bridge (to be discussed in Chap. 3) are the only choices for equipment to be used in the European market.

The double-ended forward converter works as follows. In Fig. 2.13, $Q1$ and $Q2$ are in series with the top and bottom of the transformer primary. Both of these transistors are turned on simultaneously and turned off simultaneously. When they are on, all primary and secondary dot ends are positive and power is delivered to the loads. When they turn off, current stored in the $T1$ magnetizing inductance reverses polarity of all windings. The dot end of N_p tries to go far negative but is caught at ground by diode $D1$. The no-dot end of N_p tries to go far positive but is caught at V_{dc} by diode $D2$.

Thus the emitter of $Q1$ can never be more than V_{dc} below its collector, and the collector of $Q2$ can never be more than V_{dc} above its emitter. Leakage inductance spikes are clamped so that the maximum voltage stress on either transistor can never be more than the maximum DC input voltage.

The further significant advantage is that there is no leakage inductance energy to be dissipated. Any energy stored in the leakage inductance is not lost by dissipation in some resistive element or in the power transistors. Instead, energy stored in the leakage inductance during the on time is fed back into V_{dc} via $D1$ and $D2$ when the transistors turn off. The leakage inductance current flows out of the no-dot end of N_p, through $D2$, into the positive end of V_{dc}, out of its negative end, and up through $D1$ back into the dot end of N_p.

Examination of Fig. 2.13 reveals that the core is always reset with the reset time equal to the on time. For the reverse polarity voltage across N_p when the transistors are off is equal to the forward polarity voltage across it when the transistors are on. Thus the core will always succeed in being fully reset with a 20 percent safety margin before the start of a next half cycle if the maximum on time is never required to be greater than 80 percent of a half period. This is done by choosing enough secondary turns so that the peak secondary voltage at minimum V_{dc} times the maximum duty cycle of 0.4 equals the desired output voltage (Eq. 2.25).

2.4.1.1 Practical output power limits.

It should, however, be noted that this topology still yields only one power pulse per period just as the single-ended forward converter. Thus the power available from a specific core is pretty much the same regardless of whether the single- or double-ended configuration is used. As noted in Sec. 2.3.10.6, the reset winding in the single-ended circuit carries only magnetizing current during the power transistor off time. Since that current is small, the reset winding can most often be done with No. 30 wire or narrower. Thus the absence of a reset winding in the double-ended circuit does not permit significantly larger power winding wire size and any more output power from a given core.

But because the maximum off transistor voltage stress cannot be greater than the maximum DC input voltage, the 200-W practical power limit for the single-ended forward converter discussed in Sec. 2.3.7 no longer holds. With the reduced voltage stress offered by the double-ended forward converter, output powers of 400 to 500 W are obtainable and transistors with the required voltage and current capability are easily available at adequate gain and low price.

Thus consider a double-ended forward converter operating off a nominal 120-V-AC line with ±10 percent steady-state tolerance and a ±15 percent tolerance on top of that. Maximum rectified DC voltage is $1.41 \times 120 \times 1.1 \times 1.15 = 214$ V, minimum rectified DC voltage is $1.41 \times 120 \times 0.9 \times 0.85 = 130$ V, and equivalent flat-topped primary current from Eq. 2.28 is $I_{pft} = 3.13 P_o / V_{dc}$, and for $P_o = 400$ W, $I_{pft} = 9.6$ A.

Many transistors (bipolar and MOSFET) with a 214-V, 9.6-A rating are easily and inexpensively available with adequately high gain.

A better alternative using the double-ended forward converter would be to use a voltage doubler off the 120-V-AC line (Fig. 3.1). This would double the voltage stress to 428 V and half the peak current to 4.8 A. With 4.8 A of primary current, RFI problems would be less severe. A bipolar transistor with a 400-V V_{ceo} rating could easily take 428 V if it had a -1- to -5-V reverse bias at the instant of turnoff (V_{cev} rating).

2.4.2 Design relations and transformer design

2.4.2.1 Core selection—primary turns and wire size.

The transformer design for the double-ended forward converter proceeds exactly as for the single-ended converter. A core is selected from the aforementioned selection charts (to be presented in Chap. 7 on magnetics) for the required output power and operating frequency.

The number of primary turns is chosen from Faraday's law as in Eq. 2.40. There the minimum primary voltage is $(V_{dc} - 2)$ as there are two transistors rather than one in series with the primary—but that is insignificant as V_{dc} is usually 130 V (120 V AC). Maximum on time is taken as $0.8T/2$ and dB is taken as 1600 G up to about 50 kHz or even to a higher frequency if not limited by core losses.

As mentioned, in the region of 100 to 300 kHz, peak flux density may have to be lowered down to about 1400 or possibly to 800 G as core losses increase with frequency. But the exact peak flux density chosen depends on whether the newer, lower-loss materials are available. It also depends to some extent on transformer size—smaller cores can generally operate at higher flux density as they have a larger ratio of radiating surface area to volume and hence can more easily get rid of the heat they generate (which is proportional to volume).

Since there is only one current or power pulse per period as in the single-ended forward converter, the primary current for a given output power and minimum DC input voltage is given by Eq. 2.28 and the primary wire size is chosen from Eq. 2.42.

2.4.2.2 Secondary turns and wire size. Secondary turns are chosen exactly as in Secs. 2.3.2 and 2.3.3 from Eqs. 2.25 to 2.27. Wire sizes are calculated as in Sec. 2.3.10.5 from Eq. 2.44.

2.4.2.3 Output filter design. The output inductor and capacitor magnitudes are calculated exactly as in Sec. 2.3.11 from Eqs. 2.46 to 2.48.

2.5 Interleaved Forward Converter Topology

2.5.1 Basic operation—merits, drawbacks, and output power limits

This topology is simply two identical single-ended forward converters operating on alternate half cycles with their secondary currents adding through rectifying OR diodes. The topology is shown in Fig. 2.14.

The advantage, of course, is that now there are two power pulses per period as seen in Fig. 2.14 and each converter supplies half the total output power.

Equivalent flat-topped peak transistor current is given by Eq. 2.28 as $I_{pft} = 3.13\, P_{ot}/2V_{dc}$ where P_{ot} is the total output power. This is half the transistor current if the same total output power were being produced with only a single forward converter. Thus the expense of two transistors is somewhat balanced by the fact that each has a lower

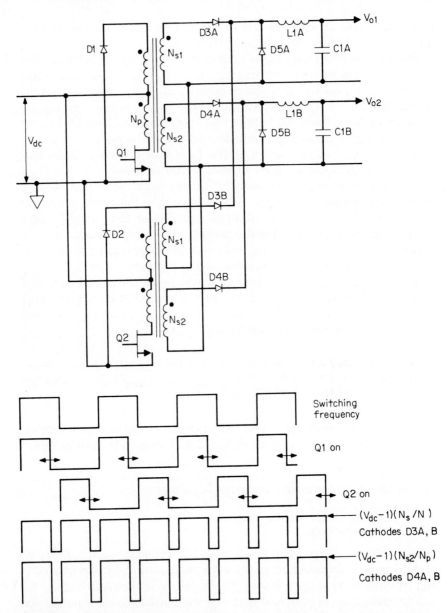

Figure 2.14 Interleaved forward converter. Interleaving the on time of $Q1$ and $Q2$ on alternate half cycles and summing their secondary output gives two power pulses per period but avoids the flux imbalance problem of the push-pull topology.

peak current rating and may be less expensive than the single one at twice the current rating.

Or looking at it another way, if two transistors of the same current rating were used and at the same peak current as one single-ended converter which had been designed for a given output power, the interleaved converter would yield twice the output power of the single converter.

Also, since the intensity of EMI generated is proportional to the peak currents, not to the number of current pulses, an interleaved converter of the same total output power as a single forward converter will generate less EMI.

The two transformers are each smaller than one for a single forward converter of the same output power. But the two together will most likely occupy more volume and cost more than the single transformer.

Thus, although there are some pluses and some minuses, a major advantage of the interleaved forward converters remains that it yields twice the output power of a single, single-ended forward converter operated at the same peak current in the transistor.

If this topology is compared to a push-pull, it might be thought that the push-pull is preferable. Although both are two-transistor circuits, the two transformers in the interleaved forward converter are most probably more expensive and occupy more space than a single large one in a push-pull circuit. But there is the ever-present uncertainty that the flux imbalance problem in the push-pull has not disappeared under odd transient line and load conditions.

The certainty that there is no flux imbalance problem in the interleaved forward converter is probably the best argument for its use.

There is one special, although not frequent case, where the interleaved forward converter is a much more desirable choice than a single forward converter of the same output power. This occurs when a DC output voltage is high—over about 200 V. In a single forward converter, the peak reverse voltage experienced by the output free-wheeling diodes ($D5A$ or $D5B$) is twice that for an interleaved forward converter as the duty cycle in the latter is twice that in the former.

This is no problem when output voltages are low, as can be seen in Eq. 2.25. Transformer secondary turns are always selected (for the single forward converter) so that at minimum DC input, when the secondary voltage is at its minimum, the duty cycle T_{on}/T need not be more than 0.4 to yield the desired output voltage. Then for a DC output of 200 V, the peak reverse voltage experienced by the free-wheeling diode is 500 V. At the instant of power transistor turnon, the free-wheeling diode has been carrying a large forward current and will suddenly be subjected to reverse voltage. If the diode has slow reverse recovery time, it will draw a large reverse current for a short time at 500-V reverse voltage and run dangerously hot.

Generally, diodes with larger reverse voltage ratings have slower recovery times and can be a serious problem in such a case. The interleaved forward converter runs at twice the duty cycle and for a 200-V-DC output, subjects the free-wheeling diode to only 250 V. This permits a lower voltage, faster-recovery diode and reduces its dissipation considerably.

2.5.2 Transformer design relations

2.5.2.1 Core selection. The core will be selected from the aforementioned charts, to be presented in Chap. 7. But they will be chosen for half the total power output as each transformer supplies half the output power.

2.5.2.2 Primary turns and wire size. The number of primary turns in the interleaved forward converter is still given by Eq. 2.40 as each converter's on time will still be $0.8T/2$ at minimum DC input. The core iron area A_e will be read from the catalogs for the selected core. Primary wire size will be chosen from Eq. 2.42 at half the total output power.

2.5.2.3 Secondary turns and wire size. The number of secondary turns will be chosen from Eqs. 2.26 and 2.27, but therein the duty cycle will be 0.8 as there are two voltage pulses, each of duration $0.8T/2$ at V_{dc}. Wire size will still be chosen from Eq. 2.44 where I_{dc} is the actual DC output current as each secondary carries that current at a maximum duty cycle of 0.4.

2.5.3 Output filter design

2.5.3.1 Output inductor design. The output inductor sees two current pulses per period exactly like the output inductor in the push-pull topology. These pulses have the same width, amplitude, and duty cycle as the push-pull inductor at the same DC output current. Hence the magnitude of the inductance is calculated from Eq. 2.20 as for the push-pull inductor.

2.5.3.2 Output capacitor design. Similarly, the output capacitor "doesn't know" whether it is filtering a full-wave push-pull waveform from a push-pull topology secondary or from an interleaved forward converter. Thus for the same inductor current ramp amplitude and permissible output ripple as the push-pull circuit, the capacitor is selected from Eq. 2.22.

Half- and Full-Bridge Converter Topologies

3.1 Introduction

Half- and full-bridge topologies subject their transistors in the off state to a voltage stress equal to the DC input voltage and not to twice that as do the push-pull, single-ended, and interleaved forward converter topologies. Thus the bridge topologies are used mainly in off-line converters where twice the rectified DC would be more than the usual switching transistors could safely tolerate. Bridge topologies hence are almost always used where the nominal AC input voltage is 220 V or higher and frequently for 120 V AC.

An additional valuable feature of the bridge topologies is that primary leakage inductance spikes (Figs. 2.1, 2.10) are easily clamped to the DC supply bus and any energy stored in the leakage inductance is returned to the input bus instead of having to be dissipated in some resistive element.

3.2 Half-Bridge Converter Topology

3.2.1 Basic operation

Half-bridge converter topology is shown in Fig. 3.1. Its major advantage is that, just as the double-ended forward converter, it subjects the off transistor to only V_{dc} and not twice that as do the push-pull and singled forward converter. It is thus widely used in equipment intended for the European market, where the AC input voltage is 220 V.

First consider the input rectifier and filter in Fig. 3.1. It is the universally used scheme when equipment is to be used with minimum changes either on 120-V-AC American or 220-V-AC European power. The circuit always yields roughly 320 V of rectified DC voltage

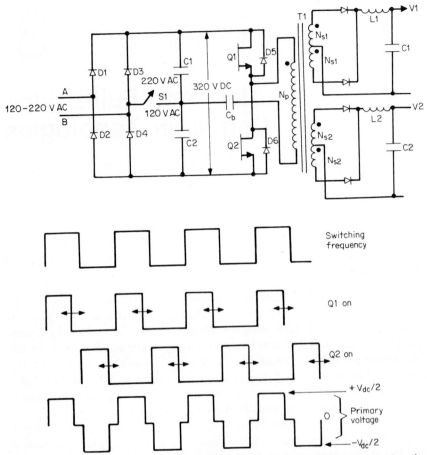

Figure 3.1   Half-bridge converter. One end of the power transformer is connected to the junction of filter capacitors $C1$, $C2$ via a small DC blocking capacitor C_b. The other end is connected to the junction of $Q1$, $Q2$ which turn on and off on alternate half cycles. With $S1$ in the lower position, the circuit is a voltage doubler; in the upper position, it is a full wave rectifier. Rectified output is thus always about 308 to 336 VDC.

whether input is 120 or 220 V AC. It does this by setting switch $S1$ to the upper position for 220-V-AC input or to the lower position for 120-V-AC input. The $S1$ component is not actually a switch; it is a linkage which is either made or not made to the lower position depending on whether the input is 120 or 220 V AC.

With the switch in the upper, 220-V-AC position, the circuit is a full-wave rectifier with filter capacitors $C1$ and $C2$ in series. It produces a peak rectified DC voltage of about $(1.41 \times 220) - 2$ or 308 V.

When the switch is in the lower 120-V-AC position, the circuit acts as a voltage doubler. On the first half cycle of the input voltage, when, say, A is positive relative to B, the top end of $C1$ is charged positively via $D1$ to a peak of $(1.41 \times 120) - 1$ or to 168 V. On the next negative half cycle, when A is negative with respect to B, the top end of capacitor $C2$ is charged positively via $D2$ to 168 V. The total output across $C1$ and $C2$ in series is then 336 V. It can be seen in Fig. 3.1 that with either transistor on, the off transistor is subjected only to the maximum DC input voltage and not twice that.

Now since the topology subjects the off transistor to only V_{dc} and not $2V_{dc}$, there are very many bipolar and MOSFET inexpensive transistors which can tolerate a nominal 336 DC V or even its maximum—a 15 percent high value of 386 V. Thus the equipment can be used off either 120 or 220 V AC with a simple switch or linkage change.

Assuming a nominal rectified DC voltage of 336 V, the topology works as follows. Ignore, for the moment, the small series blocking capacitor C_b. The bottom end of N_p can thus be assumed connected to the junction of $C1$ and $C2$. To a close approximation, if leakages in $C1$, $C2$ are assumed equal, that point will be at half the rectified DC voltage or about 168 V. It is generally good practice to place equal bleeder resistors across $C1$ and $C2$ to equalize their drop. Now $Q1$ and $Q2$ are switched on at alternate half cycles. When $Q1$ is on and $Q2$ off (Fig. 3.1), the dot end of N_p is 168 V positive with respect to its no-dot end and the off stress on $Q2$ is only 336 V. When $Q2$ is on and $Q1$ off, the dot end of N_p is 168 V negative with respect to its no-dot end and the emitter of $Q1$ is 336 V negative with respect to its collector.

This AC square-wave primary voltage produces full-wave square waveshapes on all secondaries—exactly like the secondary voltages in the push-pull topology. The selection of secondary voltages, wire sizes, and the output inductor and capacitor proceeds exactly as for the push-pull circuit.

3.2.2 Half-bridge magnetics

3.2.2.1 Maximum on time, magnetic core, primary turns selection. It can be seen in Fig. 3.1, that if $Q1$ and $Q2$ are simultaneously on—even for a very short time—there is a dead short circuit across the supply voltage and the transistors will be destroyed. The maximum $Q1$ or $Q2$ on time, which occurs at minimum DC supply voltage, will then be set at 80 percent of a half period to ensure that this does not happen. Secondary turns will be chosen so that the desired output voltages are obtained at an on time of no more than $0.8T/2$. An on-time clamp will be provided to ensure that under fault conditions, on time can never be greater than $0.8T/2$.

The core is selected from the earlier mentioned tables (to be presented in Chap. 7). These tables give maximum available output power as a function of operating frequency, peak flux density, core and iron area, and coil current density.

With a core selected and its iron area known, the number of primary turns is calculated from Faraday's law (Eq. 1.17) for the minimum primary voltage $(V_{dc}/2) - 1$, the maximum on time of $0.8T/2$. The value of dB in Faraday's law is taken as twice the desired peak flux density (1600 G below 50 kHz or less at higher frequency). The flux excursion dB is twice the desired peak value as the half-bridge core operates in the first and third quadrants of its hysteresis loop—unlike the forward converter, which (Sec. 2.3.9) operates in the first quadrant only.

3.2.2.2 Relation between primary current, output power, and input voltage.
Assume an efficiency of 80 percent. Then

$$\text{Input power} = P_{in} = 1.25P_o$$

But the input power at minimum supply voltage is the minimum primary voltage times the average primary current at minimum DC input. At minimum DC input, on time in each half period will be a maximum and will be selected as $0.8T/2$ as discussed above. Since at minimum DC input, the primary has two current pulses per period T, of width $0.8T/2$, and at a voltage $V_{dc}/2$, the input power is $1.25P_o = (V_{dc}/2)(I_{pft})(0.8T/T)$, where I_{pft} is the peak equivalent flat-topped primary current pulse. Then

$$I_{pft(\text{half bridge})} = \frac{3.13P_o}{V_{dc}} \tag{3.1}$$

3.2.2.3 Primary wire size selection.
Primary wire size in the half bridge is much larger than in a push-pull circuit of the same output power. But there are two half primaries for the push-pull, each of which has to support twice the voltage of a half bridge operated from the same supply voltage. Consequently, coil sizes for the two topologies are not much different. Half-bridge primary rms current is $I_{rms} = I_{pft}\sqrt{0.8T/T}$, and from Eq. 3.1

$$I_{rms} = \frac{2.79P_o}{V_{dc}} \tag{3.2}$$

At 500 circular mils per rms ampere, the required number of circular mils is

$$\text{Circular mils needed} = \frac{500 \times 2.79 P_o}{V_{dc}}$$

$$= \frac{1395 P_o}{V_{dc}} \tag{3.3}$$

3.2.2.4 Secondary turns and wire size selection. The number of secondary turns will be selected from Eqs. 2.1 to 2.3 for $\overline{T_{on}} = 0.8T/2$ and the term $V_{dc} - 1$ replaced by the minimum primary voltage, which is $(V_{dc}/2) - 1$.

The secondary rms currents and wire sizes are calculated from Eqs. 2.13 and 2.14 exactly as for the full-wave secondaries of a push-pull circuit.

3.2.3 Output filter calculations

The output inductor and capacitor are selected from Eqs. 2.20 and 2.22 for the same inductor current ramp amplitude and desired output ripple voltage as in a push-pull circuit.

3.2.4 Blocking capacitor to avoid flux imbalance

In Fig. 3.1, a small capacitor C_b is seen in series with the primary. Its purpose is to avoid the flux-imbalance problem discussed in connection with the push-pull circuit (Sec. 2.2.5). Recall that flux imbalance occurs if the volt-second product across the primary when the core was set (moved in one direction along the hysteresis loop) is different from the volt-second product when it had moved in the opposite direction.

Thus, if the junction of $C1$ and $C2$ is not exactly at half the supply voltage, the voltage across the primary when $Q1$ is on will differ from the voltage across it when $Q2$ is on. The core can then walk up or down the hysteresis loop into saturation and destroy the transistors.

The preceding description of the cause of flux imbalance is simply another way of stating that it comes about because there is a DC current bias in the primary. To avoid the DC current bias, the small DC blocking capacitor is placed in series in the primary. Selection of the magnitude of the capacitor is done as follows. If the capacitor is made too small, it will charge up as the primary current I_{pft} flows into it.

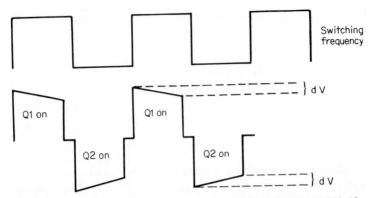

Figure 3.2 The small blocking capacitor C_b in series with the half-bridge primary (Fig. 3.1) is needed to prevent flux imbalance if the junction of the filter capacitors is not exactly at the midpoint of the supply voltage. Primary current charges the capacitor, causing a droop in the primary voltage waveform. Droop should be kept to no more than 10 percent. (dV is permissible droop in primary voltage due to charging of blocking capacitor.)

Whatever voltage it charges up to robs voltage from the flat-topped primary pulse shown in Fig. 3.2.

This robs volt-seconds from all secondary windings and forces a longer on time to achieve the desired output voltage. In general, it is desirable to keep the primary voltage pulses as flat-topped as possible.

Assume a permissible droop dV. The equivalent flat-topped current pulse which causes that droop is I_{pft} of Eq. 3.1. Then since that current flows for $0.8T/2$, the required capacitor magnitude is simply

$$C_b = \frac{I_{pft} \times 0.8T/2}{dV} \qquad (3.4)$$

It is instructive to consider an example. Assume a 150-W half bridge operating at 100 kHz from a nominal DC input of 320 V. At 15 percent low line, it is 272 V and the primary voltage is $\pm 272/2$ or ± 136 V.

A tolerable droop in the flat-topped primary voltage pulse is about 10 percent or about 14 V. For 150 W and V_{dc} of 272 V, I_{pft} is, from Eq. 3.1, $I_{pft} = 3.13 \times 150/272 = 1.73$ A. Then from Eq. 3.4, $C_b = 1.73 \times 0.8 \times 5 \times 10^{-6}/14 = 0.49$ μF. The capacitor must, of course, be a non-polarized type.

3.2.5 Half-bridge leakage inductance problems

Leakage inductance spikes, which are so troublesome in the single-ended forward converter and push-pull topology, do not exist in the half bridge. This is so because any such spikes become clamped to V_{dc} by diodes $D5$, $D6$ across transistors $Q1$, $Q2$.

Thus, if $Q1$ is on, load and magnetizing current flow through it, through the $T1$ leakage inductance, the paralleled $T1$ magnetizing inductance, and the secondary load impedances reflected by their turns ratio squared into the primary and thence through C_b into the $C1$, $C2$ junction. The dot end of N_p is positive with respect to its no-dot end.

Now, when $Q1$ turns off, the magnetizing inductance forces all winding polarities to reverse. The dot end of $T1$ tries to go far negative and if it did, would put more than V_{dc} across $Q1$ and might damage it and also might damage $Q2$ by imposing a reverse voltage across it. But the dot end of $T1$ is caught by diode $D6$ and can go no more negative than the negative end of V_{dc}.

Similarly, when $Q2$ is on, it stores current in the magnetizing inductance. The dot end of N_p is negative with respect to the no-dot end (which is close to $V_{dc}/2$). When $Q2$ turns off, the magnetizing inductance reverses all winding polarities and the dot end of N_p tries to go far positive but is caught at V_{dc} by clamp diode $D5$. Any energy stored in the leakage inductance during the on times is returned to V_{dc} via diodes $D5$, $D6$.

3.2.6 Double-ended forward converter versus half bridge

Both the half-bridge and double-ended forward converter (Fig. 2.13) subject their off transistors to only V_{dc} and not twice that. They are thus both candidates for power supplies to be used in the European market where the prime power is 220 V AC. They both have been used in such applications in enormous numbers, and it is instructive to consider the relative merits and drawbacks of each approach.

The major and probably the most significant difference between the two approaches is that the half-bridge secondary provides a full-wave output as compared to a half wave in the forward converter. Thus the square-wave frequency in the half-bridge secondary is twice that in the forward converter, and hence the output LC inductor and capacitor are smaller with the half bridge.

Peak secondary voltages are higher with the forward converter as their duty cycle is half that of the half bridge. But this is significant only if DC output voltages are high—above 200, as discussed in Sec. 2.5.1.

There are twice as many turns on the forward converter primary as on the half bridge as the former must sustain the full supply voltage as compared to half that voltage for the half bridge. The fewer turns on the half bridge primary may reduce its winding cost and result in lower parasitic capacities.

One final marginal factor in favor of the half bridge is that the coil losses in the primary due to the proximity effect (Sec. 7.5.6.1) are slightly lower than in the forward converter.

Proximity effect losses are due to induced eddy currents in one winding layer by currents in adjacent layers. Proximity losses increase rapidly with the number of winding layers and the forward converter may have more layers. The half-bridge primary has half the turns of a double-ended forward converter primary of equal output power operating from the same DC supply voltage. But this is balanced somewhat by the larger required wire size for the half bridge. Thus the required number of circular mils for a forward converter primary is given by Eq. 2.42 as $985P_o/V_{dc}$ and for a half bridge by Eq. 3.3 as $1395P_o/V_{dc}$.

In a practical case, the lower proximity effect losses for the half bridge may be only a marginal advantage. Proximity effect losses will be discussed in detail in Chap. 7.

3.2.7 Practical output power limits in half bridge

Peak primary current and maximum transistor off-voltage stress determine the practical maximum available output power in the half bridge. This limit is about 400 to 500 W for a half bridge operating off 120-V-AC input in the voltage-doubling mode of Fig. 3.1. This is equal to that for the double-ended forward converter as discussed in Sec. 2.4.1.1 and can be seen as follows. The peak equivalent flat-topped primary current is given by Eq. 3.1 as $I_{pft} = 3.13P_o/V_{dc}$. For a ± 10 percent steady-state tolerance with a 15 percent transient on top of that, the maximum off-voltage stress is $V_{dc} = 1.41 \times 120 \times 2 \times 1.1 \times 1.15$ or 428 V. The minimum DC input voltage is $V_{dc} = 1.41 \times 120 \times 2 \times 0.9 \times 0.85 = 259$ V.

Thus, for—say—500 W output, Eq. 3.1 gives the peak primary current as $I_{pft} = 3.13 \times 500/259 = 6.04$ A, and there is a large choice of transistors—either MOSFETs or bipolars—with 428-V, 6-A ratings. Bipolars, of course, would have to have a -1- to -5-V reverse bias (to permit V_{cev} rating) at turnoff to permit a safe off voltage of 428 V. Most adequately fast transistors at that current rating have only a V_{ceo} rating of 400 V.

The half bridge can be pushed to 1000-W output, but at the required 12-A rating, most available bipolar transistors with adequate current ratings and speed have too low a gain. MOSFET transistors at the required current and voltage rating have too large an on drop and are too expensive for most commercial applications at the time of this writing.

Above 500 W, the topology to consider is the full bridge, a small modification of the half bridge, capable of twice its output power.

3.3 Full-Bridge Converter Topology

3.3.1 Basic operation

Full-bridge converter topology is shown in Fig. 3.3. It is shown with the same voltage-doubling–full-wave bridge rectifying scheme as was shown for the half bridge (Sec. 3.2.1). It can be used as an off-line converter from a 440-V-AC line.

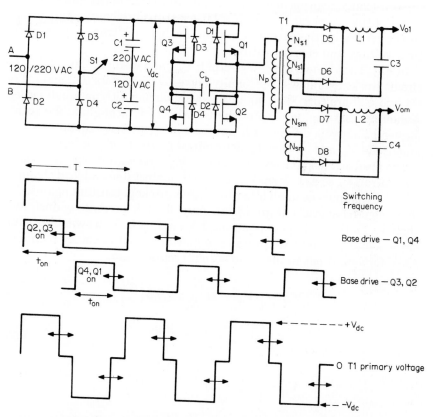

Figure 3.3 Full-bridge converter topology. Power transformer $T1$ is bridged between the junction of $Q1$, $Q2$ and $Q3$, $Q4$. Transistors $Q2$, $Q3$ are switched on simultaneously for an adjustable time during one half period; then transistors $Q4$, $Q1$ are simultaneously on for an equal time during the alternate half period. Transformer primary voltage is a square wave of $\pm V_{dc}$. This compares to the $\pm V_{dc}/2$ primary voltage in the half bridge and yields twice the available power of the half bridge.

Its major advantage is that the voltage impressed across the primary is a square wave of $\pm V_{dc}$ compared to $\pm V_{dc}/2$ for the half bridge. Further, the maximum transistor off-voltage stress is only the maximum DC input voltage—just as for the half bridge. Thus, for transistors of the same peak current and voltage ratings, the full bridge is able to deliver twice the output power of the half bridge.

The transformer primary turns must, of course, be chosen as twice that of the half bridge as it must sustain twice the primary voltage. But for the same output power as a half bridge, from the same DC supply voltage, the peak and rms currents are half that of the half bridge as the transformer primary supports twice the voltage of that in the half bridge. With twice the primary turns but half the rms current, the full-bridge transformer size is identical to that of the half bridge at equal output powers. But with a larger transformer, the full bridge can deliver twice the output of the half bridge with transistors of identical voltage and current ratings.

In Fig. 3.3 is shown a master output, V_{om} and a single slave, V_{o1}. The circuit works as follows. Diagonally opposite transistors ($Q2$ and $Q3$ or $Q4$ and $Q1$) are turned on simultaneously during alternate half cycles. Assuming that the on drop of the transistors is negligible, the transformer primary is driven with an alternating polarity square wave of amplitude V_{dc} and on time t_{on} determined by the feedback loop.

The feedback loop senses a fraction of V_{om} and with its width modulator controls t_{on} so as to keep V_{om} constant against line and load changes. The slave outputs as in all other topologies are kept constant against AC line input changes, but to within only 5 to 8 percent against load changes. Output voltages, assuming 1-V on drop in each switching transistor and 0.5 V forward drop in the master output Schottky rectifiers, 1.0-V forward drops in the slave output rectifiers are

$$V_{om} = \left[(V_{dc} - 2)\,\frac{N_{sm}}{N_p} - 0.5\right]\frac{2t_{on}}{T} \qquad (3.5a)$$

$$V_{om} \approx V_{dc}\,\frac{N_{sm}}{N_p}\,\frac{2t_{on}}{T} \qquad (3.5b)$$

$$V_{o1} = \left[(V_{dc} - 2)\,\frac{N_{s1}}{N_p} - 1.0\right]\frac{2t_{on}}{T} \qquad (3.6a)$$

$$V_{o1} \approx V_{dc}\,\frac{N_{s1}}{N_p}\,\frac{2t_{on}}{T} \qquad (3.6b)$$

As in all the other regulators, of course, as V_{dc} goes up or down by a given percentage, the width modulator decreases or increases the on time by the same percentage so as to keep the product $(V_{dc})(t_{on})$ and hence output voltages constant.

3.3.2 Full-bridge magnetics

3.3.2.1 Maximum on time, core, and primary turns selection.
In Fig. 3.3 it can be seen that, just as in the half bridge, if two transistors vertically stacked above one another (as $Q3$ and $Q4$ or $Q1$ and $Q2$) are simultaneously on, there would be a dead short circuit across the DC supply bus and the transistors would fail. To ensure against this, the maximum on time $\overline{t_{on}}$ which occurs at minimum DC input voltage V_{dc}—as can be seen in Eqs. 3.5b and 3.6b—will be chosen as 80 percent of a half period. This, of course, is "chosen" by choosing the turns ratios N_{sm}/N_p, N_{s1}/N_p so that in those equations for V_{dc} and $\overline{t_{on}}$ equal to $0.8T/2$, the correct output voltages—V_{om}, V_{o1}—are obtained.

The magnetic core and operating frequency are chosen from the core-frequency selection chart in Chap. 7. With a core selected and its iron area A_e known, the primary turns number N_p is chosen from Faraday's law (Eq. 1.17). In Eq. 1.17, E is the minimum primary voltage $(V_{dc} - 2)$ and dB is the flux change desired in the time dt of $0.8T/2$. And as discussed in Sec. 2.2.9.4, dB will be chosen as 3200 G (-1600 to $+1600$ G) for frequencies of up to 50 kHz and lesser excursions at higher frequencies as core losses increase.

3.3.2.2 Relation between primary current, output power, and input voltage.
Assume an efficiency of 80 percent from the primary input to the total output power. Then $P_o = 0.8P_{in}$ or $P_{in} = 1.25P_o$.

But at minimum DC input voltage V_{dc}, on time per half period is $0.8T/2$ and duty cycle over a complete period is 0.8. Then neglecting the power transistor on drops, input power at V_{dc} is

$$P_{in} = V_{dc}(0.8)I_{pft} = 1.25P_o$$

or
$$I_{pft} = \frac{1.56P_o}{V_{dc}} \tag{3.7}$$

where I_{pft} is the equivalent primary flat-topped current as described in Sec. 2.2.10.1.

3.3.2.3 Primary wire size selection.
Current I_{pft} flows at a duty cycle of 0.8 and hence its rms value is $I_{rms} = I_{pft}\sqrt{0.8}$. Then, from Eq. 3.7 $I_{rms} = (1.56P_o/V_{dc})\sqrt{0.8}$ or

$$I_{\text{rms}} = \frac{1.40P_o}{\underline{V_{\text{dc}}}}$$ (3.8)

And at 500 circular mils per rms ampere, the required number of circular mils is

$$\text{Circular mils needed} = \frac{500 \times 1.40P_o}{\underline{V_{\text{dc}}}}$$

$$= \frac{700P_o}{\underline{V_{\text{dc}}}}$$ (3.9)

3.3.2.4 Secondary turns and wire size. The number of turns on each secondary is calculated from Eq. 3.5a and 3.5b, where $\overline{t_{\text{on}}}$ is $0.8T/2$ for the specified minimum DC input V_{dc}, N_p is as calculated in Sec. 3.3.2.1, and all DC outputs are specified.

Secondary rms currents and wire sizes are chosen exactly as for the push-pull secondaries as described in Sec. 2.2.10.3. The secondary rms currents are given by Eq. 2.13 and the required circular mils for each half secondary is given by Eq. 2.14.

3.3.3 Output filter calculations

As for the half-bridge and push-pull topologies which also have full-wave output rectifiers, the output inductor and capacitors are calculated from Eqs. 2.20 and 2.22. Equation 2.20 specifies the output inductor for minimum DC output currents equal to one-tenth the nominal values. Equation 2.22 specifies the output capacitor for the specified peak-to-peak output ripple V_r and the selected peak-to-peak inductor current ripple amplitude.

3.3.4 Transformer primary blocking capacitor

Figure 3.3 shows a small nonpolarized blocking capacitor C_b in series with the transformer. It is needed to avoid the flux imbalance problem as discussed in Sec. 3.2.4.

Flux imbalance in the full bridge is less likely than in the half bridge, but still is possible. With bipolars, an on pair in one half cycle may have different storage times than the pair in the alternate half cycle. With MOSFETs, the on-voltage drops of the pairs in alternate half cycles may be unequal. In either case, the volt-second product applied to the transformer primary in alternate half cycles will be unequal and the core may walk off center of its hysteresis loop, saturate the core, and destroy the transistors.

Flyback Converter Topologies

4.1 Introduction

All topologies discussed thus far, with the exception of the boost regulator (Sec. 1.4) and the polarity inverter (Sec. 1.5) deliver power to their loads during the time when the power transistor is turned on.

Flyback topologies described in this chapter operate in a fundamentally different way. During their power transistor on time, they store energy in their power transformer while load current is supplied from an output filter capacitor. When the power transistor turns off, the energy stored in the power transformer is transferred to the output as load current and to the filter capacitor to replenish the charge it lost when it alone was delivering load current.

The topology has advantages and drawbacks, discussed in detail below. The major advantage is that the output filter inductors required for all forward topologies is not required for flybacks. Especially for multioutput power supplies, this is a significant saving in cost and space.

4.2 Flyback Converter—Areas of Application

Flyback converter topology is shown in Fig. 4.1. It is very widely used for output powers from about 150 down to under 5 W. Its great initial attraction—although it is not strictly so, as will soon be seen—is that it has no secondary output inductors as have all topologies discussed thus far. The consequent savings in cost and volume of the output inductors is a significant advantage.

It is widely used for high output voltages at relatively low power (≤ 5000 V at <15 W). It can also be used at powers of up to 150 W if DC supply voltages are high enough (≥ 160 V) so that primary cur-

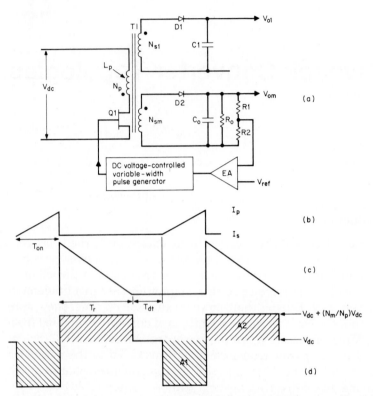

Figure 4.1 Discontinuous-mode flyback converter. When $Q1$ is on, all rectifier diodes are reverse-biased and all output capacitors supply load currents. N_p acts like a pure inductor and load current builds up linearly in it to a peak I_p. When $Q1$ turns off, the primary stored energy $\frac{1}{2}LI_p^2$ is delivered to the secondaries to supply load current and replenish the charge on output capacitors which they had lost when $Q1$ was on. The circuit is discontinuous if the secondary current has decayed to zero before the start of the next turnon.

rents are not excessive. The feature which makes it valuable for high output voltages is that it requires no output inductor. In forward converters, discussed above, output inductors become a troublesome problem at high output voltages because of the large voltages they have to sustain. Not requiring a high voltage free-wheeling diode is also a plus for the flyback in high-voltage supplies.

It is also a frequent choice for a supply with many output voltages (≤ 10 is not uncommon) in the region of 50 to 150 W. It is attractive for a multioutput supply because the output voltages track one another with line and load changes far better than they do in the forward types described earlier. The better tracking is due to the absence of output inductors.

It can be used from DC input voltages as low as 5 V up to the usual rectified 160 V from a 115-V-AC power line by proper choice of the secondary to primary turns ratios. By careful design of these turns ratios, it can also be used off the rectified DC of 160 V from a 115-V-AC power line or from the rectified 320 V DC from a 220-V-AC power line without resorting to the voltage doubling–full-wave rectifying scheme (switch $S1$) of Fig. 3.1.

The latter scheme, although very widely used, has the objectionable feature that to do the switching from 115 to 220 V AC, both ends of the switch in Fig. 3.1 have to be accessible on the outside of the supply which is a safety hazard. Or the supply must be opened to change the switch position. Both these alternatives have drawbacks. An alternative scheme not requiring switching will be discussed in Sec. 4.3.5.

4.3 Discontinuous-Mode Flybacks— Basic Operation

Referring to Fig. 4.1, the topology works as follows. Figure 4.1 shows a master and one slave output. As in all other topologies shown previously, a negative-feedback loop will be closed around the master V_{om}. A fraction of V_{om} will be compared to a reference, and the error signal will control the $Q1$ on time pulse width so as to make the sampled output equal to the reference voltage for line and load changes. The slaves will be well regulated against line changes and somewhat less against load changes. But slave changes with line and load will be better than in the previous forward-type topologies.

In Fig. 4.1, flyback operation can be immediately recognized from the dots on the transformer primary and secondary. When $Q1$ is on, dot ends of all windings are negative with respect to their no-dot ends. Output rectifier diodes $D1$ and $D2$ are reverse-biased and all the output load currents are supplied from storage filter capacitors $C1$ and $C2$. These will be chosen as described below to deliver the load currents with the maximum specified ripple or droop in output voltage.

During the $Q1$ on time, there is a fixed voltage across N_p and current in it ramps up linearly (Fig. 4.1b) at a rate of $dI/dt = (V_{dc} - 1)/L_p$, where L_p is the primary magnetizing inductance. At the end of the on time, the primary current has ramped up to $I_p = (V_{dc} - 1)T_{on}/L_p$. This current represents a stored energy of

$$E = \frac{L_p(I_p)^2}{2} \tag{4.1}$$

where E is in joules
  L_p is in henries
  I_p is in amperes

Now when $Q1$ turns off, current in the magnetizing inductance forces reversal of polarities on all windings. Assume for the moment that there are no slave windings and only the master secondary N_m. Since the current in an inductor cannot change instantaneously, at the instant of turnoff, the primary current transfers to the secondary at an amplitude $I_s = I_p(N_p/N_m)$.

After a number of cycles, the secondary DC voltage has built up to a magnitude (calculated below) of V_{om}. Now with $Q1$ off, the dot end of N_m is positive with respect to its no-dot end and current flows out of it, but ramps down linearly (Fig. 4.1c) at a rate $dI_s/dt = V_{om}/L_s$, where L_s is the secondary inductance. If the secondary current has ramped down to zero before the start of the next $Q1$ on time, all the energy stored in the primary when $Q1$ was on has been delivered to the load and the circuit is said to be operating in the discontinuous mode. Since an amount of energy E in joules delivered in a time T in seconds represents input power in watts, at the end of one period, power drawn from V_{dc} is

$$P = \frac{\frac{1}{2}L_p(I_p)^2}{T} \text{ W} \qquad (4.2a)$$

But $I_p = (V_{dc} - 1)T_{on}/L_p$. Then

$$P = \frac{[(V_{dc} - 1)T_{on}]^2}{2TL_p} \approx \frac{(V_{dc}T_{on})^2}{2TL_p} \text{ W} \qquad (4.2b)$$

As can be seen from Eq. 4.2b, the feedback loop maintains constant output voltage by keeping the product $V_{dc}T_{on}$ constant.

4.3.1 Relation between output voltage versus input voltage, on time, output load

Assume an efficiency of 80 percent.

$$\text{Input power} = 1.25 \text{ (output power)}$$

$$= \frac{1.25(V_o)^2}{R_o} = \frac{\frac{1}{2}(L_p I_p^2)}{T}$$

But $I_p = V_{dc}\overline{T_{on}}/L_p$ since maximum on time $\overline{T_{on}}$ occurs at minimum supply voltage $\underline{V_{dc}}$, as can be seen from Eq 4.2b.

Then $1.25(V_o)^2/R_o = \frac{1}{2}L_pV_{dc}^2\,\overline{T_{on}}^2/L_p^2T$ or

$$V_o = \overline{V_{dc}T_{on}}\;\sqrt{\frac{R_o}{2.5TL_p}} \tag{4.3}$$

Thus the feedback loop will regulate the output by decreasing T_{on} as V_{dc} or R_o goes up, increasing T_{on} as V_{dc} or R_o goes down.

4.3.2 Design relations and sequential decision requirements

4.3.2.1 Establishing primary/secondary turns ratio.
There are a number of decisions which should be made in the proper sequence. The first is to choose the primary/master secondary turns ratio N_p/N_{sm}; this determines the maximum off-voltage stress $\overline{V_{ms}}$ on the power transistor in the absence of a leakage inductance spike. Neglecting the leakage spike, the maximum transistor voltage stress at maximum DC input $\overline{V_{dc}}$ and for a 1-V rectifier drop is

$$\overline{V_{ms}} = \overline{V_{dc}} + \frac{N_p}{N_{sm}}\,(V_o + 1) \tag{4.4}$$

where $\overline{V_{ms}}$ is chosen sufficiently low so that a leakage inductance spike of $0.3V_{dc}$ on top of that still leaves a safety margin of about 30 percent below the maximum pertinent transistor rating (V_{ceo}, V_{cer}, or V_{cev}).

4.3.2.2 Ensuring core does not saturate, circuit remains discontinuous.
Recall that to ensure that the core does not drift up or down its hysteresis loop, the on volt-second product ($A1$ in Fig. 4.1d) must equal the reset volt-second product ($A2$ in Fig. 4.1d). Assume that the on drop of $Q1$ and the forward drop of the rectifier $D2$ are both 1 V:

$$(\underline{V_{dc}} - 1)\overline{T_{on}} = (V_o + 1)\frac{N_p}{N_{sm}}\,T_r \tag{4.5}$$

where T_r is the reset time shown in Fig. 4.1c and is the time required for the secondary current to return to zero.

To ensure the circuit operates in the discontinuous mode, a dead time (T_{dt} in Fig. 4.1c) is established so that the maximum on time $\overline{T_{on}}$, which occurs when V_{dc} is a minimum plus the reset time T_r is only 80 percent of a full period. This leaves $0.2T$ margin against unexpected decreases in R_o, which according to Eq. 4.3 would force the feedback loop to increase T_{on} in order to keep V_o constant.

As for the boost regulator (which is also a flyback type), Secs. 1.4.2

and 1.4.3 pointed out that if the error amplifier had been designed to keep the loop stable in the discontinuous mode, if the circuit momentarily entered the continuous mode, it will break into oscillation.

Thus, increasing DC load current or decreasing V_{dc} causes the error amplifier to increase T_{on} in order to keep V_o constant (Eq. 4.3). This increased T_{on} eats into the dead time T_{dt} and eventually results in the secondary current not having fallen to zero by the start of the next $Q1$ on time. This is the start of the continuous mode, and if the error amplifier has not been designed for this with a drastically lower bandwidth, the circuit will oscillate. To ensure that the circuit remains discontinuous, the maximum on time which will generate the desired maximum output power is established thus:

$$\overline{T}_{on} + T_r + T_{dt} = T$$

or
$$\overline{T}_{on} + T_r = 0.8T \tag{4.6}$$

Now in Eqs. 4.5 and 4.6, there are two unknowns as N_p/N_{sm} has been calculated from Eq. 4.4 for specified $\overline{V}_{dc}$ and $\overline{V}_{ms}$. Then from the last two relations

$$\overline{T}_{on} = \frac{(V_o + 1)(N_p/N_{sm})(0.8T)}{(V_{dc} - 1) + (V_o + 1)(N_p/N_{sm})} \tag{4.7}$$

4.3.2.3 Primary inductance versus minimum output resistance and DC input voltage. From Eq. 4.3, the primary inductance is

$$L_p = \frac{R_o}{2.5T}\left(\frac{V_{dc}\overline{T}_{on}}{V_o}\right)^2 = \frac{(V_{dc}\overline{T}_{on})^2}{2.5T\overline{P}_o} \tag{4.8}$$

4.3.2.4 Transistor peak current, maximum voltage stress. The transistor, if bipolar, should have an acceptably high gain at a peak current of

$$I_p = \frac{V_{dc}\overline{T}_{on}}{L_p} \tag{4.9}$$

where V_{dc} is specified and $\overline{T}_{on}$ is calculated from Eq. 4.7 and L_p is calculated from Eq. 4.8. If it is a MOSFET transistor, it should have a peak current rating about 5 to 10 times the value calculated from Eq. 4.9 so that its on resistance is low enough to yield a low on drop.

4.3.2.5 Primary rms current and wire size. Primary current is a triangle of peak amplitude I_p (Eq. 4.9) at a maximum duration T_{on} out of every period T. Its rms value then (see Sec. 2.2.10.6) is

$$I_{rms(primary)} = \frac{I_p}{\sqrt{3}} \sqrt{\frac{T_{on}}{T}} \tag{4.10}$$

where I_p and T_{on} are as given by Eqs. 4.9 and 4.7.

At 500 circular mils per rms ampere, the required number of circular mils is

Circular mils required (primary) $= 500 I_{rms(primary)}$

$$= 500 \frac{I_p}{\sqrt{3}} \sqrt{\frac{T_{on}}{T}} \tag{4.11}$$

4.3.2.6 Secondary rms current and wire size. Secondary current is a triangle of peak amplitude $I_s = I_p(N_p/N_s)$ and duration T_r. Primary/secondary turns ratio N_p/N_s is given by Eq. 4.4 and $T_r = (T - T_{on})$. Secondary rms current is then

$$I_{rms(secondary)} = \frac{I_p(N_p/N_s)}{\sqrt{3}} \sqrt{\frac{T_r}{T}} \tag{4.12}$$

At 500 circular mils per rms ampere, the required number of circular mils is

Secondary circular mils required $= 500 I_{rms(secondary)}$ (4.13)

4.3.2.7 Design example—discontinuous-mode flyback. Design a flyback converter with the following specifications:

V_o	5.0 V
$P_{o(max)}$	50 W
$I_{o(max)}$	10 A
$I_{o(min)}$	1.0 A
$V_{dc(max)}$	60 V
$V_{dc(min)}$	38 V
Switching frequency	50 kHz

First select the voltage rating of the transistor as this mainly determines the transformer turns ratio. Choose a device with a 200-V rating. In Eq. 4.4 choose the maximum stress V_{ms} on the transistor in the off state (excluding the leakage inductance spike) as 120 V. Then even with a 25 percent or 30-V leakage spike, this leaves a 50-V margin to the maximum voltage rating. Then from Eq. 4.4:

$$120 = 60 + \frac{N_p}{N_{sm}}(V_o + 1) \quad \text{or} \quad \frac{N_p}{N_{sm}} = 10$$

Now choose maximum on time from Eq. 4.7:

$$\overline{T}_{on} = \frac{(V_o + 1)(N_p/N_{sm})(0.8T)}{(V_{dc} - 1) + (V_o + 1)N_p/N_{sm}}$$

$$= \frac{6 \times 10 \times 0.8 \times 20)}{(38 - 1) + 6 \times 10}$$

$$= 9.9 \; \mu s$$

From Eq. 4.8

$$L_p = \frac{(V_{dc}\overline{T}_{on})^2}{2.5TP_o}$$

$$= \frac{(38 \times 9.9 \times 10^{-6})^2}{2.5 \times 20 \times 10^{-6} \times 50}$$

$$= 56.6 \; \mu H$$

From Eq. 4.9

$$I_p = \frac{V_{dc}\overline{T}_{on}}{L_p}$$

$$= \frac{38 \times 9.9 \times 10^{-6}}{56.6 \times 10^{-6}}$$

$$= 6.6 \quad A$$

From Eq. 4.10, primary rms current is

$$I_{rms(primary)} = \frac{I_p}{\sqrt{3}} \sqrt{\frac{T_{on}}{T}}$$

$$= \frac{6.6}{\sqrt{3}} \times \sqrt{\frac{9.9}{20}}$$

$$= 2.7 \; A$$

From Eq. 4.11, primary circular mils requirement is

$$I_{\text{(primary circular mils)}} = 500 \times 2.7 = 1350 \text{ circular mils}$$

This calls for No. 19 wire of 1290 circular mils, which is close enough.

From Eq. 4.12, secondary rms current is

$$I_{\text{rms(secondary)}} = \frac{I_p(N_p/N_s)}{\sqrt{3}} \sqrt{\frac{T_r}{T}}$$

But reset time T_r is

$$(0.8T - \overline{T_{\text{on}}}) = (16 - 9.9) = 6.1 \; \mu\text{s}$$

Then

$$I_{\text{rms(secondary)}} = \frac{6.6 \times 10}{\sqrt{3}} \sqrt{\frac{6.1}{20}}$$

$$= 21 \text{ A}$$

and from Eq. 4.12, the required number of circular mils is $500 \times 21 = 10,500$. This calls for No. 10 wire, which, of course, is impractically large in diameter. A foil winding or a number of smaller diameter wires in parallel with an equal total circular-mil area would be used.

Output capacitor is chosen on the basis of specified output ripple. At maximum output current, during the transistor on time of 9.9 μs, the filter capacitor C_o carries the 10 A for 10.1 μs. It slopes in voltage an amount $V = I(T - t_{\text{on}})C_o$. Then for a voltage droop of 0.05 V

$$C_o = \frac{10 \times 10.1 \times 10^{-6}}{0.05}$$

$$= 2000 \; \mu\text{F}$$

From Sec. 1.4.7, the average value of the ESR of a 2000-μF aluminum electrolytic capacitor is $R_{\text{esr}} = 65 \times 10^{-6}/C_o = 0.03 \; \Omega$.

At the instant of transistor turnoff, the peak secondary current of 66 A flows through this ESR, causing a thin spike of $66 \times 0.03 = 2$ V. This large-amplitude thin spike at transistor turnoff is a universal problem with flybacks having a large N_p/N_s ratio. It is usually solved by using a larger filter capacitor than calculated as above (since R_{esr} is inversely proportional to C_o) and/or integrating away the thin spike with a small LC circuit.

The selection of a transformer core for a flyback topology circuit is significantly different from nonflyback core selection. Recall in the flyback that when current flows in the primary, no load current flows in the secondary to buck out the primary ampere turns. Thus in the flyback, all the primary ampere turns tend to saturate the core.

In contrast, in nonflyback topologies, secondary load current flows when primary current flows and is in the direction (by Lenz' law) to cancel the ampere turns of the primary. It is only the primary magnetizing current which drives the core over its hysteresis loop and moves it toward saturation. That magnetizing current is kept a small fraction of the primary load current by providing a large magnetizing inductance and hence core saturation is never a problem with nonflyback topologies.

Thus for flyback transformers, cores must have some means of carrying large primary currents without saturating. This is done with gapped ferrite cores (Sec. 2.3.9.3) or with MPP (molybdenum permalloy powder) cores which have an inherent internal air gap. This is discussed further in the following section.

4.3.3 Flyback magnetics

Referring to Fig. 4.1*a*, it is seen from the winding dots that when the transistor is on and current flows in the primary, no secondary currents flow. This is totally different from forward-type converters where current flows in the secondary when it flows in the primary. Thus in a forward-type converter, primary current flows into a dot end and secondary current flows out of a dot end.

Primary and secondary load ampere turns then cancel each other out and do not move the core across its hysteresis loop. In the forward-type converters, it is only the magnetizing current which drives the core across the hysteresis loop and may potentially saturate it. But this magnetizing current is a small fraction (rarely >10 percent) of the total primary current.

In a flyback converter, however, the entire triangle of primary current shown in Fig. 4.1*b* drives the core across the hysteresis loop as it is not canceled out by any secondary ampere turns. Thus even at very low output power, the core would almost immediately saturate and destroy the transistor if nothing were done to prevent it.

To prevent core saturation in the flyback transformer, the core is gapped. The gapped core can be of either of two types. It can be a solid ferrite core with a known air-gap length obtained by grinding down the center leg in EE or cup-type cores. The known gap length can also be obtained by inserting a plastic shim between the two halves of an EE, cup, or UU core.

A more usual gapped core for flyback converters is the MPP or molypermalloy powder core. Such cores are toroids made of baked and hardened mix of magnetic powdered particles. These powdered particles are mixed in a slurry with a plastic resin binder and cast in the shape of toroids. Each magnetic particle in the toroid is thus encapsulated within a resin envelope which behaves as a "distributed air gap" and acts to keep the core from saturating. The basic magnetic material which is ground up into a powder is Square Permalloy 80, an alloy of 79% nickel, 17% iron, and 4% molybdenum made by Magnetics Inc. or Arnold Magnetics.

The permeability of the resulting toroid is determined by controlling the concentration of magnetic particles in the slurry. Permeabilities are controlled to within ±5 percent over large temperature ranges and are available in discrete steps ranging from 14 to 550. Toroids with low permeability behave like gapped cores with large air gaps. They require a relatively large number of turns to yield a desired inductance but tolerate many ampere turns before they saturate. Higher permeability cores require relatively fewer turns but saturate at a lower number of ampere turns.

Such MPP cores are used not only for flyback transformers where all the primary current is a DC bias current. They are also used for forward converter output inductors where, as has been seen, a unique inductance is required at the large DC output current bias (Sec. 1.3.6).

4.3.3.1 Gapped ferrite cores to avoid saturation.

Adding an air gap to the solid ferrite core achieves two results. First, it tilts the hysteresis loop as shown in Fig. 2.5 and hence decreases its permeability, which must be known to select the number of turns for a desired inductance. Second, and more important, it increases the number of ampere turns it can tolerate before it saturates.

Core manufacturers often give curves which permit calculation of the number of turns for a desired inductance and the number of ampere turns at which saturation commences. Such curves are shown in Fig. 4.2 and show A_{lg}, the inductance per 1000 turns with an air gap and the number of ampere turns (NI_{sat}) where saturation starts to set in. Since inductance is proportional to the square of the number of turns, the number of turns N_l for any inductance L is calculated from

$$N_l = 1000 \sqrt{\frac{L}{A_{lg}}} \qquad (4.14)$$

Figure 4.2 shows A_{lg} curves for a number of different air gaps and the "cliff" point at which saturation starts. It can be seen that the larger the air gap, the lower the value of A_{lg} and the larger the number of ampere turns at which saturation starts. If such curves were

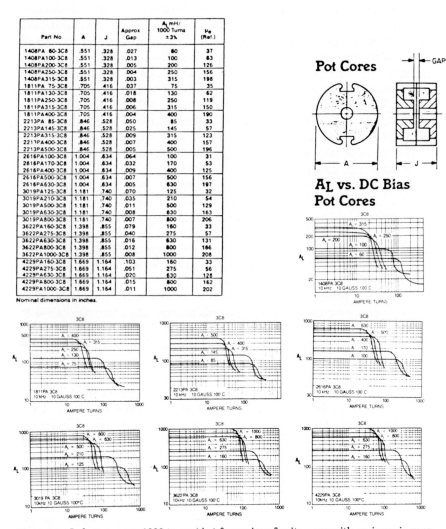

Part No	A	J	Approx Gap	A_L mH/ 1000 Turns ±3%	μ_e (Ref.)
1408PA 60-3C8	.551	.328	.027	60	37
1408PA100-3C8	.551	.328	.013	100	63
1408PA200-3C8	.551	.328	.005	200	126
1408PA250-3C8	.551	.328	.004	250	156
1408PA315-3C8	.551	.328	.003	315	198
1811PA 75-3C8	.705	.416	.037	75	35
1811PA130-3C8	.705	.416	.018	130	62
1811PA250-3C8	.705	.416	.008	250	119
1811PA315-3C8	.705	.416	.006	315	150
1811PA400-3C8	.705	.416	.004	400	190
2213PA 85-3C8	.846	.528	.050	85	33
2213PA145-3C8	.846	.528	.025	145	57
2213PA315-3C8	.846	.528	.009	315	123
2213PA400-3C8	.846	.528	.007	400	157
2213PA500-3C8	.846	.528	.005	500	196
2616PA100-3C8	1.004	.634	.064	100	31
2616PA170-3C8	1.004	.634	.032	170	53
2616PA400-3C8	1.004	.634	.009	400	125
2616PA500-3C8	1.004	.634	.007	500	156
2616PA630-3C8	1.004	.634	.005	630	197
3019PA125-3C8	1.181	.740	.070	125	32
3019PA210-3C8	1.181	.740	.035	210	54
3019PA500-3C8	1.181	.740	.011	500	129
3019PA630-3C8	1.181	.740	.008	630	163
3019PA800-3C8	1.181	.740	.007	800	206
3622PA160-3C8	1.398	.855	.079	160	33
3622PA275-3C8	1.398	.855	.040	275	57
3622PA630-3C8	1.398	.855	.016	630	131
3622PA800-3C8	1.398	.855	.012	800	166
3622PA1000-3C8	1.398	.855	.008	1000	208
4229PA160-3C8	1.669	1.164	.103	160	33
4229PA275-3C8	1.669	1.164	.051	275	56
4229PA630-3C8	1.669	1.164	.020	630	128
4229PA800-3C8	1.669	1.164	.015	800	162
4229PA1000-3C8	1.669	1.164	.011	1000	202

Nominal dimensions in inches.

Figure 4.2 Inductance per 1000 turns (A_{1g}) for various ferrite cores with various air gaps. Also the point in ampere turns "cliff" point where saturation commences. (*Courtesy Ferroxcube Corporation.*)

available for all cores at various air gaps, Eq. 4.14 would give the number of turns for any selected air gap from the value of A_{1g} read from the curve. The cliff point on the curve would tell whether, at those turns and for the specified primary current, the core had fallen over the saturation cliff.

Such curves, though, are not available for all cores and all air gaps. But this is no problem, for A_{1g} can be calculated with reasonable accuracy from Eq. 2.39 and A_l with no gap, which is always given in the manufacturers' catalogs. The cliff point at which saturation starts can be calculated from Eq. 2.37 for any air gap. The cliff point corresponds to the flux density in iron B_i, where the core material itself starts bending over into saturation.

From Fig. 2.3, it is seen that this is not a very sharply breaking point but occurs around 2500 G for this ferrite material (Ferroxcube 3C8). Thus the cliff in ampere turns is found by substituting 2500 G in Eq. 2.37. As noted in connection with Eq. 2.37, in the usual case, the air-gap length l_a is much larger than l_i/u as u is so large. Then the iron flux density as given by Eq. 2.37 is determined mainly by the air-gap length l_a.

4.3.3.2 Powdered permalloy (MPP) cores to avoid saturation. These toroidal cores are widely used and made by Magnetics Inc. (data in catalog MPP303S) and by Arnold Co. (data in catalog PC104G).

The problem in designing a core of desired inductance at a specified maximum DC current bias is to select a core geometry and material permeability, such that the core does not saturate at the maximum ampere turns to which it is subjected. There are a limited number of core geometries, each available in permeabilities ranging from 14 to 550. Selection procedures are described in the catalogs mentioned above, but the following has been found more direct and useful.

In the Magnetics Inc. catalog, one full page (Fig. 4.3) is devoted to each size toroid and for each size, its A_l value (inductance in millihenries per 1000 turns) is given for each discrete permeability. Figure 4.4, also from the Magnetics Inc. catalog, gives the falloff in permeability (or A_l value) for increasing magnetizing force in oersteds for core material of the various available permeabilities. (Recall the oersteds–ampere-turns relation in Eq. 2.6.)

A core geometry and permeability can be selected so that at the maximum DC current and the selected number of turns, the A_l and hence inductance has fallen off by any desired percentage given in Fig. 4.4. Then at zero DC current the inductance will be greater by that percentage. Such inductors or chokes are referred to as "swinging chokes" and in many applications are desirable. For example, if an inductor is permitted to swing a great deal, in an output filter, it can tolerate a very low minimum DC current before it goes discontinuous (Sec. 1.3.6). But this greatly complicates the feedback-loop stability design and most often, the inductor in an output filter or transformer in a flyback will not be permitted to "swing" or vary very much between its zero and maximum current value.

Referring to Fig. 4.3, it is seen that a core of this specific size is available in permeabilities ranging from 14 to 550. Cores with perme-

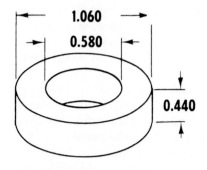

1.060

0.580

0.440

WINDOW AREA		308,000 cir. mils
CROSS SECTION	0.1014 in²	0.654 cm²
PATH LENGTH	2.50 in	6.35 cm
WEIGHT	1.3 oz	36. gm
	(.08 lb.)	

WINDING TURN LENGTH

WINDING FACTOR	LENGTH/TURN	
100% (UNITY)	0.1714 ft	5.23 cm
60%	0.1526 ft	4.66 cm
40%	0.1344 ft	4.10 cm
20%	0.1263 ft	3.85 cm
0%	0.1233 ft	3.76 cm

CORE DIMENSIONS AFTER FINISH

OD (MAX.)	1.090 in	27.7 mm
ID (MIN.)	0.555 in	14.10 mm
HT (MAX.)	0.472 in	11.99 mm

WOUND COIL DIMENSIONS

UNITY WINDING FACTOR

OD (MAX.)	1.468 in	37.3 mm
HT (MAX.)	0.944 in	24.0 mm

MAGNETIC INFORMATION

PART NO.	PERM μ	INDUCTANCE @ 1000 TURNS MH±8%	NOMINAL DC RESISTANCE OHMS/MH**	FINISHES AND STABILIZATIONS*	GRADING STATUS 2% BANDS	B/NI GAUSS PER AMP. TURN
55933–	14	18	0.457	A2	*	2.77 (<1500 gauss)
55932–	26	32	0.257	A2	*	5.15 (<1500 gauss)
55894–	60	75	0.110	ALL	YES	11.9 (<1500 gauss)
55930–	125	157	0.0524	ALL	YES	24.8 (<1500 gauss)
55929–	147	185	0.0444	ALL	YES	29.1 (<1500 gauss)
55928–	160	201	0.0409	ALL	YES	31.7 (<1500 gauss)
55924–	173	217	0.0379	ALL	YES	34.3 (<1500 gauss)
55927–	200	251	0.0327	ALL	YES	39.6 (<600 gauss)
55925–	300	377	0.0218	A2 and L6	YES	59.4 (<300 gauss)
55926–	550	740	0.0111	A2	YES	109 (<50 gauss)

14, 26, 60 and 125μ
types are available
as high flux cores.
See p. 84, "How to Order".

WINDING INFORMATION

FOR UNITY WINDING FACTOR

AWG WIRE SIZE	TURNS	Rdc OHMS	AWG WIRE SIZE	TURNS	Rdc OHMS
9	21	0.00291	24	587	2.58
10	27	0.00459	25	725	4.02
11	34	0.00726	26	906	6.37
12	42	0.01148	27	1,141	10.05
13	53	0.01805	28	1,400	15.67
14	66	0.0284	29	1,711	24.1
15	82	0.0447	30	2,139	38.1
16	103	0.0707	31	2,633	59.1
17	127	0.1102	32	3,209	89.1
18	159	0.1739	33	3,980	140.5
19	197	0.272	34	5,066	227
20	246	0.428	35	6,286	357
21	308	0.676	36	7,759	552
22	380	1.056	37	9,478	832
23	474	1.649	38	11,847	1,316

Figure 4.3 A typical MPP core. With its large distributed air gap, it can tolerate a large DC current bias without saturating. It is available in a large range of different geometries. (*Courtesy Magnetics Inc.*)

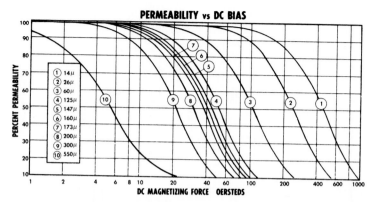

Figure 4.4 Falloff in permeability or A_1 for MPP cores of various permeabilities versus DC magnetizing force in oersteds. (*Courtesy Magnetics Inc.*)

ability above 125 have large values of A_l and hence require fewer turns for a specified inductance at zero DC current bias. But in Fig. 4.4 it is seen that the higher-permeability cores saturate at increasingly lower oersteds or ampere turns of bias. Hence in power supply usage, where DC current biases are rarely under 1 A, cores of permeability greater than 125 are rarely used. And an inductance swing or change of 10 percent from zero to the maximum specified current is most often easily acceptable.

Thus in Fig. 4.4 it is seen that for a permeability dropoff or swing of 10 percent, core materials of permeabilities 14, 26, 60, and 125, can sustain maximum magnetizing forces of only 170, 95, 39, and 19 Oe, respectively. These maximum magnetizing forces in oersteds can be translated into maximum ampere turns by Eq. 2.6 ($\overline{H} = 0.4\pi(\overline{NI})/l_m$), where l_m is the magnetic path length in centimeters, given in Fig. 4.3 for this particular core geometry as 6.35 cm.

From these maximum number of ampere turns $(\overline{NI})$, beyond which inductance falls off more than 10 percent, the maximum number of turns $(\overline{N})$ is calculated for any peak current. And from $\overline{N}$, the maximum inductance possible for any core at the specified peak current is calculated as $L_{max} = 0.9A_1 (N_{max}/1000)^2$.

Tables 4.1, 4.2, 4.3 show N_{max} and L_{max} for three often used core geometries in permeabilities of 14, 26, 60, and 125 at peak currents of 1, 2, 3, 5, 10, 20, and 50 amperes. These tables permit core geometry and permeability selection at a glance without iterative calculations.

Thus, Table 4.1 is used in the following manner. Assume that this particular core has the acceptable geometry. The table is entered horizontally to the first peak current greater than specified value. At that peak current, move down vertically until the first inductance L_{max}

TABLE 4.1 Maximum Number of Turns and Maximum Inductance at Those Turns for Various Peak Currents I_p at a Maximum Inductance Falloff of 10 Percent from Zero Current Level

Magnetics Inc. core number	Permeability	A_L, mH per 1000 turns	Maximum oersted level $\bar{H}$ for 10% falloff in inductance	Maximum $N\bar{I}$ permissible ampere turns corresponding to $\bar{H}$	Maximum permissible turns and inductance at those turns for a 10% inductance falloff at indicated peak currents							I_p
Core	μ	A_L	H	$N\bar{I}$	1A	2A	3A	5A	10A	20A	50A	N_{max} / L_{max}
								N_{max}/L_{max}				
55930	125	157	19	96	96 / 1,382	48 / 339	32 / 145	19 / 56	10 / 15	5 / 3.5	2 / 0.6	N_{max} / L_{max}
55894	60	75	39	197	197 / 2,620	99 / 662	66 / 294	39 / 103	20 / 27	10 / 7	4 / 1	N_{max} / L_{max}
55932	26	32	95	480	480 / 6,635	240 / 1,659	160 / 737	96 / 265	48 / 66	24 / 17	10 / 3	N_{max} / L_{max}
55933	14	18	170	859	859 / 11,954	430 / 2,995	286 / 1,325	172 / 479	86 / 120	43 / 30	17 / 5	N_{max} / L_{max}

Note: Magnetics Inc. MPP cores. All cores have outer diameter (OD) = 1.060 in, inner diameter (ID) = 0.58 in, height = 0.44 in, l_m = 6.35 cm. All inductances in microhenries.

greater than the desired value is reached. The core at that point is the
only one which can yield the desired inductance with only a 10 percent
swing. The number of turns N_d on that core for a desired inductance
L_d is within 5 percent given by

$$N_d = 1000 \sqrt{\frac{L_d}{0.95A_l}}$$

where A_l is the value in column 3 in Table 4.1. If, moving vertically,
no core can be found whose maximum inductance is greater than the
desired value, the core with the next larger geometry (greater OD or
greater height) must be used. The core ID must, of course, be large
enough to accommodate the number of turns of wire selected at the
rate of 500 circular mils per rms ampere or the next larger size core
must be used.

Tables 4.2 and 4.3 show similar data for a smaller (OD = 0.80 in)
and larger (OD = 1.84 in) family of cores. Similar charts can be generated for all the other available core sizes, but Tables 4.1 to 4.3
bracket about 90 percent of the possible designs for flyback transformers under 500 W or output inductors of up to 50 A.

A commonly used scheme for correcting the number of turns on a
core when an initial selection has resulted in too large an inductance
falloff should be noted. If, for an initially selected number of turns and
a specified maximum current, the inductance or permeability falloff
from Fig. 4.4 is down by P percent, the number of turns is increased by
P percent.

This moves the operating point further out by P percent as the magnetizing force in oersteds is proportional to the number of turns. The
core slides further down its saturation curve, and it might be thought
that the inductance would falloff even more. But since inductance is
proportional to the square of the number of turns, and magnetizing
force is proportional only to the number of turns, the zero current inductance has been increased by $2P$ percent but magnetizing force has
gone up only by P percent. The inductance is then correct at the specified maximum current. If the consequent swing is too large, a larger
core must be used.

4.3.4   Flyback disadvantages

Despite its many advantages, the flyback has the following drawbacks.

4.3.4.1   Large output voltage spikes.   At the end of the on time, the
peak primary current is given by Eq. 4.9. Immediately after the end of

TABLE 4.2 Maximum Number of Turns and Maximum Inductance at Those Turns for Various Peak Currents I_p at a Maximum Inductance Falloff of 10 Percent from Zero Current Level

Magnetics Inc. core number	Permeability	A_l, mH per 1000 turns	Maximum oersted level H for 10% falloff in inductance	Maximum permissible ampere turns corresponding to H	Maximum permissible turns and inductance at those turns for a 10% inductance falloff at indicated peak currents (N_{max}/L_{max})							
Core	μ	A_l	H	$\overline{NI}$	1A	2A	3A	5A	10A	20A	50A	I_p
55206	125	68	19	77	77	39	26	15	8	4	2	N_{max}
					363	93	41	14	4	1	0.24	L_{max}
55848	60	32	39	158	158	79	53	32	16	8	3	N_{max}
					719	180	81	29	7	2	0.26	L_{max}
55208	26	14	95	385	385	193	128	77	39	19	8	N_{max}
					1,868	469	206	75	19	4.5	0.8	L_{max}
55209	14	7.8	170	689	689	345	230	138	69	34	14	N_{max}
					3,333	836	371	134	33	8	1.4	L_{max}

Note: Magnetics Inc. MPP cores: OD = 0.8 in, ID = 0.5 in, height = 0.25 in, l_m = 5.09 cm. All inductances in microhenries.

TABLE 4.3 Maximum Number of Turns and Maximum Inductance at Those Turns for Various Peak Currents I_p at a Maximum Inductance Falloff of 10 Percent from Zero Current Level

Core	μ	A_l	$\bar{H}$	$\bar{NI}$	1A	2A	3A	5A	10A	20A	50A	I_p
55438	125	281	19	162	162	81	54	32	16	8	3	N_{max}
					6,637	1,659	737	259	65	16	2	L_{max}
55439	60	135	39	333	333	167	111	67	33	17	7	N_{max}
					13,473	3,389	1,497	545	132	35	6	L_{max}
55440	26	59	95	812	812	406	271	162	81	41	16	N_{max}
					35,011	8,753	3,900	1,394	348	89	14	L_{max}
55441	14	32	170	1454	1,454	727	485	291	145	73	29	N_{max}
					60,744	15,222	6,774	2,439	605	153	24	L_{max}

Note: Magnetics Inc. MPP cores: OD = 1.84 in, ID = 0.95 in, height = 0.71 in, l_m = 10.74 in. All inductances in microhenries.

the on time, that primary peak current, multiplied by the turns ratio N_p/N_s is driven into the secondary where it decays linearly as shown in Fig. 4.1c. In most cases, output voltages are low and input voltages are higher, resulting in a large N_p/N_s ratio and a consequent large secondary current.

At the initial start of turnoff, the impedance looking down into C_o is much lower than R_o (Fig. 4.1) and all the large secondary current flows down into C_o and its equivalent series resistor R_{esr}. This produces a large, thin output voltage spike, $I_p(N_p/N_s)R_{esr}$. The spike is generally less than 0.5 μs in width as it is differentiated with a time constant of $R_{esr}C_o$.

Frequently a power supply specification specifies output voltage ripple only as an rms or peak-to-peak fundamental value. Such a large, thin spike has a very low rms value and if a sufficiently large output filter capacitor is chosen, the supply can easily meet its rms ripple specification but can have disastrously high, thin output spikes. It is common to see a 50-mV fundamental peak-to-peak output ripple with a 1-V thin spike sitting on top of it.

Thus, almost always, a small LC filter is added after the main storage capacitor in flybacks. The L and C are quite small as they have to filter out a spike generally less than 0.5 μs in width. The inductor is considerably smaller than the inductor in forward-type converters, but it still has to be stocked and have space provided for it. Output voltage sensing for the error amplifier is taken before this LC filter.

4.3.4.2 Large output filter capacitor and high ripple current requirement.
A flyback filter capacitor is much larger than one for a forward-type converter. In a forward converter, when the power transistor turns off (Fig. 2.10), load current is supplied from the energy stored in both the filter inductor and the filter capacitor. But in the flyback, that capacitor is necessarily larger as it is the stored energy in it alone that supplies current to the load during the transistor on time. Output ripple is determined mostly by the ESR of the filter capacitor (see Sec. 1.3.7). An initial selection of the filter capacitor is made on the basis of output ripple specification from Eq. 1.10.

Frequently, however, it is not the output ripple voltage requirement that determines the final choice of the filter capacitor. Ultimately it may be the ripple current rating of the capacitor selected initially on the basis of the output ripple voltage specification.

In a forward-type converter (as in a buck regulator), the capacitor ripple current is greatly limited by the output inductor in series with it (Sec. 1.3.6). But in a flyback, the full DC current flows up from ground through the capacitor during the transistor on time. During the transistor off time, a current of equal (ampere)(time) product must flow down into the capacitor to replenish the charge it lost during the on time. Assuming, as in Fig. 4.1, a sum of on time plus reset time of 80 percent of a full period, the rms ripple current in the capacitor is closely

$$I_{rms} = I_{dc}\sqrt{\frac{\overline{t_{on}}}{T}} = I_{dc}\sqrt{0.8} = 0.89 I_{dc} \qquad (4.15)$$

If the initial capacitor selected on the basis of output ripple voltage specifications did not also have the ripple current rating of Eq. 4.15, a larger capacitor or more units in parallel are chosen.

4.3.5 Flybacks for 120- or 220-V-AC operation with no doubler or full-wave rectifier switching

In Sec. 3.2.1, a universally used scheme that permitted operation off either a 120-V-AC or 220-V-AC line with minimum changes was described. As seen in Fig. 3.1, at 120 V AC, switch $S1$ is thrown to the lower position and the circuit is a voltage doubler yielding a rectified voltage of 336 V. With 220 V AC, $S1$ is thrown to the upper position and the circuit is a full-wave rectifier with $C1$ and $C2$ in series yielding closely about 308 V. The converter is now designed to always work from a rectified nominal 308 to 336 V DC by proper choice of the transformer turns ratio.

In some usages, it is undesirable to have to throw $S1$ from one position to the other in changing from 120 to 220 V AC operation. To change switch position without opening the power supply case, the switch must be accessible externally, and this is a safety hazard. The alternative is not to do the switch changing externally, but this requires opening the power supply case to make the change, and this is a nuisance. Further, there is always the possibility that the switch is mistakenly thrown to the voltage doubling position when operated off 220 V AC. This, of course, would cause significant failures—the power transistor, rectifiers, and filter capacitors would be destroyed.

An alternative is not to do any switching at all whether the input is 115 or 220 V AC. Accept a rectified 160 V DC when the input is 115 V AC or a rectified 310 V DC from 220 V AC. Now a flyback converter with a small primary/secondary turns ratio can be used to ensure that the off-voltage stress at high AC input does not overstress the power transistor.

The maximum on time $\overline{T_{on}}$ at the minimum value of the 220-V-AC input is calculated from the corresponding minimum rectified DC input as in Eq. 4.7 and the rest of the magnetics design can proceed as shown in the text following Eq. 4.7. The minimum on time occurs at the maximum value of the 220-V-AC input. Since the feedback loop keeps the product of $V_{dc}T_{on}$ constant (Eq. 4.3), minimum on time is $T_{on} = \overline{T_{on}}(V_{dc}/\overline{V_{dc}})$ where V_{dc} and $\overline{V_{dc}}$ correspond to the minimum and maximum values of the 220-V-AC line.

The maximum on time with 115-V-AC input is still given by Eq. 4.7 and will be greater as the term $V_{dc} - 1$ is smaller. But the primary inductance L_p given by Eq. 4.8 is seen to be proportional to the product $V_{dc}T_{on}$ is still the same as that product is kept constant by the feedback loop. So long as the transistor can operate with the minimum on time calculated for the maximum DC corresponding to high AC input, there is no problem. With bipolar transistors operating at a high frequency, transistor storage time could prevent operation at too low an on time. An example will clarify this.

Thus Eq. 4.4 gives the maximum off stress in terms of the maximum DC input voltage, the output voltage, and the N_p/N_s turns ratio. Assume in that equation that $\overline{V_{ms}}$ is 500; many bipolar transistors can safely sustain that voltage with a negative base bias at turnoff (V_{cev} rating). At 220 V AC, nominal V_{dc} is 310 V. Assume that the maximum at high line and a worst-case transient is 375 V. Then for a 5-V output, Eq. 4.4 gives a turns ratio of 21.

Now assume that minimum DC supply voltage is 80 percent of nominal. Assume a switching frequency of 50 kHz (period T of 20 μs). Maximum on time is calculated from Eq. 4.7 at the minimum DC input corresponding to minimum AC input of 0.8 × 115 or 92 V AC. For the corresponding DC input of 1.41 × 92 or about 128 V, maximum on time calculated from Eq. 4.7 is 7.96 μs.

Minimum on time occurs at maximum DC input at highest AC input. Assuming a 20 percent high line, maximum DC input is 1.2 × 220 × 1.41 = 372 V. Since the feedback loop keeps the product of $V_{dc}T_{on}$ constant, (Eq. 4.3), on time at the 20 percent high line of 264 V AC is (128/372)(7.96) or 2.74 μs. The circuit can thus cope with either a 20 percent low AC line input of 92 V AC from a nominal 115 V AC or a 20 percent high AC input of 264 V AC from the nominal 220 V AC line by readjusting its on time from 7.96 to 2.74 μs.

But it is obvious that if this were attempted at higher switching frequencies, the minimum on time at a 220-V-AC line condition would become so low as to prohibit the use of bipolar transistors which could have 0.5- to 1.0-μs storage time. The upper-limit switching frequency at which the above scheme can be used with bipolar transistors is about 100 kHz.

It is instructive to complete the above design. Assume an output power of 150 W at 5-V output. Then $R_o = 0.167$ Ω and the primary inductance from Eq. 4.8 is

$$L_p = \left(\frac{0.167}{2.5 \times 20 \times 10^{-6}}\right)\left(\frac{128 \times 7.96 \times 10^{-6}}{5}\right)^2$$

$$= 139 \ \mu H$$

and the peak primary current from Eq. 4.9 is

$$I_p = \frac{128 \times 7.96 \times 10^{-6}}{139 \times 10^{-6}} = 7.33 \ A$$

There are many reasonably priced bipolar transistors with a V_{cev} rating above 500 V having adequate gain at 7.33 A.

Table 4.1 shows that the 55932 MPP core can tolerate a maximum of 480 ampere turns beyond which its inductance will fall off by more than 10 percent (at 5 A, column 9 shows that its maximum turns is 95 for a maximum inductance of 265 μH). For a maximum ampere turns of 480 at 7.33 A, its maximum turns is 480/7.33 = 65.4. For 66 turns, its inductance is $32{,}000 \times 0.9(66/1000)^2 = 125 \ \mu H$. If (as discussed in Sec. 4.2.3.2) 10 percent more turns are added, the inductance at 7.33 A will increase by 10 percent to 138 μH, but at zero current, the inductance will "swing" up to 20 percent above that.

If the 20 percent inductance swing is undesirable, the lower permeability core 55933 of Table 4.1 can be used. Table 4.1 shows that its maximum ampere turns is 859. For 7.33 A, the maximum number of turns is 859/7.33 or 117. Its maximum inductance for only a 10 percent swing is $(0.117)^2 \times 18000 \times 0.9$ or 222 μH. For the desired 139 μH, required turns are $1000 \ \sqrt{0.139/18 \times 0.95} = 90$ turns.

Thus a design not requiring voltage doubling/full-wave rectifier switching when operation is changed from 115 to 220 V AC is possible. But this subjects the power transistor to about 500 V plus a leakage inductance spike at turnoff. The reliability of this must be weighed against the use of a double-ended forward converter or half bridge—both of which subject the off transistor to only the maximum DC input (375 V in the preceding example) with no leakage spike. Of course, for 115/220-V-AC operation, the rectifier switching of Fig. 3.1 must be accepted.

4.4 Continuous-Mode Flybacks— Basic Operation

There are two distinctly different modes of flyback converters (discontinuous and continuous) whose waveforms are shown in Fig. 4.5.

Both modes have an identical circuit diagram, shown in Fig. 4.1, and it is only the transformer's magnetizing inductance and output load current which determines its operating mode. With a given mag-

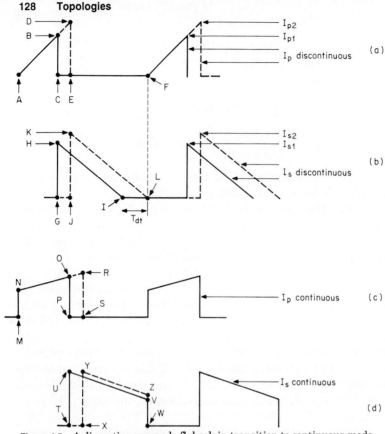

Figure 4.5 A discontinuous-mode flyback in transition to continuous-mode. Circuit is discontinuous if there is a dead time (T_{dt}) between the instant the secondary current reaches zero and the start of the next turnon. If loaded beyond this point, there is still some current left in the secondary at the end of the turnoff and the next turnon has a step at its front end. This is characteristic of the continuous mode, and if the error-amplifier bandwidth has not been drastically reduced, the circuit will oscillate.

netizing inductance, a circuit which has been designed for the discontinuous mode will move into the continuous mode when the output load current is increased beyond a unique boundary. The mechanism for this and its consequence is discussed below.

The discontinuous mode as shown in Fig. 4.5a has no front-end step in its primary current, and at turnoff as shown in Fig. 4.5b, the secondary current is a decaying triangle which has ramped down to zero before the next turnon. All the energy stored in the primary during the on time has been completely delivered to the secondary and thus to the load before the next turnon.

In the continuous mode, as seen in Fig. 4.5c, the primary current has a front-end step and the characteristic appearance of a rising ramp on a step. During the transistor off time (Fig. 4.5d), the secondary current has the shape of a decaying triangle sitting on a step with current still remaining in the secondary at the instant of the next turnon. There is thus still some energy left in the secondary at the instant of the next turnon.

The two modes have significantly different operating properties and usages. The discontinuous mode responds more rapidly and with a lower transient output voltage spike to sudden changes in load current or input voltage.

But the secondary peak current in the discontinuous mode can be between two and three times that in the continuous mode, as can be seen in Fig. 4.5b and 4.5d. Secondary DC load current is the average of the current waveshapes in those figures. Also, assuming closely equal off times, it is obvious that the triangle in the discontinuous mode must have a much larger peak than the trapezoid of the continuous mode for the two waveshapes to have equal average values.

With a larger peak secondary current, the discontinuous mode will have a larger transient output voltage spike at the instant of turnoff (Sec. 4.3.4.1) and will require a larger LC spike filter to remove it. Also, the larger secondary peak current at the start of turnoff in the discontinuous mode will cause a greater RFI problem. Even for moderate output powers, the very large initial spike of secondary current at the instant of turnoff causes a much more severe noise spike on the output ground bus because of the large di/dt into the output bus inductance.

Secondary rms currents in the discontinuous mode can be up to twice that in the continuous mode. This requires larger secondary wire size and output filter capacitors with larger ripple current ratings for the discontinuous mode. Rectifier diodes will also have larger temperature rise in the discontinuous mode because of the larger secondary rms currents.

Primary peak currents for the discontinuous mode are about twice those in the continuous mode—again because for equal average values, the triangle of Fig. 4.5a must have a larger peak than the trapezoid of Fig. 4.5c. The consequence is that the discontinuous mode with its larger peak primary current requires a higher current rating and possibly a more expensive power transistor. Also, the higher primary current in the discontinuous mode results in a greater RFI problem.

Despite all these relative disadvantages for the discontinuous mode, it is much more widely used than the continuous mode. This is so for two reasons. First, as mentioned above, the discontinuous mode, with an inherently smaller transformer magnetizing inductance, responds more quickly and with a lower transient output voltage spike to rapid changes in output load current or input voltage. Second, because of a unique characteristic of the continuous mode (its transfer function has a right-half-plane-zero, to be discussed in a later chapter on feedback loop stabilization), the error amplifier bandwidth must be drastically reduced to stabilize the feedback loop.

4.4.1 Discontinuous-mode to continuous-mode transition

In Fig. 4.5a and 4.5b the solid lines represent primary and secondary currents in the discontinuous mode. Primary current is a triangle starting from zero and rising to a level I_{p1} (point B) at the end of the power transistor on time (see Fig. 4.5a).

At the instant of turnoff, the current I_{p1} stored in the primary is dumped into the secondary at point H as $I_{s1} = (N_p/N_s)I_{p1}$. Since the dot end of the secondary is positive during the off time, secondary current ramps downward at a rate $dI_s/dt = (V_o + 1)/L_s$, where L_s is the secondary inductance, which is $(N_s/N_p)^2$ times the primary magnetizing inductance. This current reaches zero at time I, leaving a dead time T_{dt} before the start of the next turnon at point F. All the current or energy stored in the primary during the on time has now been completely delivered to the load before the next turnon. The average or DC output current is the average of the triangle GHI multiplied by its duty cycle of T_{off}/T.

Now, to remain in the discontinuous mode, there must be a dead time T_{dt} (Fig. 4.5b) between the time the secondary current has dropped to zero and the start of the next power transistor on time. As more power is demanded (by decreasing R_o), T_{on} must increase to keep output voltage constant (see Eq. 4.3). As T_{on} increases (at constant V_{dc}), primary current slope remains constant and peak current rises from B to D as in Fig. 4.5a. Secondary peak current $(= I_p N_p/N_s)$ increases from H to K in Fig. 4.5b and starts later in time (from G to J).

As output voltage is kept constant by the feedback loop, the secondary slope V_o/L_s remains constant and the point at which the secondary current falls to zero moves closer to the start of the next turnon. This reduces T_{dt} until a point L is reached where the secondary current has just fallen to zero at the instant of the next turnon. This is the load current which marks the end of the discontinuous mode. Dead time can also be completely lost at constant output power (current) as V_{dc} decreases. The on time T_{on} must also increase as V_{dc} decreases to maintain constant output voltage.

Note that as long as the circuit is in the discontinuous mode and so long as there remains a dead time, increasing the on time increases the area of the primary current triangle and also the area of the secondary triangle GHI up to the limit of the area JKL. Further, since DC output current is the average of the secondary current triangle multiplied by its duty cycle, then the very next off time after an increase in on time, more secondary current is available to the load.

When the dead time has been lost, however, any further increase in load current demand will increase the on time and decrease the off time as the back end of the secondary current can no longer move to the right. The secondary current will start later than point J (Fig. 4.5b) and from a higher point than K. Then at the start of the next on time (F in Fig. 4.5a or L in Fig. 4.5b), there is still some current or energy left in the secondary.

Now the front end of the primary current will have a small step. The feedback loop tries to deliver the increased DC load current demand by keeping the on time later than point J. Now at each successive off time, the current remaining at the end of the off time and hence the current step at the start of the next on time increases.

Finally after many switching cycles, the front-end step of primary current and the back end current at the end of the off time in Fig. 4.5d are sufficiently high so that the area $XYZW$ is somewhat larger than that sufficient to supply the output load current. Now the feedback loop starts to decrease the on time so that the primary trapezoid lasts from M to P and the secondary current trapezoid lasts from T to W (Figs. 4.5a and 4.5b).

At this point, the on volt-seconds across the transformer primary when the power transistor is on is equal to the off volt-seconds across it when the transistor is off. This is the condition that the transformer core is always reset to its original point on the hysteresis loop at the end of a full cycle. Or, what amounts to the same thing, it is the condition that the average or DC voltage across the primary is zero since it is assumed that the DC resistance in the primary is zero and it is not possible to support a DC voltage across zero resistance.

Once in the continuous mode, increased load current is supplied initially by an increase in on time (from MP to MS in Fig. 4.5c). This, oddly enough, results in a decrease in off time from TW to XW (Fig. 4.5d) as the back end of the secondary current pulse cannot move further to the right in time because the dead time has vanished. Although the peak of the secondary current has increased somewhat (from point U to Y), the area lost in the decreased off time (T to X) is greater than the area gained in the slope change from UV to YZ in Fig. 4.5d.

Thus, in the continuous mode, a sudden increase in DC output current initially causes a decrease in width and a smaller increase in height of the secondary current trapezoid. After many switching cycles, the average trapezoid height builds up and the width relaxes back to the point where the on volt-seconds again equals the off volt-seconds across the primary.

In addition, since the DC output voltage is proportional to the area of the secondary current trapezoid, the feedback loop, in attempting to keep the output voltage constant against an increased current demand, first drastically decreases the output voltage and then, after many switching cycles, corrects it by building up the amplitude of the secondary current trapezoid. This is the physical-circuits significance of the so-called right-half-plane-zero which forces the drastic reduction in error-amplifier bandwidth to stabilize the feedback loop. The right-half-plane-zero will be discussed further in the chapter on loop stabilization.

4.4.2   Design relations—continuous-mode flybacks

4.4.2.1   Relation between output voltage and on time.   Refer to Fig. 4.1. When the transistor is on, the voltage across the primary is closely $V_{dc} - 1$ with the dot end negative with respect to the no-dot end and the core is driven—say, up the hysteresis loop. With the transistor off, the magnetizing current, which is trying to remain constant, reverses the polarity of all voltages. The primary and secondary try to go far positive. But the secondary is caught and clamped to $V_{om} + 1$—assuming a 1-V forward drop across $D2$.

This reflects across to the primary as a voltage $(N_p/N_s)(V_{om} + 1)$ with the dot end now positive with respect to the no-dot end. All the current flowing in the primary (I_{PO} in Fig. 4.5c) now transfers to the secondary as I_{TU} in Fig. 4.5d. The initial magnitude of the secondary current I_{TU} is equal to the final primary current at the end of the on time (I_{PO}) times the turns ratio N_p/N_s. Since the dot end of the secondary is now positive with respect to the no-dot end, the secondary current ramps downward as the slope UV in Fig. 4.5d.

Since the primary is assumed to have zero DC resistance, it cannot sustain a DC voltage averaged over many cycles. Thus in the steady state, the volt-second product across it when the transistor is on must equal that across it when the transistor is off—i.e., the voltage across the primary averaged over a full cycle must equal zero. This is equivalent to saying the core's downward excursion on the BH loop during the off time is exactly equal to the upward excursion during the on time. Then

$$(V_{dc} - 1)\,\overline{t_{on}} = (V_{om} + 1)\frac{N_p}{N_s}\,\overline{t_{off}}$$

or
$$V_{om} = \left[\left(V_{dc} - 1\right)\frac{N_s}{N_p}\frac{\overline{t_{on}}}{t_{off}}\right] - 1 \qquad (4.16)$$

and since now there is no dead time, $\overline{t_{on}} + t_{off} = T$, then

$$V_{om} = \left[\frac{(V_{dc} - 1)(N_s/N_p)(\overline{t_{on}}/T)}{1 - \overline{t_{on}}/T} \right] - 1 \qquad (4.17a)$$

$$= \left[\frac{(V_{dc} - 1)(N_s/N_p)}{(T/\overline{t_{on}}) - 1} \right] - 1 \qquad (4.17b)$$

The feedback loop regulates against DC input voltage changes by decreasing T_{on} as V_{dc} increases, or increasing t_{on} as V_{dc} decreases.

4.4.2.2 Input, output current–power relations. In Fig. 4.6, the output power is equal to the output voltage times the average of the secondary current pulses. For I_{csr} equal to the current at the center of the ramp in the secondary current pulse

$$P_o = V_o I_{csr} \frac{t_{off}}{T}$$

$$= V_o I_{csr} (1 - \overline{t_{on}}/T) \qquad (4.18)$$

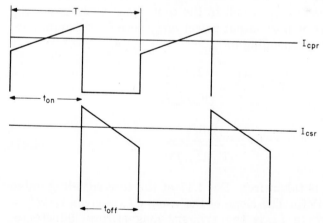

Figure 4.6 Current–on-time relations in a continuous-mode flyback. Current is delivered to the load only during the off time. At a fixed DC input voltage, t_{on} and t_{off} remain constant. Output load current changes are accommodated by the feedback loop changing the magnitude of the current at the center of the primary current ramp I_{cpr} and at the center of the secondary current ramp (I_{csr}). This occurs over many switching cycles by temporary increases in on time until the average current pulse amplitudes build up and then relax to the steady-state values of t_{on} and t_{off}.

or
$$I_{csr} = \frac{P_o}{V_o(1 - \overline{t_{on}}/T)} \qquad (4.19)$$

In Eqs. 4.18 and 4.19, $\overline{t_{on}}/T$ is given by Eq. 4.17 for specified values of V_{om} and V_{dc} and a turns ratio N_s/N_p from Eq. 4.4 chosen for an acceptably low maximum off-voltage stress at maximum DC input.

Further, for an assumed efficiency of 80 percent, $P_o = 0.8P_{in}$ and I_{cpr} equal to the current at the center of the ramp in the primary current pulse:

$$P_{in} = 1.25P_o = V_{dc}I_{cpr}\frac{\overline{t_{on}}}{T}$$

or
$$I_{cpr} = \frac{1.25P_o}{(V_{dc})(\overline{t_{on}}/T)} \qquad (4.20)$$

4.4.2.3 Ramp amplitudes for continuous mode at minimum DC input.
It has been pointed out that the start of continuous-mode operation occurs when there is just the beginning of a step at the front end of the primary current ramp. Referring to Fig. 4.6, the step begins to appear when the current at the center of the primary ramp I_{cpr} is equal to half the ramp amplitude dI_p. That value of I_{cpr} ($\underline{I_{cpr}}$) is then the minimum value at which the circuit is still in the continuous mode. From Eq. 4.20, I_{cpr} is proportional to output power and hence for the minimum output power $\underline{P_o}$ corresponding to $\underline{I_{cpr}}$

$$\underline{I_{cpr}} = \frac{dI_p}{2} = \frac{1.25\underline{P_o}}{(V_{dc})(\overline{t_{on}}/T)}$$

or
$$dI_p = \frac{2.5\underline{P_o}}{(V_{dc})(\overline{t_{on}}/T)} \qquad (4.21)$$

In Eq. 4.21, $\overline{t_{on}}$ is taken from Eq. 4.17 at the corresponding value minimum of V_{dc} ($\underline{V_{dc}}$). The slope of the ramp dI_p is given by $dI_p = (\underline{V_{dc}} - 1)\overline{t_{on}}/L_p$, where L_p is the primary magnetizing inductance. Then

$$L_p = \frac{(\underline{V_{dc}} - 1)\overline{t_{on}}}{\underline{dI_p}}$$

$$= \frac{(\underline{V_{dc}} - 1)(\underline{V_{dc}})(\overline{t_{on}})^2}{2.5\underline{P_o}T} \qquad (4.22)$$

Here again, P_o is the minimum specified value of output power and t_{on} is the maximum on time calculated from Eq. 4.17 at the minimum specified DC input voltage V_{dc}.

4.4.2.4 Discontinuous and continuous-mode flyback design example. It is instructive to compare a discontinuous- and continuous-mode flyback design at the same output power levels and input voltages. The magnitudes of the currents and primary inductances will be revealing.

Assume a 50-W, 5-V output flyback converter operating at 50 kHz from a telephone industry prime power source (38 V DC minimum, 60 V maximum). Assume a minimum output power of one-tenth the nominal or 5 W.

Consider first a discontinuous-mode flyback. Assume a bipolar transistor with a 150-V V_{ceo} rating and, wishing to be very conservative, do not bank on the V_{cer} or V_{cev} rating which permits a larger voltage. Then in Eq. 4.4, assume that the maximum off-voltage stress V_{ms} without a leakage spike is 114 V, which permits a 36-V leakage spike before the V_{ceo} limit is reached. Then Eq. 4.4 gives N_p/N_s = $(114 - 60)/6 = 9$.

Now Eq. 4.7 gives the maximum on time as

$$\overline{t_{on}} = 6 \times 9 \times 0.8 \frac{20 \times 10^{-6}}{37 + 6 \times 9}$$

$$= 9.49 \ \mu s$$

and primary inductance for R_o = 5/10 = 0.5 Ω from Eq. 4.8 is

$$L_p = \frac{0.5}{2.5 \times 20^{-6}} \left(\frac{38 \times 9.49}{5} \right)^2 \times 10^{-12}$$

$$= 52 \ \mu H$$

Peak primary current from Eq. 4.9 is

$$I_p = \frac{38 \times 9.49 \times 10^{-6}}{52 \times 10^{-6}}$$

$$= 6.9 \ A$$

and the front end of the secondary current triangle is

$$I_{s(peak)} = (N_p/N_s)I_p = 9 \times 6.9 = 62 \ A$$

Recall that in the discontinuous flyback, the reset time T_r or the time for the secondary current to decay back to zero plus the maximum on time is equal to $0.8T$ (Eq. 4.6). Reset time is then

$T_r = (0.8 \times 20) - 9.49 = 6.5$ µs, and the average value of the secondary current triangle (which should equal the DC output current of 10 A is

$$I \text{ (secondary average)} = \frac{I_{s(\text{peak})}}{2} \frac{T_r}{T}$$

$$= \left(\frac{62}{2}\right) \frac{6.5}{20} = 10 \text{ A}$$

which truly is the DC output current.

Now consider the continuous-mode flyback for the same frequency, input voltages, and output power output voltage and the same N_p/N_s ratio of 9. From Eq. 4.17b, calculate $\overline{t_{\text{on}}}/T$ for $V_{\text{dc}} = 38$ V as

$$5 = \left[\frac{(37/9)(\overline{t_{\text{on}}}/T)}{1 - \overline{t_{\text{on}}}/T}\right] - 1$$

or $\overline{t_{\text{on}}}/T = 0.5934$ and $\overline{t_{\text{on}}} = 11.87$ µs, $t_{\text{off}} = 8.13$ µs and from Eq. 4.19

$$I_{\text{csr}} = \frac{50}{(5)(1 - 0.5934)} = 24.59 \text{ A}$$

and the average of the secondary current pulse which should equal the DC output current is I (secondary average) $= I_{\text{csr}}(t_{\text{off}}/T) = 24.59 \times 8.13/20 = 10.0$ A, which checks. From Eq. 4.20 $I_{\text{cpr}} = 1.25 \times 50/(38)(11.86/20) = 2.77$ A.

From Eq. 4.22, for the minimum input power of 5 W at the minimum DC input voltage of 38 V, $L_p = 37 \times 38(11.86)^2 \times 10^{-12}/2.5 \times 5 \times 20 \times 10^{-6} = 791$ µH.

The contrast between the discontinuous and continuous mode can now be seen in the table below in the comparison between the required primary inductances and primary and secondary currents at minimum DC input of 38 V.

	Discontinuous	Continuous
Primary inductance, µH	52	791
Primary peak current, A	6.9	2.77
Secondary peak current, A	62.0	24.6
On time, µs	9.49	11.86
Off time, µs	6.5	8.13

The lower primary current and especially the secondary current for the continuous mode are certainly an advantage. But the much larger primary inductance which slows up response to load current changes and the right-half-plane-zero, which requires a very low error-amplifier bandwidth to achieve loop stabilization, make the continuous mode a less desirable choice.

4.5   Interleaved Flybacks

Interleaved flyback topology is shown in Fig. 4.7. It consists simply of two discontinuous-mode flybacks whose power transistors are turned on at alternate half cycles and whose secondary currents are summed through their rectifying diodes.

It can be used at power levels up to 300 W, limited mainly by the high peak primary and especially secondary currents. Although that power level can be reached with a single continuous-mode flyback at reasonable currents, it is more advantageous to accept the greater cost

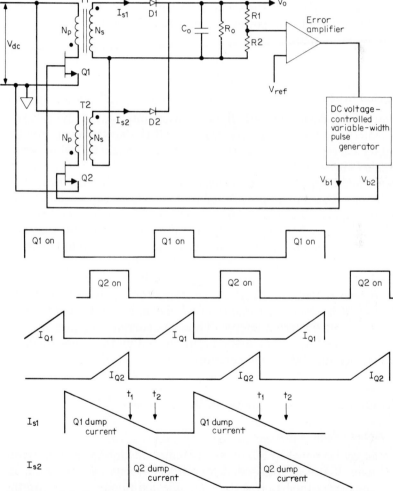

Figure 4.7 Interleaving two discontinuous-mode flyback on alternative half cycles to reduce peak currents. Output powers of up to 300 W are possible with reasonably low peak currents.

and required volume of two interleaved discontinuous-mode flybacks—if the flyback topology is chosen for some particular reason.

This is so because of the discontinuous mode's faster response to load current changes, greater error-amplifier bandwidth, and lesser feedback loop stabilization problems. A single discontinuous-mode flyback at the 300-W level is impractical because of the high peak primary and secondary currents as can be seen from Eqs. 4.2, 4.7, and 4.8.

Actually, at the 150-W level, a single forward converter is very likely a better choice than the two interleaved flybacks because of the considerably lower secondary current of the forward converter. But the interleaved flyback is shown here for the sake of completeness and its possible use at lower power levels than 150 W, but where many (over five) outputs are required.

4.5.1 Summation of secondary currents in interleaved flybacks

The magnetics design of each flyback in an interleaved flyback proceeds exactly as for a single flyback at half the power level. For the secondary currents dump into the output through their "ORing" rectifier diodes and add.

Even when both secondary diodes dump current simultaneously (as from t_1 to t_2), there is no possibility that one diode can back-bias the other and supply all the load current. This can happen when two low-impedance voltage sources attempt to sum currents simultaneously. For with low-impedance voltage sources, one source with only say 0.1 V higher open-circuit voltage or with a lower forward-drop OR diode, will back-bias the other diode and supply all the load current by itself. This can overdissipate the diode or the transistor supplying that diode.

Looking back into the secondary of a flyback, however, there is seen a high-impedance current source. Thus the current dumped out into the common load by either diode is unaffected by the other diode simultaneously supplying load current.

4.6 Double-Ended Discontinuous-Mode Flyback

4.6.1 Area of Application

The topology is shown in Fig. 4.8a. Its major advantage is that, using the scheme of the double-ended forward converter of Fig. 2.13, its power transistors in the off state are subjected to only the maximum DC input voltage. This is a significant advantage over the single-ended forward converter of Fig. 4.1, where the maximum off-voltage stress is the maximum DC input voltage plus the reflected secondary

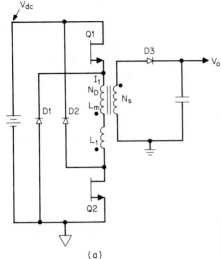

(a)

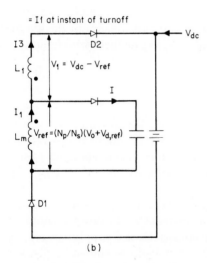

(b)

Figure 4.8 Circuit during $Q1$ and $Q2$ off time. Current I_1, stored in L_m during $Q1$, $Q2$ on time, also flows through leakage inductance L_l. During the off time, energy stored in L_m must be delivered to the secondary load as reflected into the primary across L_m. But I_1 also flows through L_l, and during the off time, the energy it represents $\frac{1}{2}L_l$, I^2) is returned to the input source V_{dc} through diodes $D1$, $D2$. This robs energy which should have been delivered to the output load and continues to rob energy until I_1, the leakage inductance current, falls to zero. To minimize the time for I_1 in L_l to fall to zero, V_i is made significantly large by keeping the reflected voltage $V_r (= N_p/N_s)(V_o + V_{D3})$ low by setting a low N_p/N_s turns ratio. A usual value for V_r is two-thirds of the minimum V_{dc}, leaving one-third for V_l.

voltage $(N_p/N_s)(V_o + 1)$ plus a leakage inductance spike which may be as high as one third of the DC input voltage.

The price paid for this advantage is, of course, the requirement for two transistors and the two clamp diodes, $D1$, $D2$.

4.6.2 Basic operation

The lower off-voltage stress comes about in the same way as for the double-ended forward converter of Fig. 2.13. Power transistors $Q1$, $Q2$ are turned on simultaneously. When they are on, the dot end of the secondary is negative, $D3$ is reverse-biased, and no secondary current flows. The primary is then just an inductor, and current in it ramps up linearly at a rate of $dI_1/dt = V_{dc}/(L_m + L_l)$, where L_m and L_l are the primary magnetizing and leakage inductances, respectively.

When $Q1$ and $Q2$ turn off, as in the previous flybacks, all primary and secondary voltages reverse polarity, $D3$ becomes forward-biased, and the stored current or energy in $L_m(= 1/2L_m(I_1)^2)$ is delivered to the load.

As always, the on or set volt-second product across the primary must equal the off or reset volt-second product. At the instant of turn-off, the bottom end of L_l attempts to go very far positive but is clamped to the positive end of V_{dc}. The top end of L_m attempts to go far negative but is clamped to the negative end of V_{dc}. Thus the maximum voltage stress at either $Q1$ or $Q2$ can never be more than V_{dc}.

The actual resetting voltage V_r across the mutual inductance L_m during the off time is given by the voltage reflected from the secondary load $(N_p/N_s)(V_o + V_{D3})$. The voltage across L_m and L_l in series is the DC supply voltage and hence as seen in Fig. 4.8b, the voltage across the leakage inductance L_l is $V_l = (V_{dc} - V_r)$.

This division of the V_{dc} supply voltage across L_m and L_l in series during the off time is a very important point in the circuit design and establishes the transformer turns ratio N_p/N_s as discussed below.

4.6.3 Leakage inductance effect in double-ended flyback

Figure 4.8b shows the circuit during the $Q1$, $Q2$ off time. The voltage across L_m and L_l in series is clamped to V_{dc} through diodes $D1$, $D2$. The voltage V_r across the magnetizing inductance is clamped against the reflected secondary voltage and equals $(N_p/N_s)(V_o + V_{D3})$. The voltage across L_l is then $V_l = V_{dc} - V_r$.

At the instant of turnoff, the same current I_1 flows in L_m and $L_l(I_3 = I_1$ at instant of turnoff). That current in L_l flows through diodes $D1$, $D2$ and returns its stored energy to the supply source V_{dc}. The L_l current decays at a rate of $dI_1/dt = V_l/L_l$ as shown in Fig. 4.9a as slope AC or AD. The current in L_m (initially also equal to I_1) decays at a rate V_r/L_m and is shown in Fig. 4.9a as slope AB.

Now the current actually delivering power to the load is I_2—the difference between the currents in L_m and L_l. This is shown as current RST in Fig. 4.9b if the L_1 current slope is AC of Fig. 4.9a or the larger area current UVW in Fig. 4.9c if the L_1 current slope is faster as AD of Fig. 4.9a. It is obvious, then, in Fig. 4.9b and 4.9c that so long as current still flows in leakage inductance L_l, through $D1$ and $D2$ back into the supply source, all the current available in L_m does not flow into the reflected load but is partly diverted back into the supply.

It can thus be seen from Fig. 4.9b and 4.9c that to maximize the transfer of L_m current to the reflected load and to avoid a delay in the

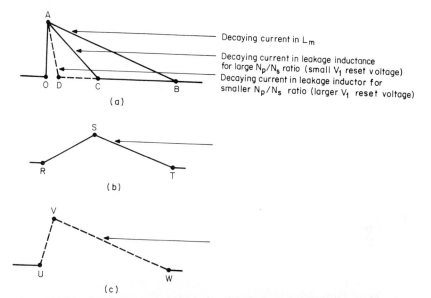

Figure 4.9 (a) Currents in magnetizing and leakage inductances in double-ended flyback. (b) Current into reflected load impedance for large N_p/N_s ratio. AB–AC of Fig. 4.9a. (c) Current into reflected load impedance for smaller N_p/N_s ratio. AB–AD of Fig. 4.9a.

transfer of current to the load, the slope of the leakage inductance current decay should be maximized (slope AD rather than AC in Fig. 4.9a). Or in magnetics–power supply jargon, the leakage inductance current should be rapidly reset to zero.

Since the rate of decay of the leakage inductance current is V_l/L_l and $V_l = V_{dc} - (N_p/N_s)(V_o + V_{D3})$, choosing lower values of N_p/N_s increases V_l and hastens leakage current reset. A usual value for the reflected voltage $(N_p/N_s)(V_o + V_{D3})$ is two-thirds of V_{dc}, leaving one-third for V_l. Too low a value for V_r will require a longer time to reset the magnetizing inductance, rob from the available $Q1$, $Q2$ on time, and decrease the available output power.

Once N_p/N_s has been fixed to yield $V_l = V_{dc}/3$, the maximum on time for discontinuous operation is calculated from Eq. 4.7, L_m is calculated from Eq. 4.8 and I_p from Eq. 4.9, just as for the single-ended flyback.

References

Billings, K., *Switchmode Power Supply Handbook*, McGraw-Hill, New York, 1989.

Chryssis, G., *High Frequency Switching Power Supplies*, 2d ed., pp. 122–131, McGraw-Hill, New York, 1989.

Dixon, L., "The Effects of Leakage Inductance on Multi-Output Flyback Circuits," *Unitrode Power Supply Design Seminar Handbook*, Unitrode Corp., Lexington, Mass., 1988.

Patel, R., D. Reilly, and R. Adair, "150 Watt Flyback Regulator," *Unitrode Power Supply Design Seminar Handbook*, Unitrode Corp., Lexington, Mass., 1988.

Current-Mode and Current-Fed Topologies

5.1 Introduction

Current-mode[1-7] and current-fed[9-20] topologies are grouped into one family despite their very significant differences. They are grouped together because they gain advantages by controlling both input current (although in different ways) and output voltage.

Current mode (Fig. 5.3) has two feedback loops: an outer one which senses DC output voltage and delivers a DC control voltage to an inner loop which senses peak power transistor currents and keeps them constant on a pulse-by-pulse basis. The end result is that it solves the magnetic flux imbalance problem in the current-mode version of the push-pull topology and restores push-pull as a viable approach in applications where the uncertainty of other solutions to flux imbalance is a drawback (Sec. 2.2.8). Further, the constant power transistor current pulses simplify the feedback-loop design.

Current-fed topology drives its power train (center tap of a push-pull or top end of a forward converter transformer) through an input inductor. Thus the power train is driven from high impedance of a current source (the input inductor) rather than the low impedance of a rectifier filter capacitor or the low source impedance of an input battery. This high output impedance of the prime power source very largely solves the flux imbalance problem when a push-pull converter is driven from the input inductor and offers other significant advantages.

In all topologies discussed thus far (voltage-mode circuits), output voltage alone is monitored and controlled directly. In those circuits, regulation against load current changes occur because current changes cause small output voltage changes which are sensed by a voltage-monitoring error amplifier which then corrects the power transistor on time to maintain output voltage constant. But output current itself is not monitored directly.

About 7 years ago, a new topology, *current mode,* appeared in which both voltage and current could be monitored. The scheme had been known previously but not widely used as it required discrete circuit components to implement it. But when, also 7 years ago, a new pulse-width-modulating (PWM) chip—the UC1846—appeared with all the features needed to implement current mode, the advantages of the technique were quickly recognized and it was widely adopted.

Where two 180° out-of-phase width-modulated outputs are required—as in the push-pull, half-bridge, full-bridge, interleaved forward converter, or flyback—the UC1846—can be used to implement current-mode control. A lower-cost, single-ended PWM controller—the UC1842—is currently available to implement current mode in single-ended circuits such as forward converters, flybacks, and buck regulators.

5.2   Current-Mode Advantages

5.2.1   Avoidance of flux imbalance in push-pull converters

Flux imbalance was discussed in Sec. 2.2.5. It occurs in a push-pull converter when the transformer core operates unsymmetrically about the origin of its hysteresis loop. The consequence is that the core moves up toward saturation and one transistor draws more current during its on time than does the opposite transistor (Fig. 2.4c).

As the core drifts further off center of the origin, it goes into deep saturation and may destroy the power transistor. A number of ways to cope with flux imbalance have been described in Sec. 2.2.8. These schemes work, but under unusual line and load transient conditions and especially with higher output powers, there is never complete certainty that flux imbalance cannot occur.

Current mode monitors each current pulse on a pulse-by-pulse basis and forces alternate pulses to have equal peak amplitudes by correcting each transistor's on time so that current amplitudes must be equal. This puts push-pull back into the running in any proposed new design and is a valuable contribution to the reservoir of possible topologies. For example, if to ensure certainty of no flux imbalance, in the absence of current mode, a forward converter which has no flux imbalance problem were chosen, a severe penalty would be paid.

Thus Eq. 2.28 shows the peak primary current in a forward converter is $3.13(P_o/V_{dc})$. But Eq. 2.9 shows it is only half that or $1.56(P_o/V_{dc})$ for the push-pull. At low output powers, it is not a serious drawback to use the forward converter with twice the peak current of a push-pull at equal output power, especially as the forward converter has only one transistor. But at higher output power, twice the peak primary current in the forward converter as compared to the push-pull becomes prohibitive.

The push-pull is a very attractive choice for telephone industry power supplies where the maximum DC input voltage is specified as only 60 V (38 V minimum). Thus having it available in its current-mode version with a certainty that flux imbalance cannot exist is very valuable.

5.2.2 Instantaneous correction against line voltage changes without the delay in an error amplifier (voltage feedforward characteristics)

It is inherent in the details of how current mode works that a line voltage change immediately causes a change in power transistor on time. This change is corrected for without having to wait for a sensed output voltage change to pass through the relatively long delay in a conventional voltage error amplifier. The details of how this comes about will be discussed below.

5.2.3 Ease and simplicity of feedback-loop stabilization

All the topologies discussed above (with the exception of flybacks) have an output LC filter. An LC filter has a possible maximum phase shift of 180° not far beyond its resonant frequency of $f_o = \frac{1}{2\pi}\sqrt{LC}$, and gain between output and input falls very rapidly with increasing frequency. As frequency increases, the impedance of the series L arm increases and that of the shunt arm decreases.

This large possible phase shift and rapid change of gain with frequency complicates the feedback-loop design. More important, the elements around the error amplifier required to stabilize the loop are more complex and can give rise to problems for rapid changes in input voltage or output current.

In current mode, however, even with an output inductor physically in series with the output shunt capacitor, in a small-signal analysis which calculates gain and phase shift to consider the possibility of oscillation, the circuit behaves as if the inductor were not there.

The circuit behaves as if there were a constant current feeding the parallel combination of the output capacitor and the output load resistor. Such a network can yield only a 90° rather than a 180° phase shift, and the gain between output and input falls half as rapidly as for a true LC filter (−20 dB per decade rather than −40 dB per decade).

This simplifies the feedback-loop design, simplifies the circuitry around the error amplifier required for stabilization, and avoids the problems arising from rapid line or load changes. The details of why this is so will be discussed below.

5.2.4 Paralleling outputs

A number of current-mode power supplies may be operated in parallel with each sharing the total load current equally. This is achieved by sensing current in each supply with equal current sensing resistors which convert peak power transistor current pulses to voltage pulses. These are compared in a voltage comparator to a common error-amplifier output voltage which forces peak current sensing voltages and hence peak currents in the paralleled supplies to be equal.

5.2.5 Improved load current regulation

Current mode has better load current regulation than does voltage mode. But the improvement is not as great as voltage regulation, which is greatly enhanced by the feedforward characteristic inherent in current mode. The improved load current regulation comes about because of the greater error-amplifier bandwidth possible in current mode.

5.3 Current-Mode versus Voltage-Mode Control Circuits

To understand the differences and advantages of current mode, it is essential to first see how voltage-mode control circuitry works. The basic elements of a typical voltage mode, PWM control circuit is shown in Fig. 5.1. That block diagram shows most of the elements of the SG1524, the very first of the integrated-circuit control chips which have revolutionized the switching power supply industry. The SG1524, originally made by Silicon General Corporation, is now manufactured by many other companies and in improved versions such as the UC1524A (Unitrode) and SG1524B (Silicon General).

5.3.1 Voltage-mode control circuitry

In Fig. 5.1, a sawtooth oscillator generates a 3-V sawtooth triangle V_{st}. The DC voltage level at the triangle base is about 0.5 V and 3.5 V at its peak. The period of the triangle is set by external discrete components R_t and C_t and is approximately equal to $T = R_t C_t$.

An error amplifier compares a fraction of the output voltage KV_o to a voltage reference V_{ref} and produces an error voltage V_{ea}; V_{ea} is compared to the sawtooth V_{st} in a voltage comparator (PWM). Note in the error

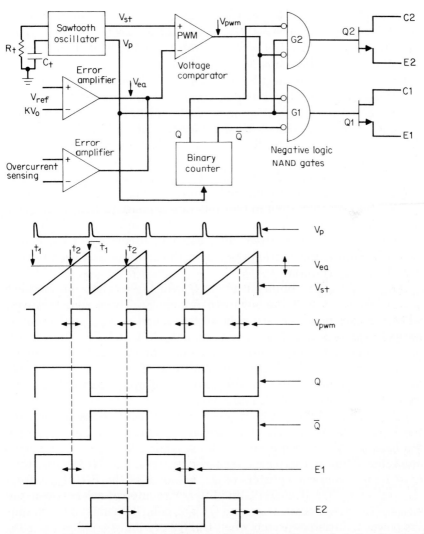

Figure 5.1 A basic voltage-mode PWM controller. Output voltage only is directly sensed by the error amplifier. Regulation against load current changes occurs only after the current changes cause small output voltage changes. The current-limit amplifier operates only to shut down the supply when a maximum current limit is exceeded. Transistor on time is from start of sawtooth until the sawtooth crosses V_{ea}.

amplifier that the fraction of the output KV_o is fed to the inverting input so that when V_o goes up, the error-amplifier output V_{ea} goes down.

In the PWM voltage comparator, the sawtooth is fed to the noninverting input and V_{ea} is fed to the inverting input. Thus the PWM output is a negative-going pulse of variable width. The pulse is negative for the entire time the sawtooth is below the DC level of the error-amplifier output V_{ea} or from t_1 to t_2. As the DC output voltage goes—say—slightly positive, KV_o goes slightly positive, and V_{ea} goes negative and closer to the bottom of the sawtooth. Thus the duration of the negative-going pulse V_{pwm} decreases.

The duration of this negative-going pulse will be the duration of the power transistor on time. Further, since in all the topologies discussed above, the DC output voltage is proportional to the power transistor on time, decreasing the on time brings the DC output voltage back down in the negative-feedback loop. The duration of the negative pulse V_{pwm} increases, of course, as the output DC voltage decreases.

The 1524 is designed for push-pull-type topologies, so the single negative-going pulse of adjustable width, coming once per sawtooth period, must be converted to two 180° out-of-phase pulses of the same width. This is done with the binary counter and negative logic NAND gates $G1$ and $G2$. A positive-going pulse V_p occurring at the end of each sawtooth is taken from the sawtooth oscillator and used to trigger the binary counter.

Outputs from the binary counter Q and $\overline{Q}$ are then out-of-phase square waves at half the sawtooth frequency. These square waves, when they are negative, are used to steer negative V_{pwm} pulses alternatively through negative logic NAND gates $G1$ and $G2$. Those gates produce a positive output only for the duration of time that all inputs are negative. Thus the bases (and emitters) of output transistors $Q1$ and $Q2$ are positive only on alternative half cycles and only for the same duration as the V_{pwm} negative pulses.

The on time of the power transistors must correspond to the time the V_{pwm} pulse is negative for the complete circuit to have negative feedback as KV_o is connected to the inverting terminal of the error amplifier. Thus if the power transistors are of the NPN type, they must be fed from the emitters of $Q1$, $Q2$; or if of the PNP type, from the collectors. Or if current amplifiers are interposed between the bases of the power transistors and $Q1$, $Q2$, polarities must be such that the power transistors are on when $Q1$, $Q2$ are on.

The narrow positive pulse V_p is fed directly into gates $G1$, $G2$. This forces both gate outputs to be simultaneously low for the duration of V_p and both output transistors to be off for that duration. This ensures that if the pulse width of V_{pwm} ever approached a full half period, it would be guaranteed that both power transistors could never be simultaneously on at the end of the half period. In a push-pull topology, if both transistors are simultaneously on even for a short time, they are subjected to high current and the full supply voltage and could be destroyed.

This, then, is a voltage-mode circuit. Power transistor or output current is never sensed directly. The power transistors are turned on at the beginning of a half period and turned off when the sawtooth V_{st} crosses the DC level of the error-amplifier output, which is a measure of output voltage only.

The complete details of the SG1524 are shown in Fig. 5.2a. The negative logic NAND gates $G1$, $G2$ of Fig. 5.1 are shown in Fig. 5.2a as positive logic NOR gates. These perform the same function for requiring all "lows" to make a "high" is identical to any one "high" forcing a "low."

In Fig. 5.2a, when pin 10 goes high, the associated transistor collector goes low and brings the error-amplifier output (pin 9) down to the base of the sawtooth. This reduces output transistor on times to zero and shuts down the supply. In the current limit comparator, if pin 4 is 200 mV more positive than pin 5, the error-amplifier output is also brought down to ground (there is an internal phase inversion, not shown) and the supply is shut down. Pins 4 and 5 are bridged across a current-sensing resistor in series with the current being monitored. If current is to be limited to I_m, the resistor is selected as $R_s = 0.2/I_m$.

5.3.2 Current-mode control circuitry

Circuitry of the first integrated-circuit current-mode control chip (Unitrode UC1846) is shown in Fig. 5.2b. Figure 5.3 shows its basic elements controlling a push-pull converter.

It is seen in Fig. 5.3 that there are two feedback loops—an outer loop consisting of output voltage sensor (EA) and an inner loop comprising primary peak current sensor (PWM) and current-sensing resistor R_i which converts ramp-on-a-step transistor currents to ramp-on-a-step voltages.

Regulation against line and load current changes is done by variation of the power transistor on time. On time is determined by both the voltage-sensing error-amplifier output V_{eao} and the PWM voltage comparator which compares V_{eao} to the ramp-on-a-step voltage at the top of the current-sensing resistor R_i.

Currents in the output transistors have the characteristic shape of a ramp on a step as the secondaries all have output inductors. This causes ramp on a step secondary currents which reflect as identical-shaped currents in the primary, lower in the ratio of N_s/N_p. Those currents flowing through R_i in the common emitters produce the ramp-on-a-step voltage waveshape shown as V_i. Power transistor on time is then determined as follows. An internal oscillator, whose period is set by external discrete components R_t, C_t, generates narrow clock pulses C_p. Oscillator period is approximately $0.9 R_t C_t$. At every clock pulse, feedforward $FF1$ is reset, causing its output Q_{pw} to go "low." The duration of the low time at Q_{pw}, it will soon be seen, is the duration of

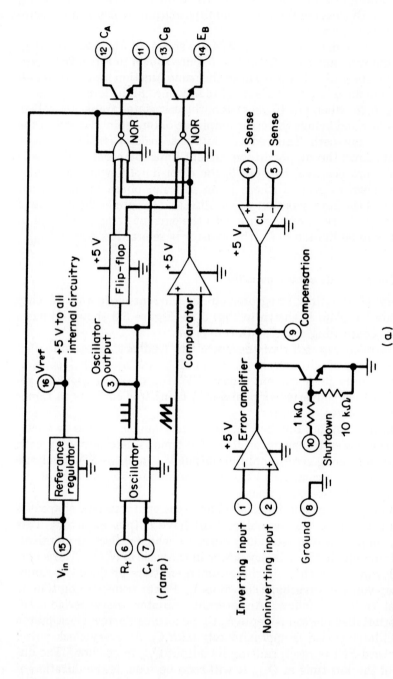

Figure 5.2 (a) PWM chip SG1524. The first integrated-circuit pulse-width-modulating control chip. (*Courtesy Silicon General Corp.*)

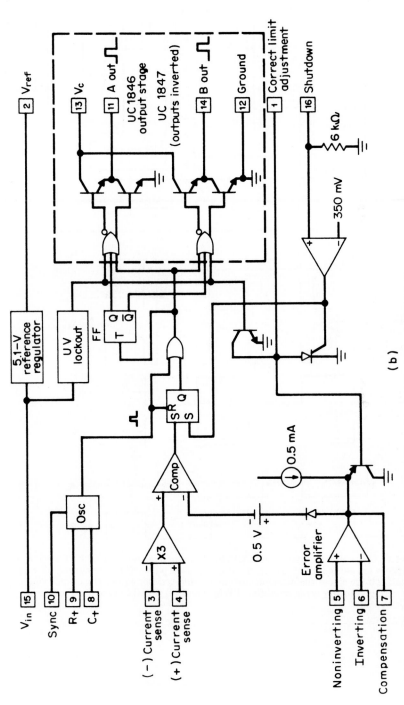

Figure 5.2 (*b*) PWM UC1846. The first integrated-circuit current-mode control chip. (*Courtesy Unitrode Corp.*)

151

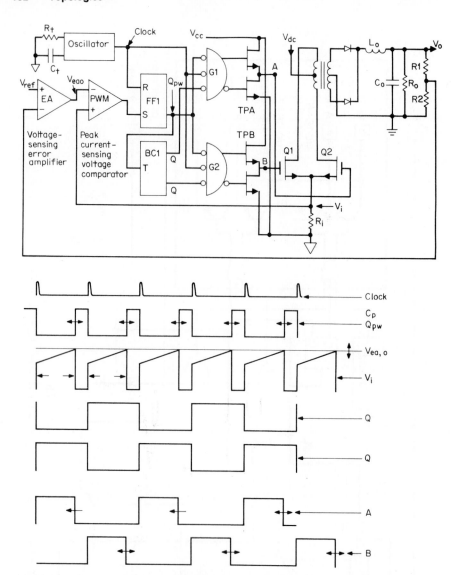

Figure 5.3   Current-mode controller (UC1846). Driving a push-pull MOSFET converter. Transistors are turned on alternatively at every clock pulse. They are turned off when the peak voltage across the common current-sensing resistor equals the output voltage of the voltage-sensing error amplifier. PWM forces all $Q1$, $Q2$ current pulses to have equal amplitude.

the "high" time at either of the chip outputs A or B and hence the duration of the power transistor on times.

Now when the PWM voltage comparator output goes high, $FF1$ is set, thus terminating the Q_{pw} low and hence the high time at A or B and turns off the power transistor which had been on. Thus the instant at which the PWM comparator output goes high determines the end of the on time.

Now the PWM comparator compares the ramp-on-a-step current-sensing voltage V_i to the output of the voltage error-amplifier EA. Hence when the peak of V_i equals V_{eao}, the PWM output goes positive, sets $FF1$, Q_{pw} goes high, and whichever of A or B had been high, goes back down low. The power transistor which had just been on is now turned off.

A low output from $FF1$ occurs once per clock period. It starts low at every clock pulse and goes back high when the PWM noninverting input equals the DC level of the EA output. Most frequently, power transistors $Q1$, $Q2$ will be N types which require positive-going signals for turnon. Thus these equal-duration negative-going pulses are steered alternately through negative logic NAND gates $G1$ and $G2$, becoming 180° out-of-phase, positive-going pulses at the chip output points A and B.

Chip output stages TPA and TPB are "totem poles." When the bottom transistor of a totem pole is on, the top one is off and vice versa. Output nodes A and B have very low output impedance. When the bottom transistor is on, it can "sink" (absorb inward-directed current) 100 mA statically and 400 mA during the high-to-low transition. When the top transistor is on, it can "source" (emit outward-directed current) 100 mA statically and 400 mA during the low-to-high transition.

The steering is done by binary counter $BC1$, which is triggered once per clock pulse by the leading edge of the pulse. The negative-going Q pulses steer the negative Q_{pw} pulses alternately through negative logic NAND gates $G1$, $G2$. The chip outputs at points A and B are 180° out-of-phase positive pulses whose duration is the same as that of the negative pulses shown as Q_{pw}.

Note that Q_{pw} is positive from the end of the on time until the start of the next turnon. This forces the bubble outputs of $G1$, $G2$ high and brings points A and B both low. This low at both power transistor inputs during the dead time between the turnoff of one transistor and the turnon of the other is a valuable feature. It presents a low impedance at the off-voltage level and prevents noise pickup from falsely turning the power transistors on. While the bubble outputs of $G1$, $G2$ are both high, their no-bubble outputs are both low. This turns off the upper transistors of the totem poles TPA and TPB and avoids overdissipating them.

It can also be seen that the narrow positive clock pulse is fed as a third input to NAND gates $G1$, $G2$. This makes bubble outputs from $G1$, $G2$ high and points A, B simultaneously low for the duration of the clock pulse. This guarantees that under fault conditions, if the controller attempted a full half period on time (Q_{pw} low and either A or B high for a full half period), there would be a dead time between the end of one on time and the start of the opposite on time. There could thus be no simultaneous conduction in the power transistors.

5.4 Detailed Explanation of Current-Mode Advantages

5.4.1 Line voltage regulation

Now consider how the controller regulates against line voltage changes. Assume that line voltage (and hence V_{dc}) goes up. Since secondary DC voltages are proportional to secondary winding peak voltages and power transistor on time, the on time must decrease as the peak secondary voltage has increased. Now as V_{dc} goes up, the peak secondary voltage will go up and after a delay in L_o, V_o will eventually go up. Then after a delay in getting through the error amplifier, V_{eao} will go down and in the PWM comparator, the ramp in V_i will equal the lowered value of V_{eao} earlier in time. Thus, on time will be decreased and the output voltage will be brought back down.

However, if this were the mechanism to correct against line voltage changes, that correction would be slow as it is slowed up by the delay in L_o and in getting through the error amplifier. But there is a shortcut around those delays. As V_{dc} goes up, the peak voltage at the input to the output inductor V_{sp} increases, the slope of inductor current dI_s/dt increases and hence the slope of the ramp of V_i increases. Now the faster ramp equals V_{eao} earlier in time and the on time is shortened without having to wait for V_{eao} to move down to shorten the on time. Output voltage transients resulting from input voltage transients will then be smaller in amplitude and shorter in duration because of this feedforward characteristic.

5.4.2 Elimination of flux imbalance

Consider the waveform V_i in Fig. 5.3. It is taken off the top of the current-sensing resistor and is hence proportional to power transistor currents. The on time ends when the peak of the ramp in V_i equals the output voltage of the error amplifier V_{eao}. It can be seen in Fig. 5.3 that peak currents on alternate half cycles cannot be unequal as in Fig. 2.4b and 2.4c because the error-amplifier output V_{eao} is pretty much a straight line and cannot change within one cycle because of its limited bandwidth.

If the transformer core got slightly off center and started walking up into saturation on one side, the voltage V_i would go slightly concave upward close to the end of that on time. It would then equal V_{eao} earlier in time and terminate that on time sooner. Flux increase in that half cycle would then cease, and in the next half cycle, since the opposite transistor does not have a foreshortened on time, the core would be brought back down in flux and away from saturation.

Since the peak of the voltage ramps in Fig. 5.3 (V_i) are equal, peak currents on alternate half cycles must be equal. Thus flux imbalance and the inequality of alternate currents shown in Fig. 2.4b is not possible.

5.4.3 Simplified loop stabilization resulting from elimination of output inductor in small-signal analysis

Refer to Fig. 5.3. In a small-signal analysis to determine whether the loop is stable, it is assumed that the loop is opened at some point and a sinusoidal signal of variable frequency is inserted at that point. The gain and phase shift versus frequency is calculated through all the elements starting from the point at which the loop was assumed opened around to the point at the other end of the loop break. By tailoring the error-amplifier gain and phase shift properly in relation to the other elements in the open loop (primarily the output LC filter), the closed loop can be made stable.

The variable frequency is generally assumed inserted in series at the input end of the error amplifier. In Chap. 12 on feedback loop stability analysis, it will be shown how gain and phase shift through the error amplifier may be calculated and tailored to achieve desired results.

In Fig. 5.3, the concept of gain and phase shift of a sinusoidal signal from the error-amplifier output to the input of the LC filter may be difficult to grasp. At the error-amplifier output V_{eao} there is a DC voltage level which, when it equals the peak of the ramp-on-a-step pulse sequence V_i, results in a sequence of negative-going pulses at Q_{pw} whose duration is dependent on the DC voltage level of V_{eao}. The Q_{pw} negative pulses result in a sequence of positive-going pulses at the input to the LC filter.

It may seem puzzling to speak of gain and phase shift of sinusoidal signals in view of this odd operation of converting a voltage level to a sequence of pulses at the switching frequency. The situation may be clarified as follows.

If there is a sinusoidal signal at the error-amplifier input, the same

signal is amplified and phase-shifted at its output. Then the DC voltage level at V_{eao} is sinusoidally modulated at that frequency. Hence
the pulse width of the Q_{pw} negative pulses is similarity modulated at
that frequency. So is the pulse width or on time of the positive-going
pulses at the output rectifiers modulated at that frequency. Hence the
voltage at the output rectifier cathodes, which is proportional to the
pulse widths, when averaged over a time long compared to the switching period, is simply the same modulating frequency as was inserted
at the error-amplifier input.

The modulation operation (so long as the modulation period is long
compared to the switching period) is then simply a sinusoid-to-pulse
width-to-sinusoid converter. The gain of this modulation operation will
be discussed further in the chapter on feedback loop stability.

Now in Fig. 5.3, there remains only the problem of calculating the
gain and phase shift versus frequency for the sinusoid through the LC
filter. If there were a sine wave of voltage at the rectifier cathodes, the
phase shift through the LC filter would be 90° at its resonant frequency $1/2\pi\sqrt{LC}$ and 180° shortly after that, and gain from input to
output would fall at a fast rate—40 dB/decade shortly after resonance.

But in current mode, the PWM comparator forces the output at the
rectifier cathodes to be a sequence of width-modulated constant-
current pulses—not voltage pulses. Thus at the input to the LC filter,
the averaged waveform is a constant-current, not a constant-voltage,
sinusoid.

With constant-current sinusoids, the filter inductor cannot act to
change phase. The circuit behaves, in this small-signal analysis, as if
the inductor were not present. Thus after the rectifier cathodes, the
gain and phase shift correspond to that of constant-current sinusoids
flowing into the paralleled combination of the output capacitor and
load resistor. Such a circuit can yield only a maximum phase shift of
90° and a gain-versus-frequency characteristic which falls at 20 dB
rather than 40 dB per decade.

Chapter 12 on feedback stability analysis, will show that this
greatly simplifies the error-amplifier design, yields greater bandwidth, and improves the response of the closed-loop circuit to step
changes in load and line. For now, Fig. 5.4a and 5.4b shows a comparison of the error-amplifier feedback networks required to stabilize a
voltage-mode circuit (Fig. 5.4a) and a current-mode circuit (Fig. 5.4b).

5.4.4 Mechanism of load current regulation

In Fig. 5.3, the V_i voltage waveforms are proportional to power transistor current waveforms which are related to secondary current
waveforms by the transformer turns ratio.

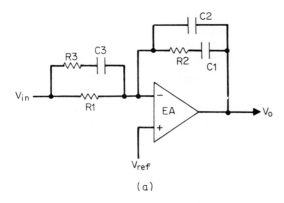

(a)

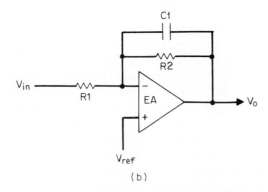

(b)

Figure 5.4 (a) Typical compensating network for a
voltage-mode power supply. The complex input-
feedback network in voltage mode is necessary because the output inductor and with the filter capacitor
together yield a 180° phase shift and a 40 dB/decade
gain versus frequency characteristic which make loop
stabilization more difficult. (b) Typical compensation
network for a current-mode power supply. In current
mode, the source driving the output inductor is an effective "current source." The output inductor thus
does not contribute to phase shift. The circuit acts at
its output as if there were a constant current driving
the parallel combination of the output filter capacitor
and the output load resistance. Such a network yields
a maximum 90° phase shift and a −20 dB/decade gain
versus frequency characteristic. This permits the simpler input-feedback network for loop stabilization. It
also copes much more easily with large-amplitude
load and line changes.

Now at a DC input voltage V_{dc}, the peak secondary voltage is $V_{sp} = V_{dc}(N_s/N_p)$. For an on time per transistor of t_{on}, the DC output voltage is $V_o = V_{sp}(2t_{on}/T)$—just as for a voltage-mode push-pull circuit. The on time starts at the clock pulse as shown and ends when the V_i ramp equals the level of the voltage error-amplifier output as shown in Fig. 5.3.

If the DC voltage goes up, initially as described, the V_i ramp rate increases and shortens the on time as it reaches the original V_{eao} level earlier in time. This yields a fast correction for a step change in input voltage and the on time remains shorter as required by the preceding relation for the peak secondary voltage has gone up.

The mechanism of load current regulation, though, is different. For a fast step—say, an increase—in DC load current, the DC output voltage drops somewhat momentarily as the LC output filter has a certain surge impedance (approximately $\sqrt{L/C}$). After the delay in the error amplifier, V_{eao} moves up an amount determined by the EA gain.

Now the V_i ramp must go out further in time and hence in amplitude for it to reach equality with the higher V_{eao}. The secondary peak current and hence the output inductor current are thus larger in amplitude. The upslope of the inductor current lasts longer and eats somewhat into the dead time before the opposite transistor turnon.

With a shorter dead time, and starting from a higher current level at the beginning of the dead time, at the opposite transistor turnon, the current remaining in the inductor will be larger than it had been in the previous cycle. Thus the front-end step in each current pulse represented by V_i is greater than in the previous cycle.

This process continues for a number of switching cycles until the step part of the ramp-on-a-step current waveform builds up sufficiently to supply the increased demand for DC load current. As this current builds up, the DC output voltage gradually builds backup and V_{eao} relaxes back down, returning the on time to its original value. The time to respond to a change in DC load current is thus seen to be dependent on the size of the output inductor (a smaller value permits more rapid current changes in it) and the bandwidth of the error amplifier.

5.5 Current-Mode Deficiencies and Problems

5.5.1 Constant peak versus constant average output inductor problems[1-4]

Current mode forces peak power transistor currents to be constant at a level needed to supply the DC load current at the DC output voltage dictated by the voltage error amplifier as shown in Fig. 5.3.

The DC load current is the average of the output inductor current, however, and keeping the peak transistor current constant keeps the peak output inductor current constant but does not keep the average inductor current constant. Because of this, in the unmodified current-mode scheme described thus far, changes in the DC input voltage will cause momentary changes in the DC output voltage. The output voltage change will be corrected by the voltage error amplifier outer feedback loop, as this is the loop which ultimately sets output voltage.

Again, however, the inner loop, in keeping peak inductor current constant, does not supply the correct average inductor current and output voltage changes again. The effect is then an oscillation which commences at every change in input voltage and which may continue for some time. The mechanism can be better understood from an examination of the upslope and downslope of the output inductor currents in Fig. 5.5.[3]

Figure 5.5a shows the upslope and downslope of the output inductor current for two different DC input voltages in current mode. Slope m_2 is the down slope $= dI_1/dt = V_o/L_o$. It is seen to be constant for the two different DC input voltages. At the high input voltage, on time is short at $t_{on,h}$ and at the lower DC input, on time is longer at $t_{on,l}$.

The peak inductor currents are constant as (see Fig. 5.3) the peak power transistor currents are kept constant by the PWM comparator. The DC voltage input V_{eao} to that comparator is constant as the outer feedback loop is keeping V_o constant. The constant V_{eao} then keeps V_i peaks constant, and hence transistor and output inductor peak currents are constant.

In Fig. 5.5a, in the steady state, the currents are drawn so that the current change during an on time are equal and opposite to those during an off time. This must be so because if not, there would be a DC voltage across the inductor; and since it is assumed that the inductor has negligible resistance, it cannot support DC voltage.

It can be seen in Fig. 5.5a, that the average inductor current at low DC input is higher than it is at high DC input voltage. This can be seen quantitatively as

$$I_{av} = I_p - \frac{dI_2}{2} = I_p - \left(\frac{m_2 t_{off}}{2}\right)$$

$$= I_p - \left[\frac{m_2(T - t_{on})}{2}\right]$$

$$= I_p - \left(\frac{m_2 T}{2}\right) + \left(\frac{m_2 t_{on}}{2}\right) \tag{5.1}$$

Since the voltage feedback loop keeps the product of $V_{dc}t_{on}$ constant, at lower DC input voltage, where the on time is higher, the average

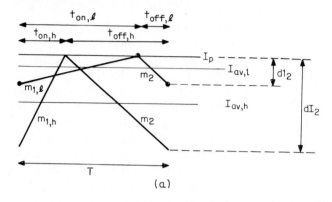

(a)

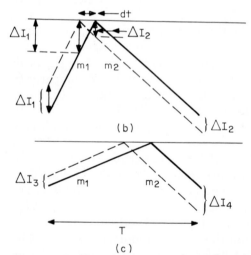

(b)

(c)

Figure 5.5 Problems in current mode. (a) Output inductor currents at high and low input voltages. In current mode, peak inductor currents are constant. At low DC input, t_{on} is maximum, yielding average inductor current I_{avl}. At high DC input, on time decreases to keep output voltage constant. But average inductor current I_{avh} is lower at high DC input. Since output voltage is proportional to average—not peak—inductor current, this causes oscillation when input voltage is changed. Slopes m_2 are inductor current downslopes. Slope m_{1l} is inductor current upslope at low line; m_{1h} is inductor current upslope at high line. (b) For a duty cycle less than 50 percent, an initial inductor current disturbance I_1 results in smaller I_2 disturbances in successive cycles until the disturbances die out. (c) For a duty cycle greater than 50 percent, an initial inductor current disturbance I_3 results in larger I_4 disturbances in successive cycles. The disturbances grow, and then decay resulting in an oscillation.

output inductor current I_{av} is higher, as can be seen from Eq. 5.1 and Fig. 5.5a.

Further, since the DC output voltage is proportional to the average, not the peak, inductor current, as DC input goes down, DC output voltage will go up. DC output voltage will then be corrected by the outer feedback loop and a seesaw action or oscillation will occur.

This phenomenon does not occur in voltage-mode control, where only DC output voltage is controlled. Also, since DC output voltage is proportional to average, not peak, inductor current, keeping output voltage constant maintains average inductor current constant.

5.5.2 Response to an output inductor current disturbance

A second problem which gives rise to oscillation in current mode is shown in Fig. 5.5b and 5.5c. In Fig. 5.5b, it is seen that at a fixed DC input voltage, if for some reason there is an initial current disturbance ΔI_1, after a first downslope the current will be displaced by an amount ΔI_2.

Further, if the duty cycle is less than 50 percent ($m_2 < m_1$) as in Fig. 5.5b, the output disturbance ΔI_2 will be less than the input disturbance ΔI_1, and after some cycles, the disturbance will die out. But if the duty cycle is greater than 50 percent ($m_2 > m_1$) as in Fig. 5.5c, the output disturbance after one cycle ΔI_4 is greater than the input disturbance ΔI_3. This can be seen quantitatively from Fig. 5.5b as follows. For a small current displacement ΔI_1, the current reaches the original peak value earlier in time by an amount dt where $dt = \Delta I_1/m_1$.

On the inductor downslope, at the end of the on time, the current is lower than its original value by an amount ΔI_2 where

$$\Delta I_2 = m_2 dt = \Delta I_1 \frac{m_2}{m_1} \qquad (5.2)$$

Now with m_2 greater than m_1, the disturbances will continue to grow but eventually decay, giving rise to an oscillation.

5.5.3 Slope compensation to correct problems in current mode[1-4]

Both current-mode problems mentioned above can be corrected as shown in Fig. 5.6, where the original, unmodified output of the error amplifier is shown as the horizontal voltage level OP. The scheme for correcting the preceding problems ("slope compensation") consists of adding a negative voltage slope of magnitude m to the output of the error amplifier. By proper selection of the m in a manner discussed

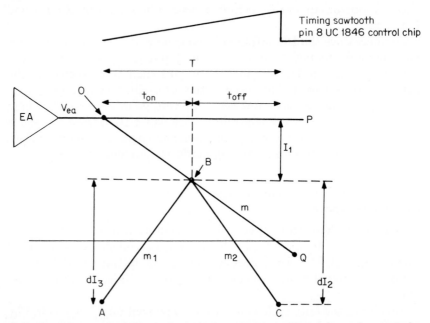

Figure 5.6 Slope compensation. By adding a negative voltage slope of magnitude $m = N_s/N_p(R_i)(m_2/2)$ to the error-amplifier output (Fig. 5.3), the two problems shown in Fig. 5.5 are corrected.

below, the output inductor average DC current can be made independent of the power transistor on time. This corrects the problems indicated by both Eqs. 5.1 and 5.2.

In Fig. 5.6, the upslope m_1 and downslope m_2 of output inductor current is shown. Recall that in current mode, the power transistor on time starts at every clock pulse and ends at the instant the output of the PWM comparator reaches equality with the output of the voltage error-amplifier as shown in Fig. 5.3. In slope compensation, a negative voltage slope of magnitude $m = dV_{ea}/dt$ starting at clock time is added to the error-amplifier output. The magnitude of m is calculated thus. In Fig. 5.6, the error-amplifier output at any time t_{on} after a clock pulse is

$$V_{ea} = V_{eao} - mt_{on} \tag{5.3}$$

where V_{eao} is the error-amplifier output at t_{on} equal to zero. The peak voltage V_i across the primary current-sensing resistor R_i in Fig. 5.3 is

$$V_i = I_{pp}R_i = I_{sp}\frac{N_s}{N_p}R_i$$

where I_{pp} and I_{sp} are the primary and secondary peak currents, respectively. But $I_{sp} = I_{sa} + dI_2/2$, where I_{sa} is the average secondary or average output inductor current and dI_2 in Fig. 5.6 is the inductor current change during the off time ($= m_2 t_{off}$). Then

$$I_{sp} = I_{sa} + \frac{m_2 t_{off}}{2}$$

$$= I_{sa} + \frac{m_2}{2}(T - t_{on})$$

Then
$$V_i = \frac{N_s}{N_p} R_i \left[I_{sa} + \frac{m_2}{2}(T - t_{on}) \right] \qquad (5.4)$$

Equating Eqs. 5.3 and 5.4, which is what the PWM comparator does, we obtain

$$\frac{N_s}{N_p} R_i I_{sa} = V_{eao} + t_{on}\left(\frac{N_s}{N_p} R_i \frac{m_2}{2} - m \right) - \left(\frac{N_s}{N_p} R_i \frac{m_2}{2} T \right)$$

It can be seen in this relation that if

$$\frac{N_s}{N_p} R_i \frac{m_2}{2} = m = \frac{dV_{ea}}{dt} \qquad (5.5)$$

then the coefficient of the t_{on} term is zero and the average output inductor current is independent of the on time. This then corrects the above two problems arising from the fact that without compensation, current mode maintains constant the peak, and not the average, output inductor current.

5.5.4 Slope compensation with a positive-going ramp voltage[3]

In the previous section it was shown that if a negative ramp of magnitude given by Eq. 5.5 is added to the error-amplifier output, the two current-mode problems described above are corrected.

The same effect is obtained by adding a positive-going ramp to the output of the current-sensing resistor V_i (Fig. 5.3) and leaving the error-amplifier output voltage V_{eao} (Fig. 5.3) unmodified. Adding the positive ramp to V_i is simpler and is the more usual approach. That adding the appropriate positive ramp to V_i also makes the average output inductor current independent of the on time can be shown as follows. A ramp voltage of slope dV/dt will be added to the voltage V_i of Fig. 5.3 and the resultant voltage will be compared in the PWM to the error-amplifier output V_{eao} of that figure. When the PWM finds equality of those voltages, its output terminates the on time. Then $V_i + dV/dt = V_{eao}$. Substitute V_i from Eq. 5.4:

$$\frac{N_s}{N_p} R_i\left[I_{sa} + \frac{m_2}{2}(T - t_{on})\right] + \frac{dV}{dt}t_{on} = V_{eao}$$

Then $$\frac{N_s}{N_p}R_i I_{sa} + \frac{N_s}{N_p}R_i\frac{m_2}{2}T + t_{on}\left(\frac{dV}{dt} - \frac{N_s}{N_p}R_i\frac{m_2}{2}\right) = V_{eao}$$

From the above, it is seen that if the slope dV/dt of the voltage added to V_i is equal to $(N_s/N_p)R_i m_2/2$, the terms involving t_{on} in the preceding relation vanish and the secondary average voltage I_{sa} is independent of the on time. Note that $m_2(= V_o/L_o)$ is the current downslope of the output inductor as defined earlier.

5.5.5 Implementing slope compensation[3]

In the UC1846 chip, a positive-going ramp starting at every clock pulse is available at the top of the timing capacitor (pin 8 in Fig. 5.2b). The voltage at that pin is

$$V_{osc} = \frac{\Delta V}{\Delta t}t_{on} \qquad (5.6)$$

where $\Delta V = 1.8$ V and $\Delta t = 0.45 R_t C_t$

As seen in Fig. 5.7, a fraction of that voltage whose slope is $\Delta V/\Delta t$ is added to V_i (the voltage across the current-sensing resistor). That slope is set to $(N_s/N_p)R_i(m_2/2)$ by resistors $R1$, $R2$. Thus in Fig. 5.7, since R_i is much less than $R1$, the voltage delivered to the current sensing terminal (pin 4) is

$$V_i + \frac{R1}{R1 + R2}V_{osc} = V_i + \frac{R1}{R1 + R2}\frac{\Delta V}{\Delta t}t_{on} \qquad (5.7)$$

and setting the slope of that added voltage equal to $(N_s/N_p)R_i m_2/2$; we obtain

$$\frac{R1}{R1 + R2} = \frac{(N_s/N_p)(R_i)(m_2/2)}{\Delta V/\Delta t} \qquad (5.8)$$

where $\Delta V/\Delta t = 1.8/(0.45 R_t C_t)$.

Since $R1 + R2$ drains current off the top of the timing capacitor, it changes operating frequency. Then either $R1 + R2$ is made large enough so that the frequency change is small or an emitter-follower is

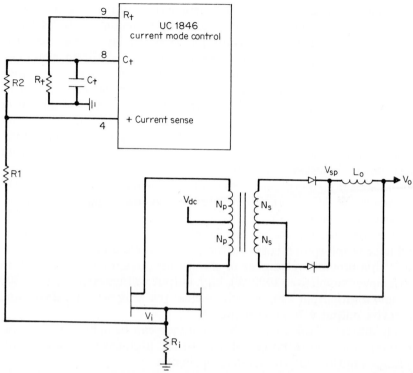

Figure 5.7 Slope compensation in the UC1846 current-mode control chip. A positive ramp voltage is taken off the top of the timing capacitor, scaled by resistors R_1, R_2 and added to the voltage at the top of the current resistor R_i. By choosing R_1, R_2 to make the slope of the voltage added to V_i equal to half the downslope of the output inductor current, reflected into the primary and multiplied by R_i, the output inductor average current is rendered independent of power transistor on times.

interposed between pin 8 and the resistors. Usually $R1$ is preselected and $R2$ is calculated from Eq. 5.8.

5.6 Voltage-Fed and Current-Fed Topologies

5.6.1 Introduction and definitions

All topologies discussed thus far have been of the voltage-fed type. *Voltage-fed* implies that the source impedance of whatever drives the topology is low and hence there is no way of limiting the current drawn from it during the unusual conditions at power switch turnon or turnoff or under various fault conditions in the topology.

Of course, there are various ways of implementing "current limiting" with additional circuitry which senses an overcurrent condition and takes some kind of corrective action such as narrowing the controller's switching pulse width or stopping it completely. But all such schemes are not instantaneous; they involve a delay over a number of switching cycles during which there can be excessive dissipation in either the power transistors or output rectifiers and dangerous voltage or current spiking. Thus such overcurrent-sensing schemes are of no help in the case of high transient currents at the instant of the power switch turnon and turnoff.

The low source impedance in voltage-fed topologies is the output impedance of the filter capacitor in off-line converters or the low output impedance of the battery in battery-powered converters. Or in compound schemes where a buck regulator preregulates the rectified DC voltage of the AC line rectifier, it is the very low output impedance of the buck regulator itself.

In current-fed topologies, the high instantaneous impedance of an inductor is interposed between the power source and the topology itself. This provides a number of significant advantages, especially in high power supplies (>1000 W), high output voltage supplies (> ~200 V), and multioutput supplies where close tracking between slaves and a master output voltage is required.

Advantages of the current-fed technique can be appreciated by examining the shortcomings of the usual high-power, high-output-voltage, multioutput voltage-fed topologies.

5.6.2 Deficiencies of voltage-fed, width-modulated full-wave bridge[9]

Figure 5.8 shows a conventional voltage-fed full bridge—the usual choice for a switching supply at 1000-W output. At higher output powers and high output voltages and for many output voltages, it has the following significant shortcomings.

5.6.2.1 Output inductor problems in voltage-fed, width-modulated full-wave bridge.

For high output voltages, the size and cost of the output inductor L_o (or inductors in a multioutput supply) become prohibitive, as can be seen from the following. The inductor is selected to prevent its going into the discontinuous mode or running dry at the specified minimum DC load current (Secs. 1.3.6, 2.2.14.1). For a minimum DC load current of one-tenth its nominal value I_{on}, Eq. 2.20 gives the magnitude of the inductor as $L_o = 0.5V_oT/I_{on}$.

Now consider a 2000-W supply at $V_o = 200$ V, $I_{o(nominal)} = 10$ A, and a minimum DC output current of 1 A. To minimize the size of the out-

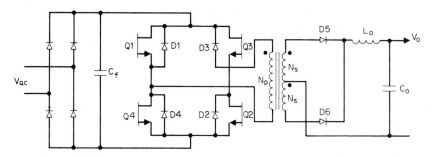

Figure 5.8 Conventional voltage-fed full bridge communally used for output powers at 1000 W. The low source of impedance seen looking back into filter capacitor C_f and the need for output inductor L_o are significant drawbacks for output powers over 1000 W and output voltages over a few hundred volts. Also, the requirement for the output inductor at each output of a multioutput power supply makes the topology expensive in dollars and required space.

put inductor, T should be minimized and a switching frequency of 50 kHz might be considered. At 50 kHz, for V_o = 200 V, I_{on} = 10 A, Eq. 2.20 yields L_o of 200 μH.

The inductor would have to carry the nominal current of 10 A without saturating. Such inductors capable of carrying large DC bias currents without saturating are discussed in a later chapter and are made either with gapped ferrite or powdered iron toroidal cores. Such a 200-μH 10-A inductor using a powdered iron toroid would be about 2.5 in in diameter and 1.0 in in height.

Although this is not too prohibitive a size for a single-output 2-kW supply, if there were many outputs, higher output voltages or higher output power, the size and cost of many such large inductors would be a serious drawback. For high output voltages (>1000 V), even at low output currents, the output inductor is far more troublesome because of the large number of turns required to support the high voltage across the inductor. The high voltage across the inductor—especially during the dead time when cathodes of $D5$, $D6$ of Fig. 5.8 are both low—can produce corona and arcing.

A further problem with a topology as shown in Fig. 5.8 requiring output inductors is the poor cross regulation or change in output voltage of a slave when current changes in the master (Sec. 2.2.2). The output inductors in both the master and slave must be large enough to prevent them from going into the discontinuous mode and causing large output voltage changes at minimum load currents.

The current-fed circuit (Fig. 5.10) to be discussed below, avoids all these problems as it does not require output inductors. It uses a single-input inductor $L1$ before the bridge and only capacitors after secondary rectification. Thus DC output voltages are the peak rather than the average of the transformer secondary voltages. Voltage regulation is achieved by width modulation of the transistor switch $Q5$ ahead of the input inductor.

5.6.2.2 Turnon transient problems in voltage-fed, width-modulated full-wave bridge.[9]   In Fig. 5.8 diagonally opposite transistors are simultaneously on at alternate half cycles. The maximum on time of each pair is designed to never have to be more than 80 percent of a half period. This ensures a $0.2T/2$ dead time between the turnoff of one transistor pair and the turnon of the other. This dead time is essential, for if the on time of alternate pairs overlapped even if only for a fraction of a microsecond, there would be a dead short circuit across the filter capacitor, and with nothing to limit current flow, the transistors would fail immediately.

Now during the dead time, all four transistors are off, the anodes of output rectifiers $D5$, $D6$ are at ground and the input end of filter inductor L_o has swung down in an attempt to keep its current constant. The input end of L_o is caught at one diode drop below ground by the cathodes of $D5$, $D6$, which now act as free-wheeling diodes. The current which had been flowing in L_o before the dead time (roughly equal to the DC output current) now continues to flow in the same direction. It flows out through the ground terminal into the secondary center tap, where it divides equally, with each half flowing through $D5$, $D6$ back into the input end of L_o.

Now at the start of the next half cycle when, say, $Q1$, $Q2$ turn on, the no-dot end of the $T1$ primary is high and the no-dot end of the $T1$ secondary (anode of $D6$) attempts to go high. But the cathode of $D6$ is looking into the cathode of $D5$, which is still conducting half the DC output current. Until $D6$ supplies a current equal to and canceling the $D5$ forward current, it is looking into the low impedance of a conducting diode ($\sim 10\ \Omega$).

This secondary low impedance reflects as a low impedance across the transformer. But this low impedance is in series with the transformer's leakage inductance, which limits the primary current during the time required to cancel the $D5$ free-wheeling current. Because of the high-impedance current-limiting effect of the leakage inductance, transistors $Q1$ and $Q2$ remain in saturation until the $D5$ free-wheeling current is canceled.

When the $D5$ current is canceled, it still has a low impedance because of its reverse-recovery time, which may range from 35 ns (ultrafast-recovery type) to 200 ns (fast-recovery type). For a reverse recovery time of t_r, supply voltage of V_{cc}, and transformer primary leakage inductance of L_l, the primary current overshoots to $V_{cc}t_r/L_l$. This overshoot current can pull the transistors out of saturation and either partially damage or destroy them.

Finally, when the output rectifier recovers abruptly, there is a damped oscillatory ring at its cathode. The first positive half cycle of this ring can more than double the reverse voltage stress on the diode and possibly destroy it. Even in lower power supplies, it is often necessary to put a series RC arm across the rectifiers to damp the oscillation. The penalty paid for this is, of course, dissipation in the resistor.

5.6.2.3 Turnoff transient problems in voltage-fed, width-modulated full-wave bridge.[9] In Fig. 5.8, there is a spike of high power dissipation at turnoff as a result of the instantaneous overlap of falling current and rising voltage across the off-turning transistors.

Thus, consider that $Q3$ and $Q4$ are on and have received turnoff signals at their bases. As $Q3$, $Q4$ commence turning off, current stored in the leakage and magnetizing inductance of $T1$ force a polarity reversal across its primary. The bottom end of $T1$ goes immediately positive and is clamped via $D1$ to the positive rail at the top of $C1$. The top end of $T1$ goes immediately negative and is clamped via $D2$ to the negative rail at the bottom end of $C1$. Now voltages across $Q3$ and $Q4$ are clamped at V_{cc} so long as diodes $D1$, $D2$ conduct. There are no leakage inductance voltage spikes across $Q3$, $Q4$ as in push-pull or single-ended forward converter topologies. Energy stored in the leakage inductance is returned without dissipation to the input capacitor C_f.

However, while voltage across $Q3$, $Q4$ is held at V_{cc}, the current in these two transistors falls linearly to zero in a time t_f determined by their reverse base drives. This overlap of a fixed voltage V_{cc} and a current falling linearly from a value I_p results in a dissipation averaged over a full period T of

$$PD = V_{cc} \frac{I_p}{2} \frac{t_f}{T} \tag{5.9}$$

It is instructive to calculate this dissipation for, say, a 2-kW supply operating at 50 kHz from a nominal V_{cc} of 336 V (typical V_{cc} for an off-line inverter operating from a 120-V-AC line in the voltage-doubling mode as in Sec. 3.1.1). Assume a minimum V_{cc} of 0.9 (336) or 302 V. Then from Eq. 3.7, the peak current is

$$I_p = \frac{1.56 P_o}{V_{dc}} = 1.56 \frac{2000}{302} = 10.3 \text{ A}$$

A bipolar transistor at this power level could be expected to have a fall time of 0.3 µs. Then since peak currents are independent of DC input voltage, calculate overlap dissipation from Eq. 5.9 at a high line of $1.1 \times 336 = 370$ V. For the dissipation in either $Q3$ or $Q4$, Eq. 5.9 gives $PD = V_{cc}(I_p/2)(t_f/T) = 370(10.3/2)(0.3/20) = 28.5$ W, and for the four transistors in the bridge, total overlap losses would be 114 W.

It is of interest to calculate the dissipation per transistor during the on time. This is $V_{ce(sat)}I_cT_{on}/T$ and for a typical $V_{ce(sat)}$ of 1.0 V and an "on" duty cycle of 0.4 is only $1 \times 10.3 \times 0.4$ or 4.1 W.

Even though the 28.5 W of overlap dissipation per transistor can be reduced with four load- and line-shaping "snubbers" (to be discussed in a later chapter), these snubbers reduce transistor losses only by diverting them to the snubber resistors with no improvement in efficiency. It will be shown that in the current-fed topology, only two snubbers will be required, reducing transistor overlap dissipation to a negligible value. There will be a price paid for this as the dissipation in each of the two snubber resistors will be somewhat greater than that for the voltage-fed full bridge.

5.6.2.4 Flux-imbalance problem in voltage-fed, width-modulated full-wave bridge. Flux imbalance or operation not centered about the origin of the transformer's BH loop was discussed in Sec. 2.2.5 in connection with the push-pull and in Sec. 3.2.4 for the half bridge. It arises because of an unequal volt-second product applied to the transformer primary on alternate half cycles. As the core drifts further and further off center on the BH loop, it can move into saturation, be unable to sustain the supply voltage, and destroy the transistor.

Flux imbalance can also arise in the conventional full-wave bridge because of a volt-second imbalance on alternate half cycles. This can come about with bipolar transistors because of unequal storage times on alternate half cycles or with MOSFET transistors because of unequal MOSFET on-voltage drops. The solution for the full-wave bridge is to place a DC blocking capacitor in series with the primary. This prevents a DC current bias in the primary and forces operation to be centered about the BH loop origin. The size of such a DC blocking capacitor is calculated just as in Sec. 3.2.4 for the half bridge.

Current-fed circuits, to be discussed below, do not require such DC blocking capacitors and thus offer another advantage over voltage-fed circuits despite the relatively small size and cost of blocking capacitors.

5.6.3 Buck-voltage-fed full-wave bridge topology—basic operation

This topology is shown in Fig. 5.9. It avoids many of the deficiencies of the voltage-fed width-modulated full-wave bridge in high-voltage high-power multioutput supplies.

Consider first how it works. It is simply a buck regulator preceding

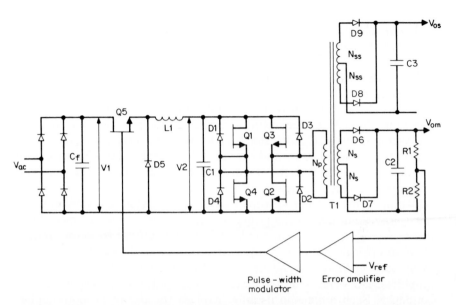

Figure 5.9 Buck-voltage-fed full bridge. The buck regulator preceding the full bridge eliminates the output inductors in a multioutput supply, but the low source impedance offered by the buck capacitor and the low output impedance of the buck regulator still leaves many drawbacks for this approach. $Q5$ is width-modulated, but $Q1$ to $Q4$ are operated at a fixed on time at about 90 percent of a half period to avoid simultaneous conduction. The output filters $C2$ are peak rather than averaging rectifiers. Practical output powers of about 2 kW to 5 kW are realizable.

a square-wave inverter which has only capacitors after the secondary rectifying diodes. Thus the DC output voltage at the filter capacitor is the peak of the secondary voltage (less, of course, the negligible rectifying diode drop). Also neglecting inverter transistor on drop, the DC output voltage is $V_o = V_2(N_s/N_p)$, where V_2 is the output of the buck regulator. Now the inverter transistors are not width-modulated. They are operated at a fixed on time—roughly 90 percent of a half period to avoid simultaneous conduction in the two transistors positioned vertically above one another. Diagonally opposite transistors are switched on and off simultaneously.

Feedback is taken from one of the secondary outputs (usually the highest current one or the one specified at tightest output voltage tolerance) and used to width-modulate the buck transistor $Q5$. This bucks down the rectified, unregulated DC voltage V_1 to a DC value V_2 arbitrarily selected to be about 25 percent lower than the lowest rectified voltage V_1 corresponding to the lowest specified AC input voltage. The turns ratio N_s/N_p is then chosen so that for the prespecified value of V_2, the correct master output voltage $V_{om} = V_2(N_s/N_p)$ is obtained.

The feedback loop, in keeping V_{om} constant against line and load changes, then keeps V_2 constant (neglecting relatively constant rectifier diode drops) at $V_2 = V_o(N_p/N_s)$. Now additional secondaries, rectifier diodes, and peak rectifying filter capacitors can be added for slave outputs.

Feedback can alternatively be taken from the top of $C1$ to keep V_2 constant. From V_2 to the outputs, the circuit is open-loop. But all output voltages are still quite constant for line and load changes as they are all proportional to V_2 and change only slightly as the forward drop in diode rectifiers and the on drop of the transistors changes only slightly with output currents.

Taking feedback from $V2$ thus results in somewhat less constant output voltages but avoids the problem of transmitting a width-modulated control voltage pulse across the boundary from output to input ground. Or if an error amplifier is located on output ground with a pulse-width modulator on input ground, it avoids the problem of transmitting the amplified DC error voltage across the output ground–input ground boundary. Such a scheme usually involves the use of an optocoupler, which has wide tolerances in gain and is not too reliable a device.

5.6.4 Buck-voltage-fed full-wave bridge advantages

5.6.4.1 Elimination of output inductors.
The first obvious advantage of the topology is that for a multioutput supply, it replaces many output inductors with a single-input inductor with consequent savings in dollars and space.

Since there are no output inductors in either the master or slaves, there is no problem of the inductors going into the discontinuous mode or running dry with consequent large output voltage changes (Secs. 1.3.6, 2.2.4). Slave output voltages will then track the master over a large range of output currents to about ±2 percent rather than the ±6 percent to ±8 percent or substantially more if output inductors were present and were permitted to go into the discontinuous mode.

The input inductor will be designed to go discontinuous just at the point where the total power or current is at its minimum. Since it is unlikely that all outputs are at minimum current simultaneously, this indicates a higher total minimum current and a smaller input inductor (Sec. 1.3.6).

Further, even after the input inductor has gone discontinuous, the master output voltage will remain substantially constant but with somewhat more output ripple and somewhat poorer load regulation. The feedback loop keeps the main output voltage constant even after onset of the discontinuous mode point by large decreases in on time of the buck transistor (Fig. 1.6a).

Further, since the slave outputs are clamped to the main output in the ratio of their respective turns ratios, slaves will also remain constant over large line and load changes.

Elimination of output inductors with their many turns required to sustain high AC voltages for high DC outputs makes 2000- to 3000-V outputs easily feasible. Higher output voltages—15,000 to 30,000 V— at relatively low output currents as for cathode-ray tubes or high-voltage–high-current outputs as for traveling-wave tubes are easily obtained by conventional diode-capacitor voltage multipliers after the secondaries.[8]

5.6.4.2 Elimination of bridge transistor turnon transients.

With respect to the full-wave width-modulated bridge of Fig. 5.8, Sec. 5.6.2.2 discussed turnon transient current stresses in the bridge transistors ($Q1$ to $Q4$) and excessive voltage stresses in the rectifying diodes ($D5$, $D6$).

It was pointed out in Sec. 5.6.2.2 that these stresses arose because the rectifier diodes were also acting as free-wheeling diodes. Thus at the instant of turnon of one diagonally opposite pair (say, $Q1$, $Q2$), $D6$ was still conducting as a free-wheeling diode. Then until the forward current in $D6$ was canceled, the impedance seen by $Q1$, $Q2$ was the leakage inductance of $T1$ in series with the low forward impedance of $D6$ reflected into the primary.

Subsequently, when $Q1$, $Q2$ forced a current into the primary sufficient to cancel the $D6$ forward current, there was still a low impedance reflected into the primary because of poor reverse recovery time in $D6$. This caused a large primary current overshoot which overstressed $Q1$, $Q2$. At the end of the recovery time, when the large secondary current overshoot terminated, it caused an oscillation and excessive voltage stress on $D6$.

But this current overstress on bridge transistors and voltage overstress on output rectifiers does not occur with the buck-voltage-fed topology of Fig. 5.9. The inverter transistors are operated with a dead time ($\sim 0.1T/2$) between the turnoff of one pair of transistors and the turnon of the other pair.

During this dead time when none of the bridge transistors are on, no current flows in the output rectifiers and output load current is supplied from the filter capacitors alone. Thus at the start of the next half period, the on-turning rectifier diode is not loaded down with a conducting free-wheeling diode as in Fig. 5.8. The opposite diode has long since ceased conducting; thus there is no current overstress in the bridge transistors and no recovery time problem in the rectifier diodes and hence no overvoltage stress in them.

5.6.4.3 Decrease of bridge transistor turnoff dissipation.

In Sec. 5.6.2.3 it was calculated that for a 2000-W supply operating from a nominal input of 120-V-AC in the input voltage-doubling mode, the bridge dissipation is 28.5 W at maximum AC input for each of the four transistors in the voltage-fed width-modulated bridge circuit of Fig. 5.8.

In the buck-voltage-fed full-wave bridge (Fig. 5.9), this dissipation is somewhat less. This is so because even at maximum AC input, the off-turning bridge transistors are subjected to bucked-down voltage V_2 (Fig. 5.9) of about 0.75 times the minimum rectified voltage as discussed in Sec. 5.6.3. For the minimum rectified DC of 302 V (Sec. 5.6.2.3), this is 0.75 × 302 or 227 V. This compares to 370 V DC at maximum AC input as calculated in Sec. 5.6.2.3.

The peak current from the bucked-down 227 V will not differ much from the calculated 10.3 A in Sec. 5.6.2.3. Thus assume a total efficiency of 80 percent as for the circuit of Fig. 5.8. Assume that half the losses are in the bridge and half in the buck regulator of Fig. 5.9.

Then for a bridge efficiency of 90 percent, its input power is 2000/0.9 or 2222 W. The bridge, with a preregulated input, can operate its transistors at a 90 percent duty cycle without concern about simultaneous conduction in two transistors vertically above one another. Input power is then $0.9 I_p V_{dc}$ = 2222. For V_{dc} of 227 V as above, this yields I_p of 10.8 A. Then, calculating bridge transistor dissipation as in Sec. 5.6.2.3 for a current fall time t_f of 0.3 μs out of a period T of 20 μs, dissipation per transistor is $(I_p/2)(V_{dc})(t_f/T)$ = (10.8/2)227 × 0.3/20 = 18.4 W. This is 74 W for the entire bridge as compared to 114 W for the circuit of Fig. 5.8 as calculated in Sec. 5.6.2.3.

5.6.4.4 Flux imbalance problem in bridge transformer. This problem is still the same as in the topology of Fig. 5.8. A volt-second unbalance can occur because of unequal storage times for bipolar bridge transistors or because of unequal on voltages for MOSFET transistors. The solution for both the Fig. 5.8 and Fig. 5.9 topologies is to insert a DC blocking capacitor in series with the transformer primary.

5.6.5 Drawbacks in buck-voltage-fed full-wave bridge[9,10]

Despite the advantages over the width-modulated full-wave inverter bridge, the buck-voltage-fed full-wave bridge has a number of significant drawbacks.

First, of course, there is the added cost, volume, and power dissipation of the buck transistor $Q5$ (Fig. 5.9) and the cost and volume of the buck LC filter ($L1,C1$). The added cost and volume of these elements is partly canceled by the saving of an inductor at each output voltage. The added dissipation of the buck regulator $Q5$ plus the free-wheeling diode $D5$ is most often a small percentage of the total losses for a ≥2000-W power supply.

Second, there are turnon and turnoff transient losses in the buck transistor which can be greater than its DC conduction losses. These can be reduced in the transistor by diverting them to passive elements in snubbers. But the losses, cost, and required space of the snubbers is still a drawback. Such turnon-turnoff snubbers will be discussed in the later section on the buck-current-fed full-wave bridge.

Turnoff transient losses in the bridge transistors, although less (as discussed in Sec. 5.6.4.3) than for the width-modulated bridge of Fig. 5.8, are still significant.

Finally, under fault conditions (unusually long storage time at high temperature and low load or low line conditions), at the turnon of one transistor pair, the opposite pair may still be on. With the low source impedance of the buck filter capacitor and the momentary short circuit across the supply bus, this will cause immediate failure of at least one and possibly all of the bridge transistors.

5.6.6 Buck-current-fed full-wave bridge topology—basic operation[9,10]

This topology is shown in Fig. 5.10.[6] It has no output inductors and is seen to be exactly like the buck-voltage-fed full-wave bridge of Fig. 5.9 with the exception that the buck filter capacitor $C1$ of Fig. 5.9 is not physically present. Instead, there is present at that point a virtual capacitor $C1V$ which is the sum of all the secondary filter capacitors reflected by the square of their respective turns ratios into the $T1$ primary. The filtering by this virtual capacitor $C1V$ is exactly the same as if a real capacitor of equal magnitude were present at the $L1$ output.

Thus, by replacing all the output inductors of the width-modulated full-wave bridge of Fig. 5.8, with a single primary side inductor as in Fig. 5.9, all the advantages described in Sec. 5.6.2.1 for the Fig. 5.9 circuit are also obtained for the circuit of Fig. 5.10.

Now bridge transistors $Q1$ to $Q4$ are not width-modulated as in Fig. 5.8. Diagonally opposite transistors are operated simultaneously on at alternate half cycles, but without the "off dead time" between the turnoff of one pair and the turnon of the next pair as was required for the voltage-fed circuit of Fig. 5.9. Each pair in Fig. 5.10 is kept deliberately on for slightly more than a half period by depending on the storage time of slow bipolar transistors or somehow delaying the turnoff time (by ~1 μs) of faster bipolars or MOSFETs. Output voltage regulation is achieved by width-modulating the on time of the buck transistor $Q5$ as was done for the buck-voltage-fed circuit of Fig. 5.9.

Significant advantages accrue from the physical removal of buck filter capacitor $C1$ of Fig. 5.9 and the deliberate overlapping on times of alternate transistor pairs. These advantages can be seen as follows.

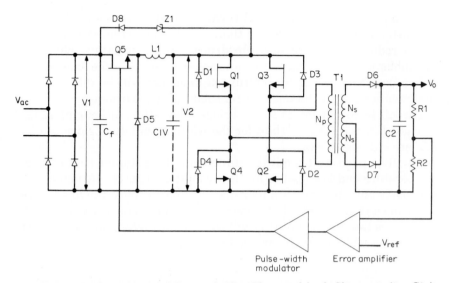

Figure 5.10 Buck-current-fed full-wave bridge. The usual buck filter capacitor $C1$ is omitted. There is a virtual capacitor $C1V$ there—it is all the output capacitors of the master and slaves, reflected back across to the primary. Diagonally opposite transistors are turned on simultaneously. By causing the off-turning and on-turning pair to overlap in the on state for a short time ($\sim 1\mu$ s), significant advantages are obtained. During the overlap of the off- and on-turning pairs, the high impedance looking into $L1$ (with $C1$ missing) forces all input and output nodes of the bridge to collapse to ground. It is this high impedance looking back into $L1$ which makes the source driving the bridge have the characteristic of a constant current generator. $Z1$, $D8$ constitute an upper clamp to limit $V2$ when the previously on transistors turn off.

5.6.6.1 Alleviation of turnon-turnoff transient problems in buck-current-fed bridge.[9,10]   For the width-modulated full-wave bridge of Fig. 5.8, Sec. 5.6.2.2 described excessive current, power dissipation stresses in the bridge transistors, and voltage stresses in output rectifier diodes at the instant of turnon. Such stresses do not occur in the current-fed circuit of Fig. 5.10 because of the overlapping on time of alternate transistor pairs and the high impedance seen looking back into $L1$ with no filter capacitor physically present at that node.

This can be seen from Figs. 5.11 and 5.12. Consider in those figures that $Q3$, $Q4$ had been on and $Q1$, $Q2$ commence turning on at T_1. Transistors $Q3$, $Q4$ remain on until T_2 (Fig. 5.12), resulting in an overlap time of $T_2 - T_1$. At T_1, as $Q1$, $Q2$ come on, a dead short circuit appears across the output of $L1$; and since the impedance looking into $L1$ is high, the voltage V_2 collapses to zero (Fig. 5.12c). But $L1$ is a large inductor and current in it must remain constant at its initial value I_L. Thus as current in $Q1$, $Q2$ rises from zero toward I_L (Fig. 5.12f and 5.12g), current in $Q3$, $Q4$ falls from I_L toward zero (Fig. 5.12d and 5.12e).

But the rising current in $Q1$, $Q2$ occurs at zero voltage at V_2 and

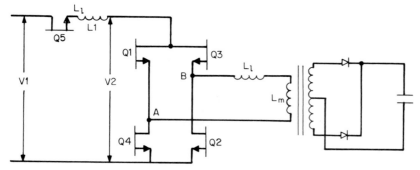

Figure 5.11 During the overlap instant, when all four transistors are on, the voltage V2 and that across nodes A, B collapse to zero. Energy stored in leakage inductance L_l is fed to the load via the transformer instead of being dissipated in a snubber resistor or being returned to the input bus as in conventional circuits. Hence, there is no turnon transient dissipation in the bridge transistors or overvoltage stress in output rectifiers.

hence also zero voltage between nodes A and B in Fig. 5.11. There is thus no voltage across $Q1$, $Q2$ as their current rises and there is no dissipation in them. At some time T_3, currents in $Q1$, $Q2$ have risen to $I_L/2$ and currents in $Q3$, $Q4$ have fallen from I_L to $I_L/2$, thus summing to the constant current I_L from inductor $L1$.

Now at T_2, $Q3$ and $Q4$ are commanded off. Assume, as a worst-case scenario, that $Q3$ is slower and $Q4$ turns off first. Since voltage V_2 is zero, $Q4$ turns off with zero voltage across it and hence no turnoff dissipation in it. As I_{Q4} falls from $I_L/2$ toward zero (T_2 to T_4), I_{Q2} rises from $I_L/2$ toward I_L to maintain the constant I_L demanded by $L1$. As I_{Q2} rises from $I_L/2$ toward I_L, I_{Q3} rises from $I_l/2$ to I_L to supply I_{Q2}. Again, since $L1$ demands a constant current I_L, as I_{Q3} rises toward I_L, I_{Q1} falls from $I_L/2$ to zero at T_4.

During the time T_1 to T_4, V_2 has collapsed to zero volts and so has the voltage across the transformer primary (A to B in Fig. 5.11). But current had been stored in the transformer leakage inductance L_L while $Q3$, $Q4$ were on. As voltage A to B collapses, voltage across the primary leakage inductance reverses in an attempt to keep the current constant. Thus the leakage inductance acts like a generator and delivers this stored current or energy through the transformer to the secondary load instead of returning it to the input supply bus or to dissipative snubbers as in conventional circuits.

Now at a later time T_5, the slower transistor $Q3$ starts turning off. As current in it falls from I_L to zero (Fig. 5.12d), current I_{Q1} tries to rise from zero to I_L to maintain the constant current I_L demanded by $L1$. But I_{Q1} rise time is limited by the transformer leakage inductance (Fig. 5.12f). Since I_{Q3} fall time is generally greater than I_{Q1} rise time,

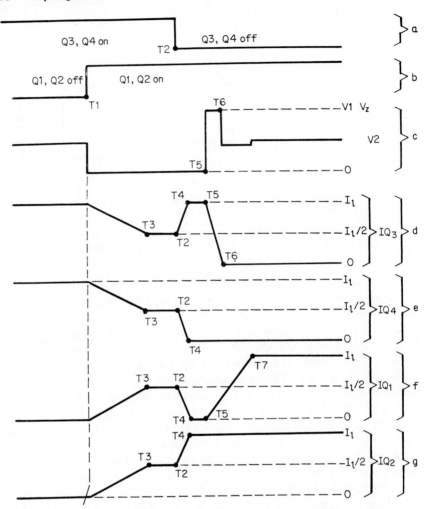

Figure 5.12   Currents in bridge transistors and voltage at bridge input. During overlapping on time of all four bridge transistors in buck-current-fed topology.

voltage V_2 will overshoot its quiescent value and must be clamped to avoid overstressing $Q3$ as its emitter is now clamped to ground by the conducting $Q2$. The clamping is done by a zener diode $Z1$ as shown in Figs. 5.10 and 5.13.

Overshooting of V_2 during the slower transistor ($Q3$) turnoff time results in somewhat more dissipation in it than in the circuit of the conventional width-modulated bridge (Fig. 5.8). This dissipation is $(V_1 + V_z)(I_L/2)(T_6 - T_5)/T$ for Fig. 5.10 but only $V_1(I_L/2)(T_6 - T_5)/T$ for Fig. 5.8. But in Fig. 5.8, there are four transistors which have relatively high turnoff dissipation. In Figs. 5.10 and 5.13, only the two

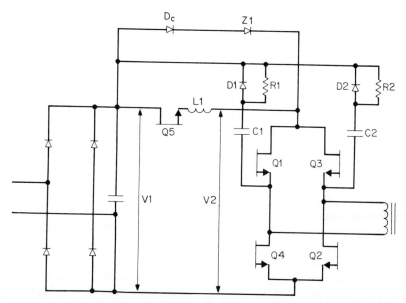

Figure 5.13 In the buck-current-fed bridge, only two turnoff snubbers ($R1$, $C1$, $D1$ and $R2$, $C2$, $D2$) are required. An upper voltage clamp ($Z1$, D_c) is required to limit $V2$ when the last of the off-turning transistors turns off.

transistors with slow turnoff time have high dissipation. As discussed above, the faster transistor suffers no dissipation at turnoff as it turns off at zero voltage; and at turnon, all transistors have negligible dissipation as they have the transformer leakage inductance in series and hence turn on at zero voltage.

The increased dissipation of the two transistors at turnoff can be diverted from the transistors to resistors by adding the snubbing networks $R1$, $C1$, $D1$ and $R2$, $C2$, $D2$ of Fig. 5.13. Design of such turnoff snubbing circuits will be discussed in the later chapter on snubbers.

5.6.6.2 Absence of simultaneous conduction problem in buck-current-fed bridge.

In the buck-voltage-fed bridge of Fig. 5.9, care must be taken to avoid simultaneous conduction in transistors positioned vertically above one another ($Q1$, $Q4$ or $Q3$, $Q2$). Such simultaneous conduction provides a low impedance across $C1$. But $C1$ has a low impedance and can supply large currents without its output (V_2) dropping in voltage. Thus the bridge transistors could be subjected to simultaneous high voltage and high current and one or more would immediately fail.

Even if a dead time between the turnoff of one transistor pair and the turnon of the other is designed in to avoid simultaneous conduction, it still may occur under various odd circumstances, such as high temperature and/or high load conditions when transistor storage time may be much lower than data sheets indicate, or low input voltage (in the absence of maximum on time clamp or undervoltage lockout) as the feedback loop increases on time to maintain constant output voltage.

But in the buck-current-fed bridge, simultaneous conduction is actually essential to its operation and provides the advantages discussed above. Further, in the buck-current-fed bridge, since the on time is slightly more than a half period for each transistor pair, the peak current is less than in the buck-voltage-fed bridge, whose maximum on time is usually set at 90 percent of a half period to avoid simultaneous conduction.

5.6.6.3 Turnon problems in buck transistor of buck-current- or buck-voltage-fed bridge.[10] The buck transistor in either the voltage- or current-fed bridge suffers from a large spike of power dissipation at the instant either of turnon and turnoff, as can be seen in Fig. 5.14.

Consider first the instantaneous voltage and current of $Q5$ during the turnon interval. The locus of rising current and falling voltage during that interval is shown in Fig. 5.14b. Just prior to $Q5$ turning on, free-wheeling diode $D5$ is conducting and supplying inductor current I_L. As $Q5$ commences turning on, its collector is at V_1, its emitter is at one diode ($D5$) drop below ground. The emitter does not move up from ground until the current in $Q5$ has risen from zero to I_L and canceled the $D5$ forward current.

Thus during the current rise time of t_r, the I_c-V_{ce} locus is along points A to B. During t_r, the average current supplied by $Q5$ is $I_L/2$ and the voltage across it is V_1. Once current in $Q5$ has risen to I_L, assuming negligible capacitance at the $Q5$ emitter node and fast recovery time in $D5$, the voltage across $Q5$ rapidly drops to zero along the path B to C. If there is one turnon of duration t_r in a period T, the dissipation in $Q5$, averaged over T, is

$$PD_{\text{turnon}} = V_1 \frac{I_L t_r}{2T} \tag{5.10}$$

It is of interest to calculate this dissipation for a 2000-W buck-current-fed bridge operating from the rectified 220-V-AC line. Nominal rectified DC voltage (V_1) is about 300 V, minimum is 270 V, and maximum is 330 V. Assume that the bucked-down DC voltage V_2 is 25 percent below the minimum V_1 or 200 V.

Further, assume the bridge inverter operates at 80 percent efficiency, giving an input power of 2500 W. This power comes from a V_2 of 200 V, and hence the average current in $L1$ is 12.5 A. Assume that $L1$ is large enough so that the ripple current in I_L can be neglected.

Then, for an assumed current rise time of 0.3-μs rise time (easily

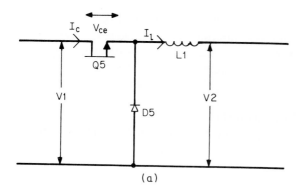

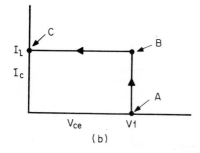

Figure 5.14 (*a*) The buck transistor in the buck-current-or voltage-fed topology has a very unfavorable voltage-current locus at the instant of turnon. It operates throughout its current rise time, at the full input voltage *V*1 until the forward current in free-wheeling diode *D*5 has been canceled. This generates a large spike of dissipation at turnon. (*b*) $I_{ce} = V_{ce}$ locus during turnon of buck transistor *Q*5. Voltage V_{ce} remains constant at *V*1 until the current in *Q*5 has risen to I_l (*A* to *B*) and canceled the forward current I_l in free-wheeling diode *D*5. Then, if capacitance at the *Q*5 emitter is low and *D*5 has a fast recovery time, it moves very rapidly to its on voltage of about 1 V (*B* to *C*).

achieved with modern bipolar transistors) and a *Q*5 switching frequency of 50 kHz, turnon dissipation at maximum AC input voltage is (from Eq. 5.10)

$$PD = 330\left(\frac{12.5}{2}\right)\left(\frac{0.3}{20}\right) = 31 \text{ W}$$

Note in this calculation that the effect of poor recovery time in *D*5 has been neglected. This has been discussed in Sec. 5.6.2.2 in connection with the poor recovery time of output rectifiers of the bridge inverter. This problem can be far more serious for the free-wheeling diode of the buck regulator, for $D5$ must have a much higher voltage rating—at least 400 V for the maximum V_1 of 330 V—and high-voltage diodes have poorer recovery time than do lower-voltage ones. Thus the $Q5$ current can considerably overshoot the peak of 12.5 A that $D5$ had been carrying. Further, the oscillatory ring after the recovery time, discussed in Sec. 5.6.2.2, can cause a serious voltage overstress in free-wheeling diode $D5$.

This turnon dissipation in $Q5$ and voltage overstress of $D5$ can be eliminated with the turnon snubber of Fig. 5.15.

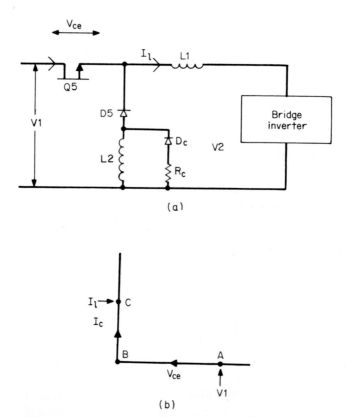

(a)

(b)

Figure 5.15 (a) Turn on snubber—$L2$, D_c, R_c—eliminates turnon dissipation in $Q5$, but at the price of an equal amount of dissipation in R_c. When $Q5$ commences turning on, the presence of $L2$ drives the $Q5$ emitter up to within 1 V of its collector. As $Q5$ current rises toward I_l, the current in $L2$ which has been stored in it by $L1$ during the $Q5$ off time decreases to zero. Thus the voltage across $Q5$ during its turnon time is about 1 V rather $V1$ V. During the next $Q5$ off time, $L2$ must be charged to a current I_l without permitting too large a drop across it. Resistor R_c limits the voltage across $L2$ during its charging time. (b) $Q5$'s locus of falling voltage (A to B) and rising current (B to C) during turnon with the snubber of Figure 5.15a.

5.6.6.4 Buck transistor turnon snubber—basic operation. The turnon snubber of Fig 5.15a does not reduce total circuit dissipation. It only diverts it from the vulnerable semiconductor $Q5$ where it is a potential failure hazard to the passive resistor R_s, which can far more easily survive the heat. It works as follows. An inductor $L2$ is added in series with the free-wheeling diode $D5$. While $Q5$ is off, the inductor load current I_L flows out of the bottom of the bridge transistors, up through the bottom end of $L2$, through free-wheeling diode $D5$, and back into the front end of $L1$. This causes the top end of $L2$ to be very slightly more negative than its bottom end.

Now as $Q5$ commences turning on, it starts delivering current into the cathode of $D5$ in an attempt to cancel its forward current. But this current flows down into $L2$, opposing the load current it is carrying. Since the current in an inductor ($L2$) cannot change instantaneously, the voltage polarity across it reverses instantaneously in an attempt to maintain constant current.

The voltage at the top end of $L2$ rises, pushing the free-wheeling diode up with it until its cathode meets the on-turning $Q5$ emitter. The $Q5$ emitter is forced up to within $V_{ce(sat)}$ of its collector and now $Q5$ continues increasing its current, but at a V_{ce} voltage of about 1 V rather than the V_1 voltage of 370 V it had to sustain in the absence of $L2$.

When the $Q5$ current has risen to I_L (in a time t_r), the forward current in $D5$ has been canceled and $Q5$ continues to supply the load current I_L demanded by $L1$. Since voltage across $Q5$ during the rise time t_r is only 1 V, its dissipation is negligible. Further, because of the high impedance of $L2$ in series with the $D5$ anode, there is negligible recovery time current in $D5$. The current-voltage locus of $Q5$ during the turnon time is shown in Fig. 5.15b.

5.6.6.5 Selection of buck turnon snubber components. For the preceding sequence of events to proceed as described, the current in $L2$ must be equal to the load current I_L at the start of $Q5$ turnon and must have decayed back down to zero in the time t_r that current from $Q5$ has risen to I_L. Since the voltage across $L2$ during t_r is clamped to V_1, the magnitude of $L2$ is calculated from

$$L2 = \frac{V_1 t_r}{I_L} \tag{5.11}$$

For the above example, V_1 was a maximum of 370 V, t_r was 0.3 μs, and I_L was 12.5 A. From Eq. 5.11, this yields $L2 = 370 \times 0.3/12.5 = 8.9$ μH.

Now the purpose of R_c, D_c in Fig. 5.15a is to ensure that at the start of $Q5$ turnon, current in $L2$ truly is equal to I_L and that it had reached that value without overstressing $Q5$.

Consider for the moment that R_c, D_c were not present. As $Q5$ turned off, since current in $L1$ cannot change instantaneously, the input end of $L1$ goes immediately negative in an attempt to keep current constant. If $L2$ were not present, $D5$ would catch the front end of $L1$ (and hence the $Q5$ emitter) at ground and permit across $Q5$ a voltage of only V_1. But with $L2$ present, the impedance looking out of the $D5$ anode is the high instantaneous impedance of $L2$. Then as $Q5$ turned off, I_L would be drawn through $L2$, pulling its top end very far negative. This would put a very large negative voltage at the $Q5$ emitter, and with its collector at V_1 (370 V in this case), it would immediately fail.

Thus R_c and D_c are shunted around $L2$ to provide a path for I_L at the instant $Q5$ turns off; and R_c is selected low enough so that the voltage drop across it at a current I_L plus V_1 is a voltage stress that $Q5$ can safely take. Thus

$$V_{Q5(max)} = V_1 + R_c I_L \qquad (5.12)$$

In the preceding example, $V_{1(max)}$ was 370 V. Assume that $Q5$ had a V_{ceo} rating of 450 V. With a -1- to -5-V reverse bias at its base at the instant of turnoff, it could safely sustain the V_{cev} rating of 650 V. Then to provide a margin of safety, select R_c so that $V_{Q5(max)}$ is only 450 V. Then from Eq. 5.12, $450 = 370 + R_c \times 12.5$ or $R_c = 6.4\ \Omega$.

5.6.6.6 Dissipation in buck transistor snubber resistor.

Examination of Fig. 5.15a shows that essentially the constant current I_L is charging the parallel combination of R_c and $L2$. The Thevinin equivalent of this is a voltage source of magnitude $I_L R_c$ charging a series combination of R_c and $L2$. It is well known that in charging a series inductor L to a current I_p or energy $\frac{1}{2}L(I_p)^2$, an equal amount of energy is delivered to the charging resistor. Then if L is charged to I_p once per period T, the dissipation in the resistor is $\frac{1}{2}L(I_p)^2/T$.

In the preceding example where $T = 20\ \mu s$, $L = 8.9\ \mu H$, $I_p = 12.5$ A

$$PD_{\text{snubber resistor}} = \frac{(1/2)(8.9)(12.5)^2}{20}$$

$$= 35\ W$$

Thus, as mentioned above, this snubber has not reduced circuit dissipation; it has only diverted it from the transistor $Q5$ to the snubbing resistor.

5.6.6.7 Snubbing inductor charging time.

The snubbing inductor must be fully charged to I_L during the off time of the buck transistor. The charging time constant is L/R, which in the above example is 8.9/

6.4 = 1.39 μs. The inductor is 95 percent fully charged in three time constants or 4.17 μs.

In the preceding example, switching period T was 20 μs. To buck down the input of 370 V to the preregulated 200 V, on time is T_{on} = 20(200/370) = 10.8 μs. This leaves a $Q5$ off time of 9.2 μs, which is sufficient, as the snubbing inductor is 95 percent fully charged in 4.17 μs.

5.6.6.8 Lossless turnon snubber for buck transistor.[10,21,22] Losses in the

snubbing resistor of Fig. 5.15a can be avoided with the circuit of Fig. 5.16. Here, a small transformer $T2$ is added. Its primary turns N_p and gap are selected so that at a current I_L, its inductance is the same $L2$ of Fig. 5.15a. The polarities at the primary and secondary are as shown by the dots.

When $Q5$ turns off, the front end of $L1$ goes negative in an attempt to keep I_L constant. Then I_L is pulled through $D5$ and N_p, producing a negative voltage V_n at the dot end of N_p and producing a voltage stress across $Q5$ of $V_1 + V_n$. Voltage V_n is chosen so that $V_1 + V_n$ is a voltage that $Q5$ can safely sustain. To maintain the voltage across N_p at V_n when $Q5$ has turned off, the turns ratio N_s/N_p is selected equal to V_1/V_n. Now when $Q5$ turns off, as the dot end of N_p goes down to V_n, the no-dot end of N_s goes positive and is clamped to V_1, holding the voltage across N_p to V_n.

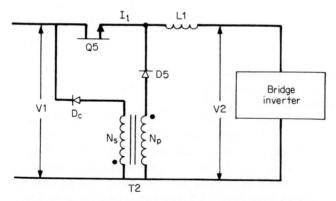

Figure 5.16 Dissipationless turnon snubber. When $Q5$ turns off, $L1$ stores a current I_l in N_p of $T1$. But the negative voltage at the dot end of N_p during this charging time is fixed by the turns ratio N_s/N_p. If the top end of N_p is to be permitted to go only V_n negative when $Q5$ turns off, the voltage stress on $Q5$ is $V1 + V_n$. When the dot end of N_p has gone negative by V_n, the no-dot end of N_s has been driven up to $V1$, D_c latches in and clamps to $V1$, clamping the voltage across N_p to the preselected V_n. Thus N_s/N_p is chosen as $V1/V_n$. The charging of N_p is thus not limited by a resistor as in Fig. 5.14 and hence there is no snubber dissipation.

Prior to Q5 turn on, L1 current flows through N_p, D5. As Q5 commences turning on, its emitter looks into the high impedance of N_p and immediately rises to within one volt of its collector. Thus, current in Q5 rises with only one volt across it, and its dissipation is negligible. All the energy stored in N_p when Q5 was off, is returned via L1 to the load with no dissipation. Q5 turn off dissipation can be minimized with a turn off snubber (Chap. 11).

5.6.6.9 Design decisions in buck-current-fed bridge. The first decision to be made on the buck-current-fed bridge is when to use it. It is primarily a high-output-power high-output-voltage topology.

In terms of cost, efficiency, and required space, it is a good choice for output powers in the range of 1 to 10 or possibly 20 kW. For high output voltages—above about 200 V—and above about 5 A output current—the absence of output inductors makes it a good choice. For output powers above 1 kW, the added dissipation, volume, and cost of the buck transistor is not a significant increase above what is required in a competing topology such as a width-modulated full-wave bridge.

It is an especially good choice for a multioutput supply consisting of one or more high output voltages (5000 to 30,000 V). In such applications, the absence of output inductors permits the use of capacitor-diode voltage multiplier chains.[8,13] Also, the absence of output inductors in the associated lower output voltages partly compensates for the cost and volume of the buck transistor and its output inductor.

The next design decision is the selection of the bucked-down voltage (V_2 of Fig. 5.10). This is chosen at about 25 percent below the lowest ripple trough at V_1 (Fig. 5.10) at the lowest specified AC input. Inductor $L1$ is chosen so as not to go discontinuous at the calculated minimum inductor current I_L corresponding to the minimum total output power at the preselected value of V_2. It is chosen exactly as in Sec. 1.3.6 for a conventional buck regulator.

The output capacitors are chosen, not to provide storage or reduce ripple directly at the output nodes because the overlapping conduction of bridge transistors minimizes this requirement. Rather they are chosen so that when reflected into the primary, the equivalent series resistance R_{esr} of all reflected capacitors is sufficiently low as to minimize ripple at V_2. Recall from Sec. 1.3.7, in calculating the magnitude of the output capacitor, it was pointed out that output ripple in a buck regulator V_{br} is given by

$$V_{br} = \Delta I\, R_{esr}$$

where ΔI is the peak-to-peak ripple current in the buck inductor and is usually set at twice the minimum DC current in it so that the inductor just about goes discontinuous at its minimum DC current. Minimum DC current in this case is the current at minimum specified output power at the preselected value of V_2. Thus with R_{esr} selected so as to yield the desired ripple at V_2, ripple at each secondary is

$$V_{sr} = V_{br} \frac{N_s}{N_p}$$

There is an interesting contrast in comparing a current to a voltage-fed bridge at the same bucked-down voltage (V_2 of Figs. 5.9, 5.10).

For the voltage-fed bridge, a maximum on time of 80 percent of a half period must be established to ensure that there is no simultaneous conduction in the two transistors positioned vertically above one another. With the low impedance looking back into the buck regulator of the voltage-fed circuit, such simultaneous conduction would subject the bridge transistors to high voltage and high current and destroy one or more of them.

In the current-fed circuit, such slightly overlapping simultaneous conduction is essential to its operation and on time of alternate transistor pairs is slightly more than a full half period at any DC input voltage. In addition, since the on time of a voltage fed bridge (Fig. 5.9) is only 80 percent of a half period, its peak current must be 20 percent greater than that of the current-fed bridge at the same output power.

It should also be noted that the number of primary turns as calculated from Faraday's law (Eq. 2.7) must be 20 percent greater in the current-fed bridge as the on time is 20 percent greater for a flux change equal to that in a voltage-fed bridge at the same V_2.

5.6.6.10 Operating frequencies—buck and bridge transistors.
The buck transistor is synchronized to and operates at twice the square-wave switching frequency of the bridge transistors. It will be recalled that it alone is width-modulated, and that the bridge devices are operated at a 50 percent duty cycle with a slightly overlapping on time.

Frequently, however, the scheme of Fig. 5.17a is used to reduce dissipation in the buck transistor. It is seen there that two buck transistors (Q5A and Q5B) are used. They are synchronized to the bridge transistor frequency and are turned on (and width-modulated) at alternate half cycles of the bridge square-wave frequency. Thus the DC and whatever AC switching losses there may be are shared between two transistors with a resulting increase in reliability.

5.6.6.11 Buck-current-fed push-pull topology.
The buck-current-fed circuit can also be used to drive a push-pull circuit as in Fig. 5.18 with the consequent saving of two transistors over the buck-current-fed

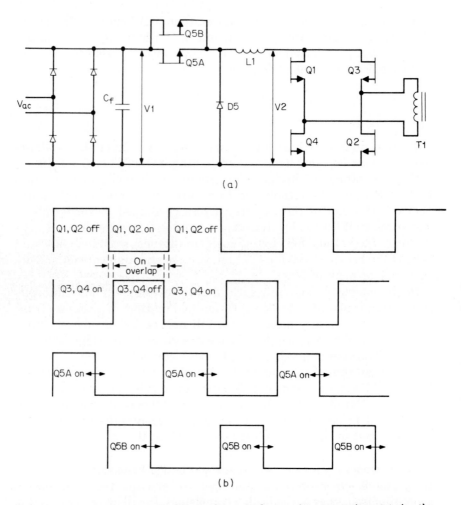

(a)

(b)

Figure 5.17 (a) Buck transistor $Q5$ may be a single transistor operating at twice the frequency of the bridge transistors and synchronized to them or, more usually, two synchronized transistors, which are width-modulated and are each on at alternate half periods of the bridge transistors. (b) To reduce dissipation in the buck transistor, it is usually implemented as two transistors, each synchronized to the bridge transistors and operated at the same square-wave frequency as the bridge devices. Transistors $Q5A$, $Q5B$ are width-modulated. Bridge transistors are not and are operated with a small "on" overlap time.

bridge. Most of the advantages of the buck-current-fed bridge are realized and the only disadvantage is that the push-pull circuit puts greater voltage stress on its power transistors. This voltage stress is now twice V_2 rather than V_2 as in the bridge circuit. But V_2 is the preregulated and bucked-down input voltage—usually only 75 percent of the minimum V_1 input. This is usually about the same as the max-

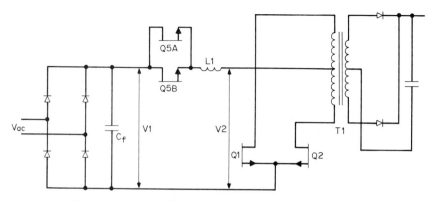

Figure 5.18 The current-fed topology can also be implemented as a buck–push-pull circuit. As in the buck-current-fed bridge, the capacitor after the buck inductor $L1$ is omitted and $Q1$, $Q2$ are operated with a deliberately overlapping on time. Only buck transistors $Q5A$, $Q5B$ are width-modulated. Output inductors are not used. All the advantages of the buck-current-fed bridge are retained. Although off-voltage stress is twice $V2$ (plus a leakage spike) instead of $V2$ as in the bridge, that is still significantly less than twice $V1$ as $V2$ is bucked down to about 75 percent of the minimum value of $V1$. This circuit is used at lower power levels than the buck-current-fed bridge and offers the saving of two transistors.

imum DC input of a competing topology—the width-modulated full-wave bridge (Fig. 5.8).

However, the major advantages of the current-fed technique—no output inductors and no possibility of flux—imbalance still exist.

The topology can be used to greatest advantage in supplies of 2 to 5 kW and especially if there are multiple outputs or at least one high voltage output.

5.6.7 Flyback-current fed push-pull topology, Weinberg Circuit[23]

This topology[23] is shown in Fig. 5.19. It is seen to have a flyback transformer in series with a push-pull inverter. It has many of the valuable attributes of the buck-current-fed push-pull (Fig. 5.18) topology, and since it requires no width-modulated input transistor ($Q5$), it has lesser dissipation, cost, volume, and greater reliability.

It might be puzzling at first glance to see how the output voltage is regulated against line and load changes since there is no LC voltage-averaging filter at the output. The diode-capacitor at the output is a peak, rather than an averaging, circuit. The answer, of course, is that the averaging or regulating is done at the $T1$ center tap to keep V_{ct} relatively constant. The output voltage (or voltages) is (are) kept constant by width modulating the $Q1$, $Q2$ on time. Output voltage is simply $(N_s/N_p)V_{ct}$ and a feedback loop sensing V_o controls the $Q1$, $Q2$ on times to keep V_{ct} at the correct value to maintain V_o constant. The

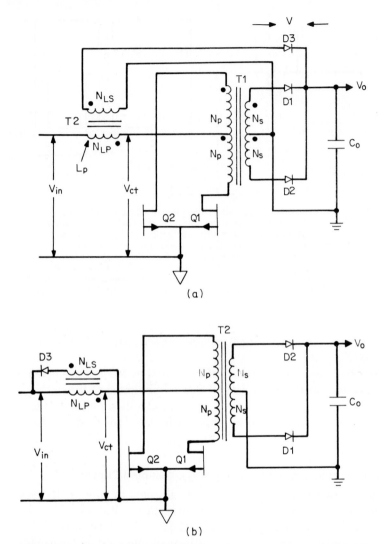

Figure 5.19 (*a*) Flyback-current-fed push-pull topology (Weinberg Circuit). This is essentially a flyback transformer in series with a width-modulated push-pull inverter. Its usage is primarily as a multioutput supply with one or more high-voltage outputs as it requires no output inductors and only the one input flyback transformer $T1$. The high impedance seen looking back into the primary of $T2$ makes it a "current fed" with all the advantages shown in Fig. 5.18. Here the $T2$ secondary is shown clamped to V_o. Transistors $Q1, Q2$ may be operated either with a "dead time" between their on times or with overlapping on times. Its advantage over Fig. 5.18 is that it requires no input switching transistors. Usual output power level is 1 to 2 kW. (*b*) Same circuit as Fig. 5.19*a* but with $D3$ clamped to V_{in}. This results in lesser input current ripple but more output voltage ripple. Courtesy Ref. 23

relation between the $Q1$, $Q2$ on times and output voltage will be shown below.

The circuit retains the major advantage of the current-fed technique—a single-input inductor but no output inductors, which makes it a good choice for a multioutput supply with one or more high-voltage outputs. Further, because of the high source impedance of the flyback transformer primary $L1$, the usual flux-imbalance problem of voltage-fed push-pulls does not result in transformer saturation and consequent transistor failure. Its major usage is at the 1- to 2-kW power level.

Two circuit configurations of the flyback-current-fed push-pull topology are shown in Fig. 5.19a and 5.19b. Figure 5.19a shows the $T2$ secondary returned to the output voltage through diode $D3$; in Fig. 5.19b the diode is returned to the input voltage. When the diode is returned to V_o, output ripple voltage is minimized; when it is returned to V_{in}, input ripple current is minimized. Consider first the configuration of Fig. 5.19a, where the diode is returned to the output.

The configuration of Fig. 5.19a can operate in two significantly different modes. In the first mode, $Q1$ and $Q2$ are never permitted to have overlapping on times at any DC input voltage. In the second mode, $Q1$ and $Q2$ may have overlapping on times throughout the entire range of specified DC input voltage or may have overlapping on times through some lower range of input voltage and automatically move (under control of the feedback loop) into the nonoverlapping mode at higher DC input voltage.

It will be shown below that in the nonoverlapping mode, power is delivered to the secondaries at a center tap voltage V_{ct} lower than the DC input voltage (bucklike operation) and in the overlapping mode, power is delivered to the secondaries at a center tap voltage V_{ct} higher than the DC input voltage (boostlike operation). Thus in the nonoverlapping mode, since V_{ct} is relatively low, $Q1$, $Q2$ currents are relatively high for a given output power. But with the lower V_{ct} voltage, off-voltage stress in $Q1$, $Q2$ is relatively low. In the overlapping mode, since V_{ct} is higher than V_{in}, $Q1$, $Q2$ currents are lower for a given output power but off-voltage stress in $Q1$, $Q2$ is higher than that for the nonoverlapping mode.

The circuit is usually designed not to remain in one mode throughout the full range of input voltages. Rather, it is designed to move from the overlapping mode with an on duty cycle T_{on}/T greater than 0.5 through to the nonoverlapping mode T_{on}/T less than 0.5 as the DC input voltage shifts from its minimum to its maximum specified values. This permits proper operation throughout a larger range of DC input voltages than if operation remained within one mode throughout the entire range of DC input voltage.

5.6.7.1 Absence of flux-imbalance problem in flyback-current-fed push-pull topology. Flux imbalance is not a serious problem in this topology because of the high-impedance current-fed source feeding the push-pull transformer center tap.

The current-fed nature of the circuit arises from the flyback transformer $T2$, which is in series with the $T2$ center tap. The impedance looking back from the $T1$ center tap is the high impedance of the magnetizing inductance of the $T2$ primary.

Now in a conventional voltage-fed push-pull inverter, unequal volt-second product across each half primary causes the flux-imbalance problem (Sec. 2.2.5). The transformer core moves off center of its hysteresis loop and moves toward saturation. Because of the low impedance of a voltage source, current to the $T2$ center tap is unlimited and the voltage at that point (V_{ct}) remains high. The core then moves further into saturation, where its impedance eventually vanishes and transistor currents increase drastically. With high currents and high voltage across the transistor, it very soon fails.

However, as shown in Fig. 5.19, with the high impedance looking back into the dot end of N_{LP}, as the $T1$ core tries to move far into saturation drawing larger currents than the load itself demands, the high currents cause a voltage drop at V_{ct}. This reduces the volt-second product on the primary half which is moving toward saturation and prevents complete core saturation.

Thus the high source impedance of N_{LP} does not fully prevent core saturation. In the worst case, it keeps the core close to the knee of the BH loop, which is sufficient to keep transistor currents from rising to disastrous levels. The major drawback of push-pull circuit flux imbalance is thus not a problem with this inverter.

5.6.7.2 Decreased push-pull transistor currents in flyback-current-fed topology. In conventional width modulated push-pulls driven at their center tap from a low-impedance voltage source, it is essential to avoid simultaneous conduction in the transistors by providing a dead time of about 20 percent of a half period between turnoff of one transistor and turnon of the other. Thus if maximum on time per transistor must be cut back from 100 percent to 80 percent of a half period, it results in a higher peak transistor current for the same output power as the output power is proportional to the average transistor current.

This dead time is essential in the voltage-fed push-pull, for if $Q1$, $Q2$ were simultaneously on, the half primaries could not sustain voltage. Then the transistor collectors would rise to the supply voltage, which would remain high, and with high voltage and high current, the transistors would fail.

But with the high impedance looking back into the dot end of N_{LP}, if both transistors were simultaneously on (under fault conditions when the DC input voltage is momentarily lower than specified and with storage times greater than specified), there is no problem. For with both transistors simultaneously on for a brief instant, V_{ct} simply drops to zero and current drawn from the input source is limited by the impedance of the $T2$ primary.

Thus even in the "nonoverlap" mode, no dead time need be provided between the turnoff of one transistor and the turnon of the other. If there is a momentary overlap because of storage time, V_{ct} simply collapses to zero and no harm results. Hence by eliminating the 20 percent dead time, the peak current required for a given output power is decreased by 20 percent at the same value of V_{ct}. Further, as discussed above, in the overlap mode, overlapping on time need not be the small amount arising from transistor storage time but can be a deliberately large fraction of a half period.

5.6.7.3 Nonoverlapping mode in flyback-current-fed push-pull topology—basic operation.
The circuit operation can be understood from examination of the significant voltage and current waveforms shown in Fig. 5.20.

Operation will be explained on the assumption that the "on" potentials of transistors $Q1$, $Q2$ are negligibly small and can be neglected. For considering their actual on drop of about 1 V would only complicate the design equations and hamper understanding of really important circuit behavior. Also, the forward drop V_d of diodes $D1$, $D2$, $D3$ are assumed equal.

Now in Fig. 5.19a, when either $Q1$ or $Q2$ is on, the voltage across the corresponding half secondary is clamped to $V_o + V_d$. Then (assuming that transistor on drop is zero) the voltage at the $T1$ center tap V_{ct} is clamped to $(N_p/N_s)(V_o + V_d)$ as can be seen in Fig. 5.20d. Now N_p/N_s is chosen so that V_{ct} is 25 percent lower than the bottom of the input ripple trough at the lowest specified value of V_{in}.

Thus when either transistor is on, the dot end of N_{LP} is negative with respect to its no-dot end and current flows through to the $T1$ center tap which is clamped to the voltage V_{ct}. The waveshapes of the currents which flow are shown in Fig. 5.20g and 5.20h. These currents have the ramp-on-a-step waveshape characteristic of any buck regulator operating in the continuous conduction mode as discussed in Sec. 1.3.2.

Now when the on transistor turns off, the dot end of N_{LP} goes positive in an attempt to maintain the L_p current constant. The dot end of N_{LS} also goes positive until $D3$ gets forward-biased and clamps to V_o. The ratio N_{LP}/N_{LS} is set equal to N_p/N_s of $T1$ (hereafter those ratios will be designated as N). The reflected voltage on the $T2$ primary is

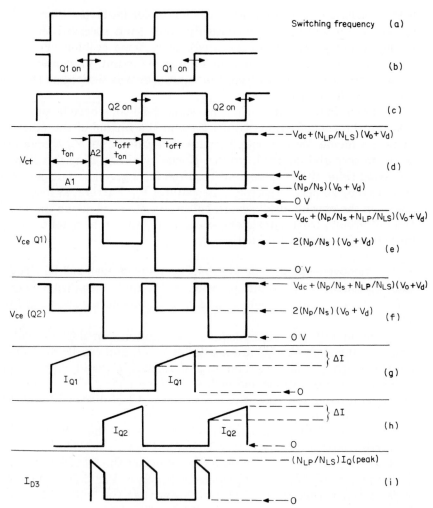

Figure 5.20 Significant voltage-current waveforms in flyback-current-fed topology when operating in nonoverlapping conduction mode. Power is delivered to the load only when either $Q1$ or $Q2$ is on. Power is delivered at a supply voltage of $(N_p/N_s)(V_o + V_d)$, which is less than V_{dc}.

then $N(V_o + V_d)$. Thus when either transistor turns off, V_{ct} rises to $V_{dc} + N(V_o + V_d)$ and stays there until the opposite transistor turns on as shown in Fig. 5.20d. The waveshape of Fig. 5.20d permits calculation of the relation between output voltage and on time as follows.

5.6.7.4 Output voltage–on-time relation in nonoverlapping mode of flyback-current-fed push-pull topology. Refer to Fig. 5.20d. It is seen that during t_{on}, V_{ct} is at a voltage level $N(V_o + V_d)$ and during t_{off}, it is at a level of $V_{dc} + N(V_o + V_d)$. But the average voltage at this point

must be equal to the V_{dc}, the DC voltage at the front end of L_p. This is because L_p is assumed to have negligible DC resistance, and hence the voltage across it, averaged over a full or half period must equal to zero. Or another way of expressing this is that in Fig. 5.20d, the volt-second area $A1$ must equal to the volt-second area $A2$.

But area $A1 = [V_{dc} - N(V_o + V_d)]t_{on}$; and

$$V_{dc}t_{on} - NV_o t_{on} - NV_d t_{on} = NV_o t_{off} + NV_d t_{off}$$

or $NV_o(t_{on} + t_{off}) = V_{dc}t_{on} - NV_d(t_{on} + t_{off})$ but $t_{on} + t_{off} = \dfrac{T}{2}$

Then
$$V_o = \left(\frac{2V_{dc}t_{on}}{NT}\right) - V_d$$

or
$$V_o = \left(2V_{dc}\frac{N_s}{N_p}\right)\frac{t_{on}}{T} - V_d \tag{5.13}$$

Thus the feedback loop regulates V_o by width-modulating t_{on}, just as in all previous circuits—to keep the product $V_{dc}t_{on}$ constant.

5.6.7.5 Output voltage and input current ripple in nonoverlapping mode.

Choosing N_{LP}/N_{LS} equal to N_p/N_s in Fig. 5.19a results in negligible ripple at V_o, as can be seen in Fig. 5.21. The voltages delivered to the anodes of either $D1$, $D2$, or $D3$ are all equal in amplitude. The currents delivered through $D1$, $D2$ are NI_{Q1} and NI_{Q2}, which are equal. Further, since $N_{LP}/N_{LS} = N_p/N_s$ during t_{off}, the current delivered through $D3$ is also NI_{Q1}. Thus there is no gap in time during which C_o must supply or absorb current. The total load current is at all times being supplied through $D1$, $D2$, or $D3$ and C_o need serve no energy storage function.

Output ripple is then the product of the secondary ripple current amplitude ΔI_s times the equivalent series resistance R_{esr} of C_o. Further, $\Delta I_s = N\,\Delta I_p$ where ΔI_p is set as twice the minimum current at the center of the $Q1$, $Q2$ ramps at minimum output power; ΔI_p is set at the desired value as discussed in Sec. 1.3.6 by choosing L_p sufficiently large that it does not run dry or go into the discontinuous conduction mode before minimum output power. Then C_o is chosen to minimize R_{esr} as discussed in Sec. 1.3.7.

There may be very narrow (<1 μs) voltage spikes at each turnon/turnoff transition as can be seen in Fig. 5.21. These may occur if the voltage fall time at the anode of $D1$, $D2$, or $D3$ is slightly faster than the voltage rise time of the next on-turning diode. Such spikes are easily eliminated with very small LC integrators.

Current drawn from V_{in} is discontinuous. As seen in Fig. 5.20i, although $T2$ secondary current flows during the off time, making output

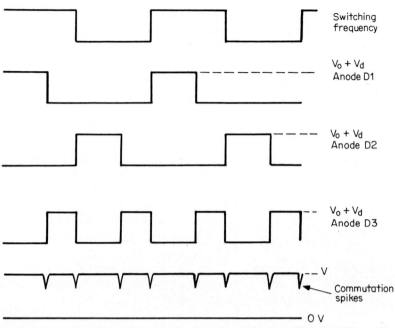

Figure 5.21 In Fig. 5.19a, peak voltages applied to the anodes of D1, D2, D3 are all equal if N_p/N_s is chosen equal to N_{LP}/N_{LS}. But if fall time at one anode is slightly faster than the rise time of the next on-coming anode, there will be narrow commutation spikes at the output.

currents continuous, input current falls to zero during each off time. These discontinuous input currents require the addition of a space-consuming RFI input filter to keep large transient currents off the input lines. By returning the T2 secondary and D3 to the input lines as in Fig. 5.19b, input currents will never fall to zero but will ramp up and down with the amplitudes shown in Fig. 5.20g and 5.20h. This will lower the size of the required RFI input filter greatly or may even make it unnecessary.

5.6.7.6 Output stage–transformer design example—nonoverlapping mode. It is instructive to run through a typical design example of the output stage and transformer for the flyback-current-fed push-pull topology operating in the nonoverlapping mode.

Only a single master secondary will be considered. Additional secondaries may be added, and their required turns will be related to the master in the ratio of their output voltages. Slave secondary output voltages will track the master to within about 2 percent—much more closely than is possible in supplies with output LC filters.

The design example will assume the following:

Output power	2000 W
Output voltage	48 V
Efficiency	80 percent
Switching frequency	50 kHz (T = 20 µs)
Diode voltage drops	1 V
DC input voltage (from 115-V, ±15 percent AC line)	Maximum, 184 V; nominal, 160 V, minimum, 136 V

The first decision to be made is selection of V_{ct} during the on time. As in Sec. 5.6.7.3, V_{ct} is set at 75 percent of the minimum DC input voltage or 0.75 × 136 = 102 V.

The turns ratio is now selected to yield 102 V during the on time. From Fig. 5.20d, V_{ct} during the on time is

$$V_{ct} = \frac{N_p}{N_s}(V_o + V_d) \qquad \text{or} \qquad \frac{N_p}{N_s} = N = \frac{102}{48 + 1} = 2$$

Now transistor current amplitudes I_{Q1}, I_{Q2} and on times are calculated to permit calculation of primary and secondary rms currents and hence wire sizes. From the on times and preselected V_{ct}, the number of primary turns will be calculated from Faraday's law once a transformer core area is selected for the specified output power.

Thus from Eq. 5.13:

$$\frac{t_{on}}{T} = \frac{(V_o + V_d)(N_p/N_s)}{2V_{dc}}$$

From this, Table 5.1 can be constructed.

Now when either transistor is on, it delivers a current whose waveshape is as shown in Fig. 5.20g·and 5.20h. This current is delivered to the $T1$ center tap at V_{ct} of 102 V. When the transistor turns off, the current shown in Fig. 5.20i is delivered via $D3$ to the secondary load. This last current (NI_Q) is delivered during the off time at a voltage $V_o + V_d$ but is equivalent to current I_Q being delivered at a

TABLE 5.1

V_{dc}, V	t_{on}/T	t_{on}, µs
200	0.245	4.9
184	0.266	5.3
160	0.306	6.12
136	0.360	7.2

voltage $N(V_o + V_d)$. Thus, effectively, this current is being delivered at 100 percent duty cycle at a voltage of $N(V_o + V_d)$ or at 102 V.

Assuming an efficiency of 80 percent outward from the T1 center tap, input power at the center tap is 2000/0.8 or 2500 W. Average current into the center tap is then 2500/102 = 24.5 A. This is very closely the current at the center of the current ramp in Fig. 5.20g and 5.20h.

Current in each T1 half primary is thus very closely approximated by an equivalent flat-topped pulse whose amplitude I_{pk} is 24.5 A and whose duration is given in Table 5.1. The rms value of this is $I_{pk}\sqrt{t_{on}/T}$. This is a maximum at minimum V_{dc}, and hence at V_{dc} = 136 V the rms current in each half secondary is I_{rms} = $24.5\sqrt{0.36}$ = 14.7 A. At a current density of 500 circular mils per rms ampere, the required number of circular mils for each half primary is 500 × 14.7 = 7350 circular mils.

The transformer core will be selected from charts in the coming section on magnetics design, which has been discussed in Sec. 2.2.9.1. Jumping ahead then, these charts will show that a Ferroxcube EC70 (also an international standard type) core with an area of 2.79 cm^2 can deliver 2536 W at 48 kHz and can be used.

The number of turns per half primary is calculated from Faraday's law (Eq.1.17) at the maximum on time (7.2 μs) in Table 5.1 and at a primary voltage of 102 V. At 50 kHz, using Ferroxcube material type 3F3 core, losses are only 60 mW/cm^3 at a peak flux density of 1600 G. For a core volume of 40.1 cm^3, total core losses are only 2.4 W. This is low enough so that copper losses of even twice that much will still leave the transformer at a safely low temperature. Then from Faraday's law $N_p = V_p t_{on} × 10^{+8}/A_e \Delta B = 102(7.2 × 10^{-6})10^{+8}/2.79 × 3200 = 8$ turns, and for N_p/N_s = 2, each half secondary has 4 turns.

Finally, the secondary wire size must be calculated. Each half secondary delivers the characteristic ramp-on-a-step waveform shown in Fig. 5.20g and 5.20h. The current at the center of the ramp is the DC output current. Their maximum width occurs at minimum DC input of 136 V and is seen in Table 5.1 to be 7.2 μs. For purposes of calculating their rms value, they can be approximated by a rectangular pulse of amplitude I_{dc} and width 7.2 μs. For an output power of 2000 W, the DC output current is 2000/48 = 41.6 A. The rms value of this rectangular current pulse of 41.6 A, 7.2-μs width, and coming once per 20 μs is $41.6\sqrt{7.2/20}$ = 24.9 A.

At a current density of 500 circular mils per rms ampere, the required wire area for the half secondaries is 500 × 24.9 = 12,450 circular mils. For such large area, the secondary would most likely be wound with metal foil of thickness and width to yield the required circular mil area. The primary with a required 7350-circular-mil area would be wound with a number of paralleled small diameter wires.

5.6.7.7 Flyback transformer for design example of Sec. 5.6.7.6. The preceding design was based on the inductor L_p operating in the continuous mode or not running dry until the minimum DC current passed through it (Sec. 1.3.6). It was shown there that the discontinuous mode starts when ΔI, the peak-to-peak ramp amplitude, is equal to twice the minimum DC current, which is the current in the center of the ramp at minimum output power.

In the design example above, assume that minimum output power is one-tenth the nominal output power. At nominal output power, current at the center of the ramp was calculated above as 24.5 A. Then current at the center of the ramp at minimum output power is 2.45 A and the peak-to-peak ramp amplitude (ΔI of Fig. 5.20g and 5.20h) is 4.9 A. But $\Delta I = V_L t_{on}/L_p$, where V_L is the voltage across L_p during t_{on}; and from Table 5.1, at $V_{dc} = 136$ V, $t_{on} = 7.2$ μs. Then

$$L_p = \frac{(136 - 102)(7.2 \times 10^{-6})}{4.9} = 50 \ \mu H$$

Wire size for the $T2$ secondary must be calculated at high DC input, for it is then that its current pulse width t_{off} is greatest (Table 5.1). Further, as above, the equivalent flat-topped pulse amplitude is I_{dc}. Then from Table 5.1, its maximum width is $10 - 5.3 = 4.7$ μs. Maximum rms current in the $T2$ secondary is then

$$I_{rms(T2 \ secondary)} = 41.6 \sqrt{\frac{t_{off}}{0.5T}}$$

$$= 41.6 \sqrt{\frac{4.7}{10}}$$

$$= 28.5 \ A$$

At 500 circular mils per rms ampere, that winding requires a circular-mil area of $500 \times 28.5 = 14{,}260$ circular mils.

Wire size for the $T2$ primary is calculated for minimum DC input voltage, for it is then that primary current has greatest width and hence largest rms value. Then from Table 5.1

$$I_{rms(T2 \ primary)} = 24.5 \sqrt{\frac{t_{on}}{0.5T}} = 24.5 \sqrt{\frac{7.2}{10}} = 20.7 \ A$$

At 500 circular mils per rms ampere, it requires $500 \times 20.7 = 10{,}394$ circular mils.

Both primary and secondary would most likely be wound with metal foil rather than round wire for those large required areas.

And of course, since $T2$ is a flyback transformer with no secondary current flowing when primary current flows, all the primary current drives the core toward saturation. To maintain the required 50-μH primary inductance at 24.5 A of primary current, the core must be a gapped ferrite, powdered Permalloy, or powdered iron type (Sec. 4.3.3).

5.6.7.8 Overlapping mode in flyback-current-fed push-pull topology—basic operation.[14]   In the nonoverlapping mode of Fig. 5.20 ($t_{on}/T < 0.5$) it is difficult to accommodate a large ratio of maximum to minimum DC input voltage. Since the maximum on time is $0.5T$ at minimum DC, then at high DC inputs, on time will be a small fraction of a period and may approach 1 to 3 μs at a 100- to 50-kHz switching rate. But bipolar transistors with their appreciable storage times cannot work reliably down to such low on times.

By operating with overlapping on times ($T_{on}/T > 0.5$) as in Fig. 5.22, however, a much larger range of maximum to minimum DC input voltages is possible.

The usual integrated-circuit pulse-width-modulating chips cannot be used for the overlapping mode as their two 180° out-of-phase outputs have a maximum duty cycle D of only 0.5. But a number of schemes using several discrete integrated-circuit packages and capable of a duty cycle of 0 to 100 percent have been described in the literature.[14,19]

Overlapping-mode operation is achieved using the same circuit as shown in Fig. 5.19 but by proper choice of the turns ratios N_p/N_s and N_{LP}/N_{LS} (hereafter designated N_1, N_2, respectively). Circuit operation will be described for the scheme of Fig. 5.19a, where diode D3 is returned to the output voltage rather than the input. It will be recalled that connection minimizes output voltage ripple rather than input current ripple.

The circuit operation can be understood from the waveforms of Fig. 5.22 and the circuit of Fig. 5.19a. For the overlapping mode, Q1 and Q2 are simultaneously on during intervals T_1 and only one of these is on during T_{off} intervals (t_2 to t_3 when Q2 is off and t_4 to t_5 when Q1 is off). Power is delivered to the load only during the T_{off} times.

When both transistors are on, the half primaries cannot support voltage and the T1 center tap voltage falls to zero as seen in Fig. 5.22d. The full input voltage V_{dc} is applied across the T2 primary inductance L_p and current ramps up it linearly at a rate $dI/dT = V_{dc}/L_p$. This current divides roughly evenly between Q1 and Q2 and is seen as the upward-going ramps at the ledges at t_3 to t_4 and t_5 to t_6. During T_1, D3 is reverse-biased, and there is no voltage across the T1 secondaries. Hence all the output power is supplied from the output filter capacitor C_o during T_1 intervals.

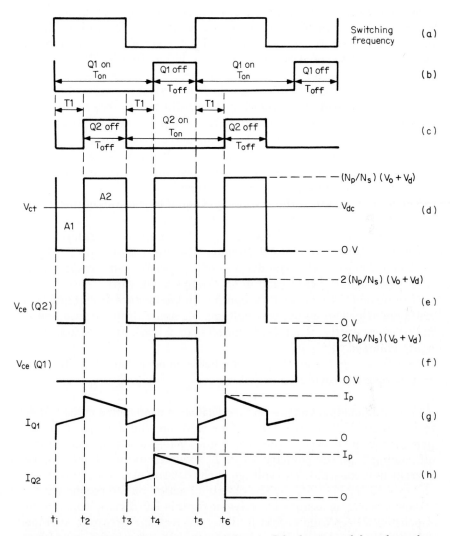

Figure 5.22 Significant voltage-current waveform in flyback-current-fed topology when operating in overlapping mode ($T_{on} > T_{off}$). This mode permits a much larger range of input voltages. Power is delivered to the load only in the interval when one transistor is on and one is off. It is delivered at voltage V_{ct}, which is higher than DC input voltage (boost operation). In the nonoverlapping mode of Fig. 5.20 it is delivered at a voltage lower then the DC input (buck operation).

When $Q2$ turns off at t_2, $Q1$ is still on. Now the $Q1$ half primary can support voltage and V_{ct} begins to rise, as does the $D1$ anode. The $D1$ anode rises until its cathode reaches V_o, the secondary is clamped to $(V_o + V_d)$ and V_{ct} is clamped to $N_1(V_o + V_d)$ as seen in Fig. 5.22d.

The turns ratio $N_{LP}/N_{LS}(= N2)$ is chosen so large that when one transistor is on and one off (intervals T_{off}), with the maximum voltage across N_{LP}, the voltage across N_{LS} is insufficient to forward-bias $D3$. This permits V_{ct} to be clamped to $N_1(V_o + V_d)$ during T_{off}. Some of the current stored in L_p during T_1 intervals and current from V_{dc} is delivered via the $T1$ primary to the load at a voltage $N_1(V_o + V_d)$. It will soon be seen that $D3$ will be forward-biased and deliver load power at some sufficiently higher DC input voltage.

The current in $Q1$ at the instant t_2 is equal to the sum of the $Q1$ and $Q2$ currents at the instant just prior to $Q2$ turnoff as the current in L_p cannot change instantly. During (t_2 to t_3), the current ramps downward (Fig. 5.22g) as N_1 will be chosen so high that $N_1(V_o + V_d)$ is greater than V_{dc}. With the dot end of L_p positive with respect to its no-dot end, current in it (and in $Q1$) ramps downward.

Now when $Q2$ turns on at t_3, again both transistors are on and their half primaries cannot support voltage, V_{ct} again drops to zero and remains there until t_4 when $Q1$ turns off (Fig. 5.22d). From t_4 to t_5, V_{ct} is again clamped to $N_1(V_o + V_d)$.

Now from Fig. 5.22d, the relation between output/input voltage and on time can be calculated as follows.

5.6.7.9 Output/input voltage–on-time relation in overlapping mode.
Refer to Fig. 5.19a. When both transistors were on, the dot end of L_p was negative with respect to the no-dot end. When one transistor turned off (during T_{off}), the polarity across L_p reversed in an attempt to keep current in it constant. The voltage at the dot end of L_p rose until it was clamped to $N_1(V_o + V_d)$ by the clamping action at the secondary.

Now since L_p is assumed to have negligible DC resistance, it cannot support a DC voltage across it. Thus the voltage across it averaged over a full or half period must equal zero. Since the input end of L_p is at V_{dc}, so must be the output end averaged over a half period. Or another way of stating this is that in Fig. 5.22d, the area $A1$ must equal area $A2$. Or

$$V_{dc}T_1 = [N_1(V_o + V_d) - V_{dc}]T_{off}$$

$$= N_1V_oT_{off} + N_1V_dT_{off} - V_{dc}T_{off}$$

$$V_oN_1T_{off} = V_{dc}(T_1 + T_{off}) - N_1V_dT_{off}$$

But $T_1 + T_{off} = T/2$; then

$$V_o = \left(\frac{V_{dc}T}{2N_1T_{off}}\right) - V_d \quad \text{and} \quad T_{off} = T - T_{on}$$

Then for $D = T_{on}/T$

$$V_o = \left[\frac{V_{dc}}{2N_1(1 - D)}\right] - V_d \tag{5.14a}$$

and from Eq. 5.14a, the duty cycle for any DC input is

$$D = \frac{2N_1(V_o + V_d) - V_{dc}}{2N_1(V_o + V_d)} \tag{5.14b}$$

5.6.7.10 Turns ratio selection in overlapping mode. Equation 5.14a gives the relation between output/input voltage and on time for the overlapping mode for a preselected choice of T_1 turns ratio N_1. As good a choice for N_1 is the value calculated from Eq. 5.14a, which makes $D = 0.5$ at the nominal value of input voltage V_{dcn}. Then for all DC input voltages less than V_{dcn}, there will be overlapping on times $(D > 0.5)$ and the output voltage–on-time relation is given by Eq. 5.14a for that calculated value of N_1.

For input voltages greater than V_{dcn}, D is less than 0.5, there is no overlapping on time, and Eq. 5.14a no longer holds. The output voltage–on-time relation will now involve N_2. It did not involve N_2 for D greater than 0.5 in Eq. 5.14a because N_2 had been made so large that during T_{off}, D3 was reverse-biased and the peak voltage at V_{ct} involved only N_1 (see Fig. 5.22d).

Thus the first choice is the value of N_1 from Eq. 5.14a, which makes $D = 0.5$ for nominal input voltage V_{dcn}. From Eq. 5.14a

$$N_1 = \frac{V_{dcn}}{2(V_o + V_d)(1 - 0.5)} = \frac{V_{dcn}}{V_o + V_d} \tag{5.15}$$

Next $N_2(= N_{LP}/N_{LS})$ must be selected so that during T_{off} in Fig. 5.22d, the maximum voltage across N_{LS} does not forward-bias D3. But the maximum N_{LS} voltage occurs at the maximum voltage across N_{LP}; and that latter is a maximum when V_{dc} is a minimum (see Fig. 5.22d). Maximum T2 secondary voltage is then $[N_1(V_o + V_d) - V_{dc(min)}]/N_2$. Further, since the D3 cathode is at V_o, in order for D3 not to be forward-biased

$$\frac{N_1(V_o + V_d) - V_{dc(min)}}{N_2} < V_o + V_d$$

or
$$N_2 > \frac{[N_1(V_o + V_d) - V_{dc(min)}]}{V_o + V_d}$$
(5.16a)

To avoid problems arising from $T1$ leakage inductance spikes, N_2 is usually selected twice this minimum value.[14] Thus

$$N_2 = \frac{2[N_1(V_o + V_d) - V_{dc(min)}]}{V_o + V_d}$$
(5.16b)

5.6.7.11 Output/input voltage–on-time relation for overlapping-mode design at high DC input voltages where operation has been forced nonoverlapping. Now with N_1 selected from Eq. 5.15 and N_2 from 5.16b, when V_{dc} is less than its nominal value, the relation between output voltage and on time is given by Eq. 5.14a. At nominal input V_{dcn}, $D = T_{on}/T$ is 0.5; and at DC input voltages greater than V_{dcn}, D is less than 0.5 and there is no overlapping on time. Waveforms for this input voltage range are shown in Fig. 5.23.

For the conditions of Fig. 5.23, whenever $Q1$ or $Q2$ are on, the secondaries are clamped to $(V_o + V_d)$ and the center tap is then clamped to $N_1(V_o + V_d)$ where N_1 is the value calculated from Eq. 5.15. When either transistor turns off, the dot end of L_p rises in an attempt to keep current in it constant. As the dot end of L_p rises, so does the dot end of N_{LS} until it clamps to $V_o + V_d$ via $D3$. This then clamps the dot end of L_p (or V_{ct}) to $V_{dc} + N_2(V_o + V_d)$ as seen in Fig. 5.23d.

Again in Fig. 5.23, since the DC voltage averaged over a half cycle must equal zero, the area $A1$ must equal area $A2$. Or

$$[V_{dc} - N_1(V_o + V_d)]T_{on} = [N_2(V_o + V_d)][(T/2) - T_{on}]$$

From this, for $T_{on}/T = D$,

$$V_o = \frac{V_{dc}D - N_2V_d(0.5 - D) - N_1V_dD}{N_2(0.5 - D) + N_1D}$$
(5.17a)

In Eq. 5.17a, since V_d, the diode forward drops, are about 1 V, the last two terms in the numerator are small compared to $V_{dc}D$ and can be neglected. The equation can then be rewritten as

$$V_o = \frac{V_{dc}D}{N_2(0.5 - D) + N_1D}$$
(5.17b)

And from Eq. 5.17b, the duty cycle at any DC input is

$$D = \frac{0.5V_oN_2}{V_{dc} - V_o(N_1 - N_2)}$$
(5.18)

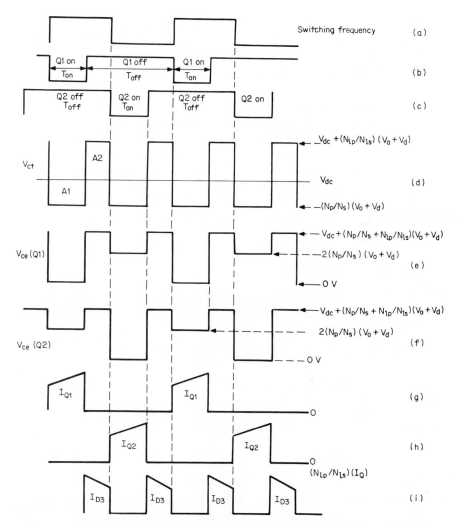

Figure 5.23 Circuit of Fig. 5.20 in overlapping mode but when DC input voltage has risen to a level which has forced it into the nonoverlapping mode. Transition between overlapping and nonoverlapping mode is continuous if turns ratios are chosen correctly.

Thus, when the design is for the overlapping mode, N_1 is calculated from Eq. 5.15 and N_2 from 5.16b. Then at DC input voltages less than nominal V_{dcn}, the feedback loop sets the duty cycle in accordance with Eq. 5.14a to maintain V_o constant. This duty cycle will be greater than 0.5.

When input voltage has risen to V_{dcn}, the duty cycle has decreased to 0.5 to keep V_o at the same value. When DC input voltage has risen above V_{dcn}, the feedback loop sets the duty cycle in accordance with Eq. 5.17b to maintain the output constant. This duty cycle will now be less than 0.5.

The transition from $D > 0.5$ to $D < 0.5$ will be smooth and continuous as V_{dc} rises through V_{dcn}. A much larger range of DC input voltages can now be tolerated than if the design were restricted to the nonoverlapping mode entirely as in Sec. 5.6.7.6.

5.6.7.12 Design example—overlapping mode. It is instructive, using the overlapping mode design, to calculate on times for a range of DC input voltages. This will be done for the design example of Sec. 5.6.7.6 which had restricted operation to the nonoverlap mode entirely. Recall in that design example that V_o was 48 V, nominal input voltage V_{dcn} was 160 V, minimum input voltage $V_{dc(min)}$ was 100 V, switching frequency was 50 kHz and P_o was 2000 W. From Eq. 5.15

$$N_1 = \frac{V_{dcn}}{V_o + V_d} = \frac{160}{48 + 1} = 3.27$$

and from Eq. 5.16b

$$N_2 = \frac{2[(3.2)(49) - 100]}{49}$$

$$= 2\left(3.27 - \frac{100}{49}\right) = 2.46$$

and for $V_{dc} < V_{dcn}$, from Eq. 5.14b

$$D = \frac{[2N_1(V_o + V_d) - V_{dc}]}{2N_1(V_o + V_d)}$$

$$= 1 - \left(\frac{V_{dc}}{2 \times 3.27 \times 49}\right)$$

$$= 1 - \left(\frac{V_{dc}}{320.5}\right) \tag{5.19}$$

and for $V_{dc} > V_{dcn}$, from Eq. 5.17b

$$D = \frac{0.5V_oN_2}{V_{dc} - V_o(N_1 - N_2)}$$

$$= \frac{0.5 \times 48 \times 2.46}{V_{dc} - 48(3.27 - 2.46)}$$

$$= \frac{59}{V_{dc} - 38.9} \tag{5.20}$$

and from Eqs. 5.19 to 5.22, we can construct Table 5.2.

Comparing this (Table 5.2) to Table 5.1, where operation was re-

TABLE 5.2

V_{dc}, V	D	T_{on}, µs	T_{off}, µs	I_p, A (Eq. 5.21)	I_{rms}, A (Eq. 5.22)
50	0.840	16.9	3.1	50.2	24.6
100	0.688	13.8	6.2	25.2	15.1
136	0.576	11.5	8.5	18.3	12.2
160	0.500	10.0	10.0	15.6	11.0
175	0.433	8.67	11.3	13.8	
185	0.404	8.08	11.9	13.1	
200	0.366	7.32	12.7	12.3	

stricted to the nonoverlapping mode, it is seen that the design for overlapping and crossing into nonoverlapping mode permits a larger range of DC input voltages and allows a larger on time at high input voltages. This latter permits the use of bipolar transistors, which would have difficulty operating reliably at the low on times close to the vicinity of their storage times.

5.6.7.13 Voltages, currents, and wire size selection for design example in overlap mode.
Transistor currents and transformer rms currents can be calculated from the waveforms of Figs. 5.22 and 5.23. Wire sizes will be selected from the rms currents at the rate of 500 circular mils per rms ampere.

Consider first operation at V_{dc} less than nominal so that there will be overlapping conduction with the waveforms of Fig. 5.22. Assume an efficiency of 80 percent as in the design example of Sec. 5.6.7.6. Input power is then $P_o/0.8 = 2000/0.8 = 2500$ W. Now note that whether V_{dc} is less or greater than nominal, power is supplied to the load through T1 at a center tap voltage of $N_1(V_o + V_d)$. For V_{dc} less than nominal (Fig. 5.22d), the center tap voltage is boosted up to $N_1(V_o + V_d)$. For supply voltages greater than nominal, center tap voltage is bucked down (Fig. 5.23d) to the same value. In this design example, $N_1(V_o + V_d) = 3.27(48 + 1) = 160$ V.

The equivalent flat-topped current pulse I_p into the T1 center tap will be calculated. This is closely the current in the center of the ramp in Fig. 5.22g. Then power into the T1 center tap is

$$P_{in} = 2500 = 160 I_p \frac{2T_{off}}{T} \quad \text{or} \quad I_p = \frac{156}{T_{off}} \quad (5.21)$$

Peak currents for supply voltages less than nominal are calculated from Eq. 5.23 and shown in Table 5.2. If $Q1$, $Q2$ are bipolar transistors, base drives will have to be adequate to saturate them at that peak current level. The transistors will be chosen for a maximum collector-emitter voltage of $V_{dc(max)} + (N_1 + N_2)(V_o + V_d)$ from Fig. 5.23e and 5.23f as this is greater than $2N_1(V_o + V_d)$ of Fig. 5.22e and 5.22f. Allowance should be made for a leakage inductance spike.

Although power and current is delivered to the load only during the two off times per period (Fig. 5.22g and 5.22h), each half secondary carries I_p during one off time but also $I_p/2$ during two T_1 times per period. Note in Fig. 5.22, $T_1 = (T/2) - T_{off}$. Then the rms current carried by each half secondary is

$$I_{rms} = I_p \left(\frac{T_{off}}{T}\right)^{1/2} + \left(\frac{I_p}{2}\right)\left(\frac{T - 2T_{off}}{T}\right)^{1/2} \tag{5.22}$$

These rms currents are shown in Table 5.2. Wire size for each half secondary will be selected at the rate of 500 circular mils per rms ampere, and it is seen in Table 5.2 that maximum rms current occurs at minimum DC input. RMS currents for supply voltages above V_{dcn} are lower than those below V_{dcn}, so the rms currents of Table 5.2 dictate the wire sizes.

The flyback transformer $T2$ secondary carries the pulses I_{D3} shown in Fig. 5.23. As DC voltage goes up, the transistor on times decrease toward zero and the I_{D3} pulses widen until they reach a full half period each. All the output load current is then fully supplied by flyback action from the $T2$ secondary. Since the $D3$ pulses at the center of the ramp constitute the DC output current, the $T2$ secondary winding should be sized for the worst-case condition, to carry the DC output current at a 100 percent duty cycle.

Finally, wire size for the $T2$ primary must be chosen. Table 5.2 gives the rms currents per half primary at supply voltages of less than nominal. Since the $T2$ primary carries the currents of both half primaries, its rms current is twice that shown in the table.

Examination of Fig. 5.22 shows that the astonishingly high currents at low DC input should be expected, for in Fig. 5.22, as the supply voltage goes lower, the T_{off} times become narrower. And since power is delivered to the load only during the T_{off} times when voltage exists at the $T1$ center tap, the very narrow T_{off} times demand high peak and rms currents to supply the output power.

References

Current Mode:
1. B. Holland, "A New Integrated Circuit for Current Mode Control," *Proceedings Powercon 10*, 1983.
2. W. W. Burns and A. K. Ohri, "Improving Off Line Converter Performance with Current Mode Control," *Proceedings Powercon 10*, 1983.
3. "Current Mode Control of Switching Power Supplies" Unitrode Power Supply Design Seminar Manual SEM 400, 1988 Unitrode Corp., Lexington, MA.

4. T. K. Phelps, "Coping with Current Mode Regulators," *Power Control and Intelligent Motion (PCIM Magazine)*, April 1986.
5. C. W. Deisch, "Simple Switching Control Method Changes Power Converter into a Current Source," 1978 IEEE.
6. R. D. Middlebrook, "Modelling Current Programmed Regulators," *APEC Conference Proceedings,* March 1987.
7. G. Fritz, "UC3842 Provides Low Cost Current Control," Unitrode Corporation Application Note U-100, Unitrode Corp. Lexington, MA.

Current Fed:

8. A. I. Pressman, *Switching and Linear Power Supply, Power Converter Design,* p. 146, Switchtronix Press, Waban, MA, 1977.
9. E. T. Calkin and B. H. Hamilton, "A Conceptually New Approach for Regulated DC to DC Converters Employing Transistor Switches and Pulse Width Control," *IEEE Transactions on Industry Applications,* 1A: 12, July 1986.
10. E. T. Calkin and B. H. Hamilton, "Circuit Techniques for Improving the Switching Loci of Transistor Switches in Switching Regulators," *IEEE Transactions on Industry Applications,* 1A: 12, July 1986.
11. K. Tomaschewski, "Design of a 1.5 kW Multiple Output Current Fed Converter Operating at 100 kHz," *Proceedings Powercon 9,* 1982.
12. B. F. Farber, D. S. Goldin, C. Siegert, and F. Gourash, "A High Power TWT Power Processing System," *PESC Record,* 1974.
13. R. J. Froelich, B. F. Schmidt, and D. L. Shaw, "Design of an 87 Per Cent Efficient HVPS Using Current Mode Control," *Proceedings Powercon 10,* 1983.
14. V. J. Thottuvelil, T. G. Wilson, and H. A. Owen, "Analysis and Design of a Push Pull Current Fed Converter," *IEEE Proceedings,* 1981.
15. J. Lindena, "The Current Fed Inverter—A New Approach and a Comparison with the Voltage Fed Inverter," *Proceedings 20th Annual Power Sources Conference,* pp. 207–210, 1966.
16. P. W. Clarke, "Converter Regulation by Controlled Conduction Overlap," U.S. Patent 3,938,024, issued Feb. 10, 1976.
17. B. Israelson, J. Martin, C. Reeve, and A. Scown, "A 2.5 kV High Reliability TWT Power Supply: Design Techniques for High Efficiency and Low Ripple, *PESC Record,* 1977.
18. J. Biess and D. Cronin, "Power Processing Module for Military Digital Power Sub System," *PESC Record,* 1977.
19. R. Redl and N. Sokal, "Push Pull Current Fed, Multiple Output DC/DC Power Converter with Only One Inductor and with 0 to 100% Switch Duty Ratio," *IEEE Proceedings,* 1980.
20. R. Redl and N. Sokal, "Push Pull, Multiple Output, Wide Input Range DC/DC Converter—Operation at Duty Cycle Ratio Below 50%," *IEEE Proceedings,* 1981.
21. L. G. Meares, "Improved Non-Dissipative Snubber Design for Buck Regulator and Current Fed Inverter," *Proceedings Powercon 9,* 1982.
22. E. Whitcomb, "Designing Non-Dissipative Snubber for Switched Mode Converters," *Proceedings Powercon 6,* 1979.
23. A.H. Weinberg, "A Boost Regulator With A New Energy Transfer Principle," *Proceedings of the Spacecraft Power Conditioning Electronics Seminar*, September 1974, European Space Research Organization Publication Sp–103.

6

Miscellaneous Topologies

6.1 SCR Resonant Topologies—Introduction

The silicon controlled rectifier (SCR) has been used in DC/AC inverters and DC/DC power supplies for over 25 years.[1,2] It is available with higher voltage and current ratings at lower cost than bipolar (single or Darlington types) or MOSFET transistors. Because of the higher voltage-current ratings, it is used primarily for supplies of over 1000 W.

It will be recalled that an SCR is a solid-state switch which is easily turned on by a narrow pulse at its input terminal (gate) and latches and stays on after the input is removed. The literature is replete with schemes for turning an SCR off ("commutating" it). Essentially all these schemes involve reducing its on current to zero by diverting it to an alternate path for a certain minimum time t_q. SCR turnoff will be discussed below.

Earlier DC/AC or DC/DC SCR supplies could not operate reliably at switching frequencies over about 8 to 10 kHz. This was because even the fastest inverter-type SCRs available then did not have a reliable high-impedance open circuit at their output terminals until about 10 to 20 μs after they had been turned off and their currents had dropped to zero. Thus they could not be subjected to high voltage until the 10 to 20 μs after their currents had been reduced to zero.

Further, early SCRs could not tolerate a large dV/dt across their output terminals even beyond the 10 to 20 μs after their output currents had fallen to zero. Most were specified at a maximum rate of change of output voltage of 200 V/μs. At a dV/dt faster than that, they would spontaneously turn back on independently of the input control voltage.

Early inverter-type SCRs also could not tolerate a large rate of change of output current dI/dt at the instant of turnon. Most were specified in the range of 100 to 400 A/µs. At dI/dt faster than their specified values, average junction temperatures would rise, local hot spots would develop on the chips, and the SCR would either fail immediately or degrade to the failure point in a short period of time.

With switching frequencies thus limited to 10 kHz, transformers, inductors, and capacitors were still relatively large and made the overall size of a DC/AC or DC/DC converter too large in many applications. Further, switching frequencies under 10,000 kHz are in the middle of the audio range, and the audible noise emitted from such converters made them unacceptable in an office or even factory environment. To be acceptable in such environments, switching frequencies must be above the highest usual audible frequency of about 18 kHz.

About 1977, RCA developed the asymmetrical silicon controlled rectifier (ASCR), which solved most of these problems and made possible DC/AC and DC/DC converters operating up to 40 and possibly 50 kHz.

Conventional SCRs can sustain or block reverse voltages across their output terminals equal to their forward-voltage blocking capability. But in a large number of SCR circuits, reverse voltage at the output terminals is clamped to one or two diode drops or to a maximum of about 2 V, making large reverse-voltage blocking capability unnecessary. Thus by certain solid-state changes on the SCR chip, RCA achieved turnoff times (t_q or the time after SCR forward current has dropped to zero until the full-rated forward voltage can be reapplied) of 4 µs. The price paid for this was a reduction of the reverse voltage blocking capability to 7 V—easily adequate in most inverter circuits.

Thus with t_q times of 4 µs, this RCA device (S7310) made possible inverters at switching frequencies of 40 to 50 kHz in a host of circuit configurations. The S7310 had many other astonishingly useful features. Its dV/dt and dI/dt ratings were 3000 V/µs (with a 1-V negative bias on its input terminal) and 2000 A/µs.

This compared to 200 V/µs and 400 A/µs for conventional SCRs. Further, the device was available in voltage ratings of 800 V and rms current ratings of 40 A. These voltage, current, and t_q ratings made possible an inverter (or DC/DC power supply) with 4000 W of output power in a two-SCR 40-kHz half-bridge circuit configuration.

In its first few years on the market the S7310 sold for about $5. No other circuit topology using transistors could remotely approach the achievement of 4000 W of output power with two switching devices costing a total of $10. Unfortunately, the S7310 is no longer manufactured by RCA, but equivalent unsymmetrical SCRs are made by other manufacturers. A very similar Marconi ASCR, type ACR25U, has a t_q of 4 µs, blocking voltage of up to 1200 V, and rms current rating of 40 A at a cost of about $17 at this writing.

A final significant feature of an SCR approach to high-power inverters is that the SCR does not suffer from the most frequent failure mode of transistors—second breakdown.

6.2   SCR Basics

The SCR symbol is shown in Fig. 6.1. Its input terminal (terminal 1) is designated the *gate,* terminal 2 is the *anode,* and 3 is the *cathode.* When it is on, current flows down from the anode to the cathode. When it is off, the maximum voltage it can sustain or block from anode to cathode is designated V_{DRM}. ASCR types are available with V_{DRM} voltage ratings ranging from 400 to 1200 V.

Once turned on, the anode-to-cathode current is determined by the supply voltage and load impedance from anode to supply source. Anode to cathode voltage versus anode current characteristics are given in the data sheets for the specific device. For the Marconi ACR25U, a 40-A rms device, anode-to-cathode voltage at 100-A anode current is typically 2.2 V (Fig. 6.2).

The device is turned on by a gate-to-cathode current pulse which is not too well specified in amplitude and duration in the data sheets. Figure 6.3 shows anode current delay and rise time (to 100 A) as a function of gate-trigger current. Gate current pulse width also determines to some extent the current rise time, but this is seldom given. Typically, for the ACR25U, gate current should be in the range of 90 to 200 mA for an anode current of 100 A.

Gate pulse duration should be greater than 400 ns for 100 A of anode current. The gate-to-cathode voltage during the duration of the gate current pulse is shown in Fig. 6.4 and is in the range of 0.9 to 3 V for a large range of gate currents. Once turned on, the anode will latch on and stay conducting after the gate turnon pulse is gone. The anode "on" potential ranges from about 1.2 to 2.2 V over an anode current range of 20 to 100 A as seen in Fig. 6.2.

Anode current rise time (shown in Fig. 6.3) is not as important for an SCR as is anode-to-cathode voltage fall time. This is obvious from Fig. 6.5, which shows that even with a 500-mA gate current pulse, with a half-sinusoid 8-μs anode current pulse, 125 A in amplitude, the

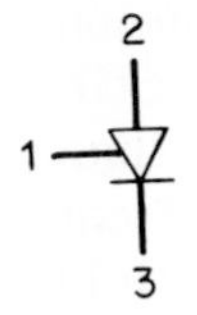

Figure 6.1   Silicon controlled rectifier symbol.

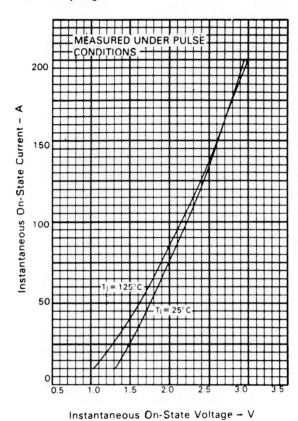

Figure 6.2   Anode current versus voltage.

anode-to-cathode voltage has fallen to only 5 V in 2.5 μs. This is still twice the anode-to-cathode quiescent voltage at that current as shown in Fig. 6.2.

The reason for this long anode voltage fall time is that it takes a long time for the anode current carriers to spread uniformly throughout the chip area. Initially, the current carriers are concentrated in only a small fraction of the chip area and instantaneous anode-to-cathode resistance is high, causing a high instantaneous on voltage. After a time, the current carriers spread uniformly throughout the chip and the on voltage drops down to the quiescent level given in Fig. 6.2.

Thus most of the dissipation in an SCR occurs during the turnon time. This dissipation is the integral $\int I_a V_a\, dt$. In most cases with SCR circuits, currents will be in the shape of half sinusoids rather than square waves, which is helpful. As seen in Fig. 6.5, if anode current pulses were square waves, the front end of the current pulse would

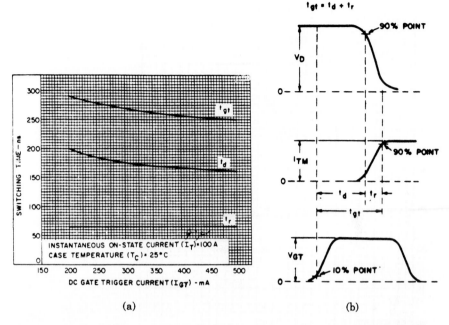

Figure 6.3 (a) Switching times. Typical switching time t_{gt}, t_d, t_r versus gate-trigger current. (b) Relationship between off-state voltage, on-state current, and gate-trigger voltage showing reference points for definition of turnon time t_{gr}. (*Note:* Figure 6.3a, 6.3b illustrate the original RCA S7310—a type of SCR very similar to the Marconi type ACR25U.)

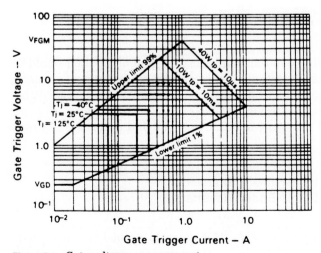

Figure 6.4 Gate voltage versus current.

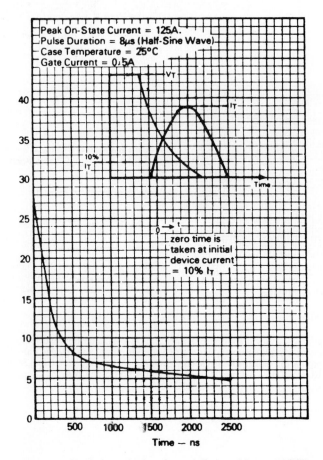

Figure 6.5 Anode-to-cathode voltage fall time. Marconi ASCR type ACR25U characteristics.

flow at an anode voltage in the vicinity of 25 V and dissipation would be high. Figure 6.5 also shows that if anode current pulses are half sinusoid, their base width should be longer than 2.5 μs to avoid an "on" anode potential greater than 5 V throughout the entire half sinusoid.

Figures. 6.6 and 6.7 show maximum dV/dt and t_q for the Marconi ACR25U.

6.3 SCR Turnoff by Resonant Sinusoidal Anode Currents—Single-Ended Resonant Inverter Topology

It was pointed out above that an SCR is easily turned on with a narrow pulse but stays latched on after the pulse has gone. To turn it off,

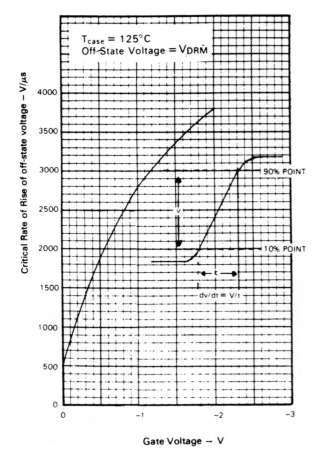

Figure 6.6 Marconi ASCR type ACR25U characteristics. Minimum linear critical rate or rise of off-state voltage versus gate voltage.

anode current must be reduced to zero for a time equal to at least the specified t_q time of the device. Further, after the t_q time, the reapplied anode voltage rise-time rate must be less than the specified dV/dt rating of the SCR.

All this and other significant advantages are easily achieved by forcing the SCR anode current to be sinusoidal in shape. The basic scheme and its advantages are most easily described with a typical single-ended SCR resonant converter such as that shown in Fig. 6.8.[3-8]

The SCR, an inductor L, and a capacitor C are arranged in series. Before the SCR is fired, capacitor C is charged to some positive voltage through the larger constant-current inductor L_c. Now when the SCR is triggered on with a narrow gate pulse, the equivalent circuit is that of

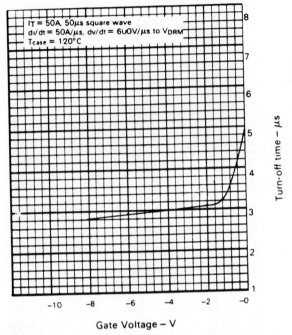

Figure 6.7 Marconi ASCR type ACR25U characteristics. Typical circuit commutated turnoff time versus gate voltage at turnoff.

a switch closure applying a step waveform to a series resonant LC circuit. Current in the circuit is shocked into a resonant "ring" whose period $t_r = 2\pi\sqrt{LC}$

Current increases in the anode sinusoidally goes through its first negative peak and decreases sinusoidally to zero at the end of a half period ($= \pi\sqrt{LC}$). Now with the antiparallel diode $D1$ across the SCR, as the sine wave of current in the SCR reaches zero at t_1, it reverses direction and flows sinusoidally for the next half cycle through $D1$. During this half cycle of diode conduction time T_d, the SCR is clamped with a reverse voltage of about 1 V by $D1$. This maximum reverse voltage is safely below the 7- to 10-V reverse-voltage specification of the asymmetrical SCR.

Now if T_d is greater than the specified t_q time of the device, at the end of T_d, the SCR has safely extinguished itself without the need for any external "commutation" circuitry and forward voltage may be safely reapplied. The half sinusoids of current through the SCR and the antiparallel diode provide power to the load resistor R_o.

After t_2, when the $D1$ current has fallen back to zero, both $Q1$ and $D1$ are safely off and the constant current from L_c commences charg-

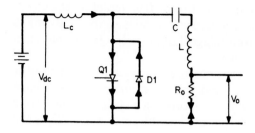

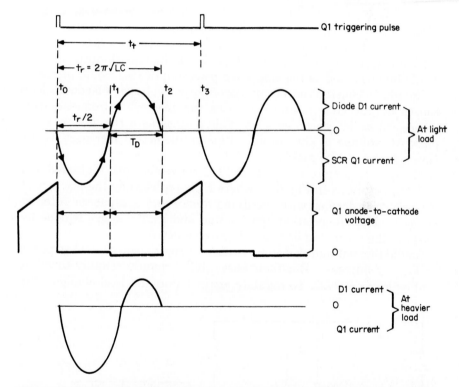

Figure 6.8 Single-ended SCR resonant converter. Inductor L_c charges C to a voltage higher than V_{dc}. When $Q1$ is fired, a sinusoidal flows through $Q1$, delivering power to R_o. At t_1, the sinusoidal current reverses direction and flows through $D1$ again, delivering power to R_o. If T_d is greater than t_q time of $Q1$, the SCR self-extinguishes. During $(t_t - t_r)$ L_c recharges C and the cycle repeats.

ing C back up with its left end positive. During the interval t_3 to t_2, C is charged up to such a DC level that some fraction of its stored energy $(CV^2/2)$ is equal to the energy delivered to the load the next time $Q1$ is triggered. After a time t_t (the triggering period), $Q1$ can be triggered on again and the cycle repeats.

As the load is increased (resistor R_o is decreased), the amplitude of the first half cycle increases and its duration increases somewhat. This decreases the duration of the second half cycle T_d, and care must be taken that the load is not increased to the point where T_d is shorter than t_q, the SCR turnoff time, or the SCR will not turn off successfully.

By choosing the triggering period t_t in the range of 1.5 to 2 times the resonant period t_r at minimum line input and maximum load, the off time $t_t - t_r$ shown in Fig. 6.8 is not too large and consequently the output across R_o is a fairly distortion-free AC sine wave over a large range of load resistors. Capacitance across R_o can reduce the distortion due to the time gap $t_t - t_r$. The circuit can thus be used as a DC/AC converter. As the supply voltage V_{dc} is increased, output power would be increased as the sine-wave peak amplitudes would increase. To maintain constant output power or output voltage, a feedback loop senses output voltage and decreases the triggering frequency (increases t_t) as V_{dc} or R_o goes up. This maintains a roughly constant peak AC voltage at the output, although distortion increases as the time (gap $t_t - t_r$) increases.

The circuit is more useful as DC/DC converter with regulated and isolated output as in Fig. 6.9., where R_o is replaced by the primary of a power transformer with rectifying diodes and a capacitor filter at the secondary. Regulation against line and load changes is done by varying the switching or triggering frequency f_t.

As the line voltage or load resistance increases, the sine-wave peaks in Fig. 6.8 increase. But their base widths remain roughly constant and equal to $\pi\sqrt{LC}$. To regulate against line and load changes, the

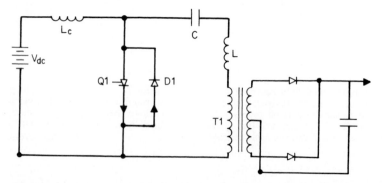

Figure 6.9 A transformer-coupled, series-loaded, single-ended SCR resonant converter.

rectified DC output is sensed with a voltage error amplifier which alters the switching frequency to maintain constant output. If output voltage rises because of an increase in line voltage or a decrease in DC load current, the switching frequency is decreased so as to take less power per unit time from the input. Similarly, a small decrease in output is corrected by an increase in switching frequency.

This method of regulating the output voltage—by variation of the switching frequency—is common to most resonant power supplies as the output current or voltage pulses are constant in width. In nonresonant topologies, regulation is done by operating at a constant switching frequency and varying pulse width to control the DC output voltage.

In such constant-frequency schemes, the power supply switching frequency is generally synchronized to the horizontal line rate in an associated display terminal or to the system's clock rate. This makes it easier to tolerate any RFI noise pickup on the display screen and lessens the possibility of computer logic errors due to noise pickup.

Since this advantage is lost in resonant-topology, variable-frequency, voltage-regulating schemes, these schemes are not acceptable in many applications. Yet it can be argued that although RFI noise pickup, if it exists, is more troublesome with variable-frequency switching supplies, it is less likely to exist. For the sinusoidal currents in resonant supplies have much slower di/dt than do the square-wave currents of fixed frequency, adjustable pulse width supplies, and hence emit less RFI.

The SCR supply was originally made resonant to ensure turnoff of the SCR at the zero crossing of the current sinusoid. This added a further significant advantage. It was seen in Sec. 1.2.4 that with square waves of current, most of the losses in the switching device occur at turnoff as a result of the overlap of falling current in it and rising voltage across it. But with sinusoidal currents, turnoff occurs at zero voltage across the device and such losses are almost nonexistent. Yet the turnon losses due to the relatively slow voltage fall time (Sec. 6.1 text and Fig. 6.5) can be high. If the sine-wave base width $\pi \sqrt{LC}$ is not less than about 8 μs, those losses are also not too great (Fig. 6.5).

This DC/DC converter, used with a single 800-V, 45-A rms SCR can generate 1-kW of output power.[4] An inductor is not needed in the secondary output. For the SCR and diode currents shown in Fig. 6.8 are constant-current pulses whose magnitude is closely equal to the voltage applied across the series LC elements divided by $\sqrt{L/C}$. These constant currents reflect into the secondary as constant currents. Those constant-current pulses flowing into the output resistor produce constant-voltage pulses of similar waveshape. The voltage averaging to obtain a constant ripple-free output voltage is done by the filter capacitor alone. Thus, not requiring an output inductor, the circuit can be used as a high output voltage supply.

A design example showing quantitative design decisions will be presented after the following discussion of more widely used two SCR resonant-bridge-type DC/DC inverters.

6.4 SCR Resonant Bridge Topologies— Introduction

The resonant half bridge (Fig. 6.10) and full bridge (Fig. 6.11) are the most useful SCR circuits. The half bridge, with two 800-V 45-A rms SCRs (Marconi ACR25UO8LG) can deliver up to 4 kW of AC or rectified DC power from a rectified 220-V AC line. A 1200-V version of that device can generate up to 8 kW in a full-bridge circuit. Full-bridge operation is much the same as the half-bridge except, of course, that SCR voltage stresses are twice as great and current levels are

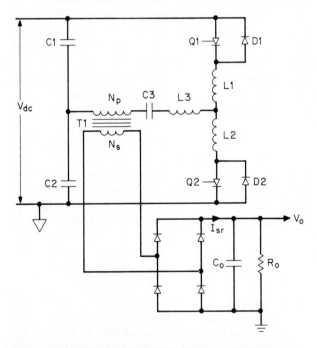

Figure 6.10 SCR resonant half-bridge series loaded. Transistors $Q1$ and $Q2$ are fired on alternate half cycles. Capacitor $C3$ resonates with $L3$ and $L1$ when $Q1$ is on and with $L3$ and $L2$ when $Q2$ is on. At the firing of either SCR, its current goes through a half sinusoid, reverses direction, and flows through the associated antiparallel diode. If the duration of the diode current is greater than the t_q time of the SCR, the SCR self-extinguishes.

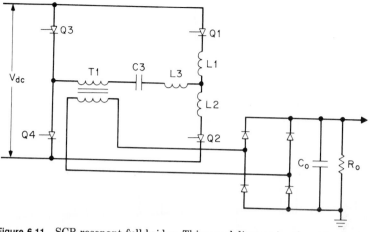

Figure 6.11 SCR resonant full bridge. This can deliver twice the output power of the half bridge.

half those of the half bridge for equal output power. Hence only the half bridge will be discussed here in detail.

The half bridge can be operated *series-loaded* as in Fig. 6.10 with the secondary load reflected via transformer $T1$ in series with a series resonant ($C3$ resonating with the series combination of $L3$ and $L1$ when $Q1$ is on or with the series combination of $L3$ and $L2$ when $Q2$ is on).

In the series-loaded circuit, the secondary load, when reflected into the primary, must not not appear as too high an impedance or the resonant circuit Q will be low and the "on" SCR may not be safely commutated off by the above described resonant current reversal. No output inductor is required in the series-loaded configuration, and hence it can be used for either high or low output DC voltages. The series-loaded circuit can safely survive an output short circuit as the normal load impedance in series with the resonating LC is already small compared to the impedance of the LC elements. But as discussed below, there is a problem when the output load is open-circuited.

Alternatively, the half bridge can be operated *shunt-loaded* as in Fig. 6.12. Here, the output load reflected into the $T1$ primary is fed in shunt with the voltage across the resonating capacitor $C3$. In this case, the output load reflected across $C3$ must not be too low or the resonant circuit Q will be so low as to prevent resonant turnoff of the SCR. Thus, this configuration can easily tolerate an open-loaded but not a short-circuited secondary.

The series-loaded configuration is analyzed as a current source driving the $T1$ primary whereas the shunt-loaded circuit is better analyzed as a voltage source driving the primary. The shunt-loaded cir-

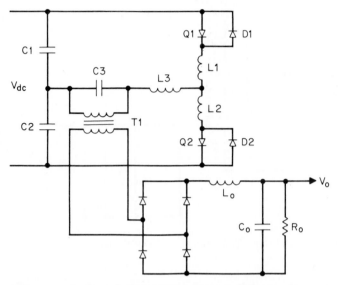

Figure 6.12 A shunt loaded SCR resonant half bridge. Power is taken in shunt across the resonant capacitor. The load reflected into the primary from the secondary must be high so as not to lower the resonant circuit Q. Too low a Q can prevent successful turnoff of the SCR.

cuit does require secondary output inductors when DC output is required, although they may be omitted if large output voltage ripple can be tolerated. For a DC/DC converter, the series-loaded circuit is a better choice.

6.4.1 SCR half-bridge resonant converter, series-loaded—basic operation[9,10]

The series-loaded SCR resonant half-bridge circuit is shown in Fig. 6.10 and its significant waveforms in Fig. 6.13. In Fig. 6.10, when $Q1$ is triggered on, the equivalent circuit is that of a voltage step of magnitude $V_{dc}/2$ applied to a series combination of $L3 + L1$ resonating with $C3$. That resonant circuit is series-loaded with the $T1$ secondary resistance reflected into the primary and that reflected primary resistance is shunted by the $T1$ magnetizing inductance.

If the Q of that equivalent circuit is not too low, current in it is shocked into a sinusoidal "ring" as shown in Fig. 6.13a. During the first half cycle, the half sinusoid of current flows through $Q1$. At the end of that half cycle at t_1, the current reverses and continues flowing through the antiparallel diode $D1$. From t_1 to t_2, current in the SCR is zero, and if that time is greater than the specified t_q time of the device, the SCR extinguishes itself and can safely sustain forward voltage again.

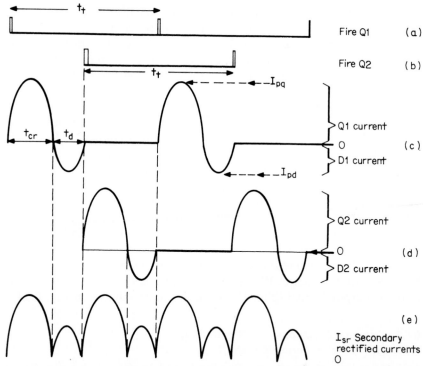

Figure 6.13 Significant currents for series loaded SCR half bridge of Fig. 6.10 for condition of minimum DC input voltage, maximum load output. As line voltage or load resistance increases, the feedback loop will decrease, triggering frequency so as to space the $Q1$, $A2$ sine waves further apart and maintain the average output current and voltage constant.

The period of the resonant ring is $t_r = 2\pi\sqrt{(L_1 + L_3)C_3}$. At light loads, the SCR and diode conduction times (t_{cr} and t_d, respectively) are equal. As the secondary load increases (R_o decreases), t_{cr} and I_{pq} increase and t_d, I_{pd} decrease. Load power must not be increased beyond the point where t_d is less than the maximum specified value of t_q, or the SCR will not turn off successfully.

Now at the next half cycle of the triggering period t_t with $Q1$ safely off, $Q2$ is fired. The resonant period is now $2\pi\sqrt{(L_2 + L_3)C_3}$. Current waveforms of $Q2$, $D2$ are similar to those of $Q1$, $D1$ and are shown in Fig. 6.13b. The $Q1$, $D1$ and $Q2$, $D2$ current waveforms, shown in Fig. 6.13c, are multiplied in the $T1$ secondary by the turns ratio N_p/N_s, rectified and summed by the output diodes.

The DC output voltage is the average of the Fig. 6.13c current waveforms multiplied by the secondary load resistor R_o. Averaging of the output current waveforms to yield a constant and ripple-free DC output voltage is done by the output filter capacitor without requiring an output inductor. After t_t the entire cycle repeats.

The timing relations shown in Fig. 6.13 will hold at minimum DC input voltage and minimum output load resistor (maximum output power). The values of resonating inductance and capacitance will be chosen so that the current amplitudes and the spacings shown in Fig. 6.13c will yield the correct average output current at the desired output voltage at minimum line and maximum load. Calculations to achieve this are shown below. As line and load change, a feedback-loop-sensing output voltage will adjust SCR triggering frequency f_t to keep output voltage constant.

Since the peak currents in Fig. 6.13c are proportional to DC input voltage, as that goes up, the feedback loop will have to decrease f_t to maintain constant secondary average current and hence constant output voltage. Further, since at a fixed DC input voltage and fixed values of L and C, peak currents (Fig. 6.13c, d) are constant, as R_o goes up, the feedback loop will also have to decrease f_t to maintain constant average output voltage. Waveshapes at DC inputs higher than minimum or output loads higher than minimum are shown in Fig. 6.14.

6.4.2 Design calculations—SCR half-bridge resonant converter, series-loaded[9,10]

The circuit configuration is shown in Fig. 6.10 and its significant waveforms, in Figs. 6.13 and 6.14. The discussion herein is based on a paper by D. Chambers.[9]

The first decision to be made is the resonant period or frequency. Assume the use of the Marconi ASCR type ACR25. Figure 6.7 shows its typical turnoff time t_q as 5 μs from an on current of 50 A with a gate bias of 0 V. Assume the worst case is 20 percent higher or 6 μs. Also assume desired operation at minimum DC input and maximum output power at the edge of the continuous mode (as in Fig. 6.13 with no gap between the zero crossing of the diode current and the start of the

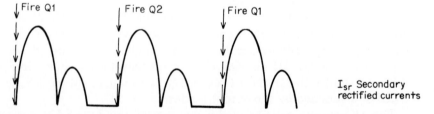

Figure 6.14 Bridge output currents I_{sr} at higher input voltage. Peak currents are higher, forcing feedback loop to decrease triggering frequency to maintain constant output voltage.

opposite SCR current). Then the absolute minimum resonant period as can be seen in Fig. 6.13c would be 12 μs or a resonant frequency of 83 kHz.

However, it was noted in Sec. 6.3, that at high output power t_d the diode conduction time shortens to a not easily calculable value. If it shortened to a value less than t_q, the SCR might not turn off successfully. Thus there should be more margin in the t_d time.

Further, Fig. 6.5 shows that the anode-to-cathode on voltage does not fall very quickly to its quiescent value of 2 to 3 V. To keep the high anode-to-cathode voltage time a small fraction of the SCR conduction time t_{cr}, the resonant half period should be increased to at least four times 2.5 μs. This, as can be seen in Fig. 6.5, puts the anode-to-cathode voltage at the peak of the sinusoidal anode current at about 3 V and is a reasonable compromise. Thus the resonant period is chosen as 20 μs (f_r = 50 kHz). Or

$$T_r = 2\pi\sqrt{(L_3+L_1)(C_3)} = 20 \times 10^{-6} \qquad (6.1)$$

Next the peak voltage on the $T1$ primary (Fig. 6.10) must be determined. Following the suggestion in the Chambers paper,[9] this will be chosen as 60 percent of the minimum voltage across one of the bridge capacitors or

$$\text{Minimum primary voltage} = V_{p(min)} = \frac{0.6 \, V_{dc(min)}}{2} \qquad (6.2)$$

Assuming a bridge output rectifier with a 1-V drop across each rectifier diode, this fixes the $T1$ turns ratio at

$$\frac{N_p}{N_s} = \frac{0.6 V_{dc(min)}}{2(V_o + 2)} \qquad (6.3)$$

At minimum line input, maximum output current, the secondary currents are as shown in Fig. 6.13e with no time gaps between the termination of current in one antiparallel diode and turnon of current in the opposite SCR. Assume, to a close approximation, that even at maximum DC current, SCR and diode currents have equal widths of a half period. Also assume—as in the Chambers paper[9]—that the diode peak current is one-fourth that of the SCR current. Then the average of these Fig. 6.13e SCR plus diode currents is

$$I_{\text{secondary average}} = I_{o(dc)} = \frac{2I_{ps}}{\pi}\frac{T}{2T} + \frac{2I_{ps}}{4\pi}\frac{T}{2T}$$

$$= \frac{1.25 I_{ps}}{\pi}$$

where I_{ps} is the peak primary SCR current after reflection into the secondary. Then

$$I_{ps} = 0.8\pi I_{o(dc)} \tag{6.4}$$

$$I_{pp} = I_{ps}\frac{N_s}{N_p} = 0.8\pi I_{o(dc)}\frac{N_s}{N_p} \tag{6.5}$$

where I_{pp} is the peak primary SCR current.

In Fig. 6.10, V_{ap}, the voltage applied to the series resonant elements when, say, $Q1$ turns on, is the voltage across the bridge capacitor $C1$ plus the transformer voltage peak of $0.6V_{dc(min)}/2$. Or

$$V_{ap} = \frac{V_{dc(min)}}{2} + \frac{0.6V_{dc(min)}}{2} = 0.8V_{dc(min)} \tag{6.6}$$

It can be shown that, to a close approximation, when a step voltage V_{ap} is applied to a series LC circuit, the peak amplitude of the first resonant current pulse is

$$I_{pp} = \frac{V_{ap}}{\sqrt{L/C}} \tag{6.7}$$

Then in this case, where $L = (L_1 + L_3)$, $C = C_3$:

$$\sqrt{(L_1 + L_3)/C_3} = \frac{V_{ap}}{I_{pp}}$$

or

$$\sqrt{(L_1 + L_3)/C_3} = \frac{0.8V_{dc(min)}}{0.8\pi I_{o[dc(min)]}(N_s/N_p)}$$

$$= \frac{V_{dc(min)}(N_p/N_s)}{\pi I_{o(dc)}} \tag{6.8}$$

Thus from Eq. 6.1, which gives the product of $(L_3 + L_1)$, (C_3), and Eq. 6.8, which gives their ratio, values of the resonating elements— $(L_3 + L_1)$ or $(L_3 + L_2)$ and C_3—are fixed for specified values of $V_{dc(min)}$ and the maximum output current $I_{o(dc)}$. The transformer turns ratio is fixed from Eq. 6.3.

The ratio of L_3/L_1 is chosen to minimize off-voltage stress on the SCRs. A smaller ratio is in the direction of lesser off stress and lesser dV/dt stress. The precise ratio is best determined empirically. Inductance L_3 constitutes the transformer primary leakage inductance plus some external inductance. It is best not to rely too much on the leakage inductance alone as it usually has a wide tolerance, and that would result in large tolerances in the resonant period.

6.4.3   Design example—SCR half-bridge resonant converter, series-loaded

The preceding relations will now be used in a design example. Assume the circuit of Fig. 6.10 with the following specifications:

Output power	2000 W
Output voltage	48 V
Output current $I_{o(dc)}$	41.7 A
Input DC voltage, nominal	310 V
Input DC voltage, maximum	370 V
Input DC voltage, minimum	270 V

Then from Eq. 6.3 $N_p/N_s = 0.6 \times 270/2(48 + 2) = 1.62$ and from Eq. 6.1

$$2\pi\sqrt{(L_3 + L_1)C_3} = 20 \times 10^{-6}$$

or

$$\sqrt{(L_3 + L_1)C_3} = 3.18 \times 10^{-6} \qquad (6.1a)$$

From Eq. 6.8

$$\sqrt{\frac{(L_3 + L_1)}{C_3}} = \frac{V_{dc(min)}(N_p/N_s)}{\pi I_{o(dc)}}$$

$$= \frac{270 \times 1.62}{\pi \times 41.7}$$

$$= 3.34 \qquad (6.8a)$$

From Eqs. 6.1a and 6.8a $C_3 = 0.95$ μF and $L_3 + L_1 = 10.6$ μH and from Eqs. 6.6 and 6.7

$$I_{pp} = \frac{V_{ap}}{\sqrt{(L_3 + L_1)/C_3}}$$

$$= \frac{0.8 \times 270}{3.34} = 64.7 \text{ A}$$

and since the maximum duty cycle of this peak SCR current is $t_r/2t_{t(min)} = 0.25$ (Fig. 6.13a and 6.13c), the SCR rms current is $I_{rms(SCR)} = 64.7 \times \sqrt{0.25}/\sqrt{2} = 22.9$ A. This is easily within 40 peak rms capability of the Marconi ACR25U. Also, as assumed above, the antiparallel diode peak current is one-fourth of the SCR current or

64.7/4 = 16.2 A. With a 1.62 turns ratio, the peak rectifier diode currents will be 104.8 and 26.2 A corresponding to the peak SCR and antiparallel diode currents. With such high rectifier diode currents, a full-wave rectifier with one series diode rather than a bridge with two diodes might be preferable.

6.4.4   SCR half-bridge resonant converter, shunt-loaded[6,12]

The ancestor of most of the practical SCR resonant bridge power supplies is Neville Mapham's classical paper.[6] That paper described an SCR shunt-loaded resonant half bridge used as a DC to AC inverter. The circuit was essentially that of Fig. 6.12 with a resistive load at the transformer secondary instead of the rectifier plus output filter.

Mapham's paper made no attempt to regulate the output but showed that over a 10/1 range of output load currents, with no feedback, the output AC voltage was constant to within 1 percent and generated a relatively distortion-free sine wave. A detailed and elegant computer analysis showed that the peak sine-wave output could be regulated against line input changes by changing the SCR triggering frequency.

The computer analysis is presented in terms of normalized relations $(R_o/\sqrt{L/C}, I_{scr}\sqrt{L/C}/E, I_{diode}\sqrt{L/C}/E, V_o/E)$, which permits a simplified design of the circuit with a resistance loaded secondary. Although the analysis is not easily extended to the configuration of a rectifier and LC filter at the output, it provides a very good guide to that circuit.

If the shunt-loaded configuration of Fig. 6.12 is used, output regulation is also achieved by varying the SCR triggering frequency. Output voltage waveshapes at the cathodes of the rectifier in Fig. 6.12 are similar to the current waveshapes of Figs. 6.13c and 6.14 for the series-loaded circuit. The output LC filter averages the voltage waveshapes for the shunt-loaded circuit, whereas the output capacitor alone is needed to average the current waveshapes for the series-loaded case.

Since the shunt-loaded circuit requires output inductors, it has no advantages over the series-loaded configuration. The shunt circuit has only been touched on here to bring attention to the Mapham paper with its useful computer analysis, which is basic to a full understanding of the series-loaded circuit. The shunt-loaded circuit has been used with MOSFETs as a much-higher-frequency DC/DC converter.[13]

6.4.5   Single-ended SCR resonant converter topology design[3,5]

The single-ended SCR resonant converter (Fig. 6.8) has been discussed in qualitative terms in Sec. 6.3. A more quantitative analysis will be presented here. The discussion herein contains some simplifying approximations but is not yet accurate enough to permit a workable design. A more rigorous discussion would require computer analysis of the circuit.

The circuit is shown again in Fig. 6.15 in a more useful configuration with the load coupled to the series resonant circuit through an

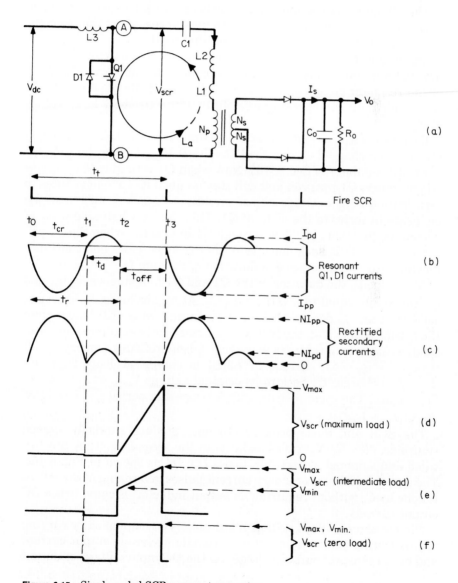

Figure 6.15 Single-ended SCR resonant converter.

isolating transformer. The circuit is a series-loaded circuit with the secondary load reflected into the primary in series with the resonating elements (C_1 and $L_1 + L_2$). The resonating inductance is the leakage inductance L_1 of $T1$ plus another discrete inductance L_2 to make up the total inductance required for the desired resonant period. If L_2 is relatively large compared to L_1, unavoidable tolerances in L_1 are not significant.

The $T1$ magnetizing inductance, although in series with the resonating elements, does not, in most circumstances, affect the resonant period or circuit operation as it is shunted by the secondary load resistance reflected into the primary. But with an open-circuited secondary, the high impedance of the magnetizing inductance can kill the Q of the resonant circuit and prevent SCR turnoff. By gapping the $T1$ core, the circuit can operate successfully with extremely large values of R_o.

Recall the basic circuit operation. Assume that the left-hand side of $C1$ has been charged up to some DC voltage $V_{\max}$ higher than V_{dc} (as the boost regulator of Sec. 1.4.1). Now when $Q1$ is fired with a narrow trigger pulse, $Q1$ turns on and will stay on until its current reduces to zero. With $Q1$ on, a voltage step of amplitude $V_{\max}$ is applied to all the elements in series to the right of $Q1$. This causes a half sine wave of current of duration t_{cr} to flow through $Q1$ in loop L_a. When the $Q1$ primary current falls back down to zero at t_1, it reverses and continues flowing as a half sine wave of duration t_d through $D1$.

At low loads, the duration of the $Q1$ and $D1$ half sine waves (t_{cr} and t_d) are closely equal to $\pi\sqrt{(L_1 + L_2)C_1}$. At higher loads, t_{cr} increases somewhat and t_d decreases. If t_d at its minimum is still longer than the t_q time of the SCR, the SCR will automatically extinguish and can safely sustain forward voltage without falsely refiring. During the off time $t_{off} = (t_3 - t_2)$, current in $L3[L_3$ is chosen at least 20 times $(L_1 + L_2)]$ charges $C1$ back to its original voltage $V_{\max}$ and $Q1$ can be fired again. The cycle repeats with a triggering period $t_t = t_r + t_{off} = (2\pi\sqrt{(L_1 + L_2)C_1}) + t_{off}$.

The SCR and diode primary currents produce similarly shaped sinusoids, $N(= N_s/N_p)$ times as large in the secondary. They are rectified and summed by rectifier diodes $D3$, $D4$ as shown in Fig. 6.15c. The average of these secondary current pulses (averaging of the pulses is done by C_o without requiring an output inductor) is equal to the DC output current.

Direct-current output voltage regulation is accomplished by varying the triggering period to maintain a constant average output current and hence constant output voltage. As the DC input voltage or output resistance R_o increase, t_t is increased by a feedback loop to maintain constant output voltage. As the input voltage or output resistance decrease, t_t is decreased.

6.4.5.1 Minimum trigger period (maximum trigger frequency) selection.

The peak SCR and diode currents I_{pcr}, I_{pd}) of Fig. 6.15b are determined by the peak voltage to which the resonating capacitor $C1$ is charged. These peak currents must be known to fix the triggering period and hence the average output current and average output voltage.

Waveshapes of voltage V_{scr} at the left-hand side of $C1$ (or across the SCR) are shown in Fig. 6.15d to 6.15f for maximum, intermediate, and zero output power. At the instant of a SCR trigger pulse, $C1$ has been charged up to a voltage V_{max} and hence has a stored energy $C_1(V_{max})^2/2$. At the end of the next diode half sine wave t_2 some of this energy has been delivered to the load by the SCR and diode half sine waves.

At intermediate powers, there still is some energy and hence voltage left on the capacitor. Thus when the diode current has fallen back to zero t_2, the left side of $C1$ is unclamped and current from $L3$ starts charging $C1$ up. With some voltage still across $C1$, V_{scr} first steps up by the amount of that voltage V_{min} and then starts rising more slowly as shown in Fig. 6.15e.

At maximum load, all the energy stored at the end of an off time t_0 has been delivered to the load, and hence at the start of the next off time t_3, there is no remaining voltage on $C1$ and hence no front-end step as shown in Fig. 6.15d.

At zero DC load, all the energy stored on $C1$ at the end of an off time still remains on it at the start of the next off time. Hence V_{max} is equal to V_{min} as in Fig. 6.15f. From the waveshapes in Fig. 6.15d to 6.15f, the minimum triggering period t_t can be established thus. Since the inductor $L3$ cannot support a DC voltage, the average voltage at its output end, must equal that at its input end, which is V_{dc}. Thus

$$V_{dc} = \frac{V_{max} + V_{min}}{2} \frac{t_{off}}{t_t}$$

or
$$V_{max} + V_{min} = \frac{2V_{dc}t_t}{t_{off}} \tag{6.9}$$

and from Fig. 6.15d, at maximum load, $V_{min} = 0$, then

$$V_{max} = \frac{2V_{dc}t_t}{t_{off}}$$

But from Fig. 6.15b, $t_{off} = t_t - t_r$, then

$$V_{max} = \frac{2V_{dc}}{1 - t_r/t_t} \qquad (6.10)$$

From Eq. 6.10, V_{max} is calculated for various ratios of t_r/t_t. Calculation will be for an off-line converter and maximum power will be assumed to occur at minimum AC line input and maximum DC output current as those are the conditions for maximum SCR current. Assume that nominal, minimum line inputs are 115 and 98 V AC, respectively, giving approximately 160 and 138 V of rectified DC. Then for the minimum V_{dc} of 138 V from Eq. 6.10, we can construct Table 6.1.

TABLE 6.1

t_r/t_t	V_{max} (at $V_{dc} = 138$ V)	V_{max}, V
0.7	$6.6V_{dc}$	911
0.6	$5.0V_{dc}$	690
0.5	$4.0V_{dc}$	552
0.4	$3.3V_{dc}$	455
0.3	$2.9V_{dc}$	393

From Table 6.1, a good compromise choice for t_r/t_t is 0.6. It still permits using a reasonably inexpensive 800-V SCR. For $t_r = 16$ μs, the resonant half period is 8 μs, which still permits the on-turning SCR to spend most of its on time at a low anode-to-cathode voltage (Fig. 6.5). Then t_t, the minimum trigger period, is 26.6 μs (maximum trigger frequency is 38 kHz). In regulating down to lower output power, the minimum trigger frequency will be about one-third of that or about 13 kHz—not too far down into the audible range.

6.4.5.2 Peak SCR current choice and *LC* component selection. The peak SCR and diode $D1$ currents are shown in Fig. 6.15b. Assume, as for the half bridge (Sec. 6.4.2), that the peak diode current is one-fourth the SCR current. Then rectified secondary currents are as shown in Fig. 6.15c. The average of those currents for a $T1$ turns ratio N is

$$I_{s(av)} = \frac{2I_{pp}N}{\pi}\frac{t_r}{2t_t} + \frac{2I_{pp}N}{4\pi}\frac{t_r}{2t_t}$$

$$= 1.25I_{pp}N\frac{t_r}{\pi t_t} \qquad (6.11)$$

where I_{pp} is the peak primary current (Fig. 6.15b). This is equal to the average or DC output current at minimum line input and maximum current output. The output voltage at minimum output load resistor R_o is

$$V_o = 1.25 N I_{pp} R_o \frac{t_r}{\pi t_t} \qquad (6.12)$$

Now the transformer turns ratio must be chosen and the magnitudes of the resonant LC components selected to yield the peak resonant currents given above.

Choose, as in Sec. 6.4.2 as per the suggestion in the Chambers paper,[9] that the $T1$ primary voltage is taken as 60 percent of the voltage across the entire loop (points A to B in Fig. 6.15a). This is the $0.6V_{max}$ of Eq. 6.10. This voltage is clamped through the turns ratio N against the output voltage plus one diode rectifier drop. Then

$$N = \frac{0.6 V_{max}}{V_o + 1} \qquad (6.13)$$

Now when the SCR is fired, the voltage applied to the series resonant circuit elements is $V_{ap} = V_{max} + 0.6V_{max} = 1.6V_{max}$ and the peak amplitude of the half-sine-wave SCR current pulse is

$$I_{pp} = \frac{V_{ap}}{\sqrt{(L_1 + L_2)/C_1}}$$
$$= \frac{1.6 V_{max}}{\sqrt{(L_1 + L_2)/C_1}} \qquad (6.14)$$

Since, in Eq. 6.11, maximum DC output current is specified and all other terms in that relation are known (Eq. 6.13 and Table 6.1), Eq. 6.14 gives the ratio of $(L_1 + L_2)/C1$. Also since the resonant period t_r was chosen in Sec. 6.4.5.1 as 16 μs, we obtain

$$t_r = 2\pi\sqrt{(L_1 + L_2)C_1} = 16 \times 10^{-6} \qquad (6.15)$$

Between Eqs. 6.14 and 6.15, there are two unknowns and two equations and so both C_1 and $(L_1 + L_2)$ are determined.

6.4.5.3 Design example. Design a single-ended SCR resonant converter with the following specifications:

Output power	1000 W
Output voltage	48 V
Output current	20.8 A

AC input, nominal	115 V AC rms
AC input, minimum	98 V AC rms
Rectified DC, nominal	160 V
Rectified DC, minimum	138 V

From Table 6. 1, chose t_r/t_t = 0.6, giving V_{max} = 690 V. From Eq. 6.13

$$N = \frac{0.6 V_{max}}{V_o + 1}$$

$$= \frac{0.6 \times 690}{49}$$

$$= 8.44$$

From Eq. 6.11

$$I_{s(av)} = I_{o(dc)} = 20.8 = 1.25 I_{pp} N \frac{t_r}{\pi t_t}$$

$$= 1.25 I_{pp} \times 8.44 \left(\frac{0.6}{\pi}\right)$$

or I_{pp} = 10.3 A. Then, from Eq. 6.14

$$I_{pp} = 10.3 = \frac{1.6 V_{max}}{\sqrt{L_1 + L_2)/C_1}}$$

$$= \frac{1.6 \times 690}{\sqrt{(L_1 + L_2)/C_1}}$$

or

$$\sqrt{\frac{(L_1 + L_2)}{C_1}} = 107.8 \tag{6.14a}$$

From Eq. 6.15

$$t_r = 16 \times 10^{-6} = 2\pi\sqrt{(L_1 + L_2)C_1}$$

or

$$\sqrt{(L_1 + L_2)C_1} = 2.55 \times 10^{-6} \tag{6.15a}$$

and from Eqs. 6.14a, 6.15a, C_1 = 0.024 μF, $L_1 + L_2$ = 275 μH.

A choice of a lower value for t_r/t_t would have yielded a lower maximum SCR voltage stress (Table 6.1) and hence possibly greater reliability. But it would have resulted in larger values of t_t (lower trigger frequencies), and at low output power, the resulting value of t_t (Eq. 6.12) would have brought trigger frequency down far into the audible frequency range.

6.5   Cuk Converter Topology—Introduction[14–16]

In its specialized area of application, this is a very imaginative and valuable topology. Its major asset is that at both input and output, ripple currents are continuous, i.e., there is no time gap where the ripple current falls to zero. Thus in the buck regulator of Fig. 1.4, it is seen that if L_o is made sufficiently large, output current is continuous (Fig. 1.4f) but input current is discontinuous (Fig. 1.4d). In the boost regulator (Figs. 1.10, 1.11), input current is continuous (Fig. 1.11, I_{L1}) but the output current through the rectifier diode is discontinuous (Fig. 1.11, I_{D1}).

In applications where very low input and output noise is essential, it is important to have ripple currents at input and output ramp up and down without going back down to zero as in Fig. 1.4f. At the inputs of most topologies (forward converters, push-pulls, bucks, flybacks, and bridges), this is usually done by adding an RFI input filter. But this adds cost and space.

6.5.1   Cuk converter—basic operation

The Cuk converter (Fig. 6.16a) has continuous current at both inputs and outputs as seen in Fig. 16.6e and 6.16f. By making $L1$ and $L2$ sufficiently large, the amplitude of the current ramps can be made extremely small. And as discussed below, by winding $L1$ and $L2$ on the same core, the ripple amplitude can be reduced to zero.

The circuit is shown in Fig. 6.16a in its basic form with its input and output having a common DC return. Input and output returns can be DC isolated by adding a transformer, as will be discussed below.

In its basic nonisolated version, the circuit works as follows (see Fig. 6.16a). When $Q1$ turns on, $V1$ goes steeply negative. Since the voltage across a capacitor cannot change instantaneously, $V2$ goes negative an equal amount, reverse-biasing $D1$ as seen in Fig. 6.16c and 6.16d. With V_{dc} across $L1$, current ramps up linearly in it, adding to its stored energy. But before $Q1$ had turned on, the left-hand end of $C1$ had been charged up to a voltage V_p and its right-hand end had been clamped to ground via $D1$. This had stored an amount of energy $C_1 V_p^2/2$ on it.

Now when $Q1$ has turned on, $C1$ acts as battery delivering current down through $Q1$, up through the bottom end of R_o, and back through $L2$ into the right-hand end of $C1$. Thus the stored energy in $C1$ plus the stored current (or energy) in $L2$ delivers power into R_o and charges the top end of output filter capacitor to a negative voltage $-V_o$.

When $Q1$ turns off, $V1$ goes positive to some voltage V_p, and V_2 follows it up but gets clamped to ground by $D1$ as discussed above. Now

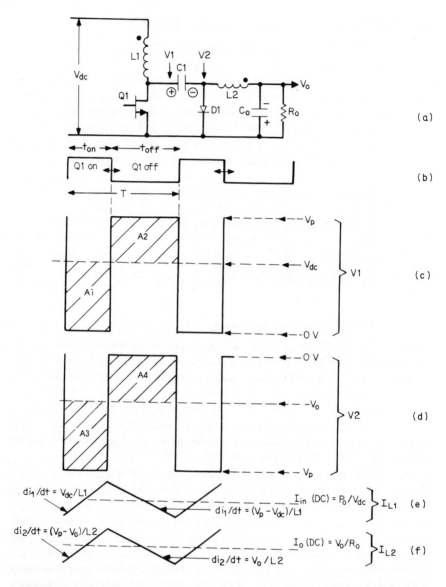

Figure 6.16 Basic Cuk converter with input and output not isolated significant voltage and currents.

with the left-hand end of $L2$ at ground and its right-hand end at $-V_o$, the stored energy or current in $L2$ flows down through $D1$, up through R_o, and back into the right-hand end of $L2$.

When $Q1$ is on, current in $L1$ ramps up at a rate $dI/dt = V_{dc}/L_1$ (Fig. 6.16e). Since $V2$ has gone down by the same amount as $V1$ (V_p), the left-hand end of $L2$ is at $-V_p$ and current in $L2$ ramps up at a rate $dI/dt = (V_o - V_p)/L_2$ as seen in Fig. 6.16f.

When $Q1$ is off, $V1$ has risen to a voltage V_p higher than V_{dc} and current in $L1$ ramps downward at a rate $dI/dt = (V_p - V_{dc})/L_1$ (Fig. 6.16e).

Then, with $Q1$ off, the left-hand end of $L2$ is clamped to ground through $D1$ and with its right-hand end at $-V_o$, current in $L2$ ramps downward at a rate $di/dt = V_o/L_2$ as in Fig. 6.16f. If $L1$, $L2$ are made large enough, these ramp currents rest on some DC level and never fall to zero.

6.5.2 Relation between output/input voltage and Q on time

Since $L1$ is assumed to have zero DC resistance, it cannot support a DC voltage. Hence the voltage at its bottom end ($V1$), averaged over one cycle, must equal the DC voltage at its top end (V_{dc}). This is equivalent to stating that in Fig. 6.16c, the area $A1$ in volt-seconds is equal to the area $A2$ in volt-seconds. Thus

$$V_p \frac{t_{off}}{T} = V_{dc} \tag{6.16a}$$

or

$$V_p = V_{dc} \frac{T}{t_{off}} \tag{1.16b}$$

Now since the voltage change at $V2$ equals the voltage change at $V1$, the bottom end of the $V2$ voltage is at $-V_p$ during t_{on}. During t_{off}, the top end of $V2$ is clamped to 0 V by diode $D1$.

Similarly, since $L2$ cannot support DC voltage, the voltage averaged over one cycle at its left-hand end ($V2$) must equal the DC voltage at its right-hand end ($-V_o$). Here, too, this is equivalent to stating that in Fig. 6.16d, the area $A3$ in volt-seconds is equal to the area $A4$ in volt-seconds. Thus

$$V_p \frac{t_{on}}{T} = V_o \tag{6.17a}$$

or

$$V_p = V_o \frac{T}{t_{on}} \tag{6.17b}$$

Equating relations 6.16b and 6.17b yields

$$V_o = \frac{V_{dc} t_{on}}{t_{off}} \tag{6.18}$$

It is seen from Eq. 6.18 that the magnitude of the DC output voltage can be less than, equal to, or greater than the DC input voltage depending on the ratio t_{on}/t_{off}.

6.5.3 Rates of change of currents in L1, L2

It is interesting to note that (for $L_1 = L_2$) the upslopes of current in $L1$ and $L2$ during t_{on} are equal and their downslopes during t_{off} are also equal. This is shown in Fig. 6.16e and 6.16f. It is this fact that makes it possible to reduce current ripple at the input completely to zero and makes this Cuk converter an ultra-low-noise circuit.

Equality of upslope and downslope currents can be shown as follows. During t_{on}, the upslope of $L1$ current is

$$\frac{+di_1}{dt} = \frac{V_{dc}}{L_1}$$

and again during t_{on}, the upslope of $L2$ current is

$$\frac{+di_2}{dt} = \frac{V_p - V_o}{L_2}$$

From Eqs. 6.16a and 6.18

$$\frac{+di_2}{dt} = \frac{1}{L_2}\left(\frac{V_{dc}T}{t_{off}} - \frac{V_{dc}t_{on}}{t_{off}}\right)$$

$$= \frac{V_{dc}}{L_2 t_{off}}(T - t_{on})$$

$$= \frac{V_{dc}}{L_2}$$

and for $L_1 = L_2$ the upslopes of current in the inductors are equal during t_{on}.

Now consider the downslopes of current during t_{off}. In $L2$, $-di_2/dt = V_o/L2$, and from Eq. 6.18

$$\frac{-di_2}{dt} = \frac{V_{dc}}{L_2}\frac{t_{on}}{t_{off}} \qquad\qquad (6.19a)$$

and in $L1$, $-di_1/dt = (V_p - V_{dc})/L_1$. But from Eq. 6.16b

$$\frac{-di_1}{dt} = \frac{(V_{dc}T/t_{off}) - V_{dc}}{L_2}$$

$$= \frac{V_{dc}}{L_2} \frac{T - t_{off}}{t_{off}}$$

$$= \frac{V_{dc}}{L_2} \frac{t_{on}}{t_{off}} \tag{6.19b}$$

Thus again, for $L_1 = L_2$, the downslopes of the inductor currents during t_{off} are equal and of magnitude given by Eq. 6.19a and 6.19b. This is seen in Fig. 6.16e and 6.16f.

6.5.4 Reducing input ripple currents to zero

Now the current ramps at the input and output can be reduced to zero, yielding pure DC in those lines if $L1$ and $L2$ are wound on the same core with the polarities as shown in Fig. 6.17.

If $L1$, $L2$ are wound on the same core as in Fig. 6.17, that core is now a transformer. During the on time, current flows from V_{dc} into the dot end of $L1$ in an upgoing ramp as seen in Fig. 6.16e. But in $L2$, its dot end is positive with respect to its no-dot end, and by transformer action, it forces a voltage across $L1$, making its dot end positive with respect to its no-dot end. This forces a "secondary" current from the dot end of $L1$ back into V_{dc}. This current is a positive-going ramp of the same upslope as the upslope of current from V_{dc}.

Since these two upslopes are of equal magnitude (as demonstrated in Sec. 6.5.3) but with the currents flowing in opposite directions, the net current change during t_{on} is zero; i.e., current flow in V_{dc} is pure DC. That current is $P_o/V_{dc}E$, where P_o is the output power and E is the efficiency.

A similar line of reasoning demonstrates that if the coupling be-

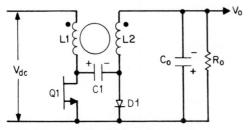

Figure 6.17 If $L1$, $L2$ are wound on the same core, input and output ripple currents are very closely equal to zero. The ramp currents into the primary are bucked out by an equal and oppositely directed ramp rate reflected into the primary from the secondary. A similar cancellation occurs in the secondary.

tween $L1$ and $L2$ is 100 percent, the current in the load is also pure DC with no ripple component. That current is V_o/R_o.

Further, since it has been shown that the current downslopes in $L1$ and $L2$ during t_{off} are equal, similar reasoning indicates that there are also no ripple currents in the input or output lines during t_{off}.

6.5.5 Isolated outputs in the Cuk converter

In most instances, output returns must be DC-isolated from input returns. This can be done with the addition of a 1/1 isolating transformer as shown in Fig. 6.18. Output voltage is still determined by the ratio t_{on}/t_{off}, and the output polarity can be either positive or negative, depending on which end of the secondary circuit is grounded.

Thus, although the Cuk converter of Fig. 6.18 is a very clever way of producing pure DC currents in input and output lines, the requirement of two pieces of magnetics (the $L1,L2$ inductor core and $T1$) is a high price to pay for the advantage.

6.6 Low Output Power "Housekeeping" or "Auxiliary" Topologies—Introduction[15–17]

These are not strictly "topologies" having a broad range of usages; rather, they are specialized circuits for unique applications. But since they generate an output voltage which serves a vital function in any switching power supply design, they are discussed here as separate topologies.

All the topologies discussed thus far require a low power (1 to 3 W) supply of about 10- to 15-V output. It is used to feed the usual

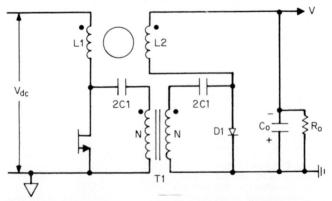

Figure 6.18 By adding a 1/1 isolating transformer, output return is DC-isolated from input return. Either a positive or negative output is now possible depending on which end of the secondary is grounded.

pulse-width-modulating (PWM) chip for the main "power train" and power the logic, sensing circuits which perform various housekeeping functions. Such housekeeping functions may include over-current, overvoltage sensing and protection, remote signaling, and correct turnon, and turnoff sequencing for each output in a multi-output supply.

These housekeeping supplies need not always be regulated as the usual loads can tolerate a relatively large range of supply voltage (± 15 percent maximum). But reliability is improved, and more pre-dictable operation of the main power train results if the housekeeping supply is regulated—usually ±2 percent is adequate. The important objectives for these supplies is that they be low in parts count and cost and occupy only a small fraction of the space that the main power train, with all its outputs, occupies.

6.6.1   Housekeeping power supply—on output or input ground?

In any new design, an initial and major decision must be made as to whether the housekeeping power supply with the PWM chip which it powers should be located on output or input ground. The load-driving outputs are located on output ground, which is, in most cases, DC-isolated from input ground. The main switching power transistors are located on input ground—one end of the rectified AC line in off-line converters or at one end of the DC prime power source in battery-operated DC/DC converters.

Thus, in regulating the output voltage, a DC error amplifier must be located on output ground to sense voltage, compare it to a reference voltage, and produce an amplified error voltage. This amplified error voltage is the difference between the reference and a fraction of the output voltage. The amplified error voltage is then used to control width of the pulse which drives the main power transistor or transistors which are located on input ground. A typical example of this is shown in Fig. 2.1.

Since output and input ground are DC-isolated and may be at DC voltage levels tens or hundreds of V apart, the width-modulated pulse cannot be DC-coupled to the power transistor.

Thus if the error amplifier and pulse-width modulator are on output ground (usually in the PWM chip), the width-modulated pulse is transferred across the output ground–input ground barrier by a pulse transformer. It is the function of the housekeeping supply, whose input power comes from the prime power source at input ground, to produce, referenced to output ground, the usual 10 to 15 V for the 1 to 3 W of housekeeping power.

Such a housekeeping supply is also often used when the PWM chip is located on input ground. Although power for the chip may be derived from an auxiliary winding on the main transformer when the main power transistor is being driven, if the drive is shut down (for overvoltage or overcurrent reasons), that power goes away and it is no longer possible to energize remote indicators. Further, on shutdown, as voltage from the auxiliary winding goes away, supply voltage for the PWM chip decays, and odd time races causing excessive pulse width can occur and may cause failures.

In general, it is far more reliable to have a housekeeping supply which is always present instead of deriving it ("bootstrapping" it) from an auxiliary winding on the main power transformer.

An alternative method of transmitting a measure of the output voltage across the output ground–input ground barrier to width-modulate the power transistor on input ground is via an optical coupler. But this also requires a housekeeping supply on input ground if bootstrapping from an auxiliary winding on the main power transformer is considered undesirable.

Some schemes for implementing these housekeeping supplies are discussed below.

6.6.2 Housekeeping supply alternatives

In an attempt to minimize the parts count of housekeeping supplies, many designers have resorted to single- or two-transistor transformer coupled feedback, self-oscillating circuits. This saves the space and cost of a PWM chip or a stable multivibrator for generating the required AC drive frequency to some kind of a driven converter. Further, by using a transformer coupled feedback oscillator, adding a separate winding on the transformer, provides output power referenced to any desired DC voltage level. The feedback from a collector to a base winding which keeps the circuit oscillating also provides sufficient drive to deliver the required power from the output winding.

Such self-oscillating housekeeping converters are very well covered in Keith Billings' handbook.[16]

These self-oscillating converters appear at first glance to be very attractive because of their simple circuit and low parts count. But without additional circuitry, most do not produce regulated DC output voltage and have various other shortcomings. Adding circuitry to regulate the output and overcome any other shortcomings increases internal dissipation, parts count, and circuit complexity.

At some point it becomes debatable whether these self-oscillating converters are a better choice than a conventional single-transistor, low-power, low-component-count-driven converter such as a flyback, fed from its own PWM chip.

With the increasingly lower price of a PWM chip, no need for an output inductor and a simple scheme for regulating its output voltage on output ground by sensing the voltage of a slave winding on input ground, the flyback is a credible alternative to a self-oscillating circuit.

Nevertheless, two of the most frequently considered self-oscillating types—the Royer and Jensen oscillating converters—are considered below and compared to a simple flyback.

6.6.3 Specific housekeeping supply block diagrams

Figures 6.19 to 6.21 show the block diagrams of three reasonable approaches for a housekeeping supply where the error amplifier and pulse width modulator are in a PWM chip on output ground.

6.6.3.1 Housekeeping supples for AC prime power.
Figure 6.19 shows the simplest and most frequently used scheme when the prime power is AC. A small (usually 2- to 6-W) 50/60-Hz transformer is powered from the AC input and has its secondary referenced to output ground. Such transformers are available from a large number of manufacturers and have tapped primaries so that they can be fed from either 115 or 220 V AC—either 50 or 60 Hz.

Typical sizes are 1.88 × 1.56 × 0.85 in for a 6VA unit or 1.88 × 1.56 × 0.65 in for a 2VA unit. They come with a large range of standard secondary voltages and usually have two secondaries which can be wired in series for full-wave center-tapped output rectifier or in

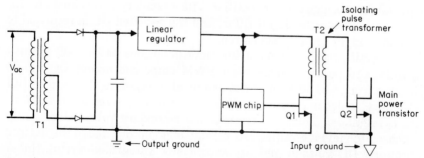

Figure 6.19 For an off-the-AC-line converter, the simplest housekeeping supply is a small (2-W) 60-Hz isolating transformer with its secondary generating a rectified 15 V, referenced to output ground. This is followed by an inexpensive linear regulator (12-V output) which is referenced to output.

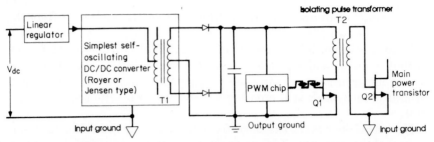

Figure 6.20 A housekeeping supply for DC input voltage. When AC voltage is not present to provide a rectified DC at output ground, a simple magnetically coupled feedback oscillator fed from the DC at input ground is used as a DC/DC converter to provide output voltage reference to output ground to power the PWM chip on output ground. The housekeeping supply output is proportional to the input voltage. Input regulator may be unnecessary if main PWM chip can tolerate ±10 percent input voltage variation.

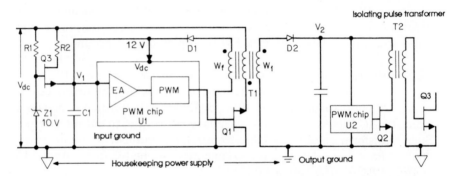

Figure 6.21 A minimum-parts-count flyback as a housekeeping supply. Although this approach may have more parts than Fig. 6.20, it generates a regulated output V_2 without requiring any linear regulators and at the 2- to 3-W power level, may require less input power than that shown in Figs. 6.19 and 6.20.

parallel for a bridge output rectifier. The secondary is rectified and filtered with a capacitor input filter, and the rectified DC is returned to output or input ground as desired.

The rectified DC will have the same tolerance as the AC input— usually ±10 percent. Since most PWM chips can accept DC inputs ranging from 8 to 40 V, it is not essential to regulate the output. But in general, safer and more predictable performance results if the output is regulated. Thus, the transformer secondary voltage frequently is chosen to yield a rectified DC voltage of about 3 V above the desired regulated DC voltage and an inexpensive integrated-circuit linear regulator in a TO 220 package is added in series after the filter capacitor as shown in Fig. 6.19. The configuration is usually designed to yield a regulated +12-V output and achieves an efficiency of about 55 percent at 3-W output at a 10 percent high-line input.

6.6.3.2 Oscillator-type housekeeping supply for AC prime power. But when the prime input power is DC, there is no AC voltage easily available to produce a rectified DC at output ground. Figure 6.20 shows a usual configuration for this case.[17] A simple magnetically coupled feedback oscillator fed from the DC input produces high-frequency square-wave output in a secondary referenced to output ground.

The secondary is rectified and filtered with a capacitor input filter, and the resultant DC is returned to output ground. Because of the high-frequency square wave, the filter capacitor after secondary rectification is far smaller than is required for the 60-Hz rectifier-filter of Fig. 6.19.

The rectified DC output in such a scheme is almost often proportional to DC input voltage. Thus, if DC output voltage variation of about ±10 percent is acceptable, this is a very efficient and low-component-count scheme if an efficient oscillator is available. There are a number of oscillator configurations which can achieve efficiencies of 75 to 80 percent at an output power level of 3 W.[16] One such particularly useful oscillator, the Royer circuit, will be discussed below.

If regulated DC output is required, the oscillator is preceded by an integrated-circuit linear regulator as shown in Fig. 6.20. Adding the linear preregulator would drop the total efficiency down to about 44 percent (assuming a telephone industry supply where the maximum DC input is 60 V and the linear preregulator drops that to 35 V—just below the minimum specification for a telephone industry supply).

At a small increase in parts count and cost, by replacing the linear regulator of Fig. 6.20 by a simple buck regulator, efficiency can be brought up to 70 and possibly 75 percent at a 3-W output power level.

6.6.3.3 Flyback-type housekeeping supplies for DC prime power. Now, however, with the added cost and component count needed to produce regulated DC in the scheme of Fig. 6.20, simple self-oscillator schemes begin to lose their attractiveness. Figure 6.21 shows a third alternative for the housekeeping supply. It is a simple flyback driven from one of the very many currently inexpensive PWM chips. It is powered from the DC prime power at input ground and a secondary winding $W1$ delivers DC voltage referenced to output ground.

In Figure 6.21, the PWM chip is powered via emitter-follower $Q3$ at initial turnon. At initial turnon, the $Q3$ output voltage is one base-emitter voltage drop less than the 10-V zener diode $Z1$. The resulting 9-V output at the $Q3$ emitter is enough to power the PWM chip ($U1$) which commences driving flyback transistor $Q1$ and delivers, via $W1$, output power to the main PWM chip ($U2$) on output ground.

As $U1$ is now powered via $Q3$, a bootstrap winding W_f on the flyback transformer starts generating output voltage. The number of turns on W_f is chosen to produce at filter capacitor $C1$, a voltage of about 12 V, which is higher than the 9 V at that point when it is being fed from the $Q3$ emitter. Thus with the emitter of $Q3$ at 12 V and its base at 10 V, its base is reverse-biased and it turns off. The auxiliary PWM chip on input ground now continues to be powered from W_f, and the main PWM chip on output ground continues to be powered via $W1$.

Resistor $R2$ is chosen small enough to deliver the current required by $U1$ during the initial turnon interval. Dissipation in $R2$ is negligible as that interval lasts only a few tens of microseconds. Resistor $R1$ carries current continuously but dissipates very little power as it carries only the $Q3$ base current which need be only about 1 mA to supply the initial startup current of about 10 to 20 mA for $U1$.

The error amplifier in $U1$ senses its own bootstrapped supply voltage V_1 and keeps it constant as a "master." The output voltage V_2, from $W1$ is a "slave" and is also quite constant (within 1 to 2 percent) as slaves track the master very well in a flyback topology.

6.6.4 Royer oscillator housekeeping supply—basic operation[17,18]

This configuration is shown in Fig. 6.22a. It was one of the earliest applications of transistors to power electronics and was conceived in 1955, only a few years after transistors were invented.[1]

It had been used to generate square-wave AC and with rectification, as a DC/DC converter up to a power level of a few hundred watts. But in its original form, it had two significant drawbacks which limited its usefulness and in some cases made it unreliable. But with the addition of three small changes and with more modern components, it has become a valuable circuit—at power levels as low as < 10 W and up to the 200- and possibly 300-W power level.

The original and basic Royer oscillator shown in Fig. 6.22a works as follows. It is a push-pull circuit with positive feedback from collectors to the base windings to keep it oscillating. The positive feedback can be seen from the dots on the collector and base windings.

Thus, assume that $Q1$ has been turned on and is in saturation. The no-dot end of its half primary N_{p1} is positive, and hence the no-dot end of its base winding N_{b1} is also positive. Voltage across N_{p1} is V_{dc} (assuming negligible V_{ce} drop); N_{p1} delivers output current to the load via N_{s1} and also enough current to the $Q1$ base via N_{b1} and $R1$ to keep $Q1$ on and in saturation at the maximum current reflected into the primary by the minimum R_o.

The $T1$ transformer core is made of material with a square hyster-

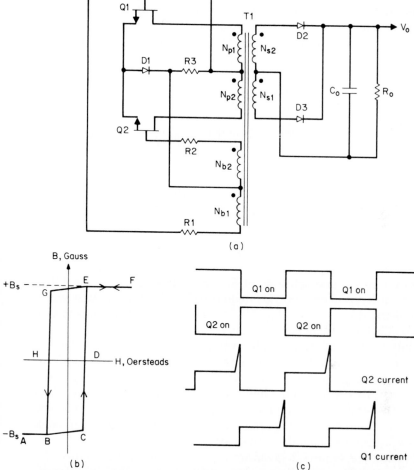

Figure 6.22 (*a*) Basic Royer oscillator. (*b*) Square hysteresis loop of *T*1 core. (*c*) Characteristic high current spikes at end of on time. These spikes are major drawbacks in Royer oscillators. As long as the core is on the vertical part of its hysteresis loop, the positive feedback from N_p to N_b widings keeps a transistor on and in saturation. When the core has moved to either the top or the bottom of its hysteresis loop, coupling between the collector and base windings immediately drops to zero as the core permeability in such a square loop material is unity. The on transistor's base voltage and current drop to zero, and its collector voltage starts to rise. Some small residual air coupling couples this rising collector voltage into the opposite base, and by positive feedback, the opposite transistor turns on. In one half period, the core moves along the path *CDEF*, then in the next half period along the path *FEGHBA*.

esis loop as seen in Fig. 6.22b. Assume that when $Q1$ turned on initially, the core was at point C on its hysteresis loop. With a voltage V_{dc} across N_{p1}, the rate of change of flux density in the core is given by Faraday's law as

$$\frac{dB}{dt} = \frac{V_{dc} \times 10^{+8}}{N_{p1}A_e} \qquad (6.20)$$

The core moves up the hysteresis loop from negative saturation $-B_s$ to positive saturation $+B_s$ along the path CDE. The time required for this is given by Eq. 6.20 as

$$T1 = \frac{T}{2} = \frac{dB\,N_{p1}A_e \times 10^{-8}}{V_{dc}}$$

$$= \frac{2B_s N_{p1}A_e \times 10^{-8}}{V_{dc}} \qquad (6.21)$$

When the core has reached point E, it is saturated, its permeability is close to unity, and coupling between the $Q1$ collector and base windings suddenly drops to zero. The $Q1$ base current quickly drops to zero and $Q1$ collector voltage starts rising.

A small residual air coupling from the dot end of N_{p1} to the dot end of N_{b2} starts turning $Q2$ on. As it commences turning on, positive feedback from the N_{p2} to the N_{b2} winding speeds up the turnon process until $Q2$ is fully on. When $Q1$ had been on, the no-dot end of N_{p1} had been positive and the core had moved up the hysteresis loop. But now with $Q2$ on, the dot end of N_{p2} is positive and the core is driven back down the hysteresis loop along the path EGHBA.

It requires the same $T/2$ given by Eq. 6.21 to move back down the hysteresis loop. The preceding cycles repeat and thus the circuit oscillates at a frequency given by

$$F = \frac{1}{T} = \frac{V_{dc} \times 10^{+8}}{4B_s N_p A_e} \qquad (6.22)$$

In Fig. 6.22a, the function of resistor $R3$ is to start the circuit oscillating. When V_{dc} is first applied, neither $Q1$ nor $Q2$ is on and the above cycles cannot commence. But current from V_{dc} flows down through $R3$ to the base windings center tap, then through either half base winding, through its base resistor and then its base, and the cycle can now start.

In general, the transistor with the highest gain will be the one to turn on first. Once the circuit is oscillating, base current flows from the outer end of one base winding, through its base resistor, its base, out of the transistor emitter, through $D1$, and then back into the base winding center tap.

The circuit of Fig. 6.22a shows only one of many possible base drive configurations. The base resistors shown serve to limit base current which may be excessive at high temperature and cause long transistor storage delay. Collector current limiting may be done with emitter resistors. Baker clamps (to be discussed in a later chapter on bipolar base drives) may be used to make the circuit less sensitive to load changes, production spread in transistor gain, and temperature.

6.6.4.1 Royer oscillator drawbacks[17].

The basic Royer oscillator has two major drawbacks, but these can be corrected by quite simple means. The effect of the first drawback can be seen in Fig. 6.22c as an ultra-high-current spike at the end of a transistor on time. This spike may last only 1 to 2 μs but may be up to three or five times the current prior to the spike.

The spike occurs at a collector voltage about equal to the supply voltage and thus adds significantly to the transistor dissipation. Since it comes at simultaneously high current and voltage, it may exceed the safe operating area (SOA) boundary and cause failure by "second breakdown" even if the average dissipation is low.

The spike is inherent to the very nature of the Royer oscillator, and it can be explained as follows. During the time—say—$Q1$ is on, $Q2$ has a reverse bias and is held off (observe the dots at the base windings). When the core has moved up—say, to the top of its hysteresis loop—it saturates, the windings can no longer support voltage and the $Q1$ collector voltage rises.

However, its base voltage does not immediately go negative to turn-off collector current. It goes negative only after the stored base charges drain away and $Q2$ has turned on sufficiently to produce a solidly negative voltage at the no-dot end of N_{p2} and hence at the no-dot end of N_{b1}. During this delay between core saturation at the end of one on time and the flipover to the opposite transistor turnon, the off-turning transistor operates with high collector voltage and a high-current spike and may fail.

The second drawback is really part of and a partial cause of the first. It is the long delay between core saturation on one side and turnon of the opposite transistor. During this delay, voltage at the base of the off-turning transistor hangs on at about the 0.5-V level and drifts slowly negative before being pulled down abruptly by opposite transistor turning solidly on.

While the off-turning base is drifting slowly down from the 0.5-V level, the transistor is still partially on at a high collector-to-emitter voltage. Frequently, while the base hangs on thus, the partially on transistor will oscillate at a very high frequency. This can easily be corrected by small capacitors—empirically chosen between 100 and 500 pF—cross-coupled from collectors to opposite bases.

There is a further drawback in that the oscillator square-wave frequency is directly proportional to supply voltage (Eq. 6.22). There are many systems-related objections to a variable-frequency switching power supply. They all relate to the fact any RFI generated will cover a wider and more continuous frequency spectrum with a variable frequency as opposed to a fixed-frequency switching power supply.

Figure 6.23a shows the schematic and critical waveforms for a typical Royer oscillator DC/DC converter for 2.4-W output operating from 38 V DC—the minimum specified input for a telephone industry power supply.

The Royer oscillator is clearly low in parts count, but Fig. 6.23c shows the aforementioned spikes at the end of turnon and also in this case at the start of turnon. Collector voltages are shown in Fig. 6.23b. The low efficiency of only 50.6 percent is a consequence of the dissipation due to the current spikes at turnon and turnoff.

6.6.4.2 Current-fed Royer oscillator[19].

By simply adding an inductor in series with Royer transformer center tap, the aforementioned current spikes at turnoff and turnon are eliminated and efficiency is greatly increased.

The addition of the series inductor makes the circuit constant-current-fed as opposed to voltage-fed and achieves all the advantages of current-fed topologies discussed in Sec. 5.6. The series inductor helps in the following way. When the core has saturated on one side, the associated transistor commences having a large current spike with a large di/dt. Since the current in an inductor cannot change instantaneously, the voltage at the transformer center tap drops down to ground and the collector current is limited to the value it had just prior to core saturation.

Now the start current from $R3$ turns on the opposite transistor and both transistors are on simultaneously at close to zero collector-to-emitter voltage—certainly for the duration of the storage time in the off-turning transistor. Now the off-turning transistor turns off at zero collector-to-emitter voltage—the condition for minimum transient turnoff dissipation (Sec. 2.2.12.1). The on-turning transistor turns on at zero collector-to-emitter voltage, which also minimizes transient turnon losses.

The benefits from this inductor or constant-current-fed Royer can be seen in Fig. 6.24. There the same Royer circuit of Fig. 6.23 was fed from an adjustable voltage power supply through a series 630-μH inductor (50 turns on 1408-3C8 ferrite core with a total 2-mil air gap).

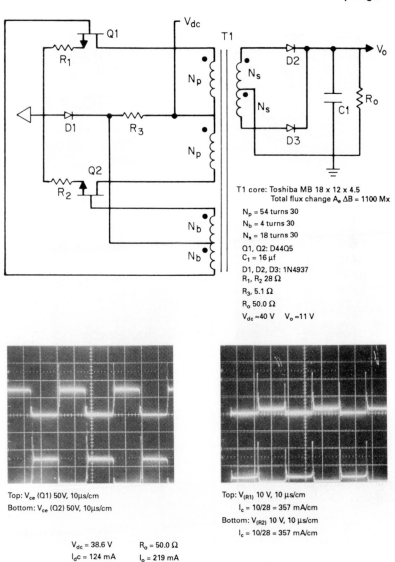

T1 core: Toshiba MB 18 x 12 x 4.5
Total flux change $A_e \, \Delta B = 1100$ Mx

N_p = 54 turns 30
N_b = 4 turns 30
N_s = 18 turns 30

Q1, Q2: D44Q5
C_1 = 16 µf
D1, D2, D3: 1N4937
R_1, R_2 28 Ω
R_3, 5.1 Ω
R_o 50.0 Ω
$V_{dc} \approx 40$ V $V_o \approx 11$ V

Top: V_{ce} (Q1) 50V, 10µs/cm
Bottom: V_{ce} (Q2) 50V, 10µs/cm

Top: $V_{(R1)}$ 10 V, 10 µs/cm
    I_c = 10/28 = 357 mA/cm
Bottom: $V_{(R2)}$ 10 V, 10 µs/cm
    I_c = 10/28 = 357 mA/cm

V_{dc} = 38.6 V	R_o = 50.0 Ω
$I_d c$ = 124 mA	I_o = 219 mA
P_{in} = 4.78 W	P_o = 2.42 W
V_o = 10.99 V	Efficiency = 50.6%

Figure 6.23 A typical Royer oscillator using a square hysteresis loop core, frequently used as a low-power "housekeeping supply" to power a PWM chip on output ground with its own power derived from power source on input ground. It is low in parts count, but the high-current spikes at the end of on time and often at start of turnon make it unreliable and undesirable despite its low parts count.

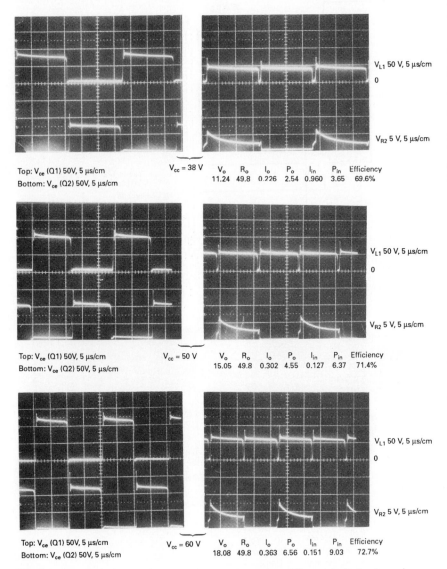

Top: V_{ce} (Q1) 50V, 5 μs/cm
Bottom: V_{ce} (Q2) 50V, 5 μs/cm

$V_{cc} = 38$ V

V_o	R_o	I_o	P_o	I_{in}	P_{in}	Efficiency
11.24	49.8	0.226	2.54	0.960	3.65	69.6%

V_{L1} 50 V, 5 μs/cm

0

V_{R2} 5 V, 5 μs/cm

Top: V_{ce} (Q1) 50V, 5 μs/cm
Bottom: V_{ce} (Q2) 50V, 5 μs/cm

$V_{cc} = 50$ V

V_o	R_o	I_o	P_o	I_{in}	P_{in}	Efficiency
15.05	49.8	0.302	4.55	0.127	6.37	71.4%

V_{L1} 50 V, 5 μs/cm

0

V_{R2} 5 V, 5 μs/cm

Top: V_{ce} (Q1) 50V, 5 μs/cm
Bottom: V_{ce} (Q2) 50V, 5 μs/cm

$V_{cc} = 60$ V

V_o	R_o	I_o	P_o	I_{in}	P_{in}	Efficiency
18.08	49.8	0.363	6.56	0.151	9.03	72.7%

V_{L1} 50 V, 5 μs/cm

0

V_{R2} 5 V, 5 μs/cm

Figure 6.24 Waveform in a current-fed Royer oscillator. By adding an inductor in series between V_{cc} and the transformer center tap, the high-current spikes at the start and end of the transistor on time (Fig. 6.22c) are eliminated and efficiency improves greatly. This occurs because the center tap voltage drops to zero when both transistors are simultaneously on for a brief instant at each transition. Waveforms are for the circuit of Fig. 6.22a with an inductor of 630 μH in series with V_{cc} and at 38, 50, and 60 V.

TABLE 6.2

$V_{dc(in)}$, V	$I_{dc(in)}$, mA	P_{in}, W	V_{out}, V	R_o, Ω	P_{out}, W	Efficiency, %
38.0	96	3.65	11.24	49.8	2.54	69.6
50.0	127	6.37	15.05	49.8	4.55	71.4
60.0	151	9.03	18.08	49.8	6.56	72.7

The transistor currents shown in Fig. 6.24 show no sign of an end of on-time spike. The numerical data of Fig. 6.24 are summarized in Table 6.2.

It is seen from Table 6.2 that efficiency has averaged about 71 percent with a constant load over the 38- to 60-V range of telephone industry specifications for power supplies. This compares to the 50.6 percent efficiency for the same Royer with the same 49.8-Ω load resistor without the series input inductor (Fig. 6.23).

The voltage drop down to zero at the transformer center tap, due to the input inductor, is clearly seen in Figs. 6.24 and 6.25.

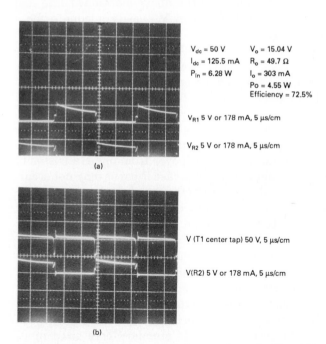

$V_{dc} = 50$ V $\qquad V_o = 15.04$ V
$I_{dc} = 125.5$ mA $\qquad R_o = 49.7$ Ω
$P_{in} = 6.28$ W $\qquad I_o = 303$ mA
$\qquad\qquad\qquad$ Po = 4.55 W
$\qquad\qquad\qquad$ Efficiency = 72.5%

V_{R1} 5 V or 178 mA, 5 μs/cm

V_{R2} 5 V or 178 mA, 5 μs/cm

(a)

V (T1 center tap) 50 V, 5 μs/cm

V(R2) 5 V or 178 mA, 5 μs/cm

(b)

Figure 6.25 (a) Voltage across emitter resistors in Fig. 6.22 with 1630 μH in series T1 center tap. (b) Circuit as in Fig. 6.24a, showing T1 center tap voltage dropping to zero at each transmission.

Thus if output voltage variations of 11 to 18 V for input changes of 38 to 60 V were acceptable, the unregulated, current-fed Royer DC/DC converter would be a very good choice because of its very low parts count.

6.6.4.3 Buck preregulated current-fed Royer converter.

In many applications, however, regulated output voltage is required. Output voltage regulation can be achieved with very little more complexity and cost by preceding the Royer with a buck regulator as in Figs. 6.26 and 6.27. Since buck regulators can quite easily be built with efficiencies of 90 percent, total efficiency does not suffer too much even though the power is handled twice—in the buck and in the Royer. Figure 6.27 shows the composite efficiency ranges from 57.9 to 69.5 percent over an input voltage range of 38 to 60 V and an output power range of 2.3 to 5.7 W.

For Fig. 6.27, the buck regulator sensed output of the buck itself, keeping it constant and running the Royer open loop. This was good enough as the Royer output voltage is constant for constant input voltage and has quite good open-loop load regulation. In Fig. 6.27 it is seen that output voltage change over the above-mentioned line and load change was only from 9.79 to 10.74 V—easily adequate for a housekeeping power supply.

But if better load regulation is desired, the error amplifier in the buck can sense a bootstrapped slave secondary off the main power transformer as described in Sec. 6.6.3.3 and Fig. 6.21.

The circuit details for the data of Fig. 6.27 are shown in Fig. 6.26.

6.6.4.4 Square hysteresis loop materials for Royer oscillators.

The transformer core for a Royer oscillator must have a square hysteresis loop. If the loop is not square, turnon flipover from one transistor to the other will be sluggish and in the worst case flipover may not occur.

The on transistor may push the core to the top of the hysteresis loop and hang up there, delivering sufficient base drive to keep itself on, yet not turning the opposite transistor on. If this occurs, the partially on transistor will fail in a few tens of microseconds.

Most ferrite core materials do not have a sufficiently square hysteresis loop, but there are various other materials which do. The earliest material was an alloy of 79% nickel, 17% iron, and 4% molybdenum available from a number of manufacturers under various trade names. Magnetics Inc. refers to its material as Square Permalloy 80 and has probably the largest selection of standard core sizes in it. Other manufacturers' trade names for roughly the same material are 4-79 Permalloy, Square Mu 79, and Square Permalloy. The material has a saturation flux density ranging between 6600 and 8200 G.

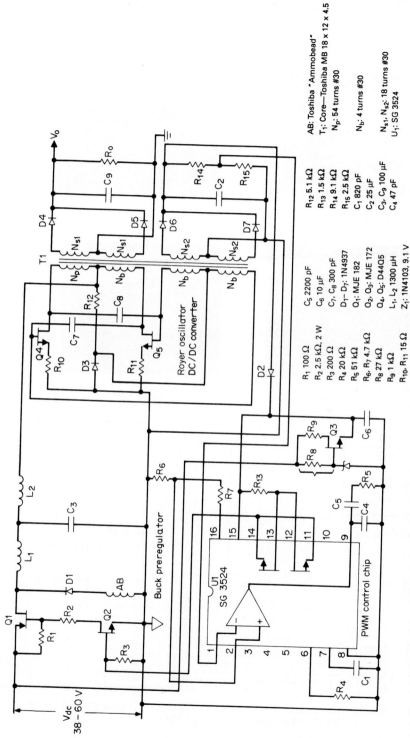

Figure 6.26 A buck regulator driving a current-fed Royer DC/DC converter for constant V_o load. Feedback can be taken in from the buck output mode with the Royer DC/DC-converter-operated open loop. This yields regulation of better than 0.5 percent over input change from 38 to 60 V, but load regulation of only ±5 percent. For better load regulation, feedback is taken from the bootstrapped slave output, which is referenced to input ground as shown.

AB: Toshiba "Ammobead"
T_1: Core—Toshiba MB 18 x 12 x 4.5
N_p: 54 turns #30

N_b: 4 turns #30

N_{s1}, N_{s2}: 18 turns #30
U_1: SG 3524

R_{12} 5.1 kΩ
R_{13} 1.5 kΩ
R_{14} 9.1 kΩ
R_{15} 2.5 kΩ
C_1 820 pF
C_2 25 µF
C_3, C_9 100 µF
C_4 47 pF

C_5 2200 pF
C_6 10 µF
C_7, C_8 300 pF
D_1–D_7: 1N4937
Q_1: MJE 182
Q_2, Q_3: MJE 172
Q_4, Q_5: D44Q5
L_1, L_2 1300 µH
Z_1: 1N4103, 9.1 V

R_1 100 Ω
R_2 2.5 kΩ, 2 W
R_3 200 Ω
R_4 20 kΩ
R_5 51 kΩ
R_6, R_7 4.7 kΩ
R_8 27 kΩ
R_9 1 kΩ
R_{10}, R_{11} 15 Ω

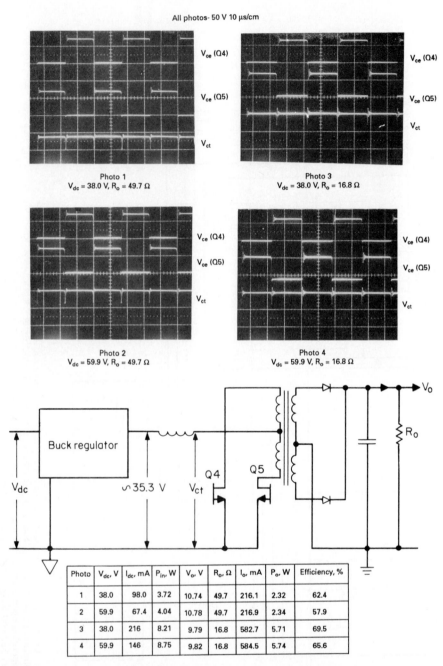

All photos- 50 V 10 μs/cm

Photo 1
$V_{dc} = 38.0$ V, $R_o = 49.7$ Ω

Photo 3
$V_{dc} = 38.0$ V, $R_o = 16.8$ Ω

Photo 2
$V_{dc} = 59.9$ V, $R_o = 49.7$ Ω

Photo 4
$V_{dc} = 59.9$ V, $R_o = 16.8$ Ω

Photo	V_{dc}, V	I_{dc}, mA	P_{in}, W	V_o, V	R_o, Ω	I_o, mA	P_o, W	Efficiency, %
1	38.0	98.0	3.72	10.74	49.7	216.1	2.32	62.4
2	59.9	67.4	4.04	10.78	49.7	216.9	2.34	57.9
3	38.0	216	8.21	9.79	16.8	582.7	5.71	69.5
4	59.9	146	8.75	9.82	16.8	584.5	5.74	65.6

Figure 6.27 Waveforms and data on the current-fed Royer driven from a buck regulator. Feedback is from the buck output. Same circuit as in Fig. 6.26.

The material is produced in a thin ribbon tape, wound on a toroidal core and then encased in either aluminum or some nonmetallic case. The tape is available in either 1- or ½-mil thickness. Core losses increase rapidly with frequency, and just as with power transformers, where higher frequencies require thinner laminations to minimize losses, beyond 50 kHz, the ½-mil tape cores should be used. But beyond 100 kHz, losses in even the ½-mil cores become prohibitive.

In the past 5 years, a new "amorphous" magnetic material with low losses at high frequencies and for flux swings between $+B_s$ and $-B_s$ has become available. It permits building Royer oscillators of up to 200 kHz with acceptably low losses and core temperature rise.

Such amorphous cores are manufactured in the United States under the trade name Metglas by Allied Corporation and Magnetics Inc. and by Toshiba under the trade name Amorphous-MB. These core materials have saturation flux densities ranging between 5700 and 6200 G.

All of these square-loop cores, since they are made of thin tapes, have relatively low iron area compared to ferrite cores. Thus at the same frequency they might be expected to require more turns than would a ferrite core (if a square-loop ferrite core were available).

However, the number of turns for a Royer is no problem with the small-area tape-wound cores as can be seen from Eq. 6.22. There it is seen that the required number of turns is inversely proportional to the saturation flux density, frequency, and iron area. Thus, although iron area of the tape-wound cores is small, their saturation flux density is close to twice that of any available square hysteresis loop ferrite. And since Royers with tape-wound cores can be built at 50 to 200 kHz, where fewer turns are necessary, there is no problem of excessive number of turns with low-iron-area tape-wound cores.

Nevertheless, if it is desired to use a ferrite core because of its larger iron area, there are some few sources for a square hysteresis loop ferrite core. One such is material Type 83 from the Fairite Corporation (Walkill, New York). It has a saturation flux density of 4000 G. But its losses operating at ±4000 G are sufficiently high that the absolute maximum operating frequency is 50 kHz. Available square hysteresis core materials are listed in Table 6.3.

It should be noted that most of these tape-wound cores have relatively small radiating surface area and hence high thermal resistance (in the range of 40 to 100°C/W). Unless bound to some kind of a heat sink, their total losses should be kept under 1 W.

Hysteresis loops for the above materials are shown in Fig. 6.28.

6.6.4.5 Future potential for current-fed Royer and buck preregulated current-fed Royer.   It may perhaps seem surprising in a text on modern power supply design to devote much space to the Royer circuit

TABLE 6.3

Core material	Saturation flux density, G	Core losses,* W/cm^3	
		50 kHz	100 kHz
Toshiba MB	6000	0.49	1.54
Metglas 2714A	6000	0.62	1.72
Square Permalloy 80 (½ mil)	7800	0.98	2.26
Square Permalloy 80 (1 mil)	7800	4.2	9.6
Fairite Type 83	4000	4.0†	30.0

*For flux excursions between positive and negative saturation.
†1 W/cm^3 at 25 kHz.

which had been cast aside 30 years ago. But the Royer, operated in the current-fed mode, with small collector-to-opposite-base flipover capacitors and with the new low-loss amorphous cores is very attractive in many applications.

If line regulation is not required, it is extremely low in parts count (Figs. 6.23, 6.24). Its major fields of application are where prime input is low-voltage DC—48 V for telephone industry supplies, 28 V for aircraft supplies, and 12 or 24 V for automotive supplies.

With the new available cores, they can generate up to 200 of possibly 300 W. Since they require no output inductors, they can easily generate high voltage—either with a multiturn secondary and/or an output voltage multiplier. If regulated output voltage is required, they can be preceded by high efficiency buck regulator (Figs. 6.26, 6.27).

It appears at this writing that in the coming years, there will be widespread renewed interest in the current-fed Royer oscillator DC/DC converter.

6.6.5 Minimum-parts-count flyback as a housekeeping supply

The low-power flyback scheme of Fig. 6.21 as a housekeeping supply is shown detailed in Fig. 6.28.

The circuit was designed as discontinuous-mode flyback from the design relations presented in Chap. 4. It was designed for 6 W of output power at a switching frequency of 50 kHz from a supply voltage of 38 to 60 V—the usual range for a telephone industry power supply. The circuit as is can easily deliver twice the output power without overstressing any components. But beyond 6 W at less than 38 V of input, it will enter the continuous mode and oscillate unless the feedback loop is changed to cope with that (Sec. 4.3).

In Fig. 6.28, the regulated output is a master secondary V_{om} referred to input ground. The housekeeping output V_o is a slave re-

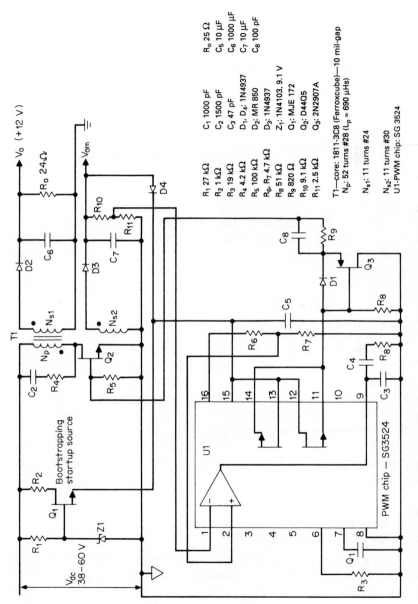

Figure 6.28 A low-power flyback housekeeping power supply with an isolated output V_o.

The component list shown in the figure:

R_1 27 kΩ
R_2 1 kΩ
R_3 19 kΩ
R_4 4.2 kΩ
R_5 100 kΩ
R_6, R_7 4.7 kΩ
R_8 51 kΩ
R_9 820 Ω
R_{10} 9.1 kΩ
R_{11} 2.5 kΩ

C_1 1000 pF
C_2 1500 pF
C_3 47 pF
D_1, D_4: 1N4937
D_2: MR 850
D_3: 1N4937
Z_1: 1N4103, 9.1 V
Q_1: MJE 172
Q_2: D44Q5
Q_3: 2N2907A

R_o 25 Ω
C_5 10 μF
C_6 1000 μF
C_7 10 μF
C_8 100 pF

T1—core: 1811-3C8 (Ferroxcube)—10 mil-gap
N_p: 52 turns #28 ($L_p = 690$ μHs)

N_{s1}: 11 turns #24

N_{s2}: 11 turns #30
U1-PWM chip: SG 3524

V_o (+12 V)
R_o 24Ω
V_{om}

PWM chip – SG3524

turned to output ground where it can drive the PWM chip for the main power supply. As discussed in Sec. 4.2.1, flybacks having no output inductors have the useful property that slaves track the master very closely. Thus regulating V_{om} on input ground keeps V_o on output ground sufficiently constant for a housekeeping supply.

In Fig. 6.28, $Q1$ provides supply voltage to the PWM chip at initial turnon. After the supply is up and delivering its output voltages, V_{om} takes over and supplies the chip via diode $D4$. The voltage at the $D4$ cathode is about 11 V. Since the base of $Q1$ is kept at 9.1 V by $Z1$, it is biased off as soon as its emitter rises to about 9 V via $D4$.

Significant waveforms and performance data for the circuit are shown in Fig. 6.29a, 6.29b, and 6.29c for input voltages of 38, 50, and 60 V, respectively. Efficiencies are seen to be about 70 percent. This is not spectacular, and no effort has been made to optimize the circuit and its efficiency.

It was intended here only to show the significant classical waveforms of an actual operating, discontinuous-mode flyback. Figure 6.29a, for a DC input voltage of 38 V, shows the circuit to be just at the end of the discontinuous mode (Sec. 4.4.1 and Fig. 4.8). Primary current is seen to start ramping up with no dead time after the instant the previous secondary current has ramped down to zero. Figure 6.29b and 6.29c shows the same waveforms at 50 and 60 V, respectively, and it is seen that there is now a dead time from the instant secondary current has ramped down to zero and the start of the next turnon.

The flyback is seen to have fewer components than the buck-current-fed Royer of Fig. 6.26. But it is seen in Fig. 6.29 that at 6 W of output power, peak secondary current for the flyback is 3 A. This compares to 0.36 A for the buck-current-fed Royer (Fig. 6.25a). The higher flyback secondary current would produce a greater RFI problem, requires a larger output filter, and possibly requires a small LC filter after the main filter capacitor to eliminate the output spike at the instant of turnoff due to ESR in the main capacitor (Sec. 4.3.4.1).

6.6.6   Buck regulator with DC-isolated output as a housekeeping supply

Figure 1.9 shows another possible, inexpensive, and low-parts-count scheme for generating a DC-isolated power supply. It is described in Sec. 1.3.8. Care must be taken in this scheme that the current drawn from the secondary is not sufficient to cause the primary current to go into the discontinuous mode, or regulation will suffer.

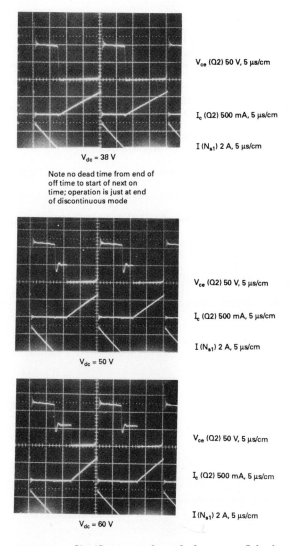

V_{ce} (Q2) 50 V, 5 µs/cm

I_c (Q2) 500 mA, 5 µs/cm

I (N_{s1}) 2 A, 5 µs/cm

V_{dc} = 38 V

Note no dead time from end of
off time to start of next on
time; operation is just at end
of discontinuous mode

V_{ce} (Q2) 50 V, 5 µs/cm

I_c (Q2) 500 mA, 5 µs/cm

I (N_{s1}) 2 A, 5 µs/cm

V_{dc} = 50 V

V_{ce} (Q2) 50 V, 5 µs/cm

I_c (Q2) 500 mA, 5 µs/cm

I (N_{s1}) 2 A, 5 µs/cm

V_{dc} = 60 V

Figure 6.29   Significant waveforms for low-power flyback
of Fig. 6.29.

References

1. B. D. Bedford and R. G. Hoft, *Principles of Inverter Circuits*, Wiley, New York, 1964.
2. *General Electric SCR Manual*, 6th ed., General Electric Co., Auburn, NY, 1979.
3. I. Martin, *Operating Characteristics of Self-Commutated Sinewave SCR Inverters*, RCA Application Note AN-6745, RCA, Somerville, NJ, 1978.
4. I. Martin, *Regulating the SCR Inverter Power Supply*, RCA Application Note AN-6856, RCA, Somerville, NJ, 1980.
5. Z. F. Chang, *Application of ASCR in 40 kHz Sine Wave Converter*, RCA Application Note ST-6867, RCA, Somerville, NJ, 1980.

6. N. Mapham, "An SCR Inverter with Good Regulation and Sine Wave Output," *IEEE Transactions on Industry and General Applications,* IGA-3 (2), 1967.
7. N. Mapham, "Low Cost Ultrasonic Frequency Inverter Using Single SCR," *IEEE Transactions on Industry and General Applications,* IGA-3 (5), 1967.
8. I. Martin, "Application of ASCR's to High Frequency Inverters," *Proceedings Powercon 4,* May 1977.
9. D. Chambers, "Designing High Power SCR Resonant Converters for Very High Frequency Operation," *Proceedings Powercon 9,* 1982.
10. D. Chambers, "A 30 kW Series Resonant X Ray Generator," *Powertechnics Magazine,* January 1986.
11. K. Check, "Designing Improved High Frequency DC/DC Converters with a New Resonant Thyristor Technique," Intel Corporation, Hillsboro, OR.
12. See Ref. 1, Chaps. 8, 10.
13. D. Amin, "Applying Sinewave Power Switching Techniques to the Design of High Frequency Off-Line Converters," *Proceedings Powercon 7,* 1980.
14. S. Cuk and D. Middlebrook, *Advances in Switched Mode Power Converters,* Vols. 1, 2, Teslaco, Pasadena, CA, 1981.
15. G. Chryssis, *High Frequency Switching Power Supplies,* 2d ed., McGraw-Hill, New York, 1989.
16. K. Billings, *Switchmode Power Supply Handbook,* McGraw-Hill, New York, 1990.
17. A. Pressman, *Switching and Linear Power Supply, Power Converter Design,* Switchtronix Press, Waban, MA, 1977.
18. G. H. Royer, "A Switching Transistor AC to DC Converter," *AIEE Transactions,* July 1955.
19. D. V. Jones, "A Current Sourced Inverter with Saturating Output Transformer," *IEEE Proceedings,* 1981.

Magnetics and Circuits Design

7

Transformer and Magnetics Design

7.1 Introduction

In Part 1, characteristics of most of the frequently used topologies were discussed in sufficient depth to permit the choice of a topology most suited to the power supply specifications.

Most frequently, the topology will be selected to minimize the power transistor's off-voltage stress at high line and peak current stress at maximum output power. Other considerations are to minimize parts count, cost, and required volume of the complete supply. Minimizing potential RFI problems is also a frequent factor in choice of topology.

After a topology is selected, the next major decisions are to select an operating frequency and transformer core size which yields the specified maximum output power for the smallest-size transformer.

To make the frequency and transformer core selection, it is necessary to know the numerical relations between available output power and transformer parameters such as iron area, core window or bobbin winding area, peak flux density, operating frequency, and coil current density. In the following sections, equations giving these relations will be derived for most of the frequently used topologies.

These relations can be used in equation form to select a transformer core and operating frequency. But in equation form, they require a tentative guess as to the required core and frequency, a calculation as to the available power from that core for some parameters, and corrected choices of a core and frequency and some of the parameters if the desired power is not available. Since all the parameters are interrelated, such iterative calculations may have to be done several dozen times before a satisfactory combination of the parameters is found.

This cumbersome procedure is avoided by throwing the equations into a chart form. The charts show frequency increasing (in multiples of 8 kHz to the right) in vertical columns and specific core sizes from various manufacturers in horizontal rows with available output power (calculated from the equations) at the column-row intersections.

The cores are arranged in horizontal rows of increasing output power. Thus at a glance one can choose an operating frequency and move vertically through the rows until the first core of sufficient power is found. Or if a specific core whose dimensions fit the available space is chosen, one can move horizontally through columns of increasing frequency until the frequency which yields the desired output power is found.

Such charts are shown for various core geometries of four major core manufacturers.

Core losses versus frequency and peak flux density for widely used core materials from various core manufacturers are shown. The available ferrite core geometries and their usages are discussed. Core and copper loss calculations are presented. A significant contributor to copper losses—proximity effect—is described. Transformer temperature rise calculation from the sum of core and copper losses is demonstrated.

7.2 Transformer Core Materials and Geometries and Peak Flux Density Selection

7.2.1 Ferrite core losses versus frequency and flux density for widely used core materials[1–4]

Most switching power supply transformers use ferrite cores. Ferrites are ceramic ferromagnetic materials having a crystalline structure consisting of mixtures of iron oxide with either manganese or zinc oxide. Their eddy current losses are negligible as their electrical resistivity is very high. Core losses are then due mainly to hysteresis losses which are so low as to permit use of some materials up to a frequency of 1 MHz.

Ferrite cores are available from about five major American manufacturers (Ferroxcube-Philips, Magnetics Inc., Ceramic Magnetics Inc., Ferrite International, Fairite) and some major overseas manufacturers (TDK, Siemens, Thomson-CSF, Tokin).

Each manufacturer has a number of different mixes of the various oxides processed in various ways to achieve different advantages. Some materials are tailored to yield the minimum core loss point at higher frequency (>100 kHz) or to shift the minimum core loss temperature point to a higher value (90°C) or to achieve minimum core losses at the most usual combination of high frequency and peak flux density.

However, most vendors' ferrites tailored for power transformer applications are quite similar in their DC hysteresis loops. They are within 10 percent of complete saturation in the region of 3000 to 3200 G at 100°C, have a coercive force of 0.10 to 0.15 Oe at 100°C, and have a residual flux density of 900 to 1200 G at 100°C.

The major factors affecting a material selection are the curves of core loss (usually in milliwatts per cubic centimeter) versus frequency and peak flux density. A typical curve showing these data plus the DC hysteresis loop is shown in Fig. 7.1 for a Ferroxcube-Philips high-frequency material 3F3. A tabulation of core losses for some widely used materials is given in Table 7.1.

Losses in Table 7.1 are taken from core manufacturer data sheets and, although seldom pointed out, are for bipolar magnetic circuits where the flux excursion extends into the first and third quadrants

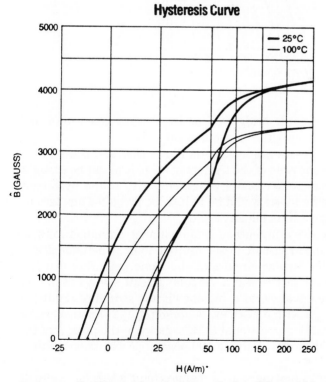

Figure 7.1 Significant characteristics of the 3F3—a high-frequency, low-loss core material. (*Courtesy of Ferroxcube-Philips Corp.*)

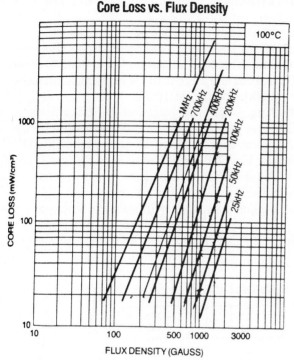

Core Loss vs. Flux Density

Figure 7.1 *Continued.*

(push-pulls, half and full bridges). But in forward converters and flybacks, operation is over the first quadrant only.

Since ferrite core losses are hysteresis losses only and these losses are proportional to the area of the hysteresis loop, it might be thought that in unipolar magnetic circuits where only half of the hysteresis loop is traversed, core losses would be half those given for bipolar circuits at the same peak flux density.

There is considerable difference of opinion among manufacturers on this. Some say unipolar circuit losses are one-fourth the quoted and measured values for bipolar circuits at the same peak flux density. They base this on the fact that if a unipolar circuit swings from 0 to $B_{\max}$ gauss, it is equivalent to a bipolar circuit swinging around a mean value of $B_{\max}/2$ with a peak excursion of $B_{\max}/2$. Further, since core losses are roughly proportional to the square of the peak flux excursion in a bipolar circuit, halving the peak flux excursion reduces losses by a factor of 4.

TDK offers a curve showing that unipolar circuit losses for a zero to $B_{\max}$ excursion are a factor K_{fc} times as great as losses in a bipolar circuit swinging from $-B_{\max}$ to $+B_{\max}$. The factor K_{fc} is shown as be-

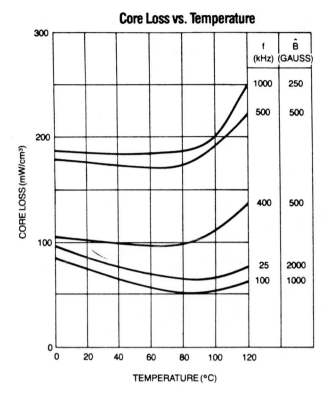

Figure 7.1 *Continued*

ing frequency-dependent. It is 0.35 at 60 kHz, 0.39 at 20 kHz, and 0.34 at 100 kHz.

A conservative approach and accepting the argument that losing half the area of a hysteresis loop (for unipolar circuits) should reduce losses measured for a bipolar circuit by a factor of 2, it will be assumed herein that unipolar circuits at the same peak flux density as listed in Table 7.1 will have losses half those shown in the table.

7.2.2 Ferrite core geometries

Ferrite cores are manufactured in a relatively small number of geometric shapes and varying dimensions within these shapes. Their shapes and dimensions are described in four core manufacturers' catalogs.[1-4]

Many of the core shapes and dimensions in those catalogs are international standards and are available from the various manufacturers in their proprietary core material. Cores which are international standards are listed in publications from the Magnetic Material Producers

TABLE 7.1   Core Losses for Various Core Materials at Various Frequencies and Peak Flux Densities at 100°C

Frequency, kHz	Material	Core loss, mW/cm^3 for various peak flux densities, G					
		1600	1400	1200	1000	800	600
20	Ferroxcube 3C8	85	60	40	25	15	
	Ferroxcube 3C85	82	25	18	13	10	
	Ferroxcube 3F3	28	20	12	9	5	
	Magnetics Inc.-R	20	12	7	5	3	
	Magnetics Inc.-P	40	18	13	8	5	
	TDK-H7C1	60	40	30	20	10	
	TDK-H7C4	45	29	18	10		
	Siemens N27	50			24		
50	Ferroxcube 3C8	270	190	130	80	47	22
	Ferroxcube 3C85	80	65	40	30	18	9
	Ferroxcube 3F3	70	50	30	22	12	5
	Magnetics Inc.-R	75	55	28	20	11	5
	Magnetics Inc.-P	147	85	57	40	20	9
	TDK-H7C1	160	90	60	45	25	20
	TDK-H7C4	100	65	40	28	20	
	Siemens N27	144			96		
100	Ferroxcube 3C8	850	600	400	250	140	65
	Ferroxcube 3C85	260	160	100	80	48	30
	Ferroxcube 3F3	180	120	70	55	30	14
	Magnetics Inc.-R	250	150	85	70	35	16
	Magnetics Inc.-P	340	181	136	96	57	23
	TDK-H7C1	500	300	200	140	75	35
	TDK-H7C4	300	180	100	70	50	
	Siemens-N27	480			200		
	Siemens-N47				190		
200	Ferroxcube 3C8				700	400	190
	Ferroxcube 3C85	700	500	350	300	180	75
	Ferroxcube 3F3	600	360	250	180	85	40
	Magnetics Inc.-R	650	450	280	200	100	45
	Magnetics Inc.-P	850	567	340	227	136	68
	TDK-H7C1	1400	900	500	400	200	100
	TDK-H7C4	800	500	300	200	100	45
	Siemens-N27	960			480		
	Siemens-N47				480		
500	Ferroxcube 3C85				1800	950	500
	Ferroxcube 3F3		1800	1200	900	500	280
	Magnetics Inc.-R		2200	1300	1100	700	400
	Magnetics Inc.-P		4500	3200	1800	1100	570
	TDK-H7F						100
	TDK-H7C4		2800	1800	1200	980	320
1000	Ferroxcube 3C85						2000
	Ferroxcube 3F3				3500	2500	1200
	Magnetics Inc.-R				5000	3000	1500
	Magnetics Inc.-P						6200

Note: Data are for bipolar magnetic circuits (first- and third-quadrant operation). For unipolar circuits (forward converter, flyback), divide by 2.

Association (MMPA)[5,6] and IEC publications from the American National Standards Institute.[7]

The various core geometries shown in Fig. 7.2 are pot or cup cores, RM cores, EE cores, PQ cores, UU or UI cores. The pot core is shown in Fig. 7.2e. It is used mostly at low power levels up to 125 W and usually in DC/DC converters. Its major advantage is that the coil on the bobbin around the center post is almost entirely enclosed by ferrite material. This decreases its radiating magnetic field and hence is used when EMI or RFI problems must be minimized.

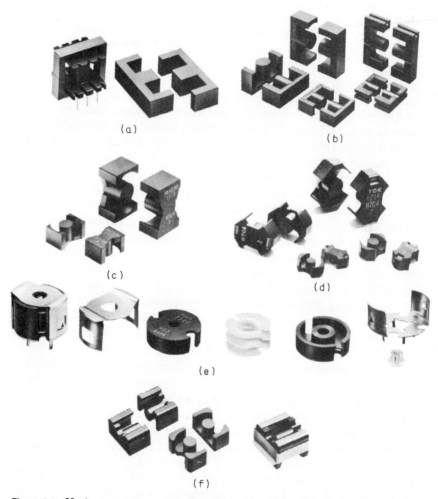

(a)

(b)

(c)

(d)

(e)

(f)

Figure 7.2 Various core geometries for power transformers: (*a*) EE cores; (*b*) EC and ETD cores; (*c*) PQ cores; (*d*) RM cores; (*e*) pot cores; (*f*) LP cores. (*Courtesy of TDK Corp.*)

The major disadvantage of the pot core is the narrow slot in the ferrite through which the coils leads exit. This makes it difficult to use it at high input or output current levels where the wire diameter is large or in multioutput supplies with many wires exiting.

It is also not a good choice for a high voltage supply, even at low power. Leads carrying a high voltage may arc because of the close spacing in the narrow exit notch in the ferrite.

Many of the pot cores are available with gaps of various sizes in the center leg so that they may carry a DC bias current without saturating. This permits their use as output inductors in buck regulators (Sec. 1.3.6), forward converters (Secs. 2.3.9.2, 2.3.9.3), push-pulls (Sec. 2.2.8.1), and flybacks (Sec. 4.3.3.1).

Most often, when a core is available with a gapped center leg, the manufacturer gives its A_l value (inductance in millihenries per 1000 turns) and the cliff point in ampere turns at which it falls over its saturation cliff.

If a gapped core is required, it is more cost effective—and from a performance viewpoint, preferable—to use a core with a gapped center leg rather than using ungapped core halves separated with the proper thickness of plastic shims. Shimming core halves will not yield reproducible A_l values over time, temperature, and production spread. Also, shimming the outer leg will increase EMI.

The most widely used cores are EE cores (Fig. 7.2a) because there is no narrow ferrite notch restricting coil leads entering or leaving the bobbin. But since the coil is not as fully surrounded by ferrite, it does produce a larger EMI-RFI field. But because the coil is not completely surrounded by ferrite, airflow past it is unimpeded and it tends to run cooler. EE cores are available with either a square or round center leg. Round-center-leg cores (EC or ETD types; Fig. 7.2b) have a small advantage in that the mean length of a turn is about 11 percent shorter than for a square-legged core of equal center-leg area. Coil resistance is thus about 11 percent less for equal numbers of turns, and copper loss and temperature rise is somewhat less for the round center leg.

There is a large range of EE core sizes, and depending on frequency and peak flux density, they can deliver output powers from under 5 W up to 5 or possibly 10 kW. By using two square-center-leg EE cores side by side, the core area is doubled, requiring half the number of turns for a fixed primary voltage, peak flux density, and frequency (Faraday's law; Eq. 2.7). This doubles the available power from a single core and may result in a smaller transformer than using a single core of the next-larger size.

The RM or "Square" core, a compromise between a pot and an EE core, is shown in Fig. 7.2d. It is effectively a pot core with a much wider notch cut out of the ferrite. It thus makes it easier to bring larger diameter or many wires in and out of the coil, and hence this core is usable for much higher output power levels and for multi-output transformers. The larger ferrite notch also provides easier access for convection air currents than in a pot core and results in lower temperature rise than that for the pot.

Because the coil is not as fully surrounded by ferrite as in a pot core, it causes more EMI-RFI radiation than does the pot core. Yet, because the ferrite surrounding the coil is still greater than in the case of an EE core, its EMI radiation is less than that for an EE of equal output power.

RM cores are available with or without a center-leg hole. The center-leg hole is used for mounting with a bolt through the hole or in frequency-sensitive applications. By inserting an adjustable ferrite "tuning rod" into the center hole, the A_l value may be adjusted up to as much as 30 percent. Although this tuning feature is not usable in power transformers because of increased energy losses, it is usable for frequency-sensitive filters.

The geometry of the PQ core (Fig. 7.2c; Magnetics Inc. and TDK) is such that it provides an optimum ratio of volume to radiating surface and coil winding area. Since core losses are proportional to core volume, and heat radiation capability is proportional to radiating surface area, these cores have a minimized temperature rise for a given output power. Further, since the PQ core volume-to-coil-winding-area ratio is optimized, the volume is minimized for a given output power.

LP cores (Fig. 7.2e; TDK) are specifically designed for low-profile transformers. They have long center legs which minimize leakage inductance.

UU or UI cores (shown in Fig. 7.2f) are used mainly for high-voltage or ultra-high-power applications. They are rarely used at power levels under 1 kW. Their large window area compared to an EE core of equal core area permits much larger wire sizes or many more turns. But their much larger magnetic path length does not yield as close primary-secondary coupling as in an EE core and results in larger leakage reactances.

7.2.3 Peak flux density selection

As discussed in Sec. 2.2.9.3, the number transformer primary turns will be selected from Faraday's law (Eq. 1.17, 2.7) for a preselected peak flux density B_{max}. It is seen in Eq. 1.17, that the larger the flux excursion (larger value of B_{max}), the fewer the primary turns and hence the larger the permissible wire size, and therefore the greater the available output power.

There are two limitations to peak flux density in the ferrite cores. The first is core losses and hence increased core temperature rise. Core losses in most ferrite materials increase as the 2.7th power of the peak flux density, and thus high peak flux densities cannot be permitted, especially at higher frequencies. But most ferrites—even the lossiest ones—have such low losses at 25 kHz and below, that core losses are not a limiting factor at those frequencies (see Table 7.1). Then at these low frequencies, peak flux excursion may possibly extend far up the hysteresis loop into the curved area of the *BH* loop. But care must be taken that the core does not move so far into saturation that the primary cannot support the applied voltage, or the power transistor will be destroyed.

Ferrite core losses also increase roughly as the 1.7th power of the switching frequency. Thus at higher frequencies, for the more lossy materials (Table 7.1), attempting a high peak flux density to minimize the number of turns results in such high losses (core losses of course are equal to the loss factor in milliwatts per cubic centimeter times the core volume in cubic centimeters) that temperature rise will be excessive.

Hence at 50 kHz and above, the less lossy (somewhat more expensive) core material must be used or peak flux density must be reduced. Reducing the peak flux density, of course, requires increasing the number of primary turns (Eq. 2.7) and hence requires smaller wire size for the same core–bobbin winding area. With smaller wire size, primary and secondary currents are smaller and available output power is decreased.

Thus at high frequencies ($> ~50$ kHz) the least lossy core material will be used and peak flux density will have to be reduced to such a value that total core and copper losses result in an acceptably low temperature rise. Temperature rise calculation for the sum of core plus coil losses will be demonstrated in Sec. 7.4.

Even at low frequencies, however, where core losses are not a limiting factor, peak flux density cannot be permitted to move very high up on the *BH* loop to minimize the number of primary turns.

It is seen in Fig. 2.3 that the *BH* loop is still linear up to 2000 G (this is closely the end of the linear portion for most ferrite materials). Going beyond this will increase the magnetizing current near the end of the transistor on time and will unnecessarily increase coil losses. But designing (choosing N_p in Eq. 2.7) for a maximum of 2000 G for most ferrites is risky. For fast transient line or load steps, if the feedback error amplifier is not fast enough for a few switching cycles, peak flux density may move up to hard saturation (>3200 G at 100°C) and destroy the power transistor. This is discussed in more detail in Sec. 2.2.9.4.

Thus, for ferrites even below 50 kHz where core loss is not a limiting factor, in all following designs herein, peak flux density will be chosen at 1600 G. At higher frequencies, where for 1600 G even the least lossy material results in excessive power losses, peak flux density will have to be reduced. The "available output power tables" to be developed below will show how easily output power may be calculated for these reduced peak flux densities.

7.3 Maximum Transformer Core Output Power, Peak Flux Density, Core and Bobbin Areas, and Coil Current Density

7.3.1 Derivation of output power relations for forward converter topology

Refer to Fig. 7.3 for the forward converter topology. The following output power relation will be based on the following assumptions:

1. Efficiency of the *power train*—from V_{dc} to the sum of all outputs and neglecting control circuit dissipation—is 80 percent.

2. The *space factor SF,* the fraction of total bobbin winding area occupied by the coil, is 0.4. This includes primary and all secondaries plus layer insulations plus any RFI or Faraday shields. This is a usual value (usually in the range 0.4 to 0.6) in transformer design because of the many factors contributing to waste of the total bobbin winding area. One significant factor is that turns within a coil layer often are widely spaced to make all bobbin layers of equal width to improve magnetic coupling between layers and reduce leakage inductances. Also, adherence to European safety specifications (VDE) requires leaving a 4-mm space from each end of a layer to the end of the bobbin. There is also the thickness of the insulation layers themselves.

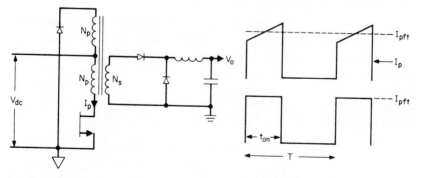

Figure 7.3 Forward converter topology and primary current waveshape I_p. Equivalent flat-topped current waveshape I_{pft} is used to calculate output power versus B_{max}, frequency, A_e, A_b, and D_{cma} relation. Turns ratio N_s/N_p is chosen to yield $t_{on} = 0.8T/2$ at minimum V_{dc} for specified V_o.

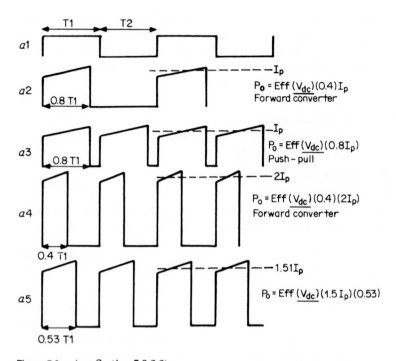

Figure 7.3a   (see Section 7.3.2.2)

VDE specifications generally require three layers of 1-mil-thick insulating material; if secondaries are to be sandwiched in between halves of the primary (as usually done to reduce proximity-effect copper losses), that wastes 6 mils of bobbin height. Finally, there is the practical problem that it is difficult to safely assemble the core and bobbin if the full bobbin height is fully utilized.

3. Primary current waveshape is as shown in Fig. 7.3. At minimum V_{dc} input, on time is a maximum at $0.8T/2$ (Secs. 2.3.2, 2.3.5). Primary current has the ramp-on-a-step waveshape because of inductors at each secondary output. The ramp swings ±10 percent about the value at its center I_{pft}. The primary current waveshape can be accurately approximated by a rectangular pulse of peak amplitude I_{pft} of duty cycle $0.8T/2T$ or 0.4 (Sec. 2.3.5). Then for minimum $V_{dc} = V_{dc(min)}$

$$P_o = 0.8P_{in} = 0.8V_{dc(min)}[I_{av} \text{ at } V_{dc(min)}]$$

$$= 0.8V_{dc(min)}(I_{pft})\frac{0.8T}{2T}$$

$$= 0.32V_{dc(min)}I_{pft} \qquad (7.1)$$

But the rms value of a rectangular waveform of amplitude I_{pft}, duty cycle of 0.4, is $I_{rms} = I_{pft}\sqrt{0.4}$ or $I_{pft} = 1.58I_{rms}$. Then

$$P_o = 0.32V_{dc(min)}(1.58I_{rms})$$

$$= 0.506V_{dc(min)}I_{rms} \qquad (7.2)$$

From Faraday's law

$$V_p = N_pA_e\frac{\Delta B}{\Delta T} \times 10^{-8}$$

where V_p = primary volts $(\approx V_{dc})$
N_p = number of primary turns
A_e = core area, cm^2
ΔB = flux change, G (0 to B_{max})
ΔT = time, s for this flux change = $0.4T$

At $V_{dc(min)}$, $\Delta B/\Delta T = B_{max}/0.4T$. Then for $f = 1/T$ from Eq. 7.2

$$P_o = \frac{0.506I_{rms}N_pA_eB_{max}f}{0.4} \times 10^{-8}$$

$$= 1.265N_pB_{max}A_ef \times 10^{-8}(I_{rms}) \qquad (7.3)$$

Now assume that primary and all secondaries operate at the same current density D_{cma} in circular mils per rms ampere. Bobbin area occupied by the reset winding is assumed negligible as it carries only magnetizing current and its wire size is usually smaller than No. 30 (AWG).

Let A_b = bobbin winding area, in^2
A_p = primary winding area, in^2
A_s = secondary winding area (total of all secondaries), in^2
A_{ti} = area of one turn of primary power winding, in^2

Then for a space factor SF of 0.4 and $A_p = A_s$

$$A_p = 0.20A_b = N_pA_{ti}$$

or $$A_{ti} = \frac{0.2A_b}{N_p} \qquad (7.4)$$

Now current density D_{cma} in circular mils per rms ampere is

$$D_{cma} = \frac{A_{tcm}}{I_{rms}}$$

where A_{tcm} is primary wire area in circular mils. Then

$$I_{rms} = \frac{A_{tcm}}{D_{cma}} \tag{7.5}$$

But area in square inches equals area in circular mils times $(\pi/4)\,10^{-6}$. Then

$$A_{tcm} = \frac{4A_{ti} \times 10^{+6}}{\pi} = \frac{4(0.20A_b)10^{+6}}{\pi N_p}$$

Then from Eq. 7.5

$$I_{rms} = \frac{0.8A_b \times 10^{+6}}{\pi N_p D_{cma}} \tag{7.6}$$

and putting Eq. 7.6 into Eq. 7.3

$$P_o = (1.265 N_p B_{max} A_e f \times 10^{-8})\,\frac{0.8A_b \times 10^{+6}}{\pi N_p D_{cma}}$$

$$= \frac{0.00322 B_{max} f A_e A_b}{D_{cma}}$$

But A_b is in square inches. If it is to be expressed in square centimeters, divide by 6.45. Then

$$P_o = \frac{0.00050 B_{max} f A_e A_b}{D_{cma}} \tag{7.7}$$

where P_o is in watts for B_{max} in gauss, A_e and A_b are in square centimeters, f is in hertz, and D_{cma} in circular mils per rms ampere.

7.3.2 Derivation of output power relations for push-pull topology

For the same assumptions as in Sec. 7.3.1, $P_o = 0.8P_{in} = 0.8V_{dc(min)}$ [I_{av} at $V_{dc(min)}$]. In a push-pull, at $V_{dc(min)}$, each transistor is on a maximum of $0.8T/2$ within its half period. For two such pulses per period, the total duty cycle of current drawn from $V_{dc(min)}$ is 0.8, and during its on time, each transistor and half primary carries an equivalent flat-topped current pulse of amplitude I_{pft}. Then

$$P_o = 0.8V_{dc(min)}(0.8I_{pft})$$

$$= 0.64V_{dc(min)}I_{pft} \tag{7.8}$$

But each half primary carries current at a duty cycle of only 0.4, so rms current in each half primary is $I_{rms} = I_{pft} \sqrt{0.4}$ or $I_{pft} = 1.58 I_{rms}$. Then

$$P_o = 0.64 V_{dc(min)}(1.58 I_{rms})$$

$$= 1.01 V_{dc(min)} I_{rms} \qquad (7.9)$$

Again for $SF = 0.4$, half the total coil area devoted to the primary and half to the secondary and each winding operating at a current density of D_{cma} circular mils per rms ampere, we obtain

$$A_p = 0.20 A_b = 2 N_p A_{ti}$$

or $$A_{ti} = \frac{0.1 A_b}{N_p} \qquad (7.10)$$

where N_p = number of turns per half primary
A_b = total bobbin winding area, in^2
A_{ti} = area of a single turn of primary wire, in^2

Now $$D_{cma} = \frac{A_{tcm}}{I_{rms}}$$

where A_{tcm} = wire area in circular mils and I_{rms} = rms current per half primary

$$I_{rms} = \frac{A_{tcm}}{D_{cma}} \qquad (7.11)$$

Now $A_{ti} = A_{tcm}(\pi/4)10^{-6}$. Putting this into Eq. 7.10, we obtain

$$A_{tcm} = 0.1273 \frac{A_b}{N_p} 10^{+6}$$

and putting this into Eq. 7.11

$$I_{rms} = 0.1273 \frac{A_b}{N_p D_{cma}} 10^{+6}$$

and putting this into Eq. 7.9

$$P_o = 1.01 V_{dc(min)} \frac{0.1273 A_b}{N_p D_{cma}} 10^{+6}$$

$$= 0.129 \frac{V_{dc(min)} A_b}{N_p D_{cma}} 10^{+6} \qquad (7.12)$$

and again from Faraday's law

$$V_{\text{primary min}} \approx V_{\text{dc(min)}} = \left(\frac{N_p A_e \, \Delta B}{\Delta T}\right) 10^{-8}$$

where here in a push-pull, flux swing is $2B_{\text{max}}$ in a time $0.4T$ at $V_{\text{dc(min)}}$. Put this into Eq. 7.12:

$$P_o = 0.129(N_p A_e) \frac{2B_{\text{max}}}{0.4T} \frac{A_b}{N_p D_{\text{cma}}} 10^{-2}$$

$$= \frac{0.00645 B_{\text{max}} f A_e A_b}{D_{\text{cma}}}$$

Again, A_b is in square inches. If it is expressed in square centimeters, divide this last relation by 6.45. Then

$$P_o = \frac{0.0010 B_{\text{max}} f A_e A_b}{D_{\text{cma}}} \tag{7.13}$$

where P_o is in watts for B_{max} in gauss, A_e and A_b are in square centimeters, f is in hertz, and D_{cma} is in circular mils per rms ampere.

This result—specifically, that the available power from a given core in a push-pull topology is twice that for the same core in a forward converter topology—could have been quite easily foreseen.

In the push-pull, each transformer half must sustain the same voltage as a forward converter fed from the same supply voltage. But in the push-pull, the available flux change is $2B_{\text{max}}$ as compared to B_{max} in the forward converter. Thus from Faraday's law, the number of turns on a half primary of the push-pull is half that in the forward converter for the same B_{max}. But since there are two half secondaries in the push-pull, the total number of turns in the push-pull is equal to the number of turns in the forward converter for equal V_{dc} and B_{max} in both circuits (neglecting the insignificant space occupied by the reset winding in the forward converter).

In the push-pull, however, half the total output power is delivered through each half secondary. Thus, for equal output powers in a push-pull and a forward converter, the peak and rms currents in each push-pull transformer half is half that in the forward converter (compare Eqs. 2.11 to 2.28 and 2.9 to 2.41). Thus the required circular-mil wire area and hence the required bobbin winding space for each half push-pull are half that for a forward converter of equal output power. Then for equal bobbin winding space, the push-pull can deliver twice the power of a forward converter from the same core, as indicated by Eqs. 7.17 and 7.13.

7.3.2.1   Core and copper losses in push-pull, forward converter topologies.

Comparing Eqs. 7.7 and 7.13, it is seen that the push-pull topology can yield twice the output power of a forward converter using the same sized (same $A_e A_b$ product) core.

There is a slight penalty paid in that the push-pull transformer, at twice the forward converter output power, will run warmer than the forward converter. Doubling a forward converter output power by going to a push-pull does double the core losses, but copper losses remain unchanged. This can be seen as follows: In the push-pull (Fig. 7.3a3), each transformer half must sustain the same voltage as the primary of the forward converter fed from the same supply voltage. In the forward converter, the flux density change is zero to some preselected value B_{max} in a time $0.8T1$ (Fig. 7.3a2). In the push-pull, the flux density change is from $-B_{max}$ to $+B_{max}$ or $2B_{max}$ in the same time $0.8T1$.

In Faraday's law, the number of turns is directly proportional to the applied voltage and inversely proportional to the flux density change. Thus, the number of turns in each half primary of the push-pull is half that of the forward converter primary for equal peak-flux densities.

For the push-pull to have twice the output power of the original forward converter, the peak current in each half period must be equal to that of the forward converter. Since the duty cycle of current flow in each half primary of the push-pull is equal to that of the forward converter of half the output power, rms current in each push-pull half primary is equal to that of the forward converter primary.

Thus, the forward converter and each push-pull primary half will use equal wire size (equal number of circular mils) since the wire size will be selected on the basis of 500 circular mils per rms ampere, and since the number of half primary turns is half that of the full primary in the forward converter of half the output power, the two half primaries of the push-pull occupy a volume equal to that of the forward converter.

The push-pull half primary has half the turns and equal rms current compared to the forward converter primary, and hence has half the $I^2 R$ copper loss of the full-forward converter primary. Thus, total copper loss for the two half-primaries of the push-pull equals that of the forward converter of half the output power.

But, core losses for the push-pull will be twice that for the forward converter. For in the push-pull, the flux-density change is from $-B_{max}$ to $+B_{max}$ and only form zero to B_{max} in the forward converter. But core losses are proportional to the area of the hysteresis loop transversed.

Thus, the push-pull operating over the first and third quadrant of the hysteresis loop will have twice the losses of the forward converter that operates only over the first quadrant of the hysteresis loop (see Sec. 7.2.1). But with the newer low-loss core material, the increased core losses will not become the limiting factor in transformer temperature rise—certainly at frequencies below about 100 kHz.

7.3.2.2 Doubling output power from a given core without resorting to a push-pull topology.

In the previous section, it is pointed out that for the same core, a push-pull topology can yield twice the output power of a forward converter. The only penalty paid is a doubling of the core losses ; copper losses remain unchanged.

But, there may be a reluctance to going to a push-pull. For push-pull with its two transistors has the added cost and space drawbacks. Also, the push-pull transformer is harder and, hence, more expensive to wind as 3 wires must be taken out of each winding as compared to 2 for a forward converter. Also, there is the always present possibility of flux imbalance (Sec. 2.25) if current-mode version of push-pull is not used.

If it is desired to double the output power of a given forward converter without increasing its core size, the following is a possible alternative to resorting to a push-pull (see Fig. 7.3a).

The push-pull yields twice the output of a forward converter from a given core because there are two current pulses per period rather than one for the forward converter. Thus, a possible alternative to the push-pull is to retain the forward converter topology, and have it give one pulse (whose amplitude is twice that of the push-pull) per half period of the originally considered push-pull. This can be seen in Fig. 7.3a4.

This, of course, is another way of saying that the forward converter frequency is doubled (forward converter frequency is defined as the inverse of the time required for a complete traversal of the hysteresis loop back to its original starting point). Equation 7.7 states the available output power from a core is directly proportional to frequency.

Thus, going to twice the original forward converter frequency would unquestionably yield twice the output power from the core. But it would result in somewhat more than twice (close to three times) the core losses. For core losses are roughly proportional to the 1.7th power of the frequency (Table 7.1 and Sec. 7.2.3).

Copper losses in a forward converter at twice the frequency and peak primary current (and hence twice the output power) would remain unchanged. This will be discussed below.

Thus, if doubling the frequency and peak primary-current amplitude of a forward converter doubles its output power and costs only a threefold increase in core losses, this may be a credible alternative to going to push-pull at the original frequency. For the push-pull at the original frequency also achieves a doubled output power but at a cost of only doubling the core losses.

Doubling the forward converter frequency and its peak current amplitude is practical only at original frequencies below 50 to 80 kHz. For, if it is attempted at higher original frequencies (say 100 kHz), the increased AC switching and snubber losses (see Chapter 11) at the doubled frequency would result in poor efficiency.

In Fig. 7.3a4, the original forward converter frequency and peak primary current were doubled to achieve a doubling of output power. But, this has its own drawbacks. First, the higher peak current will cause more severe RFI problems, and it may force the selection of a higher current, more expensive transistor.

If the doubled peak primary current is unnattractive, an alternative might be to increase the maximum transistor on-time. In Fig. 7.3a4, it was chosen as $0.8T1/2$ so as to ensure that the transformer core can be fully reset with an equal reset time and a guaranteed "dead" time before the start of the next turnon (Section 2.3.2). This is achieved by setting the ratio N_r/N_p (transformer reset winding to power winding turns ratio) equal to 1.0. (See Fig. 7.3).

In Sec. 2.3.8, it was shown that making N_r/N_p less than 1.0 permits a larger on-time, though at a cost of a larger reset voltage and, hence, higher transistor off-voltage stress. Thus, in Fig. 7.3a5, an N_r/N_p ratio of 0.5 was chosen. This yielded a larger maximum on-time of $0.53T1$ and a peak current of $1.51I_p$ as compared to $0.4T1$ and a peak current of $2I_p$ when N_r/N_p is 1.0. But the penalty is that now the peak transistor off-voltage stress is $3V_{dc}$ rather than $2V_{dc}$ for the case of $N_r/N_p = 1.0$.

Thus, as discussed in Sec. 2.3.8, setting the N_r/N_p ratio less than 1.0 decreases transistor peak current stress, but increases its peak voltage stress. Ratios of N_r/N_p less than 0.5 generally lead to unacceptably high off-voltage stress.

As stated above, going to twice the forward converter frequency and peak transistor current doubles the output power but does not increase copper losses. This can be seen below as follows:

Figure No.	Frequency	I_p	"On" duty cycle	I_{rms}	N	Wire area	Wire resistance	$(I_{rms})^2R$	P_0
7.3a2	F1	I_p	0.4	$0.632I_p$	N	A1	R1	$(I_{rms})^2R$	P_0
7.3a4	2F1	$2I_p$	0.4	$1.264I_p$	$0.5N$	2A1	0.25R1	$(I_{rms})^2R$	$2P_0$

Since the doubled-frequency forward converter has twice the rms current, it will have twice the wire area of the original converter of half the output power. And since it has half the number of primary turns, its resistance is one-fourth the resistance of the original forward converter. With twice the rms current, its I^2R losses are equal to that of the original forward converter of half the output power.

7.3.3 Derivation of output power relations for half-bridge topology

The half bridge is shown in Fig. 3.1. Again assume that minimum DC input voltage is $V_{dc(min)}$. Maximum on time per transistor is $0.8T/2$ and occurs at $V_{dc(min)}$. Thus

Efficiency = 80%

$$A_e, A_b = \text{core, bobbin area, cm}^2$$
$$A_{bi} = \text{bobbin area, in}^2$$
$$A_p = \text{primary area, in}^2$$
$$SF = 0.4, \text{primary and total secondary areas equal}$$
$$D_{cma} = \text{current density, circular mils/rms A (all windings operate at same current density)}$$
$$A_{ti} = \text{wire area, in}^2$$
$$A_{tcm} = \text{wire area, circular mils}$$
$$N_p = \text{number of primary turns}$$
$$I_{pft} = \text{equivalent flat-topped primary current pulse}$$

As I_{pft} comes at a duty cycle of 0.8, its rms value is

$$I_{rms} = I_{pft}\sqrt{0.8} = 0.894 I_{pft} \quad \text{or} \quad I_{pft} = 1.12 I_{rms}$$

Then
$$P_o = 0.8 P_{in} = 0.8 \frac{V_{dc(min)}}{2} [I \text{ average at } V_{dc(min)}]$$

$$= 0.4 V_{dc(min)} 0.8 I_{pft}$$

$$= 0.32 V_{dc(min)} I_{pft}$$

$$= 0.358 V_{dc(min)} I_{rms} \tag{7.14}$$

and
$$A_p = 0.2 A_{bi} = N_p A_{ti}$$

$$A_{ti} = \frac{0.2 A_{bi}}{N_p}$$

But $A_{ti} = A_{tcm}(\pi/4)10^{-6}$. Then

$$A_{tcm} = 0.255 \left(\frac{A_{bi}}{N_p}\right) 10^{+6} \tag{7.15}$$

$$I_{rms} = \frac{A_{tcm}}{D_{cma}}$$

$$= 0.255 \frac{A_{bi}}{N_p D_{cma}} 10^{+6} \qquad (7.16)$$

Putting Eq. 7.16 into Eq. 7.14 we obtain

$$P_o = 0.0913 \frac{V_{dc(min)} A_{bi}}{N_p D_{cma}} 10^{+6} \qquad (7.17)$$

From Faraday's law [since $V_{dc(min)}/2$ is applied to the primary]

$$V_{p(min)} = \frac{V_{dc(min)}}{2} = N_p A_e \frac{\Delta B}{\Delta T} 10^{-8}$$

where ΔB is $2B_{max}$ and ΔT is $0.4T$. Then

$$V_{dc(min)} = 10 N_p f A_e B_{max} 10^{-8}$$

Putting this into Eq. 7.17, we have

$$P_o = \frac{0.00913 B_{max} f A_e A_{bi}}{D_{cma}}$$

and dividing by 6.45 for the bobbin area in square centimeters:

$$P_o = \frac{0.0014 B_{max} f A_e A_b}{D_{cma}} \qquad (7.18)$$

where P_o is in watts, B_{max} is in gauss, f is in hertz, and A_e and A_b are in square centimeters.

7.3.4 Output power relations in full-bridge topology

A given core used in a full-bridge topology can yield no more output power than the same core used in a half bridge. The full bridge does deliver twice the output power of the half bridge, but it requires a larger core to do so. This comes about as follows. A full-bridge primary must sustain twice the supply voltage of the half bridge and hence must have twice the number of primary turns (Faraday's law and Sec. 3.3.2.1).

If the same fraction of the total bobbin area as in the half bridge is to be utilized, the wire size (area) must be halved. If the wire area is halved, operating at the same current density (circular mils per rms ampere), the permissible rms current must be halved. But the full-bridge transformer core, operating at twice the voltage and half the primary current of a half bridge, delivers the same output power as does the half bridge with the same core.

It is, of course, true that a full-bridge primary, operating at twice the voltage of a half-bridge primary but at the same primary current as a half bridge, delivers twice the half-bridge output power. But the full bridge would require a larger core winding area and hence a larger core to contain twice the number of turns at the same current density of a half bridge.

7.3.5 Conversion of output power equations into charts permitting core and operating frequency selection at a glance

Equations 7.7, 7.13, and 7.18 are valuable in selecting a core and operating frequency for a desired output power. But as discussed in Sec. 7.1, using them requires a number of time-consuming iterative calculations.

The charts of Table 7.2a and 7.2b avoid such calculations by showing the available output power as calculated from these equations for a peak flux density B_{max} of 1600 G and a coil current density D_{cma} of 500 circular mils per rms ampere.

The reason for the selection of 1600 G is discussed in Secs. 7.2.3 and 2.2.9.4. At frequencies above about 50 kHz, excessive core losses for some of the more lossy materials may dictate a lower value $B_{max,l}$ for the peak flux density. The charts make a rapid calculation of the available power simple. The lowered available power at the lowered peak flux density is then the values shown in the charts multiplied by $(B_{max,l}/1600)$.

The selection of D_{cma} = 500 circular mils per rms ampere is a compromising choice common in transformer design. A higher density (lower value of D_{cma}) would result in more copper losses, and a lower density would unnecessarily increase the coil size. Values down to 400 or possibly as low as 300 circular mils per rms ampere can be acceptable, but densities below 300 should definitely be avoided.

Actually, the choice of D_{cma} values specifies only the DC wire resistance. In subsequent sections skin and proximity effects will be discussed. These effects produce eddy currents in the wires, cause the currents to flow in only a fraction of the wire area, and hence may increase the wire resistance considerably above the values shown in wire tables for wires of a specified number of circular-mil area. Nevertheless, choosing current density of 500 circular mils per rms ampere is a good starting point.

The charts of Table 7.2 are used as follows. First, choose a topology which yields the best combination of minimum power transistor off-

TABLE 7.2a Maximum Available Ouput Power in Forward Converter Topology

Core	A_e, cm²	A_b, cm²	A_eA_b, cm⁴	Output power in watts at									Volume, cm³
				20 kHz	24 kHz	48 kHz	72 kHz	96 kHz	150 kHz	200 kHz	250 kHz	300 kHz	
EE Cores, Ferroxcube-Philips													
814E250	0.202	0.171	0.035	1.1	1.3	2.7	4.0	5.3	8.3	11.1	13.8	16.6	0.57
813E187	0.225	0.329	0.074	2.4	2.8	5.7	8.5	11.4	17.8	23.7	29.6	35.5	0.89
813E343	0.412	0.359	0.148	4.7	5.7	11.4	17.0	22.7	35.5	47.3	59.2	71.0	1.64
812E250	0.395	0.581	0.229	7.3	8.8	17.6	26.4	35.3	55.1	73.4	91.8	110.2	1.93
782E272	0.577	0.968	0.559	17.9	21.4	42.9	64.3	85.8	134.0	178.7	223.4	268.1	3.79
E375	0.810	1.149	0.931	29.8	35.7	71.5	107.2	143.0	223.4	297.8	372.3	446.7	5.64
E21	1.490	1.213	1.807	57.8	69.4	138.8	208.2	277.6	433.8	578.4	722.9	867.5	11.50
783E608	1.810	1.781	3.224	103.2	123.8	247.6	371.4	495.1	773.7	1031.6	1289.4	1547.3	17.80
783E776	2.330	1.810	4.217	135.0	161.9	323.9	485.8	647.8	1012.2	1349.5	1686.9	2024.3	22.90
E625	2.340	1.370	3.206	102.6	123.1	246.2	369.3	492.4	769.4	1025.9	1282.3	1538.8	20.80
E55	3.530	2.800	9.884	316.3	379.5	759.1	1138.6	1518.2	2372.2	3162.9	3953.6	4744.3	43.50
E75	3.380	2.160	7.301	233.6	280.4	560.7	841.1	1121.4	1752.2	2336.3	2920.3	3504.4	36.00
EC Cores, Ferroxcube-Philips													
EC35	0.843	0.968	0.816	26.1	31.3	62.7	94.0	125.3	195.8	261.1	326.4	391.7	6.53
EC41	1.210	1.350	1.634	52.3	62.7	125.5	188.2	250.9	392.0	522.7	653.4	784.1	10.80
EC52	1.800	2.130	3.834	122.7	147.2	294.5	441.7	588.9	920.2	1226.9	1533.6	1840.3	18.80
EC70	2.790	4.770	13.308	425.9	511.0	1022.1	1533.1	2044.2	3194.0	4258.7	5323.3	6388.0	40.10
ETD Cores, Ferroxcube-Philips													
ETD 29	0.760	0.903	0.686	22.0	26.4	52.7	79.1	105.4	164.7	219.6	274.5	329.4	5.50
ETD 34	0.971	1.220	1.185	37.9	45.5	91.0	136.5	182.0	284.3	379.1	473.8	568.6	7.64
ETD 39	1.250	1.740	2.175	69.6	83.5	167.0	250.6	334.1	522.0	696.0	870.0	1044.0	11.50
ETD 44	1.740	2.130	3.706	118.6	142.3	284.6	427.0	569.3	889.5	1186.0	1482.5	1779.0	18.00
ETD 49	2.110	2.710	5.718	183.0	219.6	439.2	658.7	878.3	1372.3	1829.8	2287.2	2744.7	24.20
Pot Cores, Ferroxcube-Philips													
704	0.070	0.022	0.002	0.0	0.1	0.1	0.2	0.2	0.4	0.5	0.6	0.7	0.07
905	0.101	0.034	0.003	0.1	0.1	0.3	0.4	0.5	0.8	1.1	1.4	1.6	0.13
1107	0.167	0.054	0.009	0.3	0.3	0.7	1.0	1.4	2.2	2.9	3.6	4.3	0.25

TABLE 7.2a Maximum Available Ouput Power in Forward Converter Topology (Continued)

Core	A_e, cm²	A_b, cm²	A_eA_b, cm⁴	Output power in watts at									Volume, cm³
				20 kHz	24 kHz	48 kHz	72 kHz	96 kHz	150 kHz	200 kHz	250 kHz	300 kHz	
Pot Cores, Ferroxcube-Philips (continued)													
1408	0.251	0.097	0.024	0.8	0.9	1.9	2.8	3.7	5.8	7.8	9.7	11.7	0.50
1811	0.433	0.187	0.081	2.6	3.1	6.2	9.3	12.4	19.4	25.9	32.4	38.9	1.12
2213	0.635	0.297	0.189	6.0	7.2	14.5	21.7	29.0	45.3	60.4	75.4	90.5	2.00
2616	0.948	0.407	0.386	12.3	14.8	29.6	44.4	59.3	92.6	123.5	154.3	185.2	3.53
3019	1.380	0.587	0.810	25.9	31.1	62.2	93.3	124.4	194.4	259.2	324.0	388.8	6.19
3622	2.020	0.774	1.563	50.0	60.0	120.1	180.1	240.2	375.2	500.3	625.4	750.5	10.70
4229	2.660	1.400	3.724	119.2	143.0	286.0	429.0	572.0	893.8	1191.6	1489.6	1787.5	18.20
RM Cores, Ferroxcube-Philips													
RM5	0.250	0.095	0.024	0.8	0.9	1.8	2.7	3.6	5.7	7.6	9.5	11.4	0.45
RM6	0.370	0.155	0.057	1.8	2.2	4.4	6.6	8.8	13.8	18.4	22.9	27.5	0.80
RM8	0.630	0.310	0.195	6.2	7.5	15.0	22.5	30.0	46.9	62.5	78.1	93.7	1.85
RM10	0.970	0.426	0.413	13.2	15.9	31.7	47.6	63.5	99.2	132.2	165.3	198.3	3.47
RM12	1.460	0.774	1.130	36.2	43.4	86.8	130.2	173.6	271.2	361.6	452.0	542.4	8.34
RM14	1.980	1.100	2.178	69.7	83.6	167.3	250.9	334.5	522.7	697.0	871.2	1045.4	13.19
PQ Cores, Magnetics, Inc.													
42016	0.620	0.256	0.159	5.1	6.1	12.2	18.3	24.4	38.1	50.8	63.5	76.2	2.31
42020	0.620	0.384	0.238	7.6	9.1	18.3	27.4	36.6	57.1	76.2	95.2	114.3	2.79
42620	1.190	0.322	0.383	12.3	14.7	29.4	44.1	58.9	92.0	122.6	153.3	183.9	5.49
42625	1.180	0.502	0.592	19.0	22.7	45.5	68.2	91.0	142.2	189.6	236.9	284.3	6.53
43220	1.700	0.470	0.799	25.6	30.7	61.4	92.0	122.7	191.8	255.7	319.6	383.5	9.42
43230	1.610	0.994	1.600	51.2	61.5	122.9	184.4	245.8	384.1	512.1	640.1	768.2	11.97
43535	1.960	1.590	3.116	99.7	119.7	239.3	359.0	478.7	747.9	997.2	1246.6	1495.9	17.26
44040	2.010	2.490	5.005	160.2	192.2	384.4	576.6	768.8	1201.2	1601.6	2002.0	2402.4	20.45

Note: From Eq. 7.7, $P_o = 0.00050 B_{max} f A_e A_b / D_{cma}$, where P_o is in watts, B_{max} in gauss, A_e and A_b in square centimeters, f in hertz, D_{cma} in circular mils per rms ampere, bobbin winding space factor = 40 percent. For B_{max} = 1600 G. For other B_{max}, multiply by $B_{max}/1600$. For D_{cma} = 500 circular mils/rms ampere. For other D_{cma}, multiply by $500/D_{cma}$. For push-pull topology, multiply powers by a factor of 2.

TABLE 7.2b Maximum Available Output Power In Half- or Full-Bridge Topology

Core	A_e, cm²	A_b, cm²	$A_e A_b$, cm⁴	Output power in watts at									Volume, cm³
				20 kHz	24 kHz	48 kHz	72 kHz	96 kHz	150 kHz	200 kHz	250 kHz	300 kHz	
EE Cores, Ferroxcube-Philips													
814E250	0.202	0.171	0.035	3.1	3.7	7.4	11.2	14.9	23.2	30.9	38.7	46.4	0.57
813E187	0.225	0.329	0.074	6.6	8.0	15.9	23.9	31.8	49.7	66.3	82.9	99.5	0.89
813E343	0.412	0.359	0.148	13.3	16.0	31.8	47.8	63.6	99.4	132.5	165.7	198.8	1.64
812E250	0.395	0.581	0.229	20.6	24.8	49.3	74.1	98.7	154.2	205.6	257.0	308.4	1.93
782E272	0.577	0.968	0.559	50.0	60.3	120.1	180.4	240.2	375.3	500.4	625.6	750.7	3.79
E375	0.810	1.149	0.931	83.4	100.5	200.1	300.6	400.2	625.4	833.9	1042.4	1250.8	5.64
E21	1.490	1.213	1.807	161.9	195.2	388.6	583.8	777.2	1214.6	1619.4	2024.3	2429.1	11.50
783E608	1.810	1.781	3.224	288.8	348.1	693.1	1041.2	1386.2	2166.2	2888.4	3610.4	4332.5	17.80
783E776	2.330	1.810	4.217	377.9	455.5	906.7	1362.2	1813.4	2834.0	3778.7	4723.4	5668.1	22.90
E625	2.340	1.370	3.206	287.2	346.2	689.2	1035.5	1378.5	2154.3	2872.4	3590.5	4308.6	20.80
E55	3.530	2.800	9.884	885.6	1067.5	2125.1	3192.5	4250.1	6642.0	8856.1	11070.1	13284.1	43.50
E75	3.380	2.160	7.301	654.2	788.5	1569.7	2358.2	3139.3	4906.1	6541.5	8176.9	9812.3	36.00
EC Cores, Ferroxcube-Philips													
EC35	0.843	0.968	0.816	73.1	88.1	175.4	263.6	350.9	548.4	731.2	913.9	1096.7	6.53
EC41	1.210	1.350	1.634	146.4	176.4	351.2	527.6	702.4	1097.7	1463.6	1829.5	2195.4	10.80
EC52	1.800	2.130	3.834	343.5	414.1	824.3	1238.4	1648.6	2576.4	3435.3	4294.1	5152.9	18.80
EC70	2.790	4.770	13.308	1192.4	1437.3	2861.3	4298.6	5722.6	8943.2	11924.2	14905.3	17886.4	40.10
ETD Cores, Ferroxcube-Philips													
ETD 29	0.760	0.903	0.686	61.5	74.1	147.6	221.7	295.1	461.2	614.9	768.6	922.4	5.50
ETD 34	0.971	1.220	1.185	106.1	127.9	254.7	382.6	509.4	796.1	1061.4	1326.8	1592.1	7.64
ETD 39	1.250	1.740	2.175	194.9	234.9	467.6	702.5	935.3	1461.6	1948.8	2436.0	2923.2	11.50
ETD 44	1.740	2.130	3.706	332.1	400.3	796.8	1197.1	1593.7	2490.6	3320.8	4150.9	4981.1	18.00
ETD 49	2.110	2.710	5.718	512.3	617.6	1229.4	1846.9	2458.8	3842.6	5123.4	6404.3	7685.1	24.20
Pot Cores, Ferroxcube-Philips													
704	0.070	0.022	0.002	0.1	0.2	0.3	0.5	0.7	1.0	1.4	1.7	2.1	0.07
905	0.101	0.034	0.003	0.3	0.4	0.7	1.1	1.5	2.3	3.1	3.8	4.6	0.13

TABLE 7.2*b* Maximum Available Output Power in Half- or Full-Bridge Topology (*Continued*)

Core	A_e cm²	A_b cm²	A_eA_b cm⁴	Output power in watts at									Volume, cm³
				20 kHz	24 kHz	48 kHz	72 kHz	96 kHz	150 kHz	200 kHz	250 kHz	300 kHz	
				Pot Cores, Ferroxcube-Philips (*continued*)									
704	0.070	0.022	0.002	0.1	0.2	0.3	0.5	0.7	1.0	1.4	1.7	2.1	0.07
905	0.101	0.034	0.003	0.3	0.4	0.7	1.1	1.5	2.3	3.1	3.8	4.6	0.13
1107	0.167	0.054	0.009	0.8	1.0	1.9	2.9	3.9	6.1	8.1	10.1	12.1	0.25
1408	0.251	0.097	0.024	2.2	2.6	5.2	7.8	10.4	16.3	21.8	27.2	32.7	0.50
1811	0.433	0.187	0.081	7.3	8.7	17.4	26.2	34.8	54.4	72.6	90.7	108.8	1.12
2213	0.635	0.297	0.189	16.9	20.4	40.5	60.9	81.1	126.7	169.0	211.2	253.5	2.00
2616	0.948	0.407	0.386	34.6	41.7	83.0	124.6	165.9	259.3	345.7	432.1	518.6	3.53
3019	1.380	0.587	0.810	72.6	87.5	174.2	261.6	348.3	544.4	725.8	907.2	1088.7	6.19
3622	2.020	0.774	1.563	140.1	168.9	336.1	505.0	672.3	1050.7	1400.9	1751.1	2101.3	10.70
4229	2.660	1.400	3.724	333.7	402.2	800.7	1202.9	1601.3	2502.5	3336.7	4170.9	5005.1	18.20
				RM Cores, Ferroxcube-Philips									
RM5	0.250	0.095	0.024	2.1	2.6	5.1	7.7	10.2	16.0	21.3	26.6	31.9	0.45
RM6	0.370	0.155	0.057	5.1	6.2	12.3	18.5	24.7	38.5	51.4	64.2	77.1	0.80
RM8	0.630	0.310	0.195	17.5	21.1	42.0	63.1	84.0	131.2	175.0	218.7	262.5	1.85
RM10	0.970	0.426	0.413	37.0	44.6	88.8	133.5	177.7	277.7	370.2	462.8	555.4	3.47
RM12	1.460	0.774	1.130	101.3	122.0	243.0	365.0	485.9	759.4	1012.5	1265.6	1518.8	8.34
RM14	1.980	1.100	2.178	195.1	235.2	468.3	703.5	936.5	1463.6	1951.5	2439.4	2927.2	13.19
				PQ Cores, Magnetics, Inc.									
42016	0.620	0.256	0.159	14.2	17.1	34.1	51.3	68.2	106.7	142.2	177.8	213.3	2.31
42020	0.620	0.384	0.238	21.3	25.7	51.2	76.9	102.4	160.0	213.3	266.6	320.0	2.79
42620	1.190	0.322	0.383	34.3	41.4	82.4	123.8	164.8	257.5	343.3	429.2	515.0	5.49
42625	1.180	0.502	0.592	53.1	64.0	127.4	191.3	254.7	398.1	530.8	663.4	796.1	6.53
43220	1.700	0.470	0.799	71.6	86.3	171.8	258.1	343.6	536.9	715.9	894.9	1073.9	9.42
43230	1.610	0.994	1.600	143.4	172.8	344.1	516.9	688.1	1075.4	1433.9	1792.4	2150.9	11.97
43535	1.960	1.590	3.116	279.2	336.6	670.0	1006.6	1340.1	2094.2	2792.3	3490.4	4188.4	17.26
44040	2.010	2.490	5.005	448.4	540.5	1076.1	1616.6	2152.1	3363.3	4484.4	5605.5	6726.6	20.45

Note: From Eq. 7.18, $P_o = 0.0014B_{max}fA_eA_b/D_{cma}$, where P_o is in watts, B_{max} in gauss, A_e and A_b in square centimeters, f in hertz, D_{cma} in circular mils per rms ampere, bobbin winding space factor = 40 percent. For B_{max} = 1600 G. For other B_{max}, multiply by $B_{max}/1600$. For D_{cma} = 500 circular mils/rms ampere. For other D_{cma}, multiply by $500/D_{cma}$.

voltage and peak-current stress. Or another topology selection criterion might be one that minimizes the number or cost of components.

Now note that the cores are arranged vertically in order of increasing A_eA_b product and hence increasing output power capability. If familiarity or experience dictates or suggests a particular operating frequency, that vertical frequency column is entered. Now move vertically downward and choose the first core whose output power is greater than the specified maximum power.

Or if a specific core is first chosen because it fits the available space, go to that core and move horizontally to the right to the first frequency which yields somewhat more than the specified maximum output power.

If a desired core does not yield the required output power at a selected frequency in—say—the forward converter topology, the push-pull might be considered. The push-pull (voltage or current mode) topology with the same core offers twice the output power at the same frequency. If voltage-mode push-pull is selected, all the precautions relating to flux imbalance (Sec. 2.2.8) should be kept in mind.

Thus, by moving upward to smaller cores and to the right to higher frequencies, an optimum core-frequency combination can be found. For a given output power, at higher frequencies, the core gets smaller but core losses and transformer temperature rise, and transistor switching losses increase.

7.3.5.1 Peak flux density selection at higher frequencies. Care should be taken in the use of Table 7.2a and 7.2b. The powers shown therein are available only if operation at a peak flux density of 1600 G at the selected frequency does not cause excessive temperature rise. At frequencies in the range of 20 to 50 kHz, core losses, even for the most lossy materials of Table 7.1 are so low that temperature rise at a peak flux density of 1600 G is negligibly small.

However, core losses increase roughly as the 1.6th power of the frequency and the 2.7th power of the peak flux density. Thus at higher frequencies (starting at about 50 kHz) peak flux density may have to be reduced below 1600 G (by increasing the number of primary turns) to keep the transformer temperature rise acceptably low.

In general, smaller cores can more easily tolerate a higher peak flux density at high frequencies than can larger cores. This is so because core losses are proportional to volume, but core cooling is proportional to its radiating surface area. Thus, as a core gets larger, its volume increases faster than its surface area and the internal heat generated increases more rapidly than its surface area which cools it. Note, for example, that the volume of a sphere is proportional to the third power of its radius but its radiating surface area is proportional to only the second power of its radius).

A specific example can easily demonstrate this. Consider the Ferroxcube-Philips E55 core in Table 7.2*b*. It is seen in that table that if operation at 200 kHz and 1600 G were possible, it would be capable of 8856 W of output power in a half-bridge topology. But from Table 7.1, for 3C85 material, its losses are 700 mW/cm^3 at 1600 G and 200 kHz. Then for its volume of 43.5 cm^3, its dissipation is 0.7(43.5) = 30.5 W. Coil losses (considered in the following section) probably equal this.

Consider a smaller core, the 813E343. From Table 7.2*b*, its output current capability at 1600 G, 200 kHz is 133 W in a half bridge. For a volume of 1.64 cm^3 and the same 700 mW/cm^3, its core losses are only 1.15 W. Thus, neglecting coil losses, the 813E343 with a volume of 1.64 cm^3 and core losses of 1.15 W would run at a far lower temperature than the E55 core with a volume of 43.5 cm^3 and 30.5 W of core losses.

Calculation of actual transformer temperature rise due to core plus coil losses will be demonstrated in the following section.

Thus for the larger cores, the powers shown in Table 7.2*a* and 7.2*b* may not be obtainable at frequencies above 50 kHz as operation at 1600 G may result in excessive temperature rise. Peak flux density may have to be reduced to B_{max} of somewhere in the range 1400 to 800 G. Available output powers are then the values shown in Table 7.2*a* and 7.2*b* multiplied by $B_{max}/1600$.

Table 7.2*a* and 7.2*b* shows output powers for the two major American core manufacturers. Many of their cores are interchangeable in their geometries and A_e values. But they are made in their own proprietary core materials which have different core losses in milliwatts per cubic centimeter. Core interchangeability (with regard to geometry and A_e only) and their type numbers are shown in Table 7.3 for Ferroxcube-Philips, Magnetics Inc., and TDK. Manufacturers' catalogs[1-4] also show a variety of core accessories—bobbins and assembly and mounting hardware.

7.4   Transformer Temperature Rise Calculations[8]

Transformer temperature rise above its ambient-air environment depends on its total core plus coil (copper) losses and its radiating surface area. Forced air flowing past the transformer can lower its temperature rise considerably, depending on the airflow rate in cubic feet per minute.

There is no way of calculating transformer temperature rise with

TABLE 7.3 Core Type Numbers for Geometrically Interchangeable Cores

Ferroxcube-Philips	Magnetics Inc.	TDK
	EE Cores	
814E250	41205	
813E187	41808	EE19
813E343		
812E250		
782E272		
E375	43515	
E21	44317	
783E608		EE42/42/15
783E776		
E625	44721	
E55		EE55/55/21
E75	45724	
	EC Cores	
EC35	43517	EC35
EC41	44119	EC41
EC52	45224	EC52
EC70	47035	EC70
	ETD Cores	
ETD29		
ETD34	43434	ETD34
ETD39	43939	ETD39
ETD44	44444	ETD44
ETD49	44949	ETD49
	Pot Cores	
704	40704	P7/4
905	40905	P9/5
1107	41107	P11/17
1408	41408	P14/8
1811	41811	P14/8
2213	42213	P22/13
2616	42616	P26/16
3019	43019	P30/19
3622	43622	P36/22
4229	44229	P42/29
	RM Cores	
RM4	41110	RM4
RM5	41510	RM5
RM6	41812	RM6
RM7		RM7
RM8	42316	RM8
RM10	42819	RM10
RM12	43723	RM12
RM14		RM14
	PQ Cores	
	42016	PQ20/16
	42020	PQ20/20
	42620	PQ2620
	42625	PQ26/25
	43220	PQ32/20
	43230	PQ32/30
	43535	PQ32/30
	44040	PQ40/40
		PQ50/50

Each manufacturer produces these cores in their own proprietary core materials having their unique core loss characteristic in milliwatts per cubic centimeter.

great accuracy analytically. But it can be done to within about 10°C with some empirical curves based on the concept of thermal resistance of a radiating surface area. Recall that the definition of thermal resistance R_t of a heat sink is the temperature rise (usually in degrees Celsius) per watt of dissipation in it. Then temperature rise dT for a power dissipation P is simply $dT = PR_t$.

Some core manufacturers list R_t for their various cores, implying that factor multiplied by the total core plus copper losses yields the temperature rise of the outer surface of the core. Some educated guess of about 10 to 15°C is often assumed for the temperature rise of internal hot spot (usually the core center leg) above the core's outer surface.

Temperature rise is dependent not only on the radiating surface area but also on the total dissipation. The greater the power dissipation into a radiating surface, the greater the temperature differential between the surface area and the ambient air and the more easily the surface area loses its heat or the lower the thermal resistance.

Thus transformer temperature rise will be estimated herein[8] as if the transformer's total outer surface area (2 × width × height + 2 × width × thickness + 2 × height × thickness) was the radiating area of an equivalent heat sink. The thermal resistance of this equivalent heat sink will be modified by the total dissipation (total of core plus copper losses).

A curve of heat-sink thermal resistance versus total surface area is shown in Fig. 7.4a. It is an empirical curve and is taken from the average of a large number of heat sinks of different sizes and shapes from different heat-sink manufacturers. It is the thermal resistance at a 1-W power level and is seen to lie on an averaging straight line on a log-log graph.

Although thermal resistance of a finned heat sink depends somewhat on the fin's shape and spacing and whether the surface is blackened or aluminized, these are second-order effects. To a close approximation, the thermal resistance of a heat sink depends almost entirely on only its radiating surface area.

Also from various heat-sink manufacturers' catalogs, an averaging empirical curve giving the variation of thermal resistance with power dissipation is shown in Fig. 7.4b.

From Fig. 7.4a and 7.4b, the more directly useful curves of Fig. 7.4c are derived. Figure 7.4c gives the temperature rise above ambient for various heat-sink areas (diagonal lines) and power dissipation. Thus the transformer's outer surface temperature rise will hereafter be read from Fig. 7.4c for the sum of its core plus copper losses and total radiating surface area as defined above. It is interesting to read from Fig. 7.4c the temperature rise of the two cores discussed in Sec.

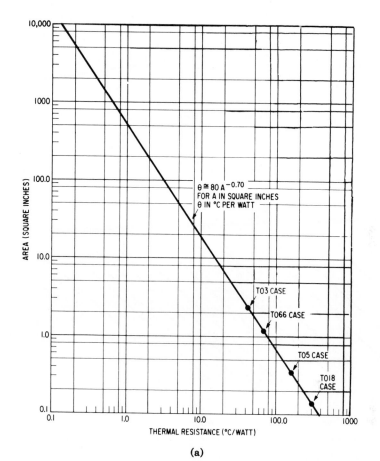

Figure 7.4 Calculating transformer temperature rise from its equivalent heat-sink area (total area of both faces plus core edge area). (a) Thermal resistance versus total heat-sink area. Total area means area of both sides of a flat plate or includes both sides of a fin in a finned heat sink. Curve is at a power dissipation of 1 W. Use multiplying factor of Fig. 7.4b for other power levels. (b) Normalized thermal resistance versus power dissipation in a heat sink. (c) Heat-sink temperature rise versus power dissipation for various heat-sink areas. From Eq. 7.19: $T = 80A^{-0.70}P^{+0.85}$. Figure 7.4b is represented analytically by $K_1 = P^{-0.15}$. Combining Fig. 7.4a (= $80A^{-0.70}$) and 7.4b gives the temperature rise for any transformer power dissipation and radiating surface areas as $T = 80A^{-0.70}P^{+0.85}$.

7.3.5.1. There it was calculated that an E55 of 43.5 cm³ volume, operated at 1600 G and 200 kHz, dissipated 30.5 W. Its radiating surface area as defined above is 16.5 in². From Fig. 7.4c, neglecting copper losses entirely, at 30.5 W of core losses, its temperature rise is 185°C.

The smaller 813E343 core of 1.64-cm³ volume also operated at 1600 G and 200 kHz has 1.15 W of core losses. Its radiating surface area,

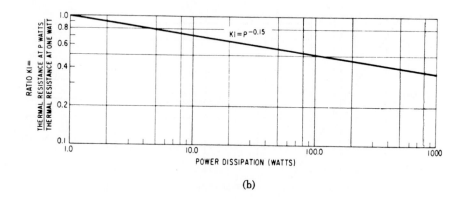

(b)

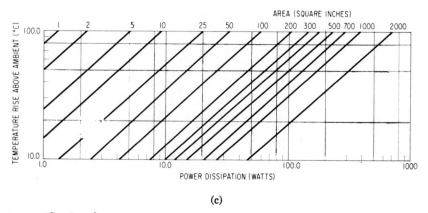

(c)

Figure 7.4   (*Continued*)

also calculated as above, is 1.90 in^2. Also from Fig. 7.4c, neglecting copper losses, its temperature rise is only 57°C. It is thus verified that it is easier for smaller cores to deliver the powers shown in Fig. 7.2a and 7.2b at 1600 G and high frequency.

It is of interest to compare the thermal resistance of some cores as measured by the manufacturer and as calculated ($R_t = 80A^{-0.70}$) from Fig. 7.4a (see Table 7.4).

7.5   Transformer Copper Losses

7.5.1   Introduction

In Sec. 7.3 it was stated that wire size for all windings would be chosen to yield a current density of 500 circular mils per rms ampere. It was assumed there that copper losses would be calculated as $(I_{\text{rms}})^2 R_{\text{dc}}$, where R_{dc} is the winding's DC resistance as calculated from

TABLE 7.4   Core Resistance

Core	Radiating surface, area, in^2	Thermal resistance, °C/W	
		Measured by manufacturer	Calculated from Fig. 7.4a
EC35	5.68	18.5	23.7
EC41	7.80	16.5	19.0
EC52	10.8	11.0	12.6
EC70	22.0	7.5	9.2

its length and resistance in ohms per foot as read from the wire tables for the selected wire size. It was also assumed that I_{rms} is the rms current as calculated from its waveshape (Secs. 2.2.10.2, 2.3.10.4).

There are two effects, *skin* and *proximity* effects, which can cause the winding losses to be significantly greater than $(I_{rms})^2 R_{dc}$.

Both skin and proximity effects arise from eddy currents which are induced by varying magnetic fields in the coil. Skin effect is caused by eddy currents induced in a wire by the magnetic field of the current carried by the wire itself. Proximity effect is caused by eddy currents induced in wires by magnetic fields of currents in adjacent wires or adjacent layers of the coil.

Skin effect causes current in a wire to flow only in a thin skin on the outer periphery of the wire. The depth of this skin or annular conducting area is inversely proportional to the square root of the frequency. Thus, as frequency increases, a progressively larger part of solid wire area is lost, increasing the AC resistance and hence copper losses.

One might not expect skin effect to increase wire resistance significantly for low frequency (say, 25 kHz) switchers as the skin depth is still a fairly large 17.9 mils at 25 kHz.

However, currents in conventional switching supplies have rectangular waveshapes which have a considerable amount of energy in their higher-frequency Fourier components. Thus high skin resistance at these high-frequency Fourier components of even a 25-kHz rectangular current waveform makes skin effect a concern even for a low-frequency 25 kHz switcher.

Skin effect will be discussed quantitatively in the following sections.

Proximity effect, caused by eddy currents induced by varying magnetic fields from adjacent conductors or adjacent coil layers, causes considerably more copper losses than does skin effect.

Proximity-effect losses can be especially high in multilayer coils. This is so only partly because the induced eddy currents crowd the net current into a small fraction of the copper wire area, increasing its resistance. What is more serious in proximity effect is that these induced eddy currents can be many times greater in amplitude than the net current flowing in the individual wire or wire layers. This will be discussed quantitatively in the following sections.

7.5.2 Skin effect

Skin effect[9-15] has been known and equations had been derived for skin depth versus frequency as far back as 1915.[9] The means by which induced eddy currents cause current to crowd into the thin outer skin of a conductor can be seen in Fig. 7.5.

A section of a round conductor sliced through a diameter is shown in Fig. 7.5. It carries its main current in the direction of OA. If not for skin effect, the current would be uniformly distributed throughout the wire area.

Now all elements of current flowing along the direction OA are encircled by magnetic flux lines normal to OA. Consider a thin filament of current flowing along the axis OA. By Fleming's right-hand rule,

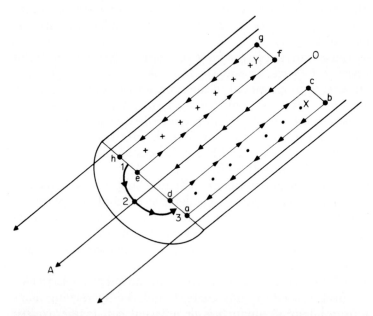

Figure 7.5 Eddy currents in a round wire causes skin effect—the canceling of current in the center of the wire and its crowding into the outer skin. The magnetic field of the current in the wire induces voltages in loops such as *abcd* and *efgh*. The polarity of these voltages is such as to cause eddy currents to flow around the boundary of these loops. The direction of these eddy currents is opposite to the main current flow on the inside of the loops (*d* to *c* and *e* to *f*) and in the same direction as the main current flow on the outside of the loops (*b* to *a* and *g* to *h*). The consequence is the canceling of current flow on the inside of the wire and its concentration in a thin skin on its outside.

its magnetic flux lines are in the direction shown by the arrow in the figure—from 1 to 2 to 3 and around back to 1.

Consider two flat loops (X and Y) within the wire. They are on a wire diameter and extend the full length of the wire. These loops are symmetrically disposed to either side of the wire axis. The magnetic flux lines flow up through loop X (shown by the dots in the center of the loop), around, and back down through loop Y (shown by the crosses in the center of loop Y).

By Faraday's law, when a varying magnetic field flows through an area, a voltage is induced in a line encircling that area. By Lenz' law, the polarity of that voltage is such as to cause an eddy current flow in such a direction that its magnetic field will be in a direction opposite to that which caused the eddy current.

Thus voltages will be induced in loops X and Y and eddy currents will flow in those loops in the direction shown. By the right-hand rule, the current in loop X flows clockwise in the direction d to c to b to a to d. That direction of current flow causes a magnetic field to go down through the center of the loop and in opposition to the field from the main filament of current along OA. Similarly, in loop Y, the eddy current flows counterclockwise (*efgh* and back to *e*) so as to cause a magnetic field to come up through the center of the loop in opposition to the magnetic field of the main current filament along OA.

Now note that the eddy currents along arms *dc* and *ef* are in the direction opposite to that of the main current filament OA and tend to cancel it. Further, eddy currents along arms *ab* and *gh* (along the outer skin of the wire) are in the same direction of the main current filaments and tend to reinforce them.

Thus the net current—the sum of the eddy currents and the main current which caused them—is canceled at the center of the wire and crowded into the outer skin. Thus at high frequency, the total current-carrying area is less than the full wire area and the AC resistance is greater than the DC resistance by an amount determined by the skin thickness.

7.5.3   Skin effect—quantitative relations

Skin depth is defined as distance below the surface where the current density has fallen to $1/e$ or 37 percent of its value at the surface. The relation between skin depth and frequency has been derived by many sources[9] and for copper wire at 70°C is

$$S = \frac{2837}{\sqrt{f}} \qquad (7.19)$$

where S is the skin depth in mils and f is frequency in hertz.

Table 7.5 shows skin depth for copper wire at 70°C at various frequencies as calculated from Eq. 7.19.

Now assume conductors of circular cross section. For a DC resistance R_{dc}, AC resistance due to skin effect of R_{ac}, and ΔR, the resistance change due to skin effect is

$$R_{ac} = R_{dc} + \Delta R = R_{dc}\left(1 + \frac{\Delta R}{R_{dc}}\right) = R_{dc}(1 + F)$$

or
$$\frac{R_{ac}}{R_{dc}} = 1 + F \tag{7.20}$$

From the skin depth relation of Eq. 7.19, the ratio R_{ac}/R_{dc} can be calculated for any wire size at any frequency. Since the resistances are inversely proportional to wire conducting area, for any skin depth S and wire radius r and diameter d, since the conducting area of the wire is the annular ring whose inner radius is $(r - S)$, then

$$\frac{R_{ac}}{R_{dc}} = \frac{\pi r^2}{\pi r^2 - \pi(r - S)^2}$$

$$= \frac{(r/S)^2}{(r/S)^2 - (r - S)^2/S^2}$$

$$= \frac{(r/S)^2}{(r/S)^2 - (r/S - 1)^2}$$

$$= \frac{(d/2S)^2}{(d/2S)^2 - (d/2S - 1)^2} \tag{7.21}$$

TABLE 7.5   Skin Depth in Copper Wire at 70°C

Frequency, kHz	Skin depth, mils*
25	17.9
50	12.7
75	10.4
100	8.97
125	8.02
150	7.32
175	6.78
200	6.34
225	5.98
250	5.67
300	5.18
400	4.49
500	4.01

*From Eq. 7.19. Skin depth $S = 2837/\sqrt{F}$; S in mils for F in hertz.

Thus Eq. 7.21 indicates that the wire's AC-to-DC resistance $R_{ac}/R_{dc} = (1 + F)$ is dependent only on the ratio of wire diameter to skin depth. Figure 7.6 plots R_{ac}/R_{dc} against the ratio d/S from Eq. 7.21.

7.5.4   AC/DC resistance ratio for various wire sizes at various frequencies

Because of skin effect, the AC-to-DC resistance of round wire is dependent on the ratio of the wire diameter to skin depth (Eq. 7.21). Further, since skin depth is inversely proportional to the square root of frequency, different-sized wires will have different AC-to-DC resistance ratios, and these ratios will increase with frequency.

Table 7.6 shows this for all even-numbered wire sizes at 25, 50, 100, and 200 kHz. In this table, d/S (wire diameter/skin depth ratio) is calculated from the maximum bare wire diameter as given in the wire tables and skin depth is calculated from Eq. 7.19 (Table 7.5). From these d/S ratios, R_{ac}/R_{dc} is calculated from Eq. 7.21 or read from Fig. 7.6.

It is obvious from Table 7.6 that large-diameter wires have a large AC/DC resistance ratio, which increases greatly with frequency. Thus No. 14 wire has a diameter of 64.7 mils and a skin depth of 17.9 mils at 25 kHz (Table 7.5). This yields a d/S ratio of 3.6, and from Fig. 7.6, its AC/DC resistance ratio is already 1.25. But the same wire at 200 kHz has a skin depth of 6.34 mils and a d/S ratio of 10.2—and from Fig. 7.6, its AC/DC resistance ratio is 3.3!

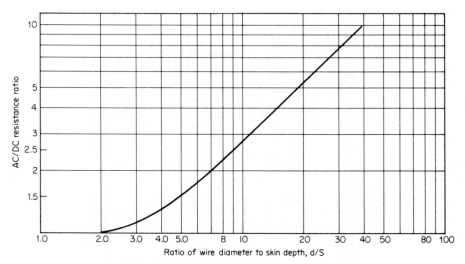

Figure 7.6   AC-to-DC resistance ratio for round wires versus ratio of wire diameter to skin depth (d/s). (*From Eq. 7.21.*)

TABLE 7.6 AC/DC Resistance Ratios Due to Skin Effects for All Even-Numbered Wire Sizes at Four Commonly Used Frequencies

Wire no.	Diameter d, mils	25 kHz			50 kHz			100 kHz			200 kHz		
		Skin depth S, mils	d/S	R_{ac}/R_{dc}	Skin depth S, mils	d/S	R_{ac}/R_{dc}	Skin depth S, mils	d/S	R_{ac}/R_{dc}	Skin depth, S, mils	d/S	R_{ac}/R_{dc}
12	81.6	17.9	4.56	1.45	12.7	6.43	1.85	8.97	9.10	2.55	6.34	12.87	3.50
14	64.7	17.9	3.61	1.30	12.7	5.09	1.54	8.97	7.21	2.00	6.34	10.21	2.90
16	51.3	17.9	2.87	1.10	12.7	4.04	1.25	8.97	5.72	1.70	6.34	8.09	2.30
18	40.7	17.9	2.27	1.05	12.7	3.20	1.15	8.97	4.54	1.40	6.34	6.42	1.85
20	32.3	17.9	1.80	1.00	12.7	2.54	1.05	8.97	3.60	1.25	6.34	5.09	1.54
22	25.6	17.9	1.43	1.00	12.7	2.02	1.00	8.97	2.85	1.10	6.34	4.04	1.30
24	20.3	17.9	1.13	1.00	12.7	1.60	1.00	8.97	2.26	1.04	6.34	3.20	1.15
26	16.1	17.9	0.90	1.00	12.7	1.27	1.00	8.97	1.79	1.00	6.34	2.54	1.05
28	12.7	17.9	0.71	1.00	12.7	1.00	1.00	8.97	1.42	1.00	6.34	2.00	1.00
30	10.1	17.9	0.56	1.00	12.7	0.80	1.00	8.97	1.13	1.00	6.34	1.59	1.00
32	8.1	17.9	0.45	1.00	12.7	0.64	1.00	8.97	0.90	1.00	6.34	1.28	1.00
34	6.4	17.9	0.36	1.00	12.7	0.50	1.00	8.97	0.71	1.00	6.34	1.01	1.00

Note: Skin depths are taken from Table 7.5; R_{ac}/R_{dc} from Eq. 7.21.

However, Table 7.6 should not be misinterpreted. Although Fig. 7.6 shows that R_{ac}/R_{dc} increases as wire diameter increases (d/S increases), R_{ac} actually decreases as wire diameter increases and larger wire sizes will yield lesser core losses. This, of course, is because R_{dc} is inversely proportional to d^2 and decreases more rapidly than R_{ac} decreases as a result of increase in d. This is because R_{ac} is inversely proportional to the area of the annular skin, which is equal to dS. Thus as d increases, R_{ac} decreases.

As is well known, large-diameter wire is much too lossy to use at high frequencies. Rather than using a single large-diameter wire, a number of paralleled smaller-diameter wires with a total equal circular-mil areas are used. This increases the total area of conducting annular skin zones. This can be seen as follows. If, say, two paralleled wires are to have a total circular mil area of a single wire, the diameter of the two smaller wires must be $D/\sqrt{2}$ (where D is the diameter of the single original wire).

Then for a skin depth of S, the single original wire has a total area in its annular skin zone of πDS. In the two smaller wires, skin depth is not related to wire diameter—only to frequency (Eq. 7.20). Thus with the two smaller wires, the total area of the two skins is $2[\pi(D/\sqrt{2})S] = \pi \sqrt{2}DS$; and the conducting area of the two skins with two smaller wires has been increased by $\sqrt{2}$ or 41 percent over that of a single wire with the same skin depth and equal circular-mil area at DC.

An extension of this is to use Litz wire.[16] This consists of a number of fine, insulated wires twisted into a bundle. Individual wires are woven together in a bundle so that each wire spends an equal distance at the center of the bundle and at its periphery. This minimizes both skin and proximity effects.[12]

Litz wire is about 5 percent more expensive than solid wire. But this is not as much of a drawback as is the difficulty of handling it in a production environment. Care must be taken that all the fine strands (usually from No. 28 to No. 50 wire) are soldered together at each end. It is reported that if some of the fine wires are broken or for some reason not picked up in the soldered connection at each end, losses increase significantly. Also, odd effects such as audible noise or vibration can occur.

General practice is to avoid Litz wire up to switching frequencies of 50 kHz. It is occasionally used at 100 kHz, and its use should be weighed against the use of two or possibly up to four paralleled smaller-diameter wires.

Some appreciation of this is obtained from Table 7.6, where it is seen that AC resistance of No. 18 wire is only 5 percent greater than No. 18 wire DC resistance at 25 kHz because of skin effect. This is not too significant. But at 50 kHz, R_{ac} is already 15 percent higher and at 100, 200 kHz, it is 40 and 85 percent higher, respectively.

These numbers do not take into account that in most switching supply topologies, currents have rectangular waveshapes in which much of the energy is in higher harmonics. When the losses of higher harmonics of the current square wave are considered, the AC/DC resistance ratios of Table 7.6 will be seen to increase significantly. This will be taken up in the following section.

For high currents (usually in secondaries above ~ 15 to 20 A), thin copper foil rather than Litz wire or multiple strands of solid wire is often used. The foil width is cut to the bobbin width (or appropriately less if VDE safety specifications must be observed). Foil thickness is chosen as about 37 percent greater thickness than the skin depth at the fundamental switching frequency. The foil is covered with a 1-mil layer of plastic (Mylar) and is wrapped as a ribbon around the bobbin for the required number of turns.

7.5.5   Skin effect with rectangular current waveshapes[14]

The ratio of AC-to-DC resistance is strongly dependent on the wire diameter/skin depth ratio (Fig. 7.6). But skin depth is dependent on frequency (Eq. 7.19). In most switching power supply topologies, current waveshapes are rectangular with much of the energy residing in the harmonics of the square-wave current waveshapes. The question thus arises as to the frequency at which skin depth should be calculated. Venkatramen has rigorously analyzed this issue.[14] A simplifying approximation has been made herein to permit estimation of the ratio of AC to DC resistance and hence calculation of copper losses.

It is assumed that the majority of the energy in the square current waveshape resides in the first three harmonics of the square-wave frequency. Skin depth S is then calculated from Eq. 7.19 for each of the three harmonics of the most usual switching frequencies (25, 50, 100, 200 kHz).

An average of these S_{av} is taken for the simplifying average skin depth for those switching frequencies. From this average skin depth, the average ratio d/S_{av} is calculated for all even-numbered wire sizes. This d/S_{av} is then used in reading R_{ac}/R_{dc} from Fig. 7.6. The results are shown in Table 7.7.

If this simplifying approximation is valid (it may be optimistic, depending on how much of the square-wave energy is contained at harmonics above the third), Table 7.6 may be giving an optimistic estimate of skin effect losses for square current waveforms. Table 7.8

TABLE 7.7 Skin Effect AC/DC Resistance Ratios for Square-Wave Currents at Four Commonly Used Switching Frequencies

Wire no.	Diameter d, mils	25 kHz			50 kHz			100 kHz			200 kHz		
		Skin depth S, mils	d/S	R_{ac}/R_{dc}	Skin depth S, mils	d/S	R_{ac}/R_{dc}	Skin depth S, mils	d/S	R_{ac}/R_{dc}	Skin depth, S, mils	d/S	R_{ac}/R_{dc}
12	81.6	13.2	6.18	1.85	9.66	8.45	2.40	6.83	11.95	3.30	4.83	16.89	4.50
14	64.7	13.2	4.90	1.50	9.66	6.70	1.90	6.83	9.47	2.65	4.83	13.40	3.70
16	51.3	13.2	3.89	1.25	9.66	5.31	1.59	6.83	7.51	2.12	4.83	10.62	2.90
18	40.7	13.2	3.08	1.13	9.66	4.21	1.35	6.83	5.96	1.75	4.83	8.43	2.36
20	32.3	13.2	2.45	1.05	9.66	3.34	1.17	6.83	4.73	1.45	4.83	6.69	1.90
22	25.6	13.2	1.94	1.00	9.66	2.65	1.07	6.83	3.75	1.25	4.83	5.30	1.56
24	20.3	13.2	1.54	1.00	9.66	2.10	1.01	6.83	2.97	1.12	4.83	4.20	1.35
26	16.1	13.2	1.22	1.00	9.66	1.67	1.00	6.83	2.36	1.04	4.83	3.33	1.17
28	12.7	13.2	0.96	1.00	9.66	1.31	1.00	6.83	1.86	1.00	4.83	2.63	1.07
30	10.1	13.2	0.77	1.00	9.66	1.05	1.00	6.83	1.48	1.00	4.83	2.09	1.01
32	8.1	13.2	0.61	1.00	9.66	0.84	1.00	6.83	1.19	1.00	4.83	1.68	1.00
34	6.4	13.2	0.48	1.00	9.66	0.66	1.00	6.83	0.94	1.00	4.83	1.33	1.00

Note: This is a simplifying approximation. It is assumed that most of the square-wave energy resides in the first three harmonics of the fundamental square-wave frequency. Average skin depth for the square-wave current is then taken as the average of the values for the first three harmonics of each fundamental as read in Table 7.5. From these average skin depths, d/S is calculated and from this, R_{ac}/R_{dc} is read from Fig. 7.6.

TABLE 7.8   AC-to-DC Resistance for No. 18 Wire

Frequency, kHz	R_{ac}/R_{dc} (Table 7.6) sine-wave currents	R_{ac}/R_{dc} (Table 7.7) square-wave currents
25	1.05	1.13
50	1.15	1.35
100	1.40	1.75
200	1.85	2.36

presents a comparison of R_{ac}/R_{dc} for No. 18 wire as read from Tables 7.6 and 7.7.

7.5.6   Proximity effect

Proximity effect[11–15] is caused by alternating magnetic fields arising from currents in adjacent wires or, more seriously, from currents in adjacent winding layers in a multilayer coil.

It is more serious than skin effect because the latter increases copper losses only by restricting the conducting area of the wire to a thin skin on its surface. But it does not change the magnitude of the currents flowing—only the current density at the wire surfaces. In contrast, in proximity effect, eddy currents caused by magnetic fields of currents in adjacent coil layers increase exponentially in amplitude as the number of coil layers increases.

7.5.6.1   Mechanism of proximity effect.

Figure 7.7 shows how proximity effect comes about. There currents are shown flowing in opposite directions (*AA'* and *BB'*) in two parallel conductors. For simplicity, the conductors are shown as having thin rectangular cross section and are closely spaced. The conductors could just as well be round wires or flat layers of closely spaced round wires such as adjacent layers in a transformer coil.

The bottom conductor is surrounded by a magnetic field which is shown coming out of its edge 1234, passing into the edge of the upper conductor, out of the opposite edge, and returning back into the far edge of the lower conductor. By Fleming's right-hand rule, the direction of the magnetic field is into edge 5678 of the upper conductor.

By Faraday's law, this varying magnetic field flowing through the area of loop 5678 induces a voltage in series with any line bounding the area. By Lenz' law, the direction of this induced voltage is to produce a current flow in the area boundary such that its magnetic field is in the direction opposite to that of the magnetic field which induced the current flow.

Thus the current flow is counterclockwise in loop 5678. It is seen

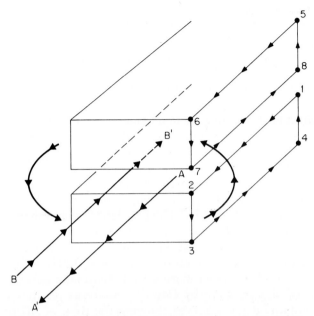

Figure 7.7   Magnetic fields of currents in one conductor induce voltages in loops of adjacent conductors. The resultant eddy currents shown in this diagram flow along the full length of the wires on their top and bottom surfaces. On the bottom conductor, eddy current is in the same direction as the main current flow (*AA'*) on its top surface and reinforces it. On the bottom surface of the bottom conductor, the eddy current is in the direction opposite to that of the main current flow and cancels it. On the bottom surface of the upper conduction, the eddy current is in the same direction as that of the main current and reinforces it. On the top surface of the top conductor, the direction of the eddy current is opposite to that of the main current and cancels it. The consequence is that current in each conductor is confined to thin skins in the surfaces facing each other.

that on the bottom end of the loop, the current flow is in the same direction of current flow (7 to 8) as the main current in the upper conductor (*B* to *B'*) and reinforces that current. On the top edge of the loop, current flow is opposite (5 to 6) to the main current and tends to cancel it. This occurs at all the loops parallel to 5678 throughout the conductor width.

The consequence of this is an eddy current flowing along the full length of the bottom surface of the upper conductor in the direction 7 to 8 and returning along the upper surface of the upper conductor where it is canceled by the main current.

A similar analysis shows an eddy current flows along the full length of the upper surface of the bottom conductor in the direction to reinforce the main current. In the bottom surface of the lower conductor, it is in the direction opposite to the main current flow and tends to cancel it.

Thus currents in the two conductors are confined to a thin skin on the surfaces of the conductor which face one another. The depth of the skin is related to frequency as in normal skin effect.

7.5.6.2 Proximity effect in adjacent layers in a transformer coil.   Current in individual wires in a layer of a transformer coil flow parallel to one another. The current in a layer can then be considered to flow in a thin rectangular sheet whose height is the wire diameter and whose width is the bobbin width. Thus there will be induced eddy currents flowing the full length of the winding. They will flow in thin skins on the interfaces between adjacent coil layers just as described in the previous section for proximity effect in two adjacent flat conductors.

However, it is very significant that the amplitude of these eddy currents increases exponentially with the number of layers. It is this that makes proximity current effect much more serious than skin effect.

A widely referenced classic paper by Dowell[13] analyzes proximity effect in transformers and derives curves showing the ratio of AC to DC resistance R_{ac}/R_{dc} as a function of the number of winding layers and the ratio of wire diameter to skin depth. A detailed summary of Dowell's results is beyond the scope of this text, but it is very well covered by Snelling.[12] A very good discussion of Dowell's curves, showing physically why R_{ac}/R_{dc} increases exponentially with the number of layers, is given by Dixon.[11]

Herein, Dowell's curves will be presented and a discussion of their use and significance on the basis of Dixon's treatment will be given.

Figure 7.8a shows an EE core with three primary layers. Each layer can be considered as a single sheet carrying a current $I = NI_t$ (say, 1 A), where N is the number of turns in the layer and I_t is the current per turn. Now recall Ampere's law which states that $\oint H\ dl = 0.4\pi I$ or the line integral of $H\ dl$ around any closed loop is equal to $0.4\pi I$, where I is the total current enclosed by the loop. This is the magnetic equivalent of Ohm's law, which states that the applied voltage to a closed loop is equal to the sum of all the voltage drops around that loop.

Now if the line integral is taken around the loop $abcd$ in Fig. 7.8b, the magnetic reluctance (magnetic analog of resistance) along the path $bcda$ is low as that path is in ferrite material which has very high permeability. Thus all the magnetic field intensity appears along the path ab which lies between sheets 1 and 2 and no magnetic field intensity lies along the leftmost surface of sheet 1. But since it is the

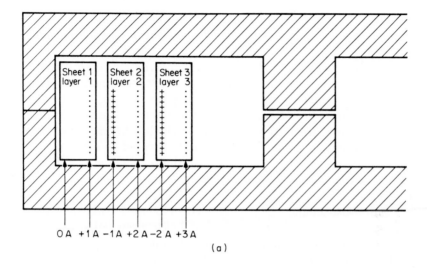

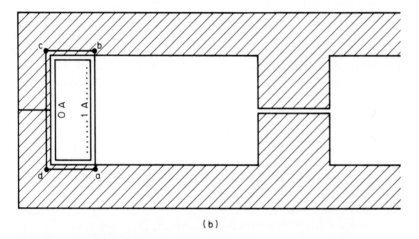

Figure 7.8 (a) Showing exponential buildup of surface eddy currents in a multilayer coil. (b) Current in the first layer is confined to a thin skin on its surface facing away from the ferrite material as dictated by Ampere's law.

magnetic field intensity along the surfaces which cause the skin currents to flow, all the current I which is carried by sheet 1 flows on its rightmost surface in say the plus direction (indicated by the dots) and no current flows on its leftmost surface.

Now consider the currents in sheet 2 (Fig. 7.8a). Proximity effect as described for Fig. 7.7 will cause eddy currents to flow on its left- and rightmost surfaces to a depth equal to the skin depth for that frequency. Now the magnetic field intensity cannot penetrate more than a skin depth below the right-hand surface of sheet 1 or the left-hand surface of sheet 2.

Hence, if the integral $\oint H \, dl$ is taken around the loop *efgh* (through the centers of sheets 1 and 2), since there is zero field intensity along that path, the net current enclosed by that path must be zero by Ampere's law. Further, since the current on the rightmost surface of sheet 1 is 1 A in the plus direction, the current in the left-hand skin of sheet 2 must be 1 A, but in the minus direction (indicated by crosses).

However, the net current in each of the three sheets is 1 A. Hence, with a -1 current in the left skin of sheet 2, the current in its right-hand skin must be $+2$ A.

In a similar argument, the current in the left-hand skin of sheet 3 is -2 A, forcing the current in its right-hand skin to be $+3$ A.

It can thus be seen from this physical or intuitive reasoning that proximity effect causes eddy currents in the skins of a multilayer coil to increase exponentially with the number of layers. The Dowell[13] analysis covered in the next section verifies this quantitatively.

7.5.6.3 Proximity effect AC/DC resistance ratios from Dowell curves.

Dowell's analysis[13] yields the widely referenced curves of Fig. 7.9. They show the ratio of AC/DC resistance ($F_R = R_{ac}/R_{dc}$) versus a factor

$$\frac{h\sqrt{F_l}}{\Delta}$$

where h = effective round wire height = 0.866 (wire diameter d) = 0.866d

Δ = skin depth (from Table 7.5)

F_l = copper layer factor = $N_l d/w$ (where N_l = number of turns per layer, w = layer width, d = wire diameter; note $F_l = 1$ for foil)

The ratio is given for a number of different values of a variable p, which is the number of coil layers per portion. A "portion" is defined as a region where the low-frequency magnetomotive force ($\oint H \, dl = 0.4\pi NI$) ranges from zero to a peak.

This "portion"—often misinterpreted—is clarified thus. Consider that the primary and secondary are both multilayer windings and stacked on the bobbin with the primary layers innermost, followed by the secondary layers on top as in Fig. 7.10a. Now moving outward from the bottom of the primary, the magnetomotive force ($\oint H \, dl = 0.4\pi NI$) increases linearly as shown in Fig. 7.10a.

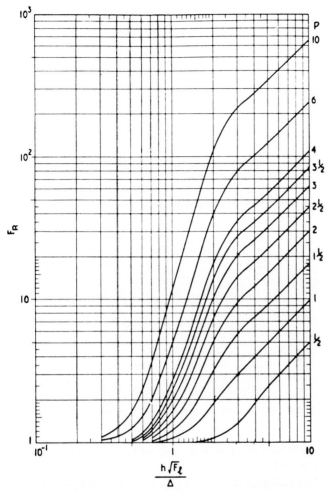

F_R as a function of $h\sqrt{F_l}/\Delta$ with number of layers, p per winding portion as a parameter.

$$R_{AC} = R_{dc}F_R \quad When \quad \frac{h\sqrt{F_l}}{\Delta} > 5 \quad F_R \rightarrow \frac{2p^2+1}{3} \cdot \frac{h\sqrt{F_l}}{\Delta}$$

Figure 7.9 Ratio of AC to DC resistance due to proximity effect. (*From Dowell, Ref. 13.*)

As the line integral is taken over an increasing distance out from the innermost primary layer, it encloses more ampere turns. Then at the secondary-primary interface, $\oint H\,dl$ has reached a peak and starts falling linearly. In a conventional transformer (unlike a flyback), the secondary ampere turns are always simultaneously in the direction opposite to that of the primary ampere turns. Or, stated otherwise,

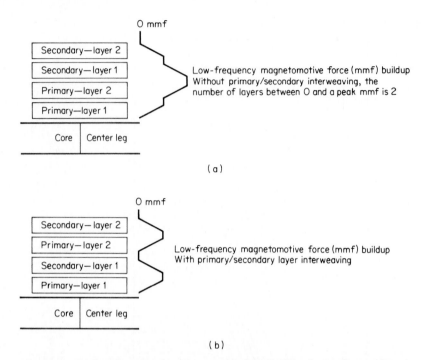

Figure 7.10   (*a*) Low-frequency magnetomotive force buildup in two-layer primary, secondary when primary and secondary layers are not interleaved. A "portion" is defined as the region between zero and a peak magnetomotive force. Here there are two layers per portion. See Fig. 7.9 for significance of "layers per portion." (*b*) By interleaving primary and secondary layers, the number of layers per portion has decreased to 1 and the AC/DC resistance ratio has decreased significantly (Fig. 7.9).

when current in a primary flows into a "dot" end, it flows in the secondary out of the dot end.

Now when the line integral is taken over the last secondary layer, $\oint H\,dl$ has fallen back to zero. This is just another way of stating "the total secondary ampere turns bucks out the primary ampere turns"—except for the small primary magnetizing current.

Thus a "portion" is the region between the zero and the peak magnetizing force and for two secondary and two primary layers, sequenced as in Fig. 7.10*a*, the number of layers per portion p is 2. In Fig. 7.9, for—say—a $(h\sqrt{F_l})/\Delta$ ratio of 4, R_{ac}/R_{dc} is about 13!

Now the number of ampere turns in each half secondary is equal to half the total ampere turns of the primary. If the two primary and secondary layers are interleaved as shown in Fig. 7.10*b*, the low-frequency magnetomotive forces are as shown in the associated diagram.

Now the number of layers between zero and a peak of magnetomotive force is only 1. For the same $(h\sqrt{F_l})/\Delta$ ratio of 4 (from Fig 7.9), the ratio R_{ac}/R_{dc} per portion is now only 4 instead of 13! Thus the total AC resistance of either the primary or secondary is only 4 instead of 13 times its DC resistance.

Note in Fig. 7.9 that the number of layers per portion is shown going down to ½. The significance of ½ layer per portion can be seen in Fig. 7.11. There it is seen that if the secondary consisted of only one layer, the point at which the low-frequency magnetomotive force came back down to zero is half way through the thickness of the secondary layer. Thus Fig. 7.9 shows that for the same $(h\sqrt{F_l})/\Delta$ ratio of 4, R_{ac}/R_{dc} is 2 instead of 4 for the case if the single-layer secondary had not been interleaved between half primaries as in Fig. 7.11.

Figure 7.9 is very valuable in selecting a primary wire size or a secondary foil thickness at a rate other than the previously quoted "500 circular mils per rms ampere." That choice usually leads to large values of h/Δ at high frequencies and, as seen in Fig. 7.9, to very large values of R_{ac}/R_{dc}.

It is often preferable to choose a smaller wire diameter or foil thickness yielding a $(h\sqrt{F_l})/\Delta$ in the region of, say, 1.5. This, of course, would increase R_{dc}. But even though R_{dc} has increased, the smaller ratio of R_{ac}/R_{dc} may yield a lesser R_{ac} and lesser copper losses.

For the case of a push-pull circuit with two layer primaries and two layer secondaries, when interleaving, the simultaneously conducting half primary and secondary should be adjacent to each other as in Fig. 7.12a. Placing the nonconducting secondary adjacent to the conducting primary (Fig. 7.12b) would induce eddy currents in it even when it is nonconducting. Placing the nonconducting secondary outside the conducting one places it in a region where the half primary and half

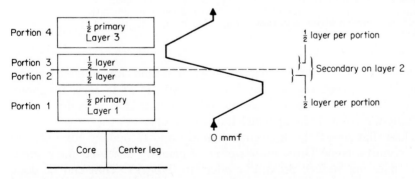

Figure 7.11 Half layers per portion (see Fig. 7.9). With a single-layer secondary sandwiched in between two half primaries, the ampere terms of a half primary are bucked out by half the current in the secondary. In the definition of "layers per portion" of Fig. 7.9, each half segment of the secondary operates at one-half layer per portion.

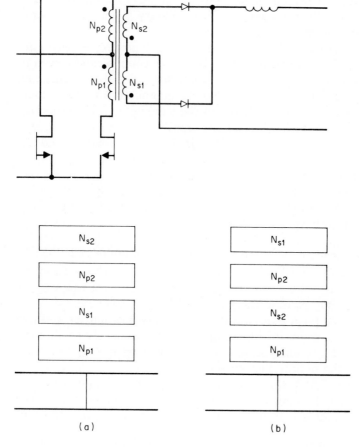

Figure 7.12 Correct (a) and incorrect (b) layer sequencing in a push-pull transformer. The sequencing of Fig. 2.12b will produce significantly more eddy current losses than that of Fig. 7.12a because of proximity effect.

secondary ampere turns cancel during conduction time at each half cycle. Then at that region, the line integral $\oint H \, dl$ is zero, magnetomotive force is zero and hence no eddy currents flow in it during the conduction time of the opposite half secondary.

Note that in a flyback circuit, primary and secondary currents are not simultaneous. Thus, interleaving of primary and secondary windings does not reduce proximity effect in flybacks. That can be done only by keeping the number of layers to a minimum and using finer wire than obtained from the rule of "500 circular mils per rms ampere." Although that increases DC resistance, it decreases R_{ac}/R_{dc}, from Fig. 7.9.

References

1. Ferroxcube-Philips Catalog, *Ferrite Materials and Components,* Saugerties, NY.
2. Magnetics Inc. Catalog, *Ferrite Cores,* Butler, PA.
3. TDK Corp. Catalog, *Ferrite Cores,* M. H. & W International, Mahwah, NJ.
4. Siemens Corp. Catalog, *Ferrites,* Siemens Corp., Iselin, NJ.
5. MMPA Publication PC100, *Standard Specifications for Ferrite Pot Cores,* MMPA, 800 Custer St., Evanston, IL.
6. MMPA Publication UE 1300 *Standard Specifications for Ferrite U, E And I Cores,* MMPA, 800 Custer St., Evanston, IL.
7. IEC Publications 133, 133A, 431, 431A, 647, American National Standards Institute, 1430 Broadway, New York.
8. A. I. Pressman, *Switching and Linear Power Supply, Power Converter Design,* pp. 116–120, Switchtronix Press, Waban, MA, 1977.
9. A. Kennelly, F. Laws, and P. Pierce, "Experimental Researches on Skin Effect in Conductors," *Transactions of AIEE,* 34: 1953, 1915.
10. F. Terman, *Radio Engineer's Handbook,* p. 30, McGraw-Hill, New York, 1943.
11. L. Dixon, *Eddy Current Losses in Transformer Windings and Circuit Wiring,* Unitrode Corp. Power Supply Design Seminar Handbook, Unitrode Corp., Watertown MA, 1988.
12. E. Snelling, *Soft Ferrites,* pp. 319–358, Iliffe, London, 1969.
13. P. Dowell, "Effects of Eddy Currents in Transformer Windings," *Proceedings IEE* (U.K.), 113(8): 1387–1394, 1966.
14. P. Venkatramen, "Winding Eddy Currents in Switchmode Power Transformers Due to Rectangular Wave Currents," *Proceedings Powercon 11,* 1984.
15. B. Carsten, "High Frequency Conductor Losses in Switchmode Magnetics," *High Frequency Power Converter Conference,* pp. 155–176, 1986.
16. A. Richter, "Litz Wire Use in High Frequency Power Conversion Magnetics," *Powertechnics Magazine,* April 1987.

Bipolar Power Transistor Base Drive Circuits

8.1 Introduction

Over the past 5 to 8 years, bipolar power transistors have increasingly been replaced by MOSFET transistors in switching power supplies. New designs in the coming years will most frequently be done with MOSFETs.

There will nevertheless remain some niche areas (perhaps low power applications, because of their lower cost) which will continue using bipolars. Thus because of some small remaining areas where bipolar transistors still offer some advantages and because the vast majority of the switching supplies still operating in the field were originally done with bipolars, it is important for designers to be familiar with their significant characteristics, in the event field failures occur with these older but still operating designs.

The first considerations for the designer of a switching supply based on bipolar transistors are, of course, selection of a device with the proper voltage and current ratings. Maximum voltage and current stresses are dependent on the topology chosen, input voltage and its tolerances, and output power. Equations giving these stresses have been derived and are presented in the discussions of each topology.

However, the means and detailed design of the bipolar base drive circuit is as important for overall reliability as choice of a transistor with adequate voltage and current ratings. The general principles of what constitutes a good base drive circuit and some widely used techniques are discussed herein.

8.2   Objectives of Bipolar Base Drive Circuits

A good base drive circuit should have the criteria and parameters described in Secs. 8.2.1 to 8.2.6.

8.2.1   Sufficiently high current throughout the on time

Base input current should be adequate to keep the on collector-to-emitter potential at a sufficiently low level (0.5 to 1.0 V) for maximum output power at minimum input voltage for the lowest gain (lowest beta) transistor at the peak current instant during the on time.

Thus, design should allow for a four-to-one production spread in transistor beta. The usual current-voltage curves (I_{ce} vs. V_{ce}) in the manufacturer's data sheets (Fig. 8.1) are for a transistor of typical or nominal beta. It should be assumed that the minimum beta is one-half and the maximum beta is twice the typical one shown in the curves.

Power transistor currents in most topologies have the shape of a ramp starting from zero or a ramp on a step. Thus the input base current should be adequate to keep V_{ce} "bottomed" to about 0.5 to 1.0 V at the peak of the I_c ramp at maximum output power at minimum input voltage for the minimum beta transistor. This is especially true for discontinuous-mode flybacks where the ratio of peak to average current is high.

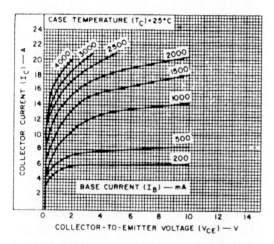

Figure 8.1   Curves of I_c versus V_{ce} for a typical high-voltage high-current transistor. 2N6676, 15 A, 450 V. (*Courtesy RCA*) Curves such as this are usually for a typical device. Depending on the manufacturer's production spread, lowest-beta device may have half the indicated beta; highest-beta device, twice that shown.

8.2.2 A spike of high base input current I_{b1} at instant of turnon

To ensure fast collector current turnon, there should be a short spike of base current about two to three times the average value during the on time. This spike need last only about 2 to 3 percent of the minimum on time (Fig. 8.2a).

The effect of this "turnon overdrive" can be seen in Fig. 8.2b. If turnon speed is not a factor, base input current I_{b1}) for a desired collector current (I_{c1})need be only that required to bottom V_{ce} to the saturation voltage $V_{ce(sat)}$ at the intersection of the collector load line and the I_c/V_{ce} curve.

At that I_{b1}, collector current will rise exponentially with some time constant t_a and get to within 5 percent of I_{c1} in three time constants $3t_a$.

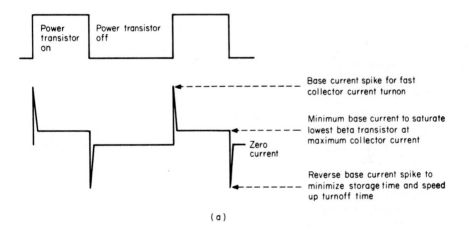

(a)

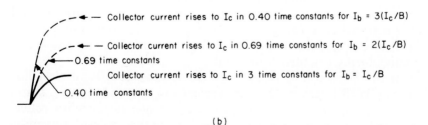

(b)

Figure 8.2 (a) Optimum base current waveforms. (b) Accelerating collector current rise time by base current overdrive.

If base input current is $2I_{b1}$ (overdrive factor of 2), however, collector current will rise as if it were heading for $2I_{c1}$ and if not limited by the load impedance and supply voltage, would reach $2I_{c1}$ in the same $3t_a$. But collector current is limited to I_{c1} by the supply voltage and load impedance. Hence the current reaches I_{c1} (the desired value) in $0.69t_a$ instead of $3t_a$.

Similarly, if an overdrive factor of 3 is used ($I_b = 3I_{b1}$), collector current will rise as if it were headed to $3I_{c1}$ and if not limited by the load resistance and supply voltage, would reach $3I_{c1}$ in the same $3t_a$. But since it is limited, it reaches the desired I_{c1} in $0.4t_a$ instead of $3t_a$.

Overdrive factors of 2 to 3 are usually used to speed up turnon time. This is an overdrive above the required base current for a nominal-beta transistor. Low-beta transistors are faster and do not require as high an overdrive factor. High-beta transistors are slower, and an overdrive of 2 for a nominal beta device corresponds to an overdrive of 4 for a high-beta transistor as its beta value is generally twice that of the nominal-beta transistor.

8.2.3 A spike of high reverse base current I_{b2} at the instant of turnoff (Fig. 8.2a)

If base input current is simply dropped to zero when it is desired to turn off, collector current will remain unchanged for a certain time (storage time t_s). Collector voltage will remain at its low $V_{ce(sat)}$ value of about 0.5 V and when it finally rises, will have a relatively slow rise time.

This comes about because the base-to-emitter circuit acts like a charged capacitor. Collector current keeps flowing until the stored base charges drain away through the external base-to-emitter resistor. There is generally a large excess of stored base charges because the base input current must be chosen sufficiently large to bottom the collector-to-emitter voltage to about 0.5 V for the lowest-beta transistor. Thus the highest or even the nominal-beta transistor has an excess of base current and long storage time.

A momentary spike of reverse base current I_{b2} is required to pull out the stored base charges. This reduces storage time and permits higher switching frequencies. It also significantly reduces power dissipation during the turnoff interval.

This can be seen (Fig. 8.3a) in the instantaneous I_c/V_{ce} curves during the turnoff interval. There it is seen (t_1 to t_2) that before V_{ce} starts rising very rapidly, it moves up out of saturation slowly while collector current hangs on at its peak value. During this interval, current is at its peak and collector-to-emitter voltage is considerably higher than its saturation level of 0.5 to 1.0 V.

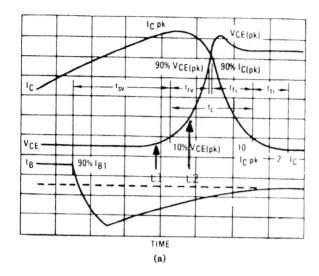

TIME

(a)

TURN-ON TIME

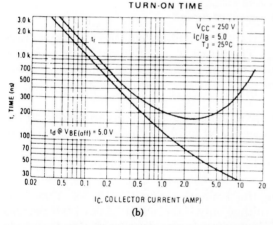

I_C, COLLECTOR CURRENT (AMP)

(b)

Figure 8.3 (a) Typical turnoff transition falling current and rising collector-to-emitter voltage for a power transistor; no snubber at collector. (b) Typical switching times for a typical high-current high-voltage transistor 2N6836, 15 A, 850 V (V_{cev}). (*Courtesy Motorola Inc.*)

This high spike of power dissipation can be a large fraction of the total dissipation in the transistor. The spike of reverse base current (Fig. 8.2a) reduces this dissipation by shortening the interval t_1 to t_2 and permits higher-frequency operation by reducing the storage time.

Manufacturers usually offer curves showing storage, rise time, and fall time for their power transistors for values of I_c/I_{b1} and I_c/I_{b2} ranging from 5 to 10 at various values of collector current (Fig. 8.3b, c).

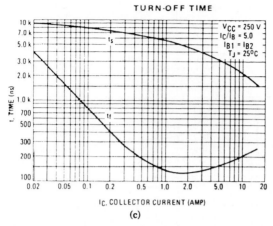

Figure 8.3   (*Continued*)

8.2.4   A base-to-emitter reverse voltage spike −1 to −5 V in amplitude at the instant of turnoff

Bipolar transistors have three significant collector-to-emitter voltage ratings: V_{ceo}, V_{cer}, and V_{cev}. The rating V_{ceo}, is the maximum collector-to-emitter voltage at turnoff when the base to emitter is open-circuited at the instant of turnoff. It is the lowest voltage rating for the device.

The transistor can tolerate a higher voltage (V_{cer} rating) during the off state if it has a "low" (usually 50 to 100 Ω) resistance from base to emitter.

The highest voltage the transistor can safely tolerate is its V_{cev} rating. This is the maximum voltage the transistor can tolerate at the instant of turnoff during the leakage inductance spike (Figs. 2.1, 2.10). It can tolerate this voltage only if there is a −1- to −5-V reverse voltage spike at the base during the instant of turnoff (Fig 8.4). This reverse-bias voltage or voltage spike must be supplied by the base drive circuit and must last at least as long as the leakage inductance spike.

8.2.5   A scheme to permit the circuit to work equally well with high- or low-beta transistors

Since production spread in beta may be four to one, if base input currrent is sufficient to safely turn on a low-beta transistor, it will greatly overdrive a high-beta transistor and result in excessive storage time. Storage times may be so long as to require unacceptably large reverse base currents to yield acceptably low storage times.

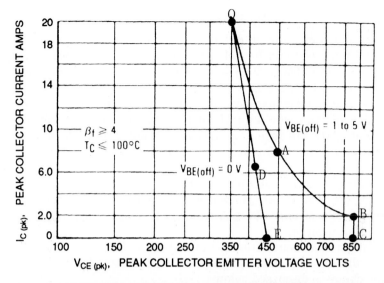

Figure 8.4 Reverse-bias safe operating area curves (RBSOA) for 2N6836. During turnoff, the I_c-V_{ce} locus must not cross the boundaries shown. Even a single crossing may destroy the transistor because of the current crowding into a small part of the chip area and causing local hot spots. With a -1- to -5-V reverse bias at the instant of turnoff, the V_{cev} boundary $OABC$ applies. For $V_{be} = 0$ at turnoff, the boundary ODE applies. (*Courtesy Motorola Inc.*)

8.2.6 High efficiency

Since high-collector-current transistors generally have low beta, the base current driver may be called on to deliver high currents. If these currents come directly from high-voltage sources without the benefit of current gain through a voltage step-down transformer, efficiency will be low.

Thus a widely used fast power transistor—the 2N6836—is rated at 15 A, V_{cev} of 850 V. It is widely used in off-the-AC-line switching supplies. At 15 A, it has a minimum current gain of 5, requiring at least 3 A of base current.

If this current came from a 6-V source for a push-pull circuit at, say, 80 percent duty cycle of base drive, base drive dissipation (at the source) would be an unacceptably high 14.4 W (for a total duty cycle of 0.8). Thus a good base drive scheme should couple the drive pulse from a DC housekeeping voltage source through a voltage step-down–current step-up transformer.

8.3 Baker clamps

The transformer-driven Baker clamp[1-4] is a widely used base drive scheme. It is inexpensive in dollars, is low in component count, and provides all six features described in Secs. 8.2.1 to 8.2.6.

Since it is transformer-driven, it also nicely solves the problem of coupling a width-modulated pulse originating on output ground (where the PWM chip and housekeeping supply are best located for off-the-AC-line supplies) to the base of the power transistor on input ground (see Fig. 6.19 and Sec. 6.6.1).

Since a transformer is involved, it is relatively simple to get a voltage step-down–current step-up ratio of 10 or more. The secondary delivers its voltage to the base at a voltage of about 1 to 1.8 V and the primary takes its current from the housekeeping power supply, which is usually 12 to 18 V.

Thus in the preceding example, for a 10/1 voltage step-down, current step-up, the 3 A of base current at the transformer secondary is obtained at a cost of only 300 mA from its housekeeping supply located at output ground.

Baker clamping is done after the secondary of $T2$ in Fig. 6.19 between the collector and the base of the power transistor. The operation of a Baker clamp is discussed below.

Normally an NPN transistor operates with its collector-to-base junction in reverse bias or with its collector positive with respect to its base. But when it is hard on and in saturation, the collector is negative with respect to its base and the base-to-collector junction is in forward bias, acting like a conducting diode.

This can be seen in Fig. 8.5a and 8.5b for the 2N6386, which is a fast 15-A, 450-V transistor. Figure 8.5a shows the on collector-to-emitter voltage at various collector currents for two values of forced beta $B_f (= I_c/I_b)$ and temperature. It is seen that V_{ce} depends strongly on I_c, B_f, and temperature; but at usual operating conditions of $I_c = 10$ A, $B_f = 5$, and 100°C junction temperature, the on V_{ce} potential is about 0.2 V. Figure 8.5b shows that at 10 A, the on base-to-emitter potential is about 0.9 V at 100°C.

With the resulting 0.7-V forward bias on the base-to-collector junction, there is an excess of stored base charges. Further, when the base current is simply reduced to zero, storage time for this very fast bipolar transistor is still a very long 3 µs (Fig. 8.5c).

Baker clamping corrects this problem by not permitting the base-to-collector junction to take on a forward bias or at the worst, by allowing only a 0.2- to 0.4-V forward bias—low enough to prevent significant storage times.

The Baker clamp can reduce storage times by a factor of 5 to 10.[4] It works nicely over a large temperature and collector current range, and very importantly, it permits equally good circuit operation with transistors whose production spread in beta can be as large as 4 to 1. Its operation is described in the following section (see also Fig. 8.6).

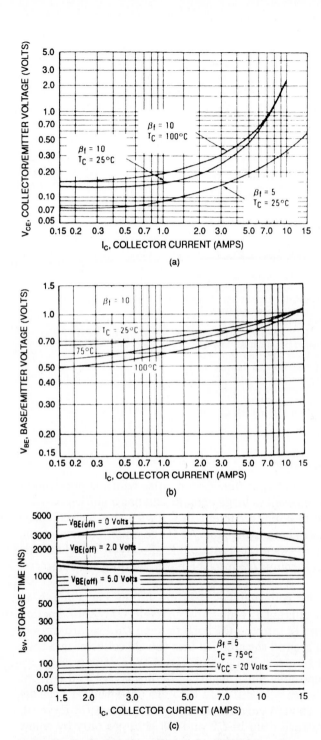

Figure 8.5 (*a, b*) Junction voltages for 2N6836 transistor at two values of forced beta. (*c*) Storage time for 2N6836 without Baker clamping. (*Courtesy Motorola Inc.*)

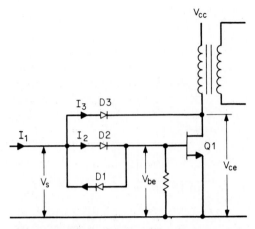

Figure 8.6 Baker clamping. The objective of the Baker clamp is to prevent a forward bias on the $Q1$ collector-to-base junction during the on time and hence minimize or eliminate storage time. If the voltage rise across $D2$ equals the drop across $D3$, V_{ce} is exactly equal to V_{be}. Small variations in the $D2$, $D3$ forward drops permit a small forward bias on the collection-to-base junction, but not enough to result in significant storage times. Currents I_2 and I_3 redistribute themselves by negative feedback so that I_2 is sufficient only to keep V_{ce} low enough to keep $D3$ in forward bias. The balance of I_1 ($= I_3$) flows through $D3$ and the $Q1$ collector to ground.

8.3.1 Baker clamp operation

In Fig. 8.6, a large current I_1 of the desired pulse width is provided at the anode of $D2$. The current is large enough and has a sufficient overdrive to turn on the maximum current in $Q1$ with the desired speed when $Q1$ is a minimum beta transistor. As $Q1$ commences turning on, $D3$ is reverse-biased, draws no current, and is effectively out of the circuit. All the I_1 flows through $D2$ into the base, yielding very fast rise time.

However, when the collector voltage has fallen low enough to forward-bias $D3$, the current I_1 redistributes itself. Only that fraction of it I_2 flows through $D2$ into the $Q1$ base to keep $D3$ forward-biased. The balance I_3 flows around through $D3$ into the $Q1$ collector and then through the emitter to ground.

The circuit now operates with negative feedback. As load current changes or as transistors with different beta are used, the $Q1$ base demands from I_1 only enough current through $D2$ to keep $D3$ forward-biased. Since the forward drop in $D2$ and $D3$ changes only by a few tens of millivolts over very large forward current changes, the potential at the $Q1$ collector does not change significantly.

Now consider the $Q1$ junction potentials. Diode $D3$ must be a high-voltage fast-recovery diode as it is subjected to twice the supply voltage plus a leakage inductance spike. Diode $D2$ is a type of the same speed but is never subjected to a reverse voltage of greater than about 0.8 V (forward voltage of $D1$). Thus, assume that $D3$ is an MUR450 (450 V, 3 A, and 75 ns of recovery time) and $D2$ is an MUR 405 (50 V, 4 A, 35 ns of recovery time).

Assume for the moment that the $D2$, $D3$ forward voltages are independent of forward current and temperature and are equal to 0.75 V. This is a good enough approximation as seen in Table 8.1. The small variations are not sufficient to change the reasoning described below.

Thus in Fig. 8.6, when $D3$ latches in and conducts, the voltage rise in $D2$ is closely equal to the drop in $D3$ and is assumed to be 0.75 V. Then for V_{be} of 1.0 V in $Q1$, its base is at $+1.0$ V with respect to ground, the $D2$ anode (V_s) is at $+1.75$, and the $Q1$ collector is back down to 1.0 V. Thus there is no forward bias on the $Q1$ base-to-collector junction and negligible storage time. As temperature rises, the forward drop in $D2$ decreases, but so does the drop in $D3$ and the collector-to-base junction still has no forward bias.

Now assume that I_1 is 3.5 A and that $Q1$ is a maximum beta transistor and requires only 0.5 A of base current, leaving 3.0 A for $D3$. Table 8.1 shows the rise in $D2$ as 0.61 V at 100°C and the drop in $D3$ at 3 A, 100°C as 0.95 V. This leaves a forward bias of only 0.34 V across the $Q1$ base-to-collector junction—not enough to cause diode-type conduction in it. Storage time is still negligible at that forward bias.

Note that Baker clamping holds the collector-to-emitter potential to about 1 V as compared to the 0.2 to 0.5 V without the Baker clamp. This increases transistor losses during the on time, but the decreased AC loss during the transition from on to off more than makes up for it (Sec. 8.2 and Fig. 8.3a).

TABLE 8.1 Forward Voltage of Two Ultra-Fast-Recovery Diodes ($D2$, $D3$ in Fig. 8.6)

I_f, A	MUR450 V_f, V		MUR405 V_f, V	
	25°C	100°C	25°C	100°C
0.5	0.89	0.75	0.71	0.61
1.0	0.93	0.80	0.74	0.65
2.0	1.01	0.90	0.78	0.70
3.0	1.10	0.95	0.80	0.73

Thus the Baker clamp has satisfactorily solved two significant problems. It prevents a sufficient forward bias on the base-to-collector junction to cause appreciable storage time. It also permits the circuit to work equally well with large changes in load current and over a large production spread in transistor beta because of the redistribution of input currents between $D2$ and $D3$ as base current demands change.

However, it is still desired to provide reverse base current to $Q1$ at the instant of turnoff to speed up turnoff time and provide a -1- to -5-V reverse base bias. This is prevented by the blocking action of $D2$, but by adding the "reach-around" diode $D1$, across $D2$, it becomes possible. It now only remains to find a low-parts-count scheme to provide the large forward current I_{b1} for turnon, an equally large reverse current I_{b2}, and a reverse voltage bias at the base for turnoff. This is easily achieved with the transformer-coupled scheme of the following section.

8.3.2 Transformer coupling into a Baker clamp

8.3.2.1 Transformer supply voltage, turns ratio selection, and primary and secondary current limiting.
The circuit of Fig. 8.7 provides all the required drive characteristics for the Baker clamp—high forward and reverse base drive for $Q2$ at relatively low primary current drawn from the housekeeping supply V_h. It also provides the reverse $Q2$ base voltage which permits it to tolerate its V_{cev} rating. It works as follows.

First, the $T1$ turns ratio N_p/N_s is chosen as large as conveniently possible so as to provide the desired secondary current with a reasonably low primary current and voltage. Since the primary current will be taken from the usual housekeeping supply V_h, which also feeds the PWM chip, V_h should be kept low to keep chip dissipation low.

Choosing a high N_p/N_s ratio to get a large current gain in $T1$ may also force too high a value of V_h. Thus a reasonable choice for V_h is the 15 to 18 V usually selected for a PWM chip. This largely fixes N_p/N_s. It will soon be seen that the $T1$ primary voltage V_p should be considerably less than V_h because of $R1$, which plays a significant part in the circuit.

The $T1$ secondary voltage V_s is clamped to $V_{be(Q_2)}$ plus the $D2$ forward drop V_{D2}. Or, in other words, $V_s = V_{be(Q2)} + V_{D2} = 1.0 + 0.75 = 1.75$ V. The voltage at the top of the $T1$ primary is

$$V_{pt} = \frac{N_p}{N_s} V_s + V_{ce(Q1)}$$

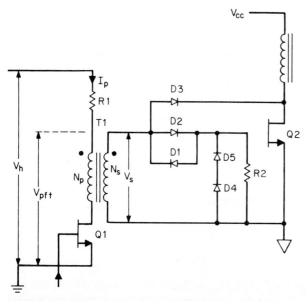

Figure 8.7 A transformer-driven Baker clamp. Transformer $T1$ provides a large current gain from primary to secondary so that secondary currents of 2 to 3 A of secondary current can be obtained from primary currents of about 600 mA, permitting use of small, inexpensive transistors in TO18 cans for $Q1$. By storing magnetizing current in N_p, large reverse currents are available in N_s at the instant of $Q2$ turnoff. Resistor $R1$ serves as a primary current limiter.

$$= \frac{N_p}{N_s} 1.75 + V_{ce(Q1)} \quad \text{V}$$

$$\approx \frac{N_p}{N_s} 1.75 + 1.0 \text{ V} \tag{8.1}$$

Now V_h will be kept constant by an inexpensive linear regulator fed from the secondary of a small 60-Hz transformer returned to output ground as in Fig. 6.19.

However, V_{pt} should be kept considerably lower than V_h so as to provide a relatively constant voltage across $R1$ (V_{R1}) when V_s varies as a result of temperature-induced variations in V_{be} and V_{D2}. The reason for keeping V_{R1} constant is that $R1$ serves to limit primary current from

$$I_{p(Q1)} = \frac{V_h - V_{\text{pt}}}{R_1}$$

$$= \frac{V_h - (N_p/N_s)V_s - 1.0}{R_1} \qquad (8.2)$$

Thus $R1$ is chosen to limit $T1$ primary and hence its secondary current and current into $D2$. Although negative feedback through the Baker clamp diode $D3$ allots current to the $Q2$ base only sufficient to supply the maximum collector current and to keep $D3$ in conduction, an excess current into $D2$ from the $T1$ secondary is simply wasted by being diverted via $D3$ into the $Q2$ collector.

Thus by choosing V_h large compared to $(N_p/N_s)V_s$, $R1$ becomes more of a constant-current source relatively independent of temperature variations in V_s.

For an initial guess, assume $N_p/N_s = 5$. For a nominal $V_s(= V_{sn})$ of 1.75 V, the nominal I_p is

$$I_{pn} = \frac{V_h - 5V_{sn} - 1.0}{R_1}$$

and the change in $I_{pn}(= dI_{pn})$ is $dI_{pn} = 5\, dV_s/R_1$, where dV_s is the anticipated change in V_s due to temperature changes. The fractional change in I_{pn} is

$$\frac{dI_{pn}}{I_{pn}} = \frac{5\, dV_s}{V_h - 5 \times 1.75 - 1.0}$$

$$= \frac{5\, dV_s}{V_h - 9.75} \qquad (8.3)$$

Then, for an anticipated temperature variation dV_s of 0.1 V, and a permissible fractional change of 0.1 in I_{pn}, from Eq. 8.3 we obtain

$$0.1 = \frac{5 \times 0.1}{V_h - 9.75}$$

or
$$V_h \cong 14.75 \text{ V}$$

$$= 15.0 \text{ V}$$

Thus if it were desired to limit the $Q1$ primary current to I_{pn}, $R1$ would be chosen as

$$R_1 = \frac{15 - (5 \times 1.75) - 1.0}{I_{pn}} \qquad (8.4a)$$

$$R_1 = \frac{5.25}{I_{pn}} \qquad (8.4b)$$

8.3.2.2 Power transistor reverse base current derived by flyback action in drive transformer. A large reverse current to the base of power transistor $Q2$ (Fig. 8.7) can be obtained by choosing a low magnetizing inductance in the $T1$ primary. During the $Q1$ on time, total current to the $T1$ primary is limited by $R1$. Part of that current is multiplied by the N_p/N_s turns ratio and delivered to the secondary to turn the $Q2$ base on.

But part of that current flows to the primary magnetizing inductance L_m and does not contribute to the secondary current. It simply ramps up linearly at a rate $dI_m/dt = (V_{pt} - 1)/L_m$. At the end of the on time t_{on} it has reached a peak $I_{pm} = (V_{pt} - 1)t_{on}/L_m$ and is stored as energy in the magnetizing inductance.

Now when $Q1$ is turned off, that magnetizing current I_{pm}, multiplied by the turns ratio N_p/N_s, is delivered by flyback action as a negative-going pulse to the secondary (note the $T1$ primary and secondary dots). At the secondary, it pulls reverse current from the base of $Q2$ through reach-around diode $D1$.

After the base current charges have been fully swept out, the base impedance is very high. As there usually is significant energy left in the $T1$ secondary, the $Q2$ base may be pulled sufficiently far negative to damage or destroy it. This is prevented by the two series diodes $D4$, $D5$ which clamp the $Q2$ base to a negative bias of about 1.6 V—far enough negative to permit $Q2$ to sustain its V_{cev} rating.

8.3.2.3 Drive transformer primary current limiting to achieve equal forward and reverse base currents in power transistor at end of the on time. Significant $T1$ current waveshapes are shown in Fig. 8.8. Current through $R1$ is shown in Fig. 8.8. For $V_h = 15$ V and $N_p/N_s = 5$, the nominal peak current is given by Eq. 8.4b as $I_{pn} = 5.25/R_1$.

Now if the $Q2$ base reverse current at the instant of turnoff is to be equal to its forward base current just the instant before turnoff, the $T1$ primary magnetizing current at the end of on time should be permitted to ramp up linearly to $I_{pn}/2$ by proper choice of its magnetizing inductance.

The $Q1$ magnetizing current is shown in Fig. 8.8b; $Q1$ primary load current is then the difference between Fig. 8.8a and 8.8b and is as shown in Fig. 8.8c. The $T1$ secondary current during the $Q2$ on time is then the $T1$ primary current of Fig. 8.8c multiplied by N_p/N_s. Its amplitude at the end of the on time, $(N_p/N_s)I_{pn}/2$, is chosen to turn on the maximum $Q2$ collector current for the minimum-beta transistor. Its amplitude at the start of the on time is twice that at its end, and consequently turnon time is very fast.

At the end of the $Q1$ on time, $T1$ magnetizing current in L_m is $I_{pn}/2$. At the very instant of $Q1$ turnoff, this reflects into the $T1$ secondary as

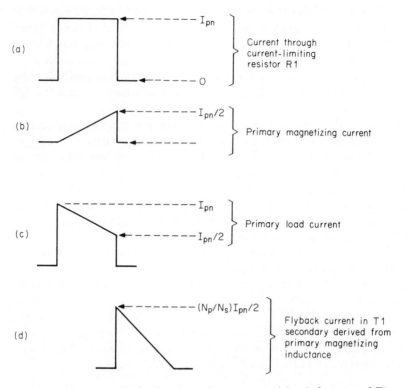

Figure 8.8 By appropriately choosing primary magnetizing inductance of $T1$, the reverse base current to $Q2$ is made equal to its forward current by flyback action in $T1$.

$(N_p/N_s)I_{pn}/2$ and provides a $Q2$ reverse base current (Fig. 8.8d) equal to its forward current just prior to turnoff.

8.3.2.4 Design example—transformer-driven Baker clamp. Assume a 500-W forward converter operating from the rectified 115-V-AC line. Assume a nominal rectified DC input of 160 V at minimum load and a minimum rectified DC input at maximum load of $0.85 \times 160 = 136$ V. From Eq. 2.28, peak primary current is

$$I_{pft} = \frac{3.13P_o}{V_{dc(min)}} = \frac{3.13 \times 500}{136} = 11.5 \text{ A}$$

Assume that $Q2$ is a 2N6836—a 15-A, 450-V (V_{ceo}) device with a V_{cev} rating of 850 V. Its minimum beta at 10 A is 8—assume 7 at 11.5 A. Maximum base current is $11.5/7 = 1.64$ A. For an N_p/N_s ratio of 5 in $T1$, primary load current is $1.64/5 = 0.328$ A.

Also from Fig. 8.8a, current in $R1$ (Fig. 8.7) must be twice that so as to store 0.328 A of $T1$ magnetizing current for the $Q2$ reverse base drive. Then from Eq. 8.4b, for V_h = 15 V, $R1$ = 5.25/2 × 0.328 = 8.0 Ω.

The $T1$ magnetizing inductance must permit a peak magnetizing current of 0.328 A at the end of the on time. Calculate the magnetizing inductance from the minimum on time of $Q1$.

Assume a switching frequency of 50 kHz and a maximum on time at minimum AC input of 0.8T/2 or 8 µs. For ±10 percent variation in AC input, the minimum on time of $Q1$ will be 0.8 × 8 = 6.4 µs. Then

$$L_{m(T1)} = \frac{(N_p/N_s)V_s t_{on(min)}}{0.328}$$

$$= \frac{5 \times 1.75 \times 6.4 \times 10^{-6}}{0.328}$$

$$= 171 \; \mu H$$

Use a Ferroxcube 1408PA3153C8 core. It is small, pill-box in shape, with diameter = 0.551 in and height = 0.328 in. It has an A_l (inductance in millihenries per 1000 turns) of 315 (Fig. 8.9). For 0.171 mH, the required number of turns is N_p = 1000$\sqrt{0.171/315}$ = 23 turns— say, 25 and for a turns ratio of 5, N_s = 5 turns. The magnetizing ampere-turns product is 0.328 × 25 = 8.2 ampere turns. Figure 8.9 shows that the cliff at which this specific core (A_l = 315) starts saturating is at about 12 ampere turns, which is safe.

Transistor $Q1$ need carry a peak current of only 2 × 328 = 656 mA.

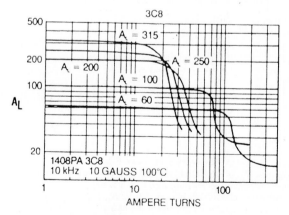

Figure 8.9 Inductance per 1000 turns A_l for Ferroxcube 1408PA3C8 pot core. A small core suitable for the transformer $T1$ of Fig. 8.7.

It can be a 2N2222A—an 800-mA 40-V device whose rise and fall times are under 60 ns. It comes in a small TO18 package and cost is under 25¢!

8.3.3 Transformerized Baker clamp[5]

By changing the circuit of Fig. 8.7 to the simpler one of Fig. 8.10, greatly improved performance with all the advantages of Baker clamping is achieved. Current gain in $T1$ can be doubled without increasing V_h, and better performance over a wider temperature range results. Also, the problem inherent in Fig. 8.7—that the forward rise in $D2$ does not track with the drop in $D3$ over large current changes— no longer exists. The circuit of Fig. 8.10 works as follows. The secondary of $T1$ in Fig. 8.10 is now center-tapped ($N_{s1} = N_{s2}$). Thus

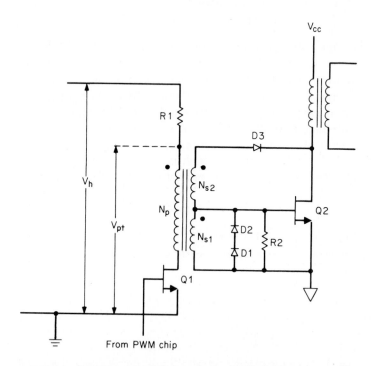

Figure 8.10 Transformerized Baker clamp. An improvement over Fig. 8.7; $N_{s1} = N_{s2}$. Thus voltage rise across N_{s2} is very closely equal to drop across $D3$ and $Q2$ collector is at same potential as its base and to a close approximation tracks it as temperature varies. With $V_{Ns1} = 1.0$ V, N_p/N_s can be 10 rather than 5 for the circuit of Fig. 8.7 at roughly the same value of V_h as for Fig. 8.7. Now current gain between N_p and N_{s1} is 10, and compared to Fig. 8.7, $Q1$ current is halved for the same $Q2$ base current.

$V_{Ns1} = V_{Ns2} = V_{be(Q2)}$, and when $D3$ has latched in and is conducting, we obtain

$$V_{ce(Q)} = V_{Ns1} + V_{Ns2} - V_{D3}$$
$$= 2V_{be(Q2)} - V_{D3}$$
$$= 2 \times 1.0 - 1.0 = 1.0 \qquad \text{(Table 8.1, Fig. 8.5}b\text{)}$$

Since $V_{be} = 1.0$ also, there is no forward bias across the base-to-collector junction and storage time is minimized.

There are, of course, changes in V_{be} and V_{D3} with current and temperature, but since there is only one diode involved as compared to two for Fig. 8.7, the maximum forward bias on the $Q2$ collector-to-base junction is considerably less than that for Fig. 8.7.

Now that $D2$ is no longer needed (it was needed only in Fig. 8.7, to provide a forward-voltage rise equal to the $D3$ forward drop), the reach-around diode $D1$ is not needed.

The greatest advantage of Fig. 8.10 is that now since V_s is approximately 1.0 rather than the 1.75 V of Fig. 8.7, the turns ratio N_p/N_{s1} can be roughly doubled without increasing V_h. Thus the same $Q2$ base current can be delivered at about half the current in $Q1$ and the $T1$ primary. The advantage of Fig. 8.10 can be appreciated by repeating the design example of Sec. 8.3.2.4 with the Fig. 8.10 circuit as below.

8.3.3.1 Design example—transformerized Baker clamp.

In Fig. 8.10, $V_{pt} = (N_p/N_{s1})V_{Ns1} + V_{ce(Q1)}$. Now choose $N_p/N_{s1} = 10$ rather than 5 as for the Fig. 8.7 circuit. With a larger $T1$ turns ratio, I_{Q1} will be smaller. Hence assume that $V_{ce(Q1)}$ will be 0.5 V rather than the 1.0 V assumed for the Fig. 8.7 circuit. Then $V_{pt} = 10 \times 1.0 + 0.5 = 10.5$ V, and keeping the same nominal 5.25 V across $R1$ (Eq. 8.4b), $V_h = 15.75$ V. For the same 1.64 A to the $Q2$ base as in the previous design example, with $N_p/N_{s1} = 10$, $Q1$ primary load current is now only 164 mA.

Also as in Sec. 8.3.2.4, choose the $T1$ magnetizing current at the end of the on time to equal the primary load current (Fig. 8.8). Thus $R1$ is chosen to limit current to 328 mA and $R_1 = 5.25/0.328 = 16\ \Omega$. And with 10 V across the $T1$ primary, for the same 6.4 μs, the magnetizing inductance $L_m = (10 \times 6.4 \times 10^{-6})/0.164 = 390\ \mu$H.

For the same Ferroxcube 1408PA3153C8 core with an A_l value of 315 mH per 1000 turns, the required number of primary turns is 1000 $\sqrt{0.390/315} = 35$. For a turns ratio of 10 N_{s1}, N_{s2} would, of course, require 3.5 turns.

Half turns are possible with pot cores, but introduce other odd, undesirable effects. Hence choose $N_{s1} = N_{s2} = 4$ turns and $N_p = 40$

turns. This makes the magnetizing inductance $(40/35)^2 \times 390$ or 509 μH and the peak magnetizing current equal to $(390/509)164 = 126$ mA. For a 10/1 turns ratio, the reverse base current to $Q2$ is now 1.26 instead of 1.64 A. This would still yield a sufficiently low storage time.

The number of magnetizing ampere turns in $T1$ is now $0.126 \times 40 = 5.04$ ampere turns—still safely below the saturation knee for the $A_l = 315$ core of Fig. 8.9.

8.3.4 Inherent Baker clamping in Darlington transistors

In a Darlington transistor, the output transistor $Q2$ is automatically Baker clamped by the base-emitter diode of the drive transistor $Q1$ acting as $D2$ of Fig. 8.7 and the base-collector diode of the drive transistor acting as $D3$ in Fig. 8.7. This can be seen in Fig. 8.11a to 8.11c.

Thus the output transistor in a Darlington has negligible forward bias on its base-collector junction and should have low storage times. But data sheets on integrated-circuit Darlingtons show storage times up to 3 and 4 μs. This is due mainly to storage times in the Darlington drive transistor, which does saturate and has a forward-biased base–collector junction.

If a Darlington configuration with lesser storage time is needed, the 3- to 4-μs storage time can be lowered by using discrete transistors for the drive and output transistors.

By implementing the Darlington with discrete drive and output transistors, the drive transistor can be chosen as an ultra-high-frequency device which can have minimized storage time despite its forward-biased base-collector junction.

Most integrated-circuit Darlingtons have a built-in reach-around

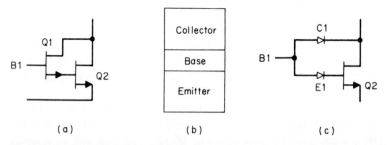

(a)   (b)   (c)

Figure 8.11 In a Darlington configuration, output transistor $Q2$ is inherently Baker clamped by the base-collector diode of $Q1$ acting as $D3$ and the base-emitter diode of $Q1$ acting as $D2$ in Fig. 8.7. Storage time in a Darlington configuration is due to saturation of the Darlington driver which is not Baker clamped. Figure 8.11b shows the junctions in a junction transistor as $Q1$.

diode as $D1$ in Fig. 8.7 which permits pulling reverse current from the output transistor base to improve its switching time.

8.3.5 Proportional base drive[2-4]

This base drive scheme (shown in Fig. 8.12) is widely used for high output power or power transistor currents over about 5 to 8 A.

The circuit does not attempt to keep the power transistor from saturating by use of Baker clamping. Rather, it ensures a large reverse base current to minimize storage time; and it always generates a base drive current proportional to its output current.

Thus even with a high base current required for high output currents, when output current is reduced from maximum to minimum, so is the input base current. Consequently, the base is never overdriven at low output currents and storage time is kept reasonably low throughout the load current range.

A particularly valuable feature is that the base current is obtained by positive feedback from the collector. For large output currents which require large base currents, this results in far less base source dissipation than if the base currents were derived from some housekeeping supply.

Circuit details are described in the following paragraphs.

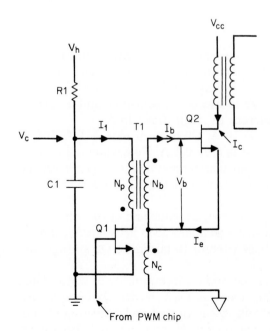

Figure 8.12 Proportional base drive. When $Q1$ turns off, the magnetizing current stored in N_p provides a short impulse to turn $Q2$ on by flyback action in $T1$. Thereafter, positive feedback from N_c to N_b holds $Q2$ on. The ratio N_b/N_c is chosen equal to $Q2$ minimum beta. When $Q1$ turns on, it couples a negative impulse to N_b which starts a regenerative turnoff sequence between N_c and N_b.

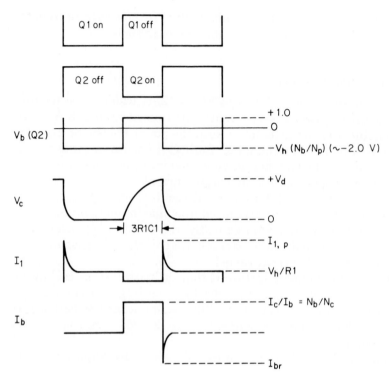

Figure 8.12 (*Continued*)

8.3.5.1 Detailed circuit operation—proportional base drive. In Fig. 8.12, there is positive feedback between windings N_c and N_b (note the dots) of drive transformer $T1$. These windings act as a current transformer with a turns ratio N_c/N_b. If $Q2$ is turned on somehow and a current $I_c(\approx I_e)$ flows in N_c, a base current $(N_c/N_b)I_c$ flows in N_b.

Thus for $(N_c/N_b) = 0.1$ if I_c is 10 A, $Q2$ base current is 1 A. If I_c is reduced to 1 A, $Q2$ base current is only 0.1 A. Now when $Q2$ is to be turned off, the stored base charges which must be removed correspond only to 0.1 and not to 1.0 A and turnoff at the 1.0-A output current level is still rapid.

The problem now is how to initiate $Q2$ turnon and at turnoff, how to break the tightly coupled positive-feedback loop between N_c and N_b and supply a large reverse base current to minimize $Q2$ storage and turnoff time.

Transistor $Q2$ can be turned on and off in a number of ways. Some designers turn on an auxiliary transistor $Q1$ to turn $Q2$ on and turn $Q1$ off to turn $Q2$ off. But herein, $Q2$ is turned on by turning $Q1$ off. Then, by flyback action (note the dots in N_p and N_b), the stored magnetizing current in the $T1$ primary is multiplied by the N_p/N_b ratio and delivered to N_b to initiate the turnon operation.

The impulse from N_p to N_b need last only a short time—long enough for $Q2$ collector current to have risen sufficiently to establish a solid positive-feedback loop between N_c and N_b. Then, for the duration of the on time, base current is supplied by transformer coupling between N_c and N_b.

Now to turn $Q2$ off, $Q1$ is turned on. It is assumed that V_c, the voltage at the top of the capacitor $C1$, is fully charged up to the supply voltage V_h. When $Q1$ comes on, the dot end of N_b goes negative with respect to its no-dot end (see dot orientation) and turns $Q2$ off. The turns ratio N_p/N_b is chosen to yield a 2-V negative pulse at N_b so as to permit $Q2$ to sustain its V_{cev} rating as it turns off.

The magnitudes of $R1$, $C1$, V_h, N_p magnetizing inductance, and all the $T1$ turns ratios are critical to the design. The quantitative design of all these components are covered in the following section.

8.3.5.2 Quantitative design of proportional base drive scheme. The first decision to be made is selection of the turns ratio N_b/N_c (Fig. 8.12). This is chosen equal to the minimum $Q2$ beta or

$$\frac{N_b}{N_c} = \beta_{\min(Q2)} \tag{8.5}$$

Proportional base drive is used mostly for $Q2$ currents over 5 to 8 A, at which level minimum transistor betas range between 5 and 10. Thus N_b/N_c is usually chosen in the range of 5 to 10.

The next decision is the choice of N_p/N_b. Below, it will be ensured that when $Q1$ is turned on, V_c, the voltage at the top of capacitor $C1$ is at the supply voltage V_h. Now when $Q1$ is turned on, it is desired to couple a 2-V negative impulse to the $Q2$ base. This permits $Q2$ to tolerate its V_{cev} voltage rating and prevents "second breakdown." Thus

$$\frac{N_p}{N_b} = \frac{V_h}{2} \tag{8.6}$$

With these ratios fixed, the transformer is almost designed. Then N_c is chosen at one turn which fixes N_b and N_p. A core will be chosen and a gap will be specified as below.

Now when $Q2$ has been turned on and is carrying its maximum current $I_{c(\max)}$, the base current to support that collector current comes from positive feedback between N_c and N_b. But to initiate that regenerative process, the current impulse delivered from N_p to N_b by flyback action when $Q1$ turns off must be large enough to ensure that the positive-feedback loop latches in securely. If the impulse from N_p is too small in amplitude or width, $Q2$ may turn on and fall back off.

To ensure that this does not happen, the short current impulse delivered to N_b from N_p will be made equal to that delivered to N_b from N_c after solid positive feedback has been established. Thus I_1 (Fig. 8.12) will be chosen, by proper selection of $R1$, to yield

$$I_1 = \frac{N_b}{N_p} \frac{I_{c(\max)}}{\beta_{\min}}$$

$$= \frac{N_b}{N_p}\left[I_{c(\max)}\left(\frac{N_c}{N_b}\right)\right] \qquad (8.7a)$$

$$I_1 = I_c \frac{N_c}{N_p} \qquad (8.7b)$$

This value of I_1 can be obtained by properly choosing the N_p inductance. It is chosen low enough (as will be calculated below) so that at the end of the minimum $Q1$ on time, the voltage across it will have collapsed to zero, and I_1 is fixed by V_h and R_1 as:

$$I_1 = \frac{V_h}{R_1} \qquad (8.8a)$$

and from Eq. 8.7b

$$R_1 = \frac{V_h}{I_c} \frac{N_p}{N_c} \qquad (8.8b)$$

8.3.5.3 Selection of holdup capacitor (C1; Fig. 8.12) to guarantee power transistor turnoff. Now at the end of the $Q1$ on time, when $Q1$ has been on long enough for the voltage across N_p to collapse to zero, N_p draws a current of only V_h/R_1. This is sufficient that at $Q1$ turnoff, the current impulse delivered to N_b by flyback action is sufficient to safely close the regenerative feedback loop between N_c and N_b.

At the initial instant when $Q1$ has just turned on, however, it is necessary for $Q1$ to draw more current than I_1. The initial current in N_p has two tasks. When $Q1$ turns on initially, it must first break the positive-feedback loop between N_c and N_b by canceling I_b, the $Q2$ forward base current. Then to turn $Q2$ off quickly with minimum storage time, it should deliver an equal reverse current I_b to the $Q2$ base. Thus to deliver $-2I_b$ to N_b requires $2I_b(N_b/N_p)$ in N_p.

Further, in delivering $-2I_b$ to N_b, the voltage at the top of N_p must remain at V_h to deliver the aforementioned momentary 2-V reverse-bias pulse to the $Q2$ base. If not for capacitor $C1$, $R1$ would not be able to remain at V_h and supply $2I_b(N_b/N_p)$ to the primary. Thus capacitor $C1$ is added at the junction of $R1$ and N_p to hold V_c up long enough to turn $Q2$ off.

This last requirement fixes the value of C_1. Capacitor $C1$ must supply the current $2I_b(N_b/N_p)$ at a voltage V_h for a time equal to the $Q2$ turnoff time t_{off}. This requires a stored energy in $C1$ of

$$\tfrac{1}{2}C_1(V_h)^2 = 2I_b\frac{N_b}{N_p}V_h t_{off}$$

$$= 2I_c\frac{N_c}{N_b}\frac{N_b}{N_p}V_h t_{off}$$

or

$$\tfrac{1}{2}C_1(V_h)^2 = 2I_c\frac{N_c}{N_p}V_h t_{off} \tag{8.9a}$$

or

$$C_1 = 4\left(\frac{I_c}{V_h}\right)\frac{N_c}{N_p}t_{off} \tag{8.9b}$$

For the usual average turnoff time t_{off} for high-current bipolar transistors of 0.30 μs, this fixes the value of C_1.

Now that $R1$ and $C1$ have been selected, care must be taken that at the instant $Q1$ is turned on to turn $Q2$ off, the voltage V_c (Fig. 8.12) has risen to V_h. For during the previous on time (Fig. 8.12), the inductance of N_p has been chosen so low that V_c has fallen to zero to permit a buildup of I_1 in $R1$. Hence at the start of the $Q1$ off time, V_c is at ground and has only the complete minimum off time to charge back up to V_h again.

Thus, to recharge $C1$ to within 5 percent of V_h, it must be true that $3R_1C_1$ = minimum $Q1$ off time.

If the preselected R_1C_1 time constant is too large, $C1$ can be recharged rapidly with an emitter-follower as in the scheme of Fig. 8.13 suggested by Dixon.[6]

8.3.5.4 Base drive transformer primary inductance and core selection. At the start of the $Q1$ on time, V_c is at V_h and at the end of the on time, it is desired that V_c collapse to ground so as to store a current I_1 in N_p. Now assume that V_c falls linearly from V_h to ground in the minimum $Q1$ on time $t_{on(min)}$. Then at the end of the on time, N_p must be carrying a current:

$$I(N_p) = I_{R1} + I_{C1}$$

$$= \frac{V_h}{R1} + \frac{C_1 V_h}{t_{on(min)}} \tag{8.10}$$

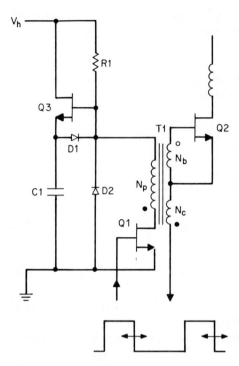

Figure 8.13 Fast *C1* recharge circuit for proportional base drive. In Fig. 8.12, if *C1* cannot be recharged to V_h in the minimum *Q2* on time, emitter-follower *Q3* is interposed between *R1* and *C1* for fast recharge.

Now in the time t_{on}, the voltage across N_p falls linearly from V_h to ground. This is the equivalent of a step of voltage $V_h/2$ applied to the N_p inductance L_p for a time t_{on}. The current rise in the inductor in a time t_{on} is then $I_1 = V_h t_{on}/2L_p$. This current rise must equal the current $I(N_p)$ of Eq. 8.10. Then

$$\frac{V_h t_{on}}{2L_p} = \frac{V_h}{R_1} + \frac{C_1 V_h}{t_{on(min)}}$$

or
$$L_p = \frac{t_{on}}{2(1/R_1 + C_1/t_{on(min)})} \tag{8.11}$$

8.3.5.5 Design example—proportional base driver. Consider a forward converter with the base drive circuit of Fig. 8.12. Assume a *Q2* collector current of 12 A. Assume the circuit is an off-line converter from the 115-V-AC line with a minimum rectified DC supply voltage of 145 V. Then from Eq. 2.28, 12 A of collector current corresponds to an output power of $12 \times 145/3.13 = 556$ W.

Assume that *Q2* is a 15-A device with a minimum beta of 6 at 12 A. Then from Eq. 8.5, $N_b/N_c = 6$ and for $N_c = 1$, $N_b = 6$ turns. Now assume a housekeeping supply voltage V_h of 12 V. From Eq. 8.6, $N_p/N_b = V_h/2 = 6$ and $N_p = 6N_b = 36$ turns.

From Eq. 8.7b, $I_1 = I_c(N_c/N_p) = 12/36 = 0.33$ A; and from Eq. 8.8b, $R_1 = (V_h/I_c)(N_p/N_c) = (12/12)(36/1) = 36\ \Omega$.

From Eq. 8.9b, for a $Q2$ turnoff time t_{off} of 0.3 μs

$$C_1 = 4\,\frac{I_c}{V_h}\frac{N_c}{N_p}\,t_{off}$$

$$= 4\left(\frac{12}{12}\right)\left(\frac{1}{36}\right)(0.3 \times 10^{-6})$$

$$= 0.033\ \mu F$$

Now assume a 50-kHz switching frequency. From Fig. 8.11, minimum $Q1$ on time occurs at maximum $Q2$ on time, which will be assumed to be a half period or 10 μs. Then from Eq. 8.11

$$L_p = \frac{t_{on(min)}}{2(1/R_1 + C_1/t_{on})}$$

$$= \frac{10 \times 10^{-6}}{2[1/36 + (0.033 \times 10^{-6}/10 \times 10^{-6})]}$$

$$= 162\ \mu H$$

Further, since N_p is calculated as 36 turns, A_l (inductance per 1000 turns) is $(1000/36)^2(0.162) = 125$ mH per 1000 turns.

Finally, from Fig. 8.9, the Ferroxcube 1408PA3C8-100 core can be used. Its A_l is 100 mH per 1000 turns, which is close enough.

8.3.6 Miscellaneous base drive schemes

A wide variety of specialized bipolar base drive schemes have evolved through the years. They are more often used at lower power levels and, by various circuit "tricks," seek to achieve two common goals. (1) a low-parts-count scheme to obtain substantial reverse base voltage, reverse base current, or a base-emitter short circuit at turnoff and at turnon and (2) forward base current adequate to drive lowest beta transistors at maximum current without long storage times for high beta transistors at lowest current. Some examples are shown below.

P. Wood devised the circuit of Fig. 8.14a for a 1000-W off-line power supply.[7] Its major features are current gain through transformer $T1$ and a 2-V reverse base bias for power transistor $Q2$ which is automatically switched on by turning $Q1$ on at the instant that $Q2$ is to be turned off. It can be used either at ground level for the bottom power transistors in a bridge or at the power supply voltage source level for the upper bridge transistors. It has also been widely used at lower

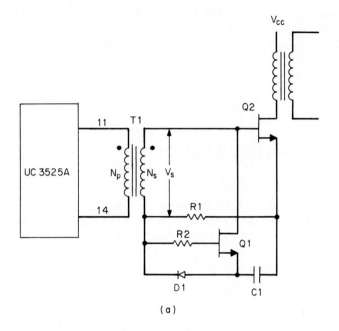

(a)

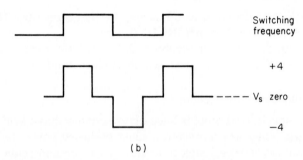

(b)

Figure 8.14   (a) Wood base drive circuit. When dot end of N_s goes positive, $Q2$ turns on with its base current limited by $R1$. Voltage V_s is chosen to provide about 4 V across $R1$ for the known base current. With 4 V across $R1$, $C1$ charges to 3 V through $D1$. While voltage exists across N_s, $Q1$ is reverse-biased and is off. When voltage across N_p drops to zero, so does voltage across N_s. Now 3-V charge on $C1$ turns on $Q1$ via $R1$ and $R2$. This brings $Q2$ base sharply down to a -3-V bias and turns it off rapidly. (c) Adding $D3$, $Z1$, and $D2$ permits driving $T1$ from the on collector in the output transistor of a 3524 chip.

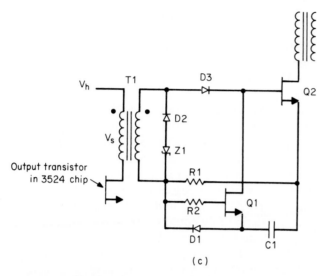

Figure 8.14 (*Continued*)

power levels. It works as follows. Assume (Fig. 8.14*b*) the voltage across N_s is high for the part of a half period that $Q2$ is supposed to be on. Then for the balance of the half period that $Q2$ is to be off ($Q2$ dead time), the voltage across N_s is clamped to zero. Then, in the following half period, the N_s voltage reverses polarity to reset the core on its hysteresis loop.

Such a waveform can be obtained using the Unitrode UC3525A PWM chip by connecting the $T1$ primary across output pins 11 and 14. Now the $T1$ turns ratio is chosen to yield a secondary voltage V_s of about 4 V. Resistor $R1$ is chosen to limit $Q2$ base current to a value sufficient to turn on and saturate the lowest beta transistor at the maximum I_c with the required speed. Then

$$R_1 = \frac{V_s - V_{be}}{I_{b(max)}}$$

$$= \frac{(V_s - 1)\beta_{(min)}}{I_{c(max)}} \tag{8.12}$$

Now for 4 V across N_s, voltage across $R1$ is about 3 V and the left-hand side of $C1$ charges down to approximately -2 V with respect to the $Q2$ emitter. With the left-hand side of $R1$ at -3 V with respect to the $Q2$ emitter, $Q1$ has a -1-V bias so long as current flows through $R1$ and is kept off.

At the start of the dead time, when V_s falls to zero, $Q2$ should turn off as rapidly as possible and with as low a storage delay as possible. At the instant V_s falls to zero, the left-hand side of $C1$ is at -2 V with respect to the $Q2$ emitter and $C1$ is a floating power supply of -2 V feeding the series combination of $R1$, $R2$ and the base-emitter of $Q1$.

Thus at the instant V_s falls to zero, $Q1$ turns on and pulls the $Q2$ base down to -2 V and turns it off. The reverse base current to $Q2$ is not uniquely determined. But $Q1$ is a small, fast 2N2222AA with a minimum gain of 50 at 500 mA. This is sufficient to yield quite low storage and turnoff time in $Q2$. As soon as the dot end of N_s goes positive again, the $Q1$ base is again reverse-biased and $Q1$ turns off.

A circuit which permits the use of the less expensive SG3524 instead of the UC3525 chip is shown in Fig. 8.14c. Here, when the V_s polarity reverses, zener diode $Z1$ (3.3 V) and diode $D2$ clamp it and reset the core in a time approximately equal to its setting time. Diode $D3$ blocks the resetting voltage from being clamped by $Q1$.

Now the voltage to which $C1$ had charged via $D1$ is the floating bias voltage which turns $Q1$ on via $R1$ and $R2$ in series. As $Q1$ turns on, it pulls the $Q2$ base down hard to -2 V and turns it off. The addition of diode $D3$ requires the $T1$ turns ratio to be set to a value which yields a V_s of about 5 V.

If power transistor reverse base bias is not critical, the components $Q1$, $C1$, and $D1$ of the Wood circuit can be eliminated by the use of a UC3525 chip as shown in Fig. 8.15. Although the scheme does not offer a reverse base bias, it does provide a dead short circuit at the power transistor base immediately after turnoff. This minimizes storage and turnoff time but does not provide the reverse base bias which enables the transistor to sustain its V_{cev} rating.

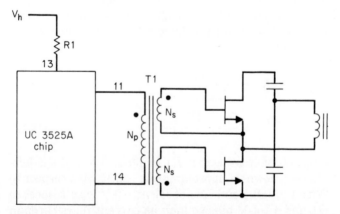

Figure 8.15 Base drive to upper and lower transistors in a bridge through a transformer whose primary is fed directly from UC3525A output.

The circuit is shown in Fig. 8.15 providing base drive to the upper and lower transistors in a half bridge—or, alternatively, to a pair of push-pull transistors.[8] Resistor $R1$ is used for current limiting, and to be a good constant-current source, the voltage across it should be relatively independent of voltage drops in the internal source and sink drivers at pins 11 and 14.

These source and sink drivers in the UC3525 are each specified to have about a 2-V drop at 200 mA. Thus for $V_s (= V_{be}) = 1$ V and a current gain of 10, the primary voltage at pins 11 and 14 is 10 V. Further, since the primary current flows out of the source driver and returns through the sink driver to ground, for 10 V across the primary, pin 13, the top of the source driver is at 14 V. For $R1$ to be a fairly good constant-current source, the voltage across it is set at 6 V, making the housekeeping supply $V_h = 20$ V.

Then for primary current limiting at 200 mA, $R_1 = 6/0.2 = 30\ \Omega$. For a 10/1 turns ratio, this yields 2 A of power transistor base current. At maximum power transistor current, turnoff and storage delay are minimized because with the UC3525, both output terminals are short-circuited together immediately after the end of an on time.

Note, though, that unlike with Baker clamping or proportional base drive, the same power transistor base current is delivered at maximum and minimum collector current. Thus, if base currents are adequate at maximum collector current, bases will be very heavily overdriven at minimum current and storage and turnoff time will be long at those currents.

Figure 8.16 shows another alternative with some desirable features. Transistor $Q4$ is the power transistor which is being Baker clamped

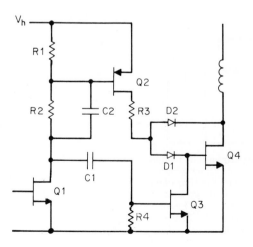

Figure 8.16 DC-coupled power transistor base drive. When $Q1$ in PWM chip turns on, it turns $Q2$ on, which, via $R3$, turns $Q4$ on. When $Q1$ turns off, a positive-going differentiated spike is coupled via $C1$ into $Q3$ base, turning $Q4$ base to ground to turn it off rapidly; $Q1$ turnoff also couples a positive spike into $Q2$ base to turn if off rapidly.

by diodes $D1$, $D2$. Turnon drive comes from the PNP emitter-follower $Q2$ (2N2907A—a small, fast 800-mA device). Resistor $R3$ is chosen to provide the desired maximum $Q4$ base current [$I_{R3} = (V_h - 2)/R3$]. When $Q1$, the PWM output transistor, turns on, it turns on $Q2$, which then turns $Q4$ on.

Normally $Q3$ is off and does not rob any base drive from $Q4$. When it is desired to turn $Q4$ off, $Q1$ is turned off, removing base drive from $Q2$. Its collector current ceases and forward drive is removed from $Q4$, which then starts turning off.

As $Q1$ starts turning off, its collector voltage rises steeply. A differentiated positive pulse is coupled via $C1$ into the $Q3$ base and turns it on momentarily. This short-circuits the $Q4$ base to ground, minimizing its storage and current fall time.

As $Q1$ starts turning off, $Q2$ does not turn completely off until the bottom end of $R2$ has risen almost to V_h. To speed up the $Q4$ turnoff time, in addition to the differentiated positive pulse coupled to the $Q3$ base via $C1$, a differentiated positive pulse is coupled to the $Q2$ base via $C2$ to accelerate its turnoff time.

A final base drive scheme is shown in Fig. 8.17, where $Q1$ is the output transistor in the PWM chip, $Q4$ is the power transistor, and $Q2$ and $Q3$ constitute an NPN-PNP emitter-follower totem pole. For $Q2$ a 2N2222A, $Q3$ a 2N2907A, it is capable of "sourcing" up to 800 mA when $Q2$ is on and "sinking" 800 mA when $Q3$ is on. Both $Q2$ and $Q3$ are fast 300-mHz transistors.

On the way up, when $Q2$ is turning on, $Q3$ has a 0.6-V reverse base-

Output transistor in PWM chip

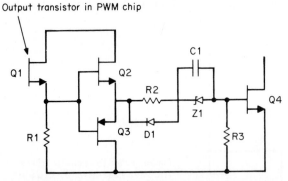

Figure 8.17 Direct coupling from emitter of output transistor in PWM chip. When $Q1$ is on, totem-pole driver $Q2$ turns on power transistor $Q4$ with base current limiting determined by $R2$, $Z1$. Capacitor $C1$ takes on a charge equal to the zener voltage (~ 3.3 V). When $Q1$ turns off, $Q3$ emitter falls to about +0.6 V and right-hand side of $C1$ forces $Q4$ base down to about −3 V, turning it off rapidly.

emitter bias and is off. On the way down, when $Q3$ is turning on, $Q2$ has a 0.6-V reverse base-emitter bias and is off.

In Fig. 8.17 $Z1$ is a 3.3-V zener diode. When $Q1$ and $Q2$ are on, $C1$ charges up to 3.3 V with its $Q4$ base end negative with respect to its $R2$ end. $R2$ serves to limit $Q4$ base current $(= [V_h - V_{ce(Q2)} - V_{be(Q4)} - V_{Z1}]/R_2)$

When $Q1$ turns off, $R1$ brings the $Q2$, $Q3$ base quickly to ground as the capacity at the bases of the totem-pole transistors is very low. The $Q3$ emitter comes to +0.6 and $Q3$ is hard on. Now the 3.3-V negative charge at the right-hand side of $C1$ brings the $Q3$ base down to -3.3 V and quickly turns $Q4$ off.

References

1. A. I. Pressman, *Switching and Linear Power Supply, Power Converter Design,* pp. 322–323, Switchtronix Press, Waban, MA, 1977.
2. K. Billings, *Switchmode Power Supply Handbook,* pp. 1.132–1.133, McGraw-Hill, New York, 1989.
3. G. Chryssis, *High Frequency Switching Power Supplies,* 2d ed., pp. 68–71, McGraw-Hill, New York, 1989.
4. P. Wood, *High Efficiency, Cost Effective Off Line Inverters,* TRW Power Semiconductor Application Note 143-1978, Lawndale, CA, 1978.
5. R. Carpenter, "A New Universal Proportional Base Drive Technique for High Voltage Switching Transistors," *Proceedings Powercon 8,* 1981.
6. L. Dixon, "Improved Proportional Base Drive Circuit," Unitrode Power Supply Design Seminar, Unitrode Corp., 1985.
7. P. Wood, "Design of a 5 Volt, 1000 Watt Power Supply," TRW Power Semiconductor Application Note 122, Lawndale, CA, 1975.
8. Unitrode Corp. Application Note 89-1987, Unitrode Corp., Watertown, Mass.

9

MOSFET Power Transistors and Input Drive Circuits

9.1 Introduction

Over about the past 10 years, the power MOSFET has revolutionized the power supply industry and in an enormous way changed the rest of the electronics industry. The faster switching speed of MOSFETs has permitted increasing power supply switching frequencies from about 50 to 200 or 400 kHz. It has thus made power supplies smaller and made possible a host of new products which were feasible only with smaller power supplies. The increasingly smaller size of personal computers is a prime example.

The higher frequencies spurred a wide variety of changes in the components industries. The semiconductor industry, of course, changed drastically first. More of the research funds were spent on MOSFETs, and their voltage and current ratings improved dramatically and prices dropped, making a large number of new applications possible—even at lower frequencies.

Magnetic materials with lesser losses at high frequencies and high magnetic flux density were developed. Pulse-width-modulating chips capable of operating at higher frequencies were introduced. Higher frequencies and thus smaller transformers and smaller filter capacitors required everything else to get smaller, and there was thus a greater emphasis on manufacturing processes such as surface-mount techniques.

A new industry and field for researchers—resonant power supplies—was developed. Resonant power supplies using silicon controlled rectifiers at about 20 to 30 kHz had been in use for many years. But with the high frequencies possible with MOSFETs, an army of researchers stepped in to develop dozens of new resonant circuit topologies operating at 0.3 to 5 MHz.

Phenomena which could be ignored at frequencies up to 100 kHz now had to be considered by designers. Thus skin-effect and especially proximity-effect losses in transformer coils had to be taken into account as these became a larger fraction of total transformer losses at higher frequencies. With faster-rise-time current waveforms, $L\ di/dt$ spikes on ground buses and supply rails became more troublesome and more attention had to be paid to wiring layout, low-inductance buses and supply rails, and capacitive decoupling at critical points.

Yet with all these attractive new possibilities and problems, the power supply designer, familiar with bipolar design, could quickly learn to design with MOSFETs by acquiring a surprisingly small amount of information about their characteristics. Material on the internal, solid-state physics structure of the MOSFET which determines its circuits behavior is not of great importance to the circuit designer and will not be considered herein. The MOSFET's various DC volt-ampere characteristics, terminal capacitances, temperature characteristics, and turnon-turnoff speed information are all that is needed for circuit design, and only such material will be considered here.

In very many ways, design with MOSFETs is simpler than with bipolars. MOSFET input terminal (gate) drive circuitry is far simpler than the complex base drive schemes for bipolar transistors discussed in the previous chapter. Specifically, because MOSFETs have no storage times, the complexities of Baker clamps and proportional base drive are unnecessary. The problems arising from the four-to-one production spread of transistor beta in bipolars do not exist.

During the turnoff transition, because of the fast MOSFET current fall time, the overlap of falling current and rising voltage at the output terminal occurs at lower current levels and decreases overlap or AC switching losses (Sec. 1.3.4). This simplifies or makes unnecessary the design of load-line-shaping circuits (snubbers, to be discussed in Chap. 11).

Basic MOSFET characteristics and MOSFET design will be discussed in the following sections.

9.2   MOSFET Basics

The MOSFET[1,2] is a three-terminal voltage-controlled switch—in contrast to the bipolar transistor, which is three-terminal current-controlled switch. In switching power supply circuits, it is used just as a bipolar transistor—either fully on with an input drive which should minimize its on-voltage drop or fully off at zero current and sustaining the supply voltage or some multiple of it.

The symbol for a MOSFET is shown in Fig. 9.1*a*, but herein, the simplified version shown in Fig. 9.1*b* will be used.

The three MOSFET terminals are called the *drain, gate,* and *source,* corresponding to the collector, base, and emitter of a bipolar transistor. MOSFETs, just as bipolars, are available for operation from either positive or negative power supply buses.

The N-channel type (equivalent to a bipolar N type) is fed from a positive supply voltage. The load impedance is connected between the positive supply source and the drain. Current, controlled by a positive gate-to-source voltage, flows from the positive rail through the load impedance into the drain and returns from the source to the negative rail (Fig. 9.2*a*).

The P-channel type (equivalent to a bipolar P type) is fed from a negative supply source. The load impedance is connected between the drain and negative rail. Current, controlled by a negative gate-to-source voltage, flows into the source from the positive rail, out through the drain, and through the load impedance to the negative rail (Fig. 9.2*b*).

Most power transistors are N-channel types. There are two further distinct types—either *enhancement* or *depletion* types. In the N enhancement channel type, drain-to-source current is zero at zero gate-to-source voltage. It requires a positive gate-to-source voltage to turn on drain to source current.

In the N depletion type, drain-to-source current is a maximum at zero gate-to-source voltage. It requires a negative gate-to-source voltage to turn off drain-to-source current. Depletion-type MOSFETs are never used for power transistors. They are still—but increasingly rarely—used in low-current signal-type MOSFETs.

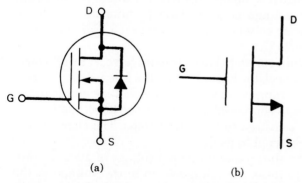

Figure 9.1 (*a*) Symbol for an N-type MOSFET. The diode is inherent in its structure and has forward current, reverse voltage ratings identical to the MOSFET itself. (*b*) Simplified N-type MOSFET symbol used herein.

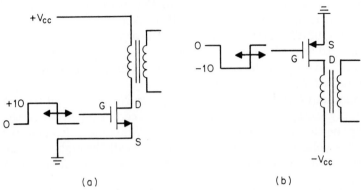

(a)   (b)

Figure 9.2   (a) A drain-loaded N-type MOSFET. (b) A drain loaded P-type MOSFET.

9.2.1   MOSFET drain current versus drain-to-source voltage characteristics (I_d – V_{ds})

These are shown in Fig. 9.3a for a typical 7-A 450-V device (Motorola MTM7N45). They correspond to the I_c – V_{ce} curves of a bipolar transistor (see Fig. 8.1). Note that they are voltage-controlled and that drain current is turned on by a positive gate-to-source voltage. This can be seen more clearly in the "transfer" characteristics of Fig. 9.3b, which shows drain-to-source current versus gate-to-source voltage.

The transfer characteristics show a very significant advantage of the MOSFET over the bipolar transistor. Note in Fig. 9.3b that drain current does not begin to turn on until the gate-to-source voltage reaches about 2.5 V. Thus positive noise pickup spikes at the gate terminal cannot falsely turn drain current on until the 2.5-V threshold is reached. This is in contrast to bipolar transistors, where the diodelike base-to-emitter input voltage characteristic permits false collector current turnon with noise voltage spikes as low as 0.6 V or even lower at temperatures above 25°C.

Note in Fig. 9.3a, drain current characteristics have a "knee" somewhat like the bipolar transistor knee. Beyond the knee, drain current is constant over a large range of drain-to-source voltage and is determined only by the gate-to-source voltage. Below the knee, the I_d – V_d curves asymptotically converge to a constant slope. The slope of that asymptote (dV/dI) is referred to as r_{ds}.

It is seen in Fig. 9.3a that a gate-to-source voltage of 10 V is sufficient to drive the drain-to-source voltage down to the voltage at the intersection of a load line with the r_{ds} slope (point $P1$). Higher gate voltages will not decrease the on V_{ds} significantly unless operating

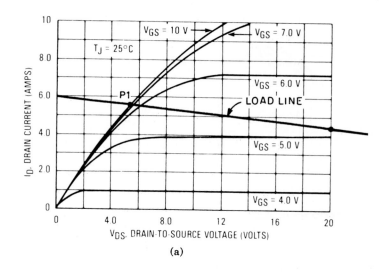

(a)

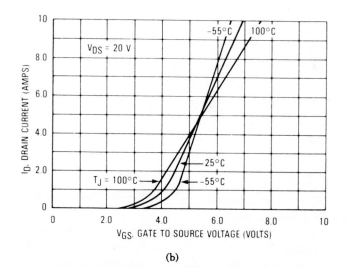

(b)

Figure 9.3 (a) The $I_d - V_{ds}$ characteristics of the MTM7N45—a typical 7-A 450-V MOSFET. (b) The $I_d - V_{gs}$ or "transfer" characteristics of the MTM7N45. (c, d) $I_d - V_d$ and transfer characteristics of the MTM15N40. (*Courtesy of Motorola Inc.*)

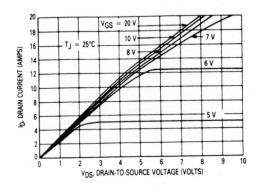

On-Region Characteristics

(c)

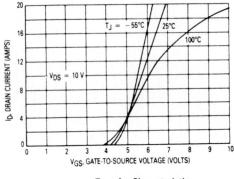

Transfer Characteristics

(d)

Figure 9.3   (*Continued*)

current is close to the maximum-rated current where the $(I_d - V_d)$ curve bends away from the r_{ds} slope.

Thus, in contrast to the bipolar transistor, where the collector to emitter on voltage is about 0.3 to 0.5 V over a very large range of collector currents, in a MOSFET, the drain "on" potential is equal to $I_{\mathrm{ds}}R_{\mathrm{ds}}$. Generally, it will be found that to have an on V_{ds} voltage of about 1 V, at a current I_d, a MOSFET with a maximum continuous current rating of about $3I_d$ to $5I_d$ should be selected as r_{ds} is inversely proportional to maximum current rating.

This can be seen in Fig. 9.3a for the 7-A MTM7N45 ($r_{\mathrm{ds}} = 0.8\ \Omega$). If it were to be used at 7 A, for a gate-to-source voltage V_{gs} of 10 V at 7 A, Fig. 9.3a shows its V_{ds} to be 7 V. This would yield an unacceptable 49 W of dissipation during the on time. The MTM15N40—a 15-A, 400-

V Motorola device (r_{ds} = 0.4 Ω) is shown in Fig. 9.3c and 9.3d. There it is seen that at V_{gs} of 10 V and 7 A, its V_{ds} is still about 2.5 V.

It is customary to keep bipolar V_{ce} on voltages at 1 V or less to keep their total dissipation low. With a bipolar, the on dissipation ($I_c V_{ce}$) may be only half to a third of the total—the balance being the overlap or AC switching dissipation. But MOSFETs generally can be operated with an on V_{ds} of up to 2 or 3 V. Drain current turnoff time is so fast that the dissipation due to the overlap of falling current and rising voltage is generally negligible. Total dissipation is thus $I_{ds} V_{ds}(t_{on}/T)$ dissipation alone.

9.2.2 MOSFET input impedance and required gate currents

The MOSFET's DC input impedance is extremely high. At V_{gs} of 10 V, the gate draws only nanoamperes of current. Thus once the gate has been driven up to, say, the 10 V "on" level, the current it draws is negligible.

However, there is considerable capacity at the gate-to-source terminal. This requires relatively large currents to drive the gate up and down the 10 V required to switch drain current on and off with the required speed. The required gate drive currents are calculated as follows (Fig. 9.4).

In Fig. 9.4, the current I_g required to move the gate up 10 V from ground consists of the two currents I_1 and I_2. Two capacitors, C1 and C2, are involved. Capacitance C_1 is the capacitance from gate to source and is referred to in the data sheets as "C_{iss}," the input capacitance. Capacitance C_2 is the capacitance from gate to drain and is referred to in the data sheets as "C_{rss}," the reverse-transfer capacitance.

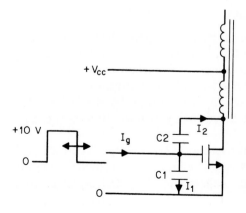

Figure 9.4 The gate driver must supply I_1 to C_1 and I_2 to C_2. Because of the Miller effect, I_2 may be greater than I_1 even though C_1 may be 10 times as large as C_2.

To drive the gate up to the 10-V "on" level in a time t_r, the required current I_1 is

$$I_1 = \frac{C_1 \, dV}{dt} = \frac{C_1 \times 10}{t_r} \tag{9.1}$$

However, in driving the gate up 10 V, the drain turns on and drops from the supply voltage V_{dc} (Fig. 2.10) to the V_{ds} on voltage, which for simplicity will be taken as ground. Thus, as the top end of C2 moves down V_{dc} volts, its bottom end moves up 10 V. The current required to achieve this is

$$I_2 = C_2 \frac{dV}{dt}$$

$$= \frac{C_2(V_{dc} + 10)}{dt} \tag{9.2}$$

It is revealing to calculate these currents in a typical case. Assume an off-line forward converter operating from a nominal 115-V-AC line with ±10 percent tolerance. Then the maximum rectified DC voltage is $1.1 \times 115 \times 1.41 = 178$ V. Assume an MTM7N45 whose C_1 is 1800 pF and whose C_2 is 150 pF. Then from Eq. 9.12, for a gate rise time of 50 ns, we obtain

$$I_1 = \frac{1800 \times 10^{-12} \times 10}{50 \times 10^{-9}}$$

$$= 360 \text{ mA}$$

and from Eq. 9.2

$$I_2 = \frac{(150 \times 10^{-12})(178 + 10)}{50 \times 10^{-9}}$$

$$= 564 \text{ mA}$$

and the total current required from the gate driving source is $I_g = I_1 + I_2 = (0.36 + 0.564) = 0.924$ A. Thus, the smaller capacitor, C2, requires about 50 percent more current than does C1. This, of course, is the well-known Miller effect, which multiplies the input-to-output capacity by the gain from input to output. By a similar calculation, the current required to move the gate down 10 V is the same 0.924 A.

Generally, the effective input capacity of low-voltage MOSFETs will be lower than high-voltage devices. The input capacitance C_{iss} will be higher and the reverse-transfer capacitance C_{rss} will be lower than those for higher-voltage devices. But more importantly, the Miller effect multiplication of C_{rss} will be less as the voltage change across C_{rss} is less as the transistor operates from a lower supply voltage.

Thus, consider an MTH15N20—a 15-A, 200-V device. Assume that it operates from a nominal supply voltage of 48 V in a telephone industry supply where minimum voltage is usually assumed to be 38 V and maximum, 60 V. Capacities are C_{iss} = 2000 pF and C_{rss} = 200 pF. Then total input capacity, assuming turnon from a supply voltage of 60 V, is

$$C_{in} = C_{iss} + \left(\frac{70}{10}\right)C_{rss} = 2000 + 7 \times 200 = 3400 \text{ pF}$$

and to move the effective input capacity up 10 V in the same 50 ns requires a gate input current of $I_g = C_{in}\, dv/dt = 3400 \times 10^{-12}$ $(10/50 \times 10^{-9}) = 0.68$ A.

Such input currents, although large, are not too serious as they must last only 50 ns (or whatever is desired for the gate rise time t_r).

9.2.3 MOSFET gate rise and fall times for desired drain current rise and fall times

Very rapid drain current rise and fall times are undesirable as they cause large $L\, di/dt$ spikes on ground buses, supply rails, and large $C\, dV/dt$ capacitatively coupled spikes into adjacent wires or nodes.

The question thus arises as to what gate voltage rise time is required to yield a desired drain current rise time. This can be seen from the transfer characteristics shown in Fig. 9.3b and 9.3d.

In a MOSFET, switching time between zero and a drain current I_d is only the times required for the gate voltage to traverse the DC voltage level from the threshold to the gate voltage V_{gI} in Fig. 9.3b, which yields I_d. The time for the gate to move up from ground to the threshold voltage of about 2.5 V is simply a delay time. Drain current turnon time is not accelerated by overdriving the input terminal as with bipolars (Sec. 8.2 text and Fig. 8.2b).

Further, MOSFETs have no storage time. There is only a turnoff delay corresponding to the time required for the gate to fall from its uppermost level of about 10 V to the DC level V_{gI} in Fig. 9.3b, which corresponds to the current I_d. Once gate voltage V_{gI} is reached, drain current fall time is the time required for the gate to fall from V_{gI} to the threshold.

Thus, consider turning on an MTM7N45 to 2.5 A. If a 50-ns gate rise time were used for the first 2.5 V, no drain current at all would result (see Fig. 9.3b). There would only be a delay equal to the time required for the gate to rise the first 2.5 V, and by the time the gate rose to about 5 V, most of the 2.5 A would have been turned on.

Then, for a 0- to 10-volt gate rise time in 50 ns, the drain current would rise from 0 to 2.5 A in about $(2.5/10)50$ or 12.5 ns (Fig. 9.5). Thus, 10-V gate voltage transition times can be two to three times the desired drain current transition times because of the narrow range of gate voltage across which drain current changes. The gate currents calculated above thus need be only about one-half to one-third the values calculated as above.

9.2.4 MOSFET gate drive circuits

As described above, the gate driver must be able to deliver outward-directed current or be a "source" to drive gates in a positive direction to turn drain current on. It must also be able to absorb inward-directed current or to be a "sink" to pull gates in a negative direction to ground to turn drain current off.

Most of the earlier PWM chips (SG1524 family) could not both source and sink large currents—they could only source or sink fairly large currents, as can be seen from their output stage circuit in Fig. 9.6a.

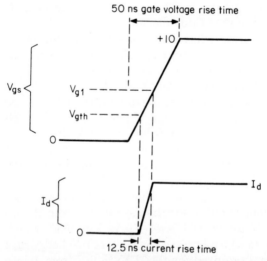

Figure 9.5 A 0- to 50-ns gate voltage rise time causing a 12.5-ns drain current rise time. The first 2.5 V on the gate voltage rise time to the gate threshold voltage is simply a delay time. At a gate voltage level of about 5 to 7 V, most of the drain current has already been turned on.

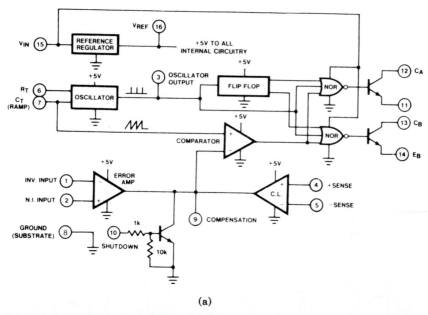

(a)

Figure 9.6 (a) The SG1524 PWM chip with its output transistors (pins 11, 12 and 13, 14). The output transistors can either source or sink (but not both) 200 mA. (b) An output transistor-emitter driving the high input capacity at a MOSFET gate. The 200-mA source current can drive the high MOSFET gate rapidly in a positive direction, but it is only R_1 which pulls the gate negative in a time $3R_1C_{in}$. (c) A PNP emitter-follower for a high-current sink driver and the chip output transistor as 200-mA source driver. Resistor R_2 can now be fairly large.

The output stage of an SG1524-type PWM chip consists simply of a transistor with an "uncommitted" emitter and collector. When the transistor is turned on, it can sink 200 mA into its collector or source 200 mA out of its emitter. When used as a source driver, it is only the emitter resistor which can sink current from the gate to pull it low and turn the MOSFET off. Most often, the power transistor must be on when the chip's output transistor is on. Thus for an N-type MOSFET, its gate is driven from the emitter of the output stage as shown in Fig. 9.6b.

Such an emitter driving stage can source or deliver 200 mA of outward-directed current to turn a MOSFET gate on relatively rapidly. Thus, as mentioned in Sec. 9.2.2, it required 0.924 A to drive the MTM7N45 gate up 10 V in 50 ns.

The 200 mA of SG1524 source current can thus drive the gate up 10 V in only $(0.924/0.2)50 = 231$ ns. Also, as mentioned in Sec. 9.2.3, because drain current rise time is within the 2.5- to 5.0-V level of the gate voltage rise time, drain current rise time will be only (2.5/

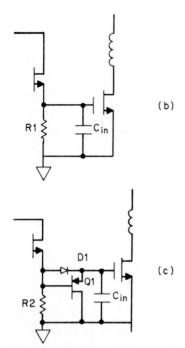

(b)

R1 $\quad$ C_{in}

D1

Q1

R2 $\quad$ C_{in}

(c)

Figure 9.6 *(Continued)*

10) = 58 ns. The first 2.5 V of gate rise time until the threshold is reached yields a delay of only 58 ns. Although this slows up maximum switching frequency, it does not, of course, cause any switching losses.

The gate voltage rise time of 231 ns within the 0- to 10-V level is thus fast enough. But in the circuit of Fig. 9.6*b*, gate voltage fall time is determined only by the emitter resistor R_e and the gate input capacity as there is no constant current discharging that capacity.

In Fig. 9.6*b*, when the base of the chip output transistor goes low (internal to the chip), the output transistor emitter is held up by the large MOSFET input capacity. This biases the chip output transistor fully off and leaves only the emitter resistor to discharge the MOSFET input capacity. That capacity (Sec. 9.2.2) is the input plus the Miller capacity or 1800 + (180/10)150 = 4500 pF!

Thus, even with a—say—200-Ω emitter resistor, MOSFET gate fall time is $3R_1C = 3 \times 200 \times 4500 = 2.70$ μs—obviously impossibly long if switching frequencies of over 100 kHz are to be achieved. Hence driving the high MOSFET gate input capacitances requires the use of active transistors which can source and sink currents of about 200 to 400 mA.

For use with SG1524-type PWM chips which have only source or sink capability, but not both, a simple but, in most cases, adequate

MOSFET gate driver is the NPN-PNP emitter-follower totem pole of Fig. 8.17, where $Q2$, $Q3$ are 2N2222A, 2N2907A transistors in TO18 cans costing under 10¢. They are capable of sourcing and sinking 800 mA with current rise times of about 60 ns. The upper transistor of the totem pole can be eliminated by using the PWM chip's output transistor as a source driver as shown in Fig. 9.6c. Although it has less source capability (200 mA) than the external 2N2222A, in many instances it is adequate.

Second-generation PWM chips such as the Unitrode Corp. UC1525A[3] have a built-in totem pole consisting of an NPN emitter-follower resting on top of an NPN inverter. These transistors can source and sink over 200 mA. The emitter-follower and the inverter are driven by 180° out-of-phase signals so that when either is on, the other is off as shown in Fig. 9.7a. By using a transformer with two isolated secondaries as in Fig. 9.7b, the top and bottom transistors of a half or full bridge which are at different DC voltage levels can be driven. Similarly, of course, the MOSFET gates which are at the same DC voltage level in a push-pull circuit can be driven.

In Fig. 9.7b, the transformer primary is connected between pins 11 and 14 of the PWM chip. During the on time in one half period, when pin 11 is, say, positive with respect to pin 14 and is sourcing 200 mA, it is at about $+(V_h - 2)$ V with respect to ground and pin 14 is at about +2 V with respect to ground. During the dead time within that half period, pins 1, 14 are both short-circuited to ground. In the next half period, the polarity across pins 11, 14 reverses for the on time in that half period. Thus for ±10 V across the primary, the supply voltage V_h should be about 14 V.

9.2.5 MOSFET R_{ds} temperature characteristics and safe operating area limits[4,5]

The most common failure mode in bipolar transistors—second breakdown—comes about because their on-voltage drop $V_{ce(sat)}$ decreases with temperature. This imposes limits (RBSOA curve of Fig. 8.4) on the $I_c - V_{ce}$ trajectory the transistor may not cross during the turnoff transition. Manufacturers state that only a single crossing of this limit curve may cause the bipolar to fail in the second-breakdown mode.

However, MOSFETs, because their on-voltage drop or r_{ds} increases with temperature, do not suffer from second breakdown and consequently have a much larger switching SOA as shown in Fig. 9.8. This is the boundary which if crossed for over 1 μs during either the turnon or turnoff trajectory may damage or destroy the transistor. The bound-

366

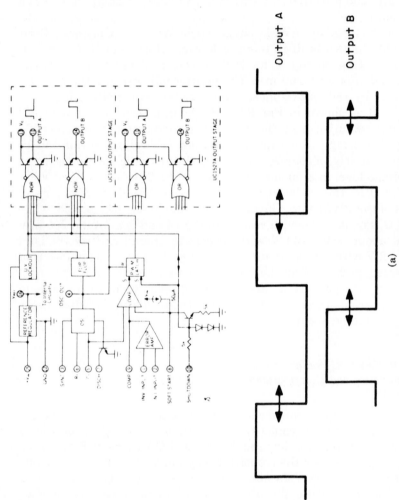

(a)

Figure 9.7 (a) Second-generation PWM chip UC1525A with totem-pole outputs (outputs A and B) for sourcing and sinking high currents. (Courtesy Unitrode Corp.) (b) Totem-pole outputs at A, B can drive high input capacity of MOSFETs either directly when gates are as same DC voltage level as in a push-pull or via a transformer when gates are at different DC voltage levels as in a half or full bridge.

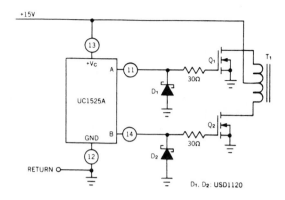

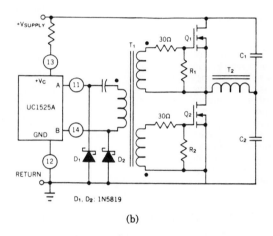

(b)

Figure 9.7   (*Continued*)

ary limits are the maximum pulsed current ($I_{dm,pulsed}$) and maximum drain-to-source V_{dss} voltage ratings for the device.

An explanation of why the negative temperature coefficient of V_{ce} causes second breakdown in the bipolar and the V_{ds} positive temperature prevents it in the MOSFET is as follows. Second breakdown in bipolars comes about because of local hot spots on the chip. These hot spots are considerably hotter than the average junction temperature as calculated from the chip's junction to case thermal resistance and total transistor dissipation. Such a calculation assumes a uniform distribution of current carriers throughout the collector area.

If current is not uniformly distributed but is, for some reason, initially bunched up or crowded into a small fraction of the collector area, that area runs slightly hotter than the rest of the chip. Further, since the collector-to-emitter resistance decreases with increasing tempera-

368   **Magnetics and Circuit Design**

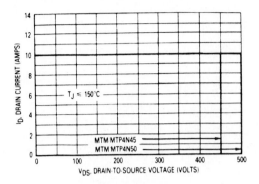

**MAXIMUM RATED SWITCHING
SAFE OPERATING AREA**

Figure 9.8 Reverse-biased safe operating area of 4
A, 400-V MOSFET. This is a far larger area than
that for a 4-A 400-V bipolar transistor. For the
MOSFET it is a rectangle bounded by I_{dm} (maximum pulsed current rating) which is two to three
times I_d (maximum continuous current rating) and
V_{dss}, the maximum drain-to-source voltage rating.
The switching safe operating area is the boundary
that the load line may traverse without incurring
damage to the device. The fundamental limits are
the maximum rated peak drain current I_{dm}, the
minimum   drain-to-source   breakdown   voltage
$V_{(br)dss}$ and the maximum rated junction temperature. The boundaries are applicable for both turnon
and turnoff of the devices for rise and fall times of
less than 1 μs. (*Courtesy Motorola Inc.*)

ture, any incipient local hot spot has slightly less resistance than its
surrounding areas and robs current carriers from adjacent areas. This
causes the hot spot to get even hotter, decrease even more in resistance and rob even more current from adjacent areas. This process
builds up rapidly until the local hot spot reaches a high current density and temperature sufficient ($>200°C$) to cause failure.

However, MOSFETs, with their positive r_{ds} temperature coefficient,
tend to wipe out or cool off incipient local hot spots. If a point on the
chip started operating at a slightly higher current density than its
neighbors, its temperature would rise slightly. Because r_{ds} has a positive temperature, its resistance would increase and it would shift off
some of its current carriers to neighboring areas and cool down. The
result is the much larger SOA of Fig. 9.8 for the MOSFET as compared to Fig. 8.2 for the bipolar.

Curves showing the variation of r_{ds} with temperature and drain current are seen in Fig. 9.9 for a typical 15-A, 450-V MOSFET
(MTM15N45). The variation of r_{ds} with temperature is also dependent
on the voltage rating of the MOSFET as shown in Fig. 9.10. It is seen

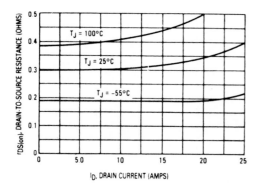

Figure 9.9 Variation of $r_{ds(on)}$ with drain current and temperature for the MTM15N45 (*Courtesy Motorola Inc.*)

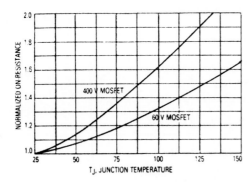

Figure 9.10 The influence of junction temperature on resistance varies with breakdown voltage. (*Courtesy Motorola Inc.*)

there that higher-voltage MOSFETs have larger r_{ds} temperature coefficients than do lower voltage devices.

9.2.6 MOSFET gate threshold voltage and temperature characteristic[4,5]

The major American MOSFET manufacturers—Motorola and International Rectifier—specify the gate threshold voltage V_{gsth} differently. Motorola specifies it as the gate-to-source voltage for which I_{ds} equals 1 mA at $V_{ds} = V_{gs}$. International Rectifier (IR) defines it as the gate-to-source voltage for which $I_{ds} = 0.25$ mA at $V_{ds} = V_{gs}$. There appears to be a two-to-one production spread in V_{gsth} in either Motorola or IR devices.

The gate threshold voltage V_{gsth} has a negative temperature coefficient and falls about 5 percent for each 25°C rise in temperature (Fig. 9.11) and quickly falls to zero in a radiation environment.[6] A negative gate-to-source voltage is required to keep the MOSFET off under radiation. The transfer characteristic is strongly dependent on type, duration, and intensity of radiation (Fig. 9.12). Discussion of MOSFETs in a radiation environment is beyond the scope of this text.

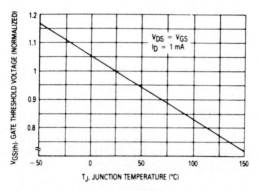

Figure 9.11   Gate threshold voltage variation with temperature. (*Courtesy Motorola Inc.*)

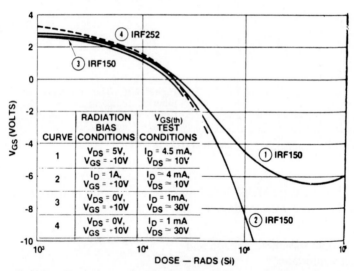

CURVE	RADIATION BIAS CONDITIONS	$V_{GS(th)}$ TEST CONDITIONS
1	$V_{DS} = 5V$, $V_{GS} = -10V$	$I_D = 4.5 \text{ mA}$, $V_{DS} \approx 10V$
2	$I_D = 1A$, $V_{GS} = +10V$	$I_D \approx 4 \text{ mA}$, $V_{DS} \approx 10V$
3	$V_{DS} = 0V$, $V_{GS} = +10V$	$I_D = 1\text{mA}$, $V_{DS} \approx 30V$
4	$V_{DS} = 0V$, $V_{GS} = +10V$	$I_D = 1 \text{ mA}$, $V_{DS} \approx 30V$

Figure 9.12   Typical gate threshold voltage versus total gamma dose. Under radiation, a negative gate bias is required to keep a MOSFET turned off. Gate threshold voltage depends strongly on the type, intensity, and duration of radiation. (*Courtesy Unitrode Corp.*)

9.2.7 MOSFET switching speed and temperature characteristics

MOSFET switching speed is significantly independent of temperature. Drain current rise and fall times depend only on the time required for the gate voltage to cross the narrow boundary between the gate threshold voltage (V_{gsth}) and V_{gl} in Fig. 9.3b. This depends on the output resistance of the source-sink driver and the effective gate input capacity. The source-sink output resistance is usually a discrete external resistance which has a low-temperature coefficient. Further, since gate input capacity is so independent of temperature, drain current rise and fall times are also independent of temperature.

Turnon and turnoff delays are somewhat temperature-dependent. Turnon delay is the time for the gate voltage to rise from 0 to the threshold voltage V_{gsth}. Since V_{gsth} falls 5 percent for each 25°C rise in temperature, turnon delay will decrease with temperature. Also since there is a two-to-one production spread in V_{gsth}, turnon delay will vary from device to device even at the same temperature. Note, though, that devices with large variation in V_{gsth} may not have a large variation in delay to turn on to a relatively large specific current. The lower tails of the transfer characteristic can vary significantly without changing V_{gI}—the gate voltage for a given current I.

Turnoff delay is the time required for the gate to fall from its usual on voltage of 10 V to V_{gI} (Fig. 9.3b). Since gate threshold voltage and transconductance vary with temperature, so will turnoff delays.

Turnon and turnoff delays are significant only when paralleling MOSFETs.

9.2.8 MOSFET current ratings

For bipolar transistors, maximum output current is limited by the fact that current gain falls drastically as output current rises. Thus unacceptably high base input currents are required as output current increases. This is shown in Fig. 9.13 for the 2N6542—a typical 5-A, 400-V bipolar transistor.

With MOSFETs, however, output-input gain (transconductance or $dI_{\text{ds}}/dV_{\text{gs}}$) does not decrease with output current, as can be seen in Fig. 9.14. Thus the only limitation on drain current is power dissipation or maximum MOSFET junction temperature.

Maximum MOSFET junction temperature is 150°C. Good standard design practice is to derate this to 105°C or at most to 125°C.

Manufacturers rate the current carrying capability of their device in terms of I_d, the maximum continuous drain current.

Apparently Motorola and IR, the major American MOSFET manufacturers, have rated I_d as that current, which at the maximum $V_{\text{ds(on)}}$ voltage for that current yields a power dissipation at 100 percent duty cycle such that when multiplied by the thermal resistance brings the MOSFET junction temperature to the maximum of 150°C when the transistor case is at 100°C. Thus

$$dT = 50 = PDR_{\text{th}} = V_{\text{ds(on)}}I_d R_{\text{th}} \quad \text{or} \quad I_d = \frac{50}{V_{\text{ds(on)}}R_{\text{th}}}$$

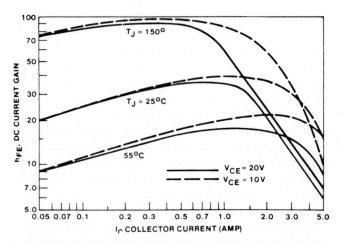

Figure 9.13 Typical DC current gain for the 2N6542/3 bipolar transistor. Gain of a bipolar transistor falls off with increasing output current, but that of a MOSFET does not. Maximum current in a MOSFET is limited only by junction temperature rise. (*Courtesy Motorola Inc.*)

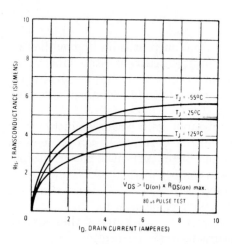

Figure 9.14 Transconductance versus drain current of the IRF330. Gain of a bipolar transistor falls off with increasing output current, but that of a MOSFET does not. Maximum current in a MOSFET is limited only by junction temperature rise. (*Courtesy International Rectifier.*)

where $V_{ds(on)}$ is the maximum drain-to-source on voltage at 150°C and R_{th} is the thermal resistance in degrees Celsius per watt.

This I_d rating is not a useful guide for selecting a MOSFET for a given peak current in a switching supply application. In such usage, duty cycle is never 100 percent. For reliability, it is desired to operate at junction temperatures derated to 125°C or the usual military-specified 105°C. But it does show the relative current-carrying capability of various MOSFETs operated at 100 percent duty cycle.

In general, there are two ways of selecting a MOSFET for a specified output power in a switching supply. First, the equivalent flat-topped primary current I_{pft} is calculated for specified output power and minimum DC input voltage. This current is given in Eqs. 2.9, 2.28, 3.1, and 3.7 for the push-pull, forward converter, half and full bridge, respectively. Then for these currents, a MOSFET of r_{ds} is chosen so that the on drain-to-source voltage $I_{pft}r_{ds})$ is a small percentage (usually no more than 2 percent) of the minimum supply voltage so as to rob no more than 2 percent of the transformer's minimum primary voltage.

In selecting a device with a desired r_{ds}, it should be recalled that the data sheets give it at a case temperature of 25°C. Also noteworthy is the fairly large variation of r_{ds} with temperature and device voltage rating as shown in Figs. 9.9 and 9.10. Thus, Fig. 9.10 shows that an r_{ds} of a 400-V MOSFET at 100°C is 1.6 times its value at 25°C.

As a design example, consider a 150-W forward converter operating from a nominal 115-V-AC line. Assume that maximum and minimum rectified DC voltages are 184 and 136 V, respectively. Peak flat-topped current from Eq. 2.28 is I_{pft} = 3.13(150/136) = 3.45 A, then, for the MOSFET on voltage to be 2 percent of the minimum supply voltage, V_{on} = 0.02 × 136 = 2.72 = $I_{pft}r_{ds}$ = 3.45r_{ds} or r_{ds} = 0.79Ω at, say, 100°C or 0.79/1.6 = 0.49 Ω at 25°C.

Possible plastic-cased 450-V MOSFET choices from the Motorola catalog are shown in Table 9.1.

The choice would be made on an engineering judgment of the relative importance of cost and performance. The 7-A MTH7N45 is not quite good enough. It would have more than the sought on drop of 2.72 V at 3.45 A. That itself is not prohibitive; it would run at a junction temperature somewhat higher than the MTH13N45. That would have to be weighed against the higher cost of the 13-A MTH13N45.

An alternative way to chose the MOSFET is to preset its maximum junction temperature—say, to 100°C for reliability. Then assume a reasonably low MOSFET junction-to-case temperature rise so as not to require too low a heat-sink temperature—for, of course, the further the case temperature is below the MOSFET junction, the larger must be the heat sink on which the case rests.

TABLE 9.1 Motorola MOSFETs

Device	I_d, A	V_{dss}, V	r_{ds}, Ω at 25°C
MTH7N45	7	450	0.8
MTH13N45	13	450	0.4

Thus assume a reasonably low 5°C case-to-junction temperature rise. Then

$dT = 5 =$ power dissipation $\times$ thermal resistance (junction to case)

and assuming that there are negligible AC switching losses

$$dT = (I_{rms})^2 (r_{ds}) R_{th} \qquad \text{or} \qquad r_{ds} = \frac{5}{(I_{rms})^2 R_{th}}$$

where I_{rms} is the rms current in the MOSFET.

For a forward converter where the maximum on time per period is $0.8T/2$, the rms current is $I_p(\sqrt{t_{on}/T}) = 0.632\, I_p$. Then for the preceding design example of a 150-W forward converter where I_p is 3.45 A, we obtain

$$r_{ds} = \frac{5}{(0.632 I_p)^2 R_{th}}$$

and for the usual thermal resistance of 0.83°C/W for MOSFETs of this current and package size

$$r_{ds} = \frac{5}{(0.632 \times 3.45)^2 \times 0.83}$$

$$= 1.26 \ \Omega \ \text{at} \ 100°C$$

This is the r_{ds} at 100°C junction temperature, which causes a 5°C junction-to-case temperature differential with a 3.45-A peak current pulse at 0.4 percent duty cycle. The r_{ds} at 25°C junction temperature is then 1.26/1.6 or 0.78 Ω.

Thus, on the basis of a 5°C junction-to-case temperature differential, Table 9.1 shows that the MTH7N45 would be an adequate choice. But it would rob $1.26 \times 3.45 = 4.34$ V from the primary voltage at 100°C. The MTH13N45 would be a better choice if its somewhat higher cost were acceptable.

9.2.9 Paralleling MOSFETs[7]

In paralleling MOSFETs, two situations must be considered: (1) whether the paralleled devices share current equally—in the static case when they are fully on and (2) whether they share current equally during the dynamic turnon-to-turnoff transition.

With paralleled MOSFETs, in either the static or dynamic case, the concern is that if one MOSFET hogs a disproportionate part of the current, it will run hotter, and long-term reliability will decrease or, in the short run, will fail.

Unequal static current sharing comes about because of unequal r_{ds}

between paralleled devices. The lower r_{ds} device draws more than its numerical share of the total current—just as with a group of paralleled discrete resistors, the lowest resistor draws the most current.

In describing the absence of second breakdown with MOSFETs, it was pointed out that this is so because of the positive temperature coefficient of r_{ds} in MOSFETs. Thus, if a small portion of the chip tends to hog a disproportionate part of the total current, it runs hotter, its r_{ds} increases, and it shifts off some of its current to some neighboring areas to equalize current density.

This mechanism also works to some extent with paralleled discrete MOSFETs. By itself, however, it is not sufficient to minimize the temperature of the hottest device. This is so because the temperature coefficient of r_{ds} is not very large and a large temperature differential between devices is required to shift off excess current. But with a large required temperature differential, the hottest device is at a high temperature, and this is exactly what reduces reliability and is to be avoided.

The mechanism does work well within a chip because all elementary areas of the chip are thermally coupled. But it does not work as well if thermal coupling between the parallel MOSFETs is poor as with discrete MOSFETs in separate cases and physically separated on a common or in the worst case on separate heat sinks.

To improve the equality of static current sharing, MOSFETs, if in discrete cases, should be located as close as possible on the same heat sink. If possible, MOSFETs in discrete chips should be located close together on the same substrate within the same package. Such packages containing multiple paralleled MOSFETs on a common substrate–heat sink are currently available from a number of manufacturers. As a last resort, if MOSFETs in discrete packages must be used, and close location on a common heat sink does not suffice, matching the r_{ds} of paralleled devices will guarantee equal current sharing.

For equal dynamic current sharing, the transconductance curves of paralleled devices must lie on top of one another. This is obvious from Fig. 9.15. If all gates have identical voltage at the same time, and the transconductance curves are not superimposed, the drains carry different currents at that time, on either turnon or turnoff.

It is not so important that the gate thresholds match. If n devices are to be paralleled for a total current of I_t, they should be matched to have as closely as possible the same I_t/n at the same gate voltage—even if there is a large mismatch in gate threshold voltages.

Symmetrical circuit layout is also important for equal dynamic current sharing (Fig. 9.16). Lead lengths from the common output point of the gate driver to the gate terminals should be equal. Leads from

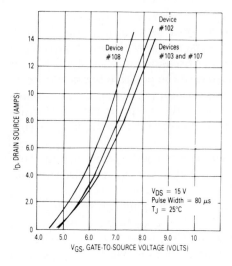

Figure 9.15 Widest variation in transconductance curves of 250 additional MTPBN2O. For equal dynamic current sharing, MOSFET transconductance curves must coincide. (*Courtesy Motorola Inc.*)

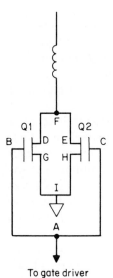

Figure 9.16 Symmetrical circuit layout for equal dynamic current sharing in parallel MOSFETs. To ensure equal dynamic current sharing in parallel MOSFETs, circuit layout should be symmetrical. Thus $AB = AC$, $GI = HI$, $DF = EF$.

the source terminals directly at the MOSFETs to a common tie point should be equal, and that common tie point should be brought directly as possible to a common tie point on the ground bus. That ground bus tie point should be common (with as short a lead as possible) with the negative rail of the housekeeping supply. Then, finally, to prevent oscillations with paralleled MOSFETs, resistors of 10 to 20 Ω or ferrite beads should be placed in series with gate leads.

9.2.10   MOSFETs in push-pull topology

MOSFETs in the push-pull topology minimize the transformer flux-imbalance problem significantly. It will be recalled (Sec. 2.2.5) that if the volt-second product applied to the transformer during one half period is not equal to that in the next half period, the transformer core moves off center of its hysteresis loop. After a number of such periods, the core drifts very far off center, saturates, and cannot support the supply voltage, and the transistor is destroyed.

MOSFETs alleviate this problem for two reasons. First, there is no storage time with MOSFETs and for equal gate on times, drain voltage on times are always equal in alternate half periods. There is hence no inequality in volt-second product applied to the transformer due to unequal transistor on times. In contrast, with bipolars, the main reason for unequal volt-seconds on alternate half periods is the inequality in storage times. Second, with MOSFETs, the positive temperature coefficient of r_{ds} acts in a negative-feedback way to prevent severe flux imbalance. If there is a certain amount of flux imbalance, the core walks partly up its hysteresis loop. This causes the magnetizing current and hence total current on one half period to be larger than that on the alternate half period (Figs. 2.4b and 2.4c). But now the MOSFET with the larger peak current runs hotter and its r_{ds} increases, increasing its on drop. This robs voltage from its half primary, its volt-second product decreases, and the core moves back down toward the center of its hysteresis loop.

Qualitatively, both these effects are in the direction to prevent a catastrophic flux imbalance. But it is not easily feasible to demonstrate quantitatively that it works at all power levels, at all temperatures, and for all core materials. A certain solution to the flux-imbalance problem is to go to current-mode topology (Sec. 2.2.8.5). But if for some reason it is not desired to go to current mode, MOSFETs in a conventional push-pull circuit may be used with no flux-imbalance problem up to power levels of 150 W; many designers have used this approach successfully.

One final interesting advantage of MOSFETs in a push-pull circuit is shown in Fig. 9.17. This simple scheme makes it possible to totally eliminate any residual flux imbalance due possibly to differences in r_{ds}. If there is an incipient flux imbalance, it manifests itself by the current in one transistor being somewhat larger than the current in the other (Figs. 2.4b and 2.4c). The MOSFET with the higher peak current has, for some reason, a larger volt-second product than the other device.

This is corrected as illustrated in Fig. 9.17 by adding a small, empirically selected resistor r_b in series with the gate of the MOSFET with the larger peak current. This integrates away some of the front

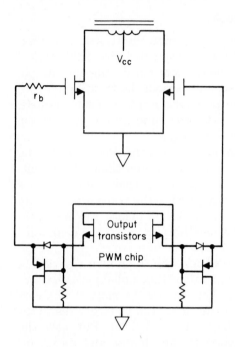

Figure 9.17 Flux-imbalance correction in a MOSFET push-pull circuit. An empirically selected resistor inserted in series in the gate of the MOSFET which originally had the higher peak current forces currents in Q_1, Q_2 to be exactly equal. It does this by integrating away part of the front end of the gate drive pulse and forces the volt-second product on each transformer half to be equal.

edge of its gate turnon pulse, narrows it, equalizes the volt-second products on each side, and equalizes peak currents on alternate periods.

Although some (military) programs do not permit empirical "Select At Test" components, once a resistor is selected, it corrects peak current imbalance independently of temperature, supply voltage, and load current. Thus the only objection to the scheme is that if either transistor is changed, a new "Select At Test" resistor must be chosen. This may be unacceptable in the field where the proper test equipment is not available.

9.2.11   MOSFET maximum gate voltage specifications

Most MOSFET gates have a maximum gate-to-source voltage specification of ± 20 V. The gate is easily destroyed if that limit is exceeded.

A problem arises in this respect when a MOSFET has a gate input resistor and is turned off in a circuit with a large supply voltage. Thus, consider a forward converter operating from a nominal supply voltage of 160 DC V (maximum of 186 V). Then, when the MOSFET turns off (at maximum supply voltage), its drain goes to twice the supply voltage or 372 V. A fraction of this positive-going front edge is coupled back and voltage divided down by C_{rss} and C_{iss}. For the

MTH7N45, C_{rss} = 150 pF, C_{iss} = 1800 pF. Then the voltage coupled back down to the gate is 372 × 150/(150 + 1800) = 29 V.

This may not damage the gate even though it exceeds the 20-V limit. The gate resistor will also load down and decrease its amplitude. But it is close to the point of causing a possible failure as line transients and the leakage inductance spike have not yet been considered. Thus, good design practice is to shunt the gate with an 18-V zener diode. Note that a high frequency oscillation may often result from the capacitive drain to gate feedback.

9.2.12 MOSFET drain-to-source ("body") diode

Inherently in solid-state structure of a MOSFET, a parasitic "body" diode is located across the drain-source terminals as shown in Fig. 9.18.

The diode polarity is such as to prevent reverse voltage across the MOSFET. The forward current handling capability and reverse voltage rating of the diode are identical to those of the MOSFET itself. Its reverse recovery time is faster than a conventional AC power rectifier diode, but not as fast as discrete fast-recovery types. Manufacturers' data sheets show the diode reverse recovery time for each specific MOSFET.

The diode is of no importance for most switching supply topologies

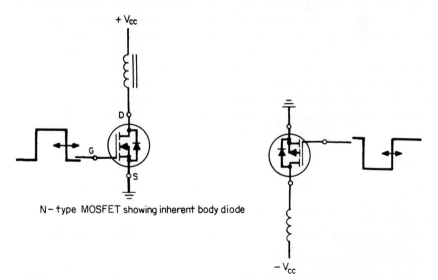

N – type MOSFET showing inherent body diode

P – type MOSFET showing inherent body diode

Figure 9.18 Inherent body diodes in N- and P-type MOSFETs. In the N-channel MOSFET, the diode prevents a negative drain-to-source voltage. In the P-channel MOSFET, the diode prevents a positive drain-to-source voltage.

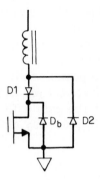

Figure 9.19 Scheme to avoid using a MOSFET body diode when reverse current must be allowed to flow around a MOSFET. To prevent forward current from flowing through the MOSFET's body diode which does not have good reverse recovery characteristics, blocking diode D_1 is added in series in the drain. D_2 with better reverse recovery characteristics is shunted around the D_1 anode and the Q1 source.[9]

as the drain to source is never subjected to a reverse voltage (drain negative with respect to source for an N-type MOSFET, positive with respect to source for a P-type MOSFET).

There are some exceptions—specifically, the half- or full-bridge topologies of Figs. 3.1 and 3.3. But in these circuits there is almost always a dead time between the time the diode conducts (when it is returning to the supply source, energy stored in the transformer leakage inductance) and the time it is subjected to reverse voltage. Because of this delay between forward current and reverse voltage, the relatively poor reverse recovery time of the MOSFET body diode is not harmful.

However, if a specific new circuit configuration requires reverse voltage across the MOSFET, a blocking diode must be placed in series with the drain. Various motor drive circuits or circuits with highly inductive loads may have problems because of the body diode.[8]

High-frequency resonant circuit topologies (Chap. 13) frequently must be able to support reverse voltage immediately after carrying forward current. When this is necessary, the circuit of Fig. 9.19 is used. Diode D_1 prevents forward current from flowing through the MOSFET body diode, and the fast-reverse-recovery-time diode D_2 carries the required forward current.

References

1. *International Rectifier Power MOSFET Data Book,* HDB-3, International Rectifier, El Segundo, CA.
2. *Power MOSFET Transistor Data,* Motorola Inc., Motorola Literature Distribution, Phoenix, AZ.
3. *Linear Integrated Circuits Databook—PWM chip UC3525A,* Unitrode Corp., Merrimack, NH.
4. Reference 1, Chaps. 1, 4.
5. Reference 2, Chap. 2.
6. Radiation Resistance of Hexfets, Ref. 1, p. B10.
7. Reference 1, Chap. 1; Ref. 2, Chap. 7; International Rectifier Application Note AN-941.
8. "Hexfet's Integral Body Diode," Ref. 1, p. A65.
9. Reference 1, page A65.

Magnetic-Amplifier
Postregulators

10.1 Introduction

In Secs. 2.2.1 and 2.3.3, multi-output-voltage push-pull and forward converter topologies were discussed. As was described, in either circuit, a feedback loop is closed around a main or "master" (usually the highest-current or 5-V) output. The feedback loop keeps the master output constant against line or load changes.

Additional secondaries on the power transformer yield "slave" output voltages whose magnitudes are proportional to their respective numbers of turns. These slaves are operated open-loop. Their on time, or duration of high voltage at the secondaries, is fixed by the master feedback loop so as to keep the master output voltage constant. These on times are unaffected by the slave output currents and are proportional to the DC supply voltage.

These slave voltages are thus as well regulated against line input changes as is the master. But the slaves are not well regulated against load current changes—either in the master or in themselves. Slave output change due to current changes in the master is referred to as *cross regulation* and may be as high as ±8 percent for the maximum specified current change in the master.

Slave output changes due to current change in themselves are considerably less so long as the master or slave output inductor does not go discontinuous or run dry (Sec. 2.2.4). If either the master or an individual slave output inductor is permitted to go discontinuous by decreasing its output current, that slave DC output voltage may change up to 50 percent.

If their magnitudes of inductance are chosen very large, the output inductors can be kept from going discontinuous. But larger output inductors cause larger and longer lasting output voltage transients in response to step output current changes.

A final drawback to open-loop slave output voltages is that they cannot be set precisely to a desired value. Their DC voltage level can be set to within only 1 or 2 V of a specific value.

The preciseness of setting depends on the volts per turn of the transformer core. Further, since either primary or secondary can be changed only in whole multiples of a single turn, output voltage can only be changed in coarse steps. Moreover, since, from Faraday's law, the volts per turn is directly proportional to switching frequency, the coarseness of these steps increases with increasing frequency.

This scheme of a multioutput supply with a master, well regulated against line and load changes but with slaves poorly regulated against master or slave load current changes is nevertheless widely used.

Usually it is only the master—the 5-V output that feeds crucial logic circuits—which must be well regulated against line and load changes. Slaves usually feed motors on disk or tape drives or error amplifiers. Such loads can most often tolerate a DC voltage which is as much as 1 to 2 V off a specified nominal value. For motor drives, this changes the motor acceleration times only slightly. For various linear circuits, it changes internal dissipation only somewhat.

Yet there are numerous applications where the slave outputs must be precisely set to a specified value and must be well regulated (better than 1 percent) against line and load changes. Heretofore, when slaves well regulated against line and load changes were required, the solution was to postregulate a semiregulated slave with either a linear regulator for output currents of under 1.5 A or a buck regulator for higher output currents.

These approaches have their merits and drawbacks, which are discussed below. A better solution for poorly regulated slaves is the magnetic-amplifier postregulator.[1,2] It uses an old basic technique, but with a simpler circuit and better magnetic material, it made a dramatic reappearance about 7 years ago and has rapidly been adopted throughout the industry.

10.2 Linear and Buck Regulator Postregulators

A linear regulating postregulator is the best approach for output currents up to 1.5 A. The 1.5-A limit comes about because of low cost and low internal dissipation.

Linear regulators with up to 1.5 A of output current are available as integrated circuits in plastic TO220 packages at a cost of about 50¢. They require no additional external components other than a small filter capacitor.

They are usually specified as requiring 2 V (typically, 3 V for the worst case) minimum input-output differential or headroom as discussed in Sec. 1.2.3). Thus, for 1.0 A of output current at 3 V of headroom, their internal dissipation is 3.0 W.

They are also available as integrated circuits at much higher currents in metal TO66 or TO3 cases. But they are not widely used at currents above 1.0 A—not so much because of excessive junction temperature, for that can be handled by heat-sinking—but rather because of the excessive dissipation and consequent total supply inefficiency due to the 3-V headroom requirement, which limits their use at currents above 1.0 A.

Integrated-circuit linear regulators with only 0.5- to 1.0-V headroom requirement (Sec. 1.2.5) are available, but these are considerably more expensive.

Postregulators for output currents above 1.5 or possibly 3.0 A are most often implemented as buck regulators. The slave output voltage is usually set at a minimum of about 4 V above the desired output and is then bucked down (Sec. 1.3.1) to the desired output.

This yields better efficiency than does a linear step-down regulator. But it is more expensive in dollars, number of components, and required space. Further, the new frequency of the buck transistor introduces an additional source of RFI and may produce beats with the main switching frequency causing problems in other parts of the frequency spectrum.

The magnetic-amplifier postregulator, discussed below, is a better approach than a buck regulator at currents over 1.5 A and is even a credible alternative at lower currents.

10.3   Magnetic Amplifiers—Introduction

Referring to Figs. 2.1 and 2.10, it is seen that the slave output voltages are not well regulated, primarily because they are operated open-loop and their "high" time, or time that their secondary voltages are high, is determined only by the master feedback loop. If there were independent control of the slave secondary high times, through separate feedback loops, they, too, could be constant.

High time of the slave secondary of a forward converter can be controlled by a symbolic switch $S1$ as in Fig. 10.1. Switch $S1$ is in series between the slave secondary output terminal and its rectifying diode $D1$. By independently controlling its on/off-time ratio, the duty cycle of voltage supplied to the slave LC filter and hence the slave DC output voltage can be controlled.

Assume that the high time directly at the slave secondary output (before $S1$) is t_h out of a period T as in Fig. 10.1. The time t_h is set by

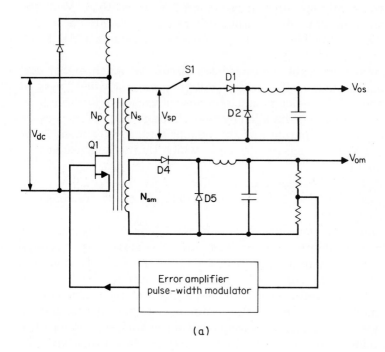

(a)

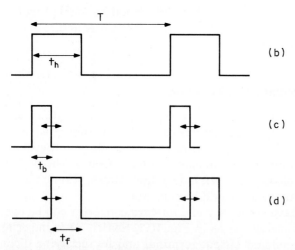

(b)

(c)

(d)

Figure 10.1 Width modulation of a slave secondary pulse with a symbolic switch $S1$. If the open and closed times of $S1$ could be controlled in a separate feedback loop independently of the on and off times of $Q1$, the slave output voltage could be regulated independently of the master.

the main feedback loop to maintain constant main output DC voltage V_{om}. Thus

$$V_{om} = \left[(V_{dc} - V_{ce})\frac{N_{sm}}{N_p} - V_{D4}\right]\frac{t_h}{T} \tag{10.1a}$$

$$V_{om} \approx \left[(V_{dc} - 1)\frac{N_{sm}}{N_p} - 1\right]\frac{t_h}{T} \tag{10.1b}$$

Of this time, t_h, assume that $S1$ is open and blocking the slave secondary voltage V_{sp} from getting through to the $D1_s$ anode for a time t_b (Fig. 10.1c) and that $S1$ is closed with zero resistance for a firing time t_f (Fig. 10.1d). The slave DC output voltage is then

$$V_{os} = (V_{sp} - V_{D1})\frac{t_f}{T} \tag{10.2a}$$

$$V_{os} \approx (V_{sp} - 1)\frac{t_f}{T} \tag{10.2b}$$

Now $t_f + t_b = t_h$, or

$$t_f = t_h - t_b \tag{10.3}$$

The slave output voltage will be kept constant, as indicated by Eq. 10.2, by controlling t_f. But the physical nature of the switch $S1$ is such that it is not t_f directly that will be controlled, but rather t_b, the blocking time.

Thus in Eq. 10.2a, if the peak secondary voltage $V_{sp} = (V_{dc} - V_{Q1})$ (N_s/N_p) varies—say, increases—because the supply voltage V_{dc} increases, t_f will be decreased by increasing t_b or cutting away a larger piece of the front end of the t_h pulse.

The switch $S1$ is a *magnetic amplifier*. It consists simply of a toroidal magnetic core of square hysteresis loop material with a few turns of wire. It works as follows.

10.3.1 Square hysteresis loop magnetic core as a fast acting on/off switch with electrically adjustable on/off time

Figure 10.2 shows the *BH* loop of a typical square hysteresis loop material (Toshiba MB amorphous core material[3]). Other square-loop materials usable in magnetic amplifiers will be discussed below.

The slope of the *BH* loop ($\mu = dB/dH$) is its permeability. A coil wound around the core will have an impedance proportional to the core permeability μ. Thus, so long as the core is on the vertical of its

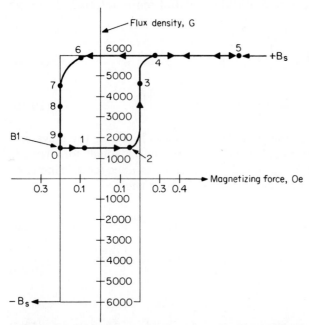

Figure 10.2 Toshiba MB amorphous core, *BH* loop at 100 kHz. In magnetic-amplifier operation, the core moves along a minor loop O1234567890. In going from 1 to 4, the core is on the steep part of the hysteresis loop and the MA has high impedance. At point 4, the core saturates and the MA has essentially zero impedance. At the end of the Q1 on time (Fig. 10.1), the core is reset to B_1. The time to move from B_1 to $+B_s$ is the switch-open time. The further down B_1 is pushed, the longer the blocking or switch-open time. The level to which B_1 is reset is determined by the current forced into the no-dot end of MA by Q2 (Fig. 10.3). That current is controlled by the error amplifier.

hysteresis loop, its permeability and hence the coil impedance is very high. It is effectively a single-pole switch in the open position.

When the core is in saturation on the horizontal axis of its hysteresis loop (beyond point 4 in Fig. 10.2), the *BH* loop is so square that the slope dB/dH or permeability is unity. The coil impedance is thus the very low impedance of an air core coil of an equal number of turns. The coil is thus effectively a single-pole switch in the closed position.

Such a core with a few turns of wire constitutes the switch S1 of Fig. 10.1. It is shown in Fig. 10.3 with the error amplifier and the scheme for controlling the on/off time of the switch.

Throughout one switching cycle (t_0 to t_3 in Fig. 10.4) the core moves around a so-called minor hysteresis loop—the path 01234567890 shown in Fig. 10.2. The blocking (t_b) and firing (t_f) times of the magnetic core switch are controlled as follows. Assume that at the start of a cycle (t_0),

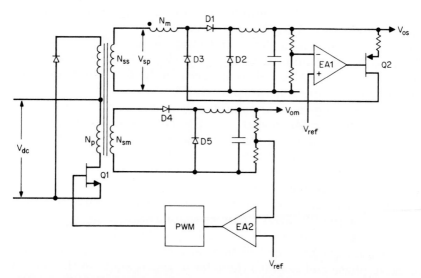

Figure 10.3 Magnetic-amplifier regulation of a slave output. The switch $S1$ of Fig. 10.1 is implemented with magnetic amplifier MA. The MA has high impedance as long as it is below saturation on the steep part of its hysteresis loop. That high-impedance time is determined by the amount of reset current pushed into the no-dot end of MA during the $Q1$ off time. The MA is simply a square hysteresis loop core with a few turns of wire.

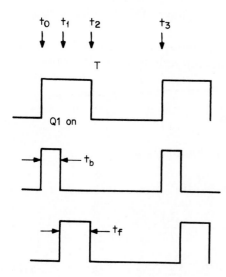

Figure 10.4 Critical timing intervals for magnetic amplifier (Fig. 10.3).

the core had been pushed down to B_1 on Fig. 10.2. When $Q1$ turns on, a voltage $V_{sp} \approx (V_{dc} - 1)N_{ss}/N_p$ appears across the slave secondary.

Just prior to t_0, $D2$ had been conducting and its cathode was one diode drop below ground. At t_0, a voltage $(V_{sp} + 1)$ appears across the magnetic amplifier MA and $D1$ in series in the direction to drive the core up toward saturation at point P4 (Fig. 10.2).

Until the core gets up to point 4, only a very small "coercive" current flows through MA and $D1$ into $D2$. This coercive current is considerably smaller than the free-wheeling current $D2$ is carrying. Thus the $D2$ cathode does not move substantially; it remains at one diode drop below ground and the voltage V_{sp} is blocked from getting through and raising the voltage at the front end of L_s.

Diode $D1$ carries the MA coercive current, and although it is much smaller than the $D2$ current, assume that forward drops in $D1$ and $D2$ are equal (and equal to 1 V). The full V_{sp} voltage thus appears across MA, whose right-hand end remains at ground. The MA is now in its blocking phase and remains there for a time t_b equal to the time required to move the core up from B_1 to saturation at B_s (= point 4).

Once the core has reached saturation at point 4, the MA impedance becomes negligible within a few nanoseconds and it cannot support the voltage V_s. A large current flows from the top end of N_{ss} into $D2$ and unclamps it, and its cathode voltage rises to one diode drop ($D1$) below V_{sp} and remains there for the duration of the $Q1$ on time.

The time from the onset of saturation to the instant $Q1$ turns off is the firing time t_f. The LC output filter is thus presented with a square pulse of amplitude $(V_{sp} - V_{D1})$, duration t_f, and duty cycle t_f/T. It averages this pulse to produce the slave DC output voltage of $(V_{sp} - V_{D1})t_f/T$.

Regulation against line and load variation is achieved by controlling the firing time t_f. This is done indirectly by controlling the blocking time t_b.

10.3.2 Blocking and firing times in magnetic-amplifier postregulators

Blocking time t_b is calculated from Faraday's law:

$$V_{sp} = N_m A_e \frac{dB}{dT} 10^{-8}$$

$$= N_m A_e \frac{(B_s - B_1)}{t_b} 10^{-8}$$

or
$$t_b = N_m A_e \frac{(B_s - B_1)}{V_{sp}} 10^{-8} \qquad (10.4)$$

where N_m = number of turns on magnetic amplifier MA
    A_e = MA core area, cm^2
    B_s = saturation flux density, G
    B_1 = starting point in flux density, G
    V_{sp} = peak slave secondary voltage, V
    t_b = blocking time, s (Fig. 10.4)

Now note (from Eq. 10.2b) $V_{os} = (V_{sp} - 1)t_f/T$ and (from Eq. 10.3) $t_f = t_h - t_b$.

If V_{sp} increases for any reason, V_{os} can be kept constant by decreasing the firing time t_f (Eq. 10.3), and from Eq. 10.2, t_f can be decreased by increasing t_b. From Eq. 10.4, t_b can be increased by decreasing B_1, that is, by pushing B_1 further down on the hysteresis loop. Similarly, if for some reason V_{os} decreases, t_f must be increased by decreasing the blocking time t_b. This is accomplished by increasing the flux level B_1 so that less time is required for the voltage V_{sp} to drive the core up into saturation.

10.3.3 Magnetic-amplifier core resetting and voltage regulation

Thus far only the transition of the core from its starting point B_1 up to saturation has been discussed. During t_f, the MA impedance is essentially zero and it delivers the characteristic ramp-on-a-step current waveform demanded by the output LC filter.

At the end of the $Q1$ on time and prior to the start of the next on time, the core must be restored to the B_1 level on the hysteresis loop, which yields the correct blocking time on the next switching cycle. If no current is delivered into MA in the reverse direction (into its no-dot end) immediately after the end of the ramp-on-a-step pulse, the MA core would return to $+B_s$ at 0 Oe.

The core is reset to the appropriate B_1 by a current-reset technique. In magnetic-amplifier practice, cores are reset to desired flux levels by either a voltage-reset or current-reset scheme. In voltage reset, the core is reset to any desired flux level by applying a unique amount of volt-seconds product to it (recall from Faraday's law, $dB = E \, dt/NA$). In this particular circuit, core reset is more simply done by current reset.

Current reset to the appropriate B_1 and line and load regulation is achieved with the voltage error amplifier, blocking diode $D3$, and the voltage-controlled current source $Q2$ of Fig. 10.3. The core is reset to that B_1 level which yields a blocking t_b and hence firing time t_f which gives the desired DC output voltage.

The resetting is done by pushing the appropriate DC current into the no-dot end of MA at the end of the $Q1$ on time.

When $Q1$ is on, $D3$ is reverse-biased and blocks $Q2$ from loading

down the secondary. When $Q1$ turns off, the top end of N_{ss} goes negative and current from the $Q2$ collector is driven into the no-dot end of
MA. The amount of this current is controlled by the voltage error amplifier (error amplifier 1) such as to make the sampled fraction of the
DC output voltage equal to the reference voltage.

If, for any reason, the DC output voltage goes up, t_f must go down,
which means that t_b must go up. Thus, if the DC output voltage goes
up, the error-amplifier output goes down and the $Q2$ collector current
goes up, pushing more reset current into the no-dot end of MA. This
pushes the initial flux level B_1 down further and, by Eq. 10.4, increases t_b, thus decreasing t_f and bringing the DC output voltage back
down.

Similarly, of course, a decrease in V_{os} causes an increase in error-
amplifier output voltage and a decrease in $Q2$ reset current. As B_1
flux level rises, t_b decreases, t_f increases, and V_{os} is brought back up.

All this, of course, occurs over a number of switching cycles and is
accomplished in a time dependent on the error-amplifier bandwidth.

Stabilization of this negative-feedback loop will not be considered
here. It is treated by C. Jamerson in Ref. 4 and C. Mullett in Ref. 2.

10.3.4   Slave output voltage shutdown with magnetic amplifiers

Heretofore, the magnetic amplifier was presented only as a means of
voltage regulating the slave output voltage. That was done by controlling the flux level B_1 to which the core is reset at the end of the power
transistor on time. The further down B_1 was pushed, the longer the
blocking time t_b, the shorter the firing time t_f, and hence the lower the
DC output voltage.

The magnetic amplifier can also be used to shut down the DC output
voltage completely. This is done by pushing the initial flux level $+B_1$
down to $-B_s$. Blocking time, from Eq. 10.4, is $t_b = N_m A_e (2B_s) 10^{-8}/V_{sp}$.
The core area A_e and N_m will be chosen so that this blocking time is
greater than the maximum $Q1$ on time.

Flux level B_1 can be brought down to $-B_s$ in a number of different
ways by forcing the $Q2$ current to be sufficiently large. Thus the error-
amplifier output can be overridden by forcing it down to a sufficiently
low-impedance, low-voltage source. Or V_{ref} at the error-amplifier input terminal can be short-circuited to ground with an isolating resistor from the reference voltage source to the error-amplifier input terminal to avoid overloading the reference source.

It should be noted that if the magnetic-amplifier core is used only
for voltage regulation (as it generally is), it moves around a minor
hysteresis loop as in Fig. 10.2. The area of this loop may be a small

fraction of the total hysteresis loop area—depending on the minimum B_1 flux level, which is dependent on the maximum and minimum supply voltage and load current specifications.

Generally, for a voltage-regulation-only design, the minor loop area will be about one-fourth the total hysteresis loop area. Since core losses are proportional to the area of the hysteresis loop traversed, this ordinarily will result in quite low core dissipation and temperature rise.

However, if the design is to shut the slave voltage down completely to zero and the core flux excursion is over the full area of the major hysteresis loop from $+B_s$ to $-B_s$, higher core losses and temperature rise will result. Losses and core temperature rise should thus be calculated from the manufacturer's curves of core loss versus total flux excursion. This will be demonstrated below.

Note also that in Fig. 10.3, supply voltage for the error amplifier and $Q2$ is the slave output voltage source itself. If it is desired to shut the slave output down completely to zero, supply voltage for the error amplifier and $Q2$ will have to be taken from a source which is always present—possibly another slave output.

10.3.5 Square hysteresis loop core characteristics and sources

When interest in magnetic amplifiers resumed about 7 years ago, only one material having the required characteristics for an efficient high-frequency magnetic amplifier was available.

This material is an alloy of 79% nickel, 17% iron, and 4% molybdenum. It is available from various manufacturers under their particular brand names. Magnetics Inc. of Butler, Pennsylvania[3] is the foremost American supplier and has the largest range of available core sizes and iron areas. It calls its material Square Permalloy 80. Other manufacturers' brand names for similar material are 4-79 Molypermalloy, Square Mu 79, Square Permalloy, and Hy Ra 80.

Square Permalloy 80 is available from Magnetics Inc.[5] in tapes of various thicknesses wound on toroidal bobbins. Available tape thicknesses are 0.5, 1.0, 2.0, 4.0, 6.0, and 14.0 mils. Since the material is electrically conductive, eddy currents contribute a large fraction of the total losses, and at high frequencies, the thinner tapes must be used to keep losses down.

Generally, 1-mil tape thickness is used up to a switching frequency of 50 kHz, and ½ mil for frequencies of 50 to 100 kHz. Beyond 100 kHz, the newer "amorphous" core materials, to be discussed below, are used because of their lower losses.

The two characteristics required for an efficient, high-frequency magnetic amplifier are a very square hysteresis loop and low losses at high peak flux density. The ½-mil tape is more expensive than 1-mil tape and should be used only if low loss is more important than low cost. If the design is only to provide voltage regulation by traversing minor loops rather than the full major loop, the higher loss 1-mil tape can be used even above 50 kHz.

The square hysteresis loop requirement is necessary for a very low impedance in the saturated state. If the hysteresis loop is not sufficiently square, its permeability (dB/dH in saturation, as shown in Fig. 10.2) is appreciable and its impedance at the top of the loop will be significantly greater than that of an air core coil of an equal number of turns.

Thus, in Fig. 10.3, the voltage at the output of the MA will be less than V_{sp} during the firing time and the drop across MA will be dependent on the secondary current. Further, if the loop is not square, the transition from high to low impedance may take a considerable time, prohibiting its use at high frequencies.

Core losses in watts per pound as a function of peak flux density and operating frequency are shown in Fig. 10.5a and 10.5b for 1- and ½-mil Square Permalloy tapes. Flux density on those curves are half the peak-to-peak excursion. The Magnetics Inc. catalog does not give the tape weight for each core, but this can be calculated from the core area, mean path length, and material density of 8.75 g/cm^3 which are given in the catalogs.

Temperature rise of the outer surface of the case enclosing the magnetic toroid can be estimated from its thermal resistance as read from Fig. 7.4a or 7.4c and the core losses. A reasonable estimate of the temperature differential between the magnetic core itself and the outer surface of the case is about 15°C.

The core temperature rise can be quite high since the Curie temperature of Square Permalloy is 460°C. Thus the limiting factor for core losses is either the temperature rating of the wire or the specified magnetic-amplifier efficiency.

About 4 years after the renewed interest in magnetic amplifiers commenced, a new type of magnetic material was introduced. It is not crystalline in structure, but amorphous, and has lower core losses and a squarer hysteresis loop at higher frequencies than does Square Permalloy. Although ½-mil Permalloy can be used up to 100 kHz and possibly somewhat higher, beyond that frequency, this new material is preferable.

This amorphous material is available from two sources—Allied Signal in Parsippany, New Jersey,[6] and Toshiba Corporation[7] (the American sales agent is Mitsui in New York).

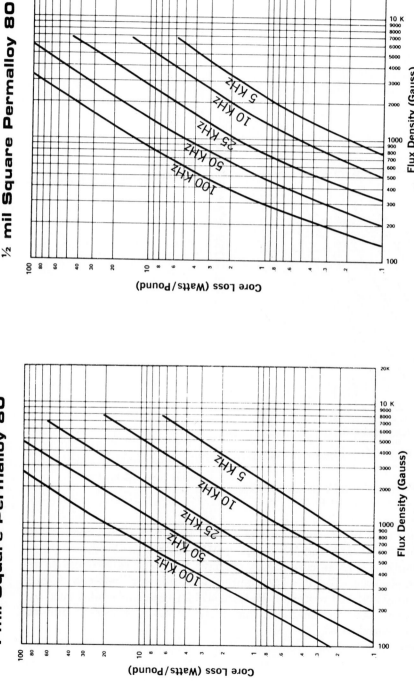

Figure 10.5 (a) Core losses, 1-mil Square Permalloy. (*Courtesy Magnetics Inc.*) (b) Core losses, ½-mil Square Permalloy. (*Courtesy Magnetics Inc.*) (c) Core losses, amorphous core material, Metglas 27144. (*Courtesy Magnetics Inc.*) (d) Core losses, Toshiba MA (watts/LB = 56.8 × watts/CC). (*Courtesy Toshiba Corp.*)

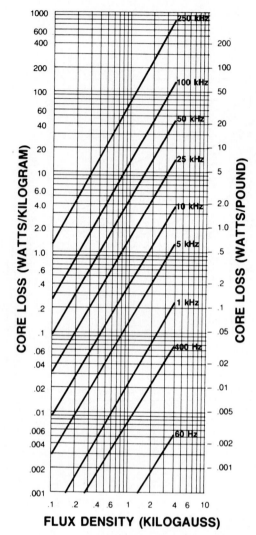

FLUX DENSITY (KILOGAUSS)

Figure 10.5c *(Continued)*

Allied calls its product Metglas 2714A. Toshiba has two amorphous core materials: MA and MB. Toshiba MB material is closely identical to Metglas 2714A in core losses, coercive force and squareness of its hysteresis loop. Toshiba MA material is midway between ½-mil Permalloy and MB material. Metglas 2714A material is also used by Magnetics Inc. for magnetic amplifier cores in its own line of standard-sized cores.

Curves of core loss versus peak flux density at various frequencies

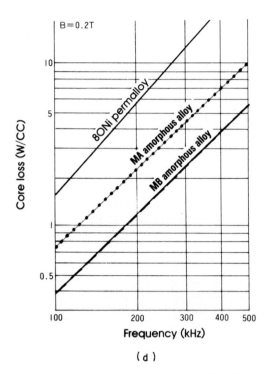

Figure 10.5d   (*Continued*)

(d)

for Metglas 2714A are shown in Fig. 10.5c. Data comparing core loss versus frequency at a peak flux density of 2000 G for Toshiba MA, MB material and 1-mil Permalloy are given in Fig. 10.5d. Note that figure gives loss in watts per cubic centimeter. For MA, MB density of 8.0 g/cm^3, loss in watts per pound is 56.8 × loss in watts per cubic centimeter.

The *BH* loops at 100 kHz for Toshiba MA, MB material and ½-mil Permalloy are shown in Fig. 10.6a. Figure 10.6c compares 100-kHz *BH* loops for Metglas 2417A, ½- and 1-mil Permalloy.

The *BH* loops for increasing frequency have a characteristic appearance. As frequency increases, coercive force increases but saturation flux density remains fixed. This, of course, explains the increase in core loss with frequency as the loss is proportional to the area of the hysteresis loop. The increase in coercive force with frequency is shown in Fig. 10.6b for Toshiba MA, MB and Permalloy material.

Standard-sized MA and MB cores available from Toshiba are shown in Fig. 10.7a and 10.7b. Metglas 2714A cores available from Magnetics Inc.[8] are shown in Fig. 10.8a and from Allied Signal, in Fig. 10.8b.

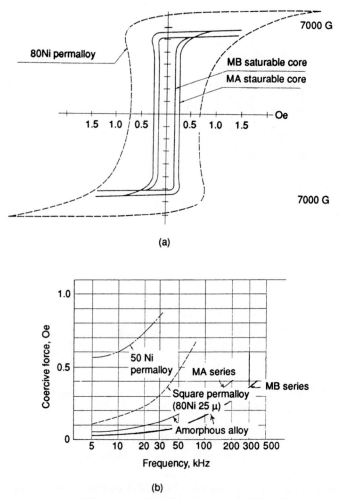

(a)

(b)

Figure 10.6 (a) *BH* loops at 100 kHz. (*Courtesy Toshiba Corp.*) (b) Coercive force versus frequency. (*Courtesy Toshiba Corp.*) (c) *BH* loops at 100 kHz, 1-mil and ½-mil Permalloy, Metglas 2714A. (*Courtesy Magnetics Inc.*)

10.3.6 Core loss and temperature rise calculations

Toshiba provides curves useful in calculating core temperature rise for each of its cores. Figures 10.9, 10.10, and 10.11 show core loss versus total flux change in maxwells for its three largest MB cores.

Recall that flux change in maxwells equals flux density change in

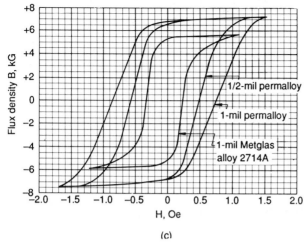

Figure 10.6   (*Continued*)

gauss multiplied by core area in square centimeters. Thus, dividing the maxwells shown in the curves by the core area gives the flux density change in gauss. The maximum maxwells shown on the curves then correspond to the total maximum flux density change from negative to positive saturation flux density ($-B_s$ to $+B_s$). Toshiba's MA, MB materials have B_s of 6500 and 6000 G, respectively.

Losses at the maximum maxwells shown in Figs. 10.9 to 10.11 then correspond to operation around the total major loop as when the magnetic amplifier is used to fully shut down the slave output voltage. Losses at the lesser maxwell level correspond to operation around a minor loop as in Fig. 10.2, where the magnetic amplifier is used only for voltage regulation.

Thus, whatever the total maxwell excursion is, Figs. 10.9 to 10.11 give core loss for each core at that flux excursion. From this core loss, Fig. 10.12 gives the core temperature rise. Actually, Fig. 10.12 is a measure of the thermal resistance of each core and is related to the radiating surface area of the core which can be calculated from its outer dimensions as given in Fig. 10.7*b*.

It is interesting to note that the temperature rise given by Toshiba in Fig. 10.12 coincides to within a very few degrees with the rise as calculated from Fig. 7.4*c* for any power dissipation and core area (calculated from Fig. 10.7*b*).

Type No.	Standard core dimensions (mm)			Finished dimensions (mm)			Effective core cross section (mm²)	Mean flux path length (mm)	Total flux 2Φ₁ (×10⁻⁸WB)	Insulating covers
	Outer dia.	Inner dia.	Height	Outer dia.	Inner dia.	Height				
MA 26×16×4.5W	26	16	4.5	29.5 max.	13.0 min.	8.0 max.	16.9	66.0	1800	Resin casing
" 22×14×4.5W	22	14	4.5	25.5 "	11.0 "	8.0 "	13.5	56.5	1440	"
" 18×12×4.5X	18	12	4.5	20.5 "	10.2 "	8.0 "	10.1	47.1	1080	Epoxy resin coating
" 14× 8×4.5X	14	8	4.5	16.3 "	6.3 "	7.5 "	10.1	34.6	1080	"
" 10× 6×4.5X	10	6	4.5	12.3 "	4.4 "	7.5 "	6.75	25.1	720	"
" 8× 6×4.5X	8	6	4.5	10.0 "	4.4 "	7.5 "	3.38	22.0	360	"
" 7× 6×4.5X	7	6	4.5	9.0 "	4.4 "	7.5 "	1.69	20.4	180	"

(a)

Type No.	Standard core dimensions (mm)			Finished dimensions (mm)			Effective core cross section (mm²)	Mean flux path length (mm)	Total flux 2Φ₁ (×10⁻⁸WB)	Insulating covers
	Outer dia.	Inner dia.	Height	Outer dia.	Inner dia.	Height				
MB 21×14×4.5	21	14	4.5	24.0 max.	12.0 min.	8.5 max.	11.8	55.0	1105	Epoxy resin coating
" 18×12×4.5	18	12	4.5	20.5 "	10.2 "	8.0 "	10.1	47.1	935	"
" 15×10×4.5	15	10	4.5	17.5 "	8.3 "	7.5 "	8.44	39.3	790	"
" 12× 8×4.5	12	8	4.5	14.3 "	6.3 "	7.5 "	6.75	31.4	629	"
" 10× 7×4.5	10	7	4.5	12.3 "	5.4 "	7.5 "	5.06	26.7	476	"
" 9× 7×4.5	9	7	4.5	11.0 "	5.4 "	7.5 "	3.38	25.1	315	"
" 8× 7×4.5	8	7	4.5	10.0 "	5.4 "	7.5 "	1.69	23.6	158	"
" 15×10×3W	15	10	3.0	17.0 "	8.0 "	5.0 "	5.63	39.3	526	Resin casing
" 12× 8×3W	12	8	3.0	14.0 "	6.0 "	5.0 "	4.5	31.4	420	"

(b)

Figure 10.7 (a) Available MA amorphous cores for magnetic amplifiers. (*Courtesy Toshiba Corp.*) (b) Available MB amorphous cores for magnetic amplifiers. (*Courtesy Toshiba Corp.*)

| Part Number* | DIMENSIONS | | | | | | Core loss (w) @ 50KHz, 2000 gauss (Max.) | ml cm | Ac cm² | Wa cr m | Core wt. grams | Wa Ac cr m cm² (×10⁻⁶) |
| | I.D. (in.) | | O.D. (in.) | | Ht. (in.) | | | | | | | |
	core	case (Min.)	core	case (Max.)	core	case (Max.)						
50B10-5D	.650	.580	.900	.970	.125	.200	.118	6.18	.051	348,000	2.7	.0177
50B10-1D	.650	.580	.900	.970	.125	.200	.22	6.18	.076	348,000	4.0	.0264
50B10-1E	.650	.580	.900	.970	.125	.200	.092	6.18	.076	348,000	3.5	.0264
50B11-5D	.500	.430	.625	.695	.125	.200	.044	4.49	.025	194,000	1.0	.0048
50B11-1D	.500	.430	.625	.695	.125	.200	.083	4.49	.038	194,000	1.5	.0074
50B11-1E	.500	.430	.625	.695	.125	.200	.034	4.49	.038	194,000	1.3	.0074
50B12-5D	.375	.305	.500	.570	.125	.200	.035	3.49	.025	99,000	8	.0025
50B12-1D	.375	.305	.500	.570	.125	.200	.066	3.49	.038	99,000	1.2	.0038
50B12-1E	.375	.305	.500	.570	.125	.200	.027	3.49	.038	99,000	1.04	.0038
50B45-5D	.500	.430	.750	.820	.250	.325	.194	4.99	.101	194,000	4.4	.0143
50B45-1D	.500	.430	.750	.820	.250	.325	.363	4.99	.151	194,000	6.6	.0214
50B45-1E	.500	.430	.750	.820	.250	.325	.149	4.99	.151	194,000	5.7	.0214
50B66-5D	.500	.430	.750	.820	.125	.200	.097	4.99	.050	194,000	2.2	.0071
50B66-1D	.500	.430	.750	.820	.125	.200	.182	4.99	.076	194,000	3.3	.0108
50B66-1E	.500	.430	.750	.820	.125	.200	.075	4.99	.076	194,000	2.9	.0108

*For other sizes, refer to factory.

Figure 10.8 Available Square Permalloy 80 and Metglas 2714A cores for magnetic amplifiers. (*Courtesy Magnetics Inc.*) (*b*) Standard Metglas 2714A amorphous magnetic-amplifier cores. (*Allied Signal.*)

PART NUMBER CODE

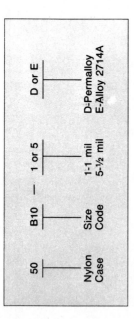

MATERIAL CHARACTERISTICS

	Alloy 2714A	½ mil Permalloy	1 mil Permalloy
Bm (gauss min.)	5000	7000	7000
Br/Bm (min.)**	.9	.83	.80
H₁ (oersted max.)**	.025	.045	.040
Core loss (w/lb. max. @ 50 kHz, 2000 gauss)	12	20	25

**Measured @ 400 Hz, CCFR Test

Figure 10.8 *(Continued)*

CORE NUMBER	DIMENSIONS (mm)*				(cm)	A (cm²)	Mass (g)	Flux Capacity 2φ (μWb)	Wₐ (cm²)	WₐA (cm⁴)
		OD	ID	HT						
MP1303	CORE CASE	12.8 14.6	9.5 7.9	3.2 5.1	3.50	0.041	1.1	4.7	0.49	0.021
MP1603	CORE CASE	15.9 17.8	12.7 11.1	3.2 5.1	4.50	0.041	1.4	4.7	0.96	0.039
MP1903	CORE CASE	19.2 21.0	12.7 11.1	3.2 5.1	5.00	0.082	3.1	9.3	0.96	0.079
MP2303	CORE CASE	22.9 25.0	16.5 14.6	3.2 5.1	6.19	0.081	3.8	9.2	1.68	0.14
MP1305	CORE	12.5	9.5	4.8	3.46	0.057	1.5	6.5	0.49	0.028
MP1505	CORE	15.1	9.5	4.8	3.87	0.11	3.1	12	0.49	0.049
MP1805	CORE CASE	18.4 20.8	12.7 10.8	4.8 6.7	4.88	0.11	4.0	12	0.92	0.10
MP1906	CORE CASE	19.1 21.3	12.7 10.7	6.4 8.4	4.99	0.16	6.1	18	0.90	0.14
MP3506	CORE CASE	35.2 37.3	25.4 23.4	6.4 8.4	9.52	0.241	17.4	27.5	4.29	1.04
MP2510	CORE CASE	25.6 27.8	19.1 17.0	9.5 11.8	7.01	0.241	12.8	27.5	2.28	0.552

NOTE: 1 circular mil = 5.067 × 10⁻⁶ cm²

PART NUMBER CODE:

MP   13   03
Metglas   OD   HT
Products

P or E
P - Plastic Box
E - Encapsulated

4A
Alloy
2714A

S
Square
Loop

(b)

Figure 10.8   (Continued)

401

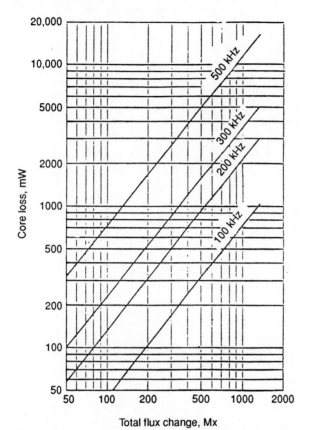

Figure 10.9 Core loss versus total flux change. Toshiba MB 21 × 14 × 4.5 core. Core area = 0.118 cm²; ΔB = $\Delta\phi$(maxwells)/0.118. (*Courtesy Toshiba Corp.*)

10.3.7 Design example—magnetic-amplifier postregulator

Design a magnetic-amplifier postregulator for the output of the forward converter shown in Fig. 10.13a. Specifications are

Forward converter switching frequency	100 kHz
Slave output voltage	15 V
Slave output current	10 A

The main output voltage is $V_{om} = V_{dc}(N_{sm}/N_p)(t_{on}/T)$. The main feedback loop, in keeping V_{om} constant, then must keep the product $V_{dc}t_{on}$ constant. Thus t_{on} is a maximum when V_{dc} is a minimum.

In the usual case, the number of turns on the $T1$ reset winding N_r is set equal to the turns on the power winding N_p. This forces the voltage

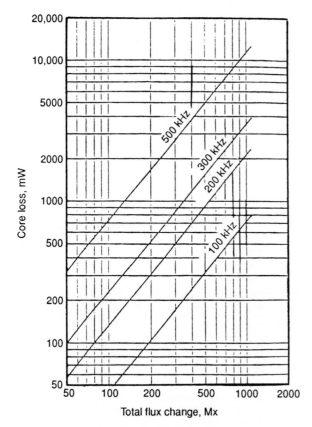

Figure 10.10 Core loss versus total flux change. Toshiba MB 18 × 12 × 4.5 core. Core area = 0.101 cm²; $\Delta B =$ $\Delta\phi$(maxwells)/0.101. (*Courtesy Toshiba Corp.*)

across N_p when $Q1$ is off to be equal (and opposite, of course) to the voltage across it when $Q1$ is on.

Within one cycle, the volt-second product across N_p when $Q1$ is on must be equal and opposite to the volt-second product across it when $Q2$ is off. Otherwise, from Faraday's law, the core would move in gauss in one direction on the hysteresis loop and at the start of the next cycle, would not have been returned to its starting point on the loop. After a number of such cycles, the core would drift up the hysteresis loop, saturate, and—being unable to support voltage—destroy the power transistor the next time it is turned on.

Thus the absolute maximum $Q1$ on time at minimum DC input voltage is $0.5T$ or 5 μs so that $+V_{dc}t_{on}$ can equal $-V_{dc}t_{off}$.

To ensure that the core can always be reset during transient power-line dips below its specified minimum, in the above expression for

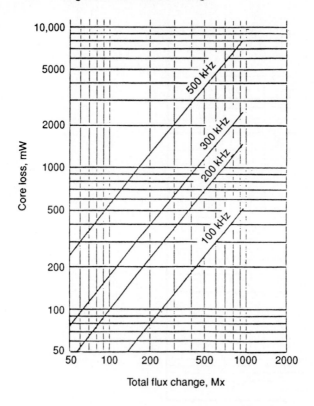

Figure 10.11 Core loss versus total flux change. Toshiba MB 15 × 10 × 4.5 core. Core area = 0.0843 cm²; ΔB = Δφ(maxwells)/0.0843. (*Courtesy Toshiba Corp.*)

V_{om}, N_{sm} will be chosen so that V_{om} is obtained for a maximum on time of $0.4T$ or 4 μs at the specified minimum V_{dc}. This yields a guard band of $0.1T$ or 1 μs to allow for line input dips.

The slave peak voltage V_{sp} (at the input end of MA) is then high for 4 μs at minimum DC input voltage. The MA will block this voltage for a time t_b (Fig. 10.13c), leaving a high voltage V_{sp1} for a time t_f at the no-dot end of the MA after it has saturated or fired.

If the MA has zero impedance when it has saturated, then $V_{\text{sp1}} = V_{\text{sp}}$. Then, assuming a 1-V drop across rectifier diode $D1$, the peak voltage at the front end of L_s when MA has fired is $(V_{\text{sp}} - 1)$. Now of the 4-μs duration of V_{sp} at low V_{dc} input, arbitrarily set $t_f = 3$ μs and $t_b = 1$ μs. This permits t_1 (Fig. 10.13b) to move either left or right, increasing or decreasing t_f to regulate against load changes.

Then for a slave output voltage of the specified 15 V

$$15 = (V_{\text{sp}} - 1)\left(\frac{t_f}{T}\right) = (V_{\text{sp}} - 1)\left(\frac{3}{10}\right) \quad \text{or} \quad V_{\text{sp}} = 51 \text{ V}$$

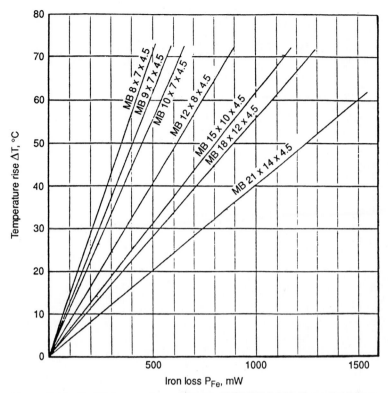

Figure 10.12 Toshiba amorphous MB cores. Temperature rise versus core losses. (*Courtesy Toshiba Corp.*)

Now the number of turns on MA and its iron area must be chosen to block 51 V. But they will be chosen to block not for the 1 μs of minimum blocking time, but for the full 4 μs corresponding to the maximum duration of V_{sp} on the assumption that the MA may be used to force the slave output voltage completely down to zero.

Assume that for a 100-kHz magnetic amplifier, an amorphous core such as the Toshiba MB (Fig. 10.7b) will be used. Arbitrarily select the one with the largest iron area as it will require the least turns to block the 51 V for 4 μs for a given flux change. This minimizes the residual air core inductance of the MA in its saturated state. Thus the MB 21 × 14 × 4.5, of iron area 0.118 cm², is chosen.

From Faraday's law, to minimize the number of turns, the flux change should be maximized or the core should traverse the full *BH* loop from $-B_s$ to $+B_s$. From Fig. 10.6a, B_s for the Toshiba MB material is 6000 G. Then from Faraday's law, to block 51 V for 4 μs with a core area of 0.118 cm²:

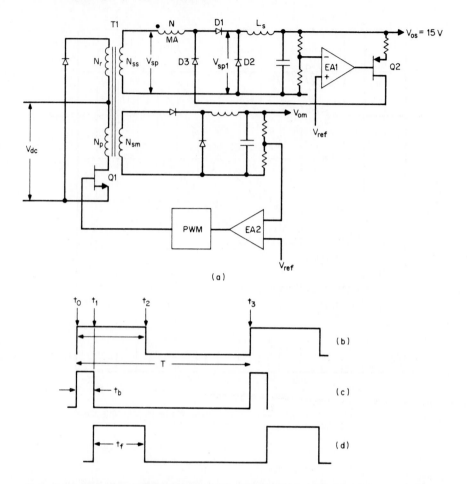

Figure 10.13 Design example of magnetic-amplifier postregulator. Magnetic amplifier blocks V_{so} for a time t_b and is a zero-impedance short circuit for a time t_r. Then $V_{os} = V_{so} (t_r/T)$. Time t_f is controlled in a negative-feedback loop by the current that $Q2$ forces into MA via D_m. That current is controlled by error amplifier 1.

$$E = 51 = NA_e \frac{dB}{dt} 10^{-8}$$

$$= 51 = N(0.118) \frac{2B_s}{4 \times 10^{-6}} 10^{-8}$$

or $N = 14$ turns.

For DC output current of 10 A, MA will be carrying the 10 A for a maximum of only 3 μs (maximum t_f) at low DC input. Maximum rms current is then $10\sqrt{3/10} = 5.48$ A. At 500 circular mils per rms ampere, a wire area of 2739 circular mils is required.

Two No. 19 wires in parallel provide 2 × 1290 or 2580 circular mils, which is close enough. The inner periphery of the Toshiba MB21 $\times$ 14 $\times$ 4.5 core is $\pi \times 0.55 = 1.73$ in. For the 0.0391-in diameter of No. 19 wire, the inner periphery can hold 1.73/0.0391 or 44 turns on a single layer. The 14 turns of two paralleled No. 19 wires can thus easily be accommodated in a single layer on the inner periphery.

If the core is operated in the shutdown mode, the full major loop is traversed each cycle. Figure 10.9 shows that for the MB 21 $\times$ 14 $\times$ 4.5, this corresponds to a total flux change of 1400 Mx or 12000 G $(- B_s$ to $+B_s)$ and core loss of 1 W, and Fig. 10.12 shows that the core temperature rise is only 40°C.

10.3.8 Magnetic-amplifier gain

When the MA has fired, it has close to zero impedance and the DC current through it is determined only by the DC output impedance and the slave output voltage. That is simply the specified DC output current. But to bring the MA to its fired state, a current equal to twice the coercive current I_c is required to force the core from the left to the right side of the hysteresis loop (Fig. 10.2). That current comes from the transformer secondary V_{sp}. Similarly, when the core is reset to the left side of the hysteresis loop (Fig. 10.2), a current equal to the coercive current must be supplied from $Q2$ via $D3$.

Magnetic-amplifier gain from $Q2$ to the output is then I_o/I_c. From Ampere's law, the coercive force $H_c = 0.4\pi N_m I_c/L_p$, where N_m is the number of turns, I_c is the coercive current, and L_p is the mean path length in centimeters.

For the MB core at 100 kHz, the coercive force is 0.18 Oe (Fig. 10.6b). Mean path length L_p of the MB 21 $\times$ 14 $\times$ 4.5 core is 5.5 cm, from Fig. 10.7b. Then for N_m of 14 turns, the coercive current is

$$I_c = \frac{H_c L_p}{0.4\pi N_m}$$

$$= \frac{0.18 \times 5.5}{0.4 \, \pi \times 14}$$

$$= 56.3 \text{ mA}$$

Thus a current of 56.3 mA from $Q2$ can control the 10-A output—or, stated another way, the magnetic-amplifier gain is 10/0.056 = 178.

It is of interest to realize the physical significance of this and to appreciate that a magnetic amplifier is very different from a usual saturable reactor. In the magnetic amplifier, when the control current (from $Q2$) flows, no load current flows as $D1$ is reverse-biased. Thus the control current does not have to "buck out" the load current.

In a saturable reactor (a variable-inductance reactor controlled by current in a control winding) in series with a load, however, current flows to the load at the same time the control current flows. Thus the control winding ampere turns must buck out the load ampere turns and gain is low.

10.3.9 Magnetic amplifiers for a push-pull output

For a full-wave output (push-pull or half-bridge topology), the circuit of Fig. 10.14 is often presented. But it has serious problems in that the dead time between transitions, the magamps, carry primary magnetizing current (Fig. 2.6). This is fully discussed in Ref. 15.

10.4 Magnetic-Amplifier Pulse-Width Modulator and Error Amplifier

Thus far, in this chapter, magnetic amplifiers as postregulators only have been considered. In this section, an interesting example of the use of a magnetic amplifier used simultaneously as a pulse-width modulator and error amplifier is described.[9]

It may be puzzling why, with the current enormous proliferation of inexpensive semiconductor pulse-width modulating chips with their built-in width modulators and error amplifiers, there is interest in magnetic elements to perform these functions.

The circuit to be described below does have advantages in specialized applications where a semiconductor integrated circuit cannot be used for some reason. The circuit consists of only square hysteresis loop core material and wire which is far more reliable than that in an integrated circuit.

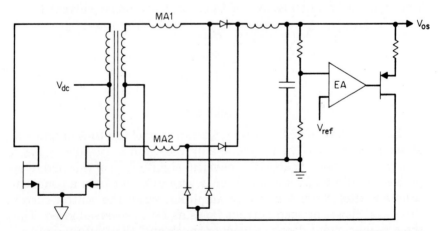

Figure 10.14   Two magnetic-amplifier cores driven from the same EA and PNP current source are required for a push-pull output.

There are some environmental conditions—such as excessive temperature—where the magnetic amplifier can survive more easily than an integrated circuit. Since discrete transistors which can survive high temperatures can be found easily, a circuit consisting of discrete transistors and a magnetic amplifier PWM–error amplifier is a more survivable circuit than one with discrete transistors and an integrated-circuit PWM chip.

Finally, the circuit described below offers a simple solution to an omnipresent problem in switching power supplies. That problem is how to sense a voltage on output ground and deliver to the power transistor on input ground, the appropriate width-modulated pulse, without requiring a housekeeping power supply to power the error amplifier on output ground.

The circuit works as follows.

10.4.1 Circuit details, magnetic amplifier pulse-width modulator–error amplifier[9]

The circuit is shown in Fig. 10.15. It was originally devised by Dulskis and Estey (cited in Ref. 9). It is a conventional push-pull topology using Darlington power transistors. A 40-kHz, ±8-V, 50/50 duty cycle square wave is applied at points AB via transformer $T1$.

The heart of the design is the magnetic amplifier $M1$. It consists of two square hysteresis loop cores sitting on top of one another. There are two equal turn gate windings N_{g1}, N_{g2} and a control winding N_c. Gate winding N_{g1} links core A only, N_{g2} links core B only, and N_c links both cores.

On alternate half cycles, a +8-V, 12.5-μs appears at points A, B. Consider the half period when, say, A is positive. That 8 V is divided across $D1$, the base-emitters of $Q3$, $Q1$, and $R5$. Resistor $R5$ is a current limiter.

At the start of the half period, magnetic-amplifier core $M1A$ is on the steep part of its hysteresis loop (B_0 of Fig. 10.16a) and has a sufficiently high impedance so that it does not short-circuit out the voltage from the $Q3$ base to ground. The Darlington, $Q3$, $Q1$, is energized and a voltage of roughly $V_{dc} - 1$ is applied to its half primary of $T2$.

The voltage across $M1A$ is the sum of the base-emitter drops of $Q1$ and $Q3$ (~1.6 V). This voltage drives $M1A$ upward toward saturation along the minor hysteresis loop $B0$–$B1$–$B2$–$B3$–B_s. At B_s, $M1A$ saturates, $Q3$ loses its base drive, and Darlington $Q3$, $Q1$ turn off. The $Q3$, $Q1$ on time is given by Faraday's law as

$$t_{\text{on}(Q1, Q3)} = \frac{N_g A_e (B_s - B_0)}{1.6} 10^{-8}$$

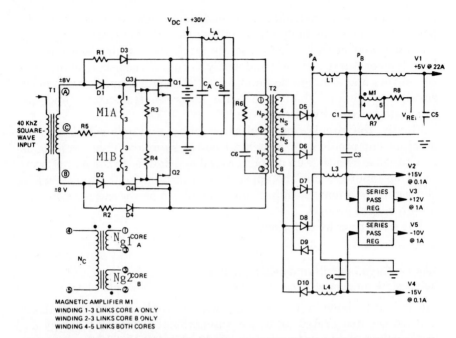

Figure 10.15 Magnetic-amplifier-controlled switching regulator. The magnetic amplifier serves as both a pulse-width modulator and an error amplifier. DC current through
control winding N_c determines the initial flux bias in gate windings and hence their
time to saturate, which fixes the Darlington on times. (*From R. Dulskis, J. Estey, and
A. Pressman, "A Magnetic Amplifier Controlled 40 kHz Switching Regulator," Wescon
Proceedings, San Francisco, 1977.*)

where N_g = number of turns of $M1A$
      A_e = core iron area
      B_0 = initial starting point on the hysteresis loop
      1.6 = voltage across $M1A$ driving it toward saturation

It is seen that the further down B_0 is from B_s, the longer the on
time. On-time control will be accomplished by controlling the level B_0
to which the core is reset at the start of the positive half cycle.

Now, as $M1A$ is being push up toward saturation with a voltage of
1.6 V across its N_g turns, it induces a voltage of $(N_c/N_g)1.6$ across N_c.
That couples a voltage back down to 1.6 V across $M1B$. But because of
the winding polarities, that voltage is in the direction to push $M1B$
down to B_0 if in the previous half period it had been pushed up to $+B_s$
by point B having been positive.

Thus in one half period, as—say—$M1A$ goes from B_0 to B_s, its
Darlington is on and $M1B$ is driven down from B_s to B_0. But the $M1B$
Darlington is off as its input diode $D2$ is reverse-biased. During the

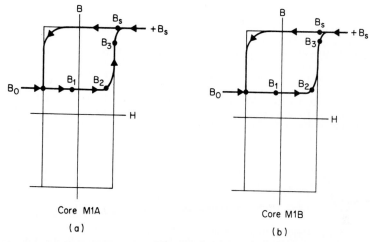

Figure 10.16   The BH loop operating locus of magnetic-amplifier cores (Fig. 10.15). As core $M1A$ moves from B_0 to $+B_s$, core $M1B$ is pushed down from $+B_s$ to B_0. Time to move from B_0 to B_s is the on time of the power transistors. On time is determined by how far down from B_s the initial starting ping B_0 has been pushed. This is determined by the DC current in control winding N_c, which is proportional to the output voltage (Fig. 10.15).

next half period the sequence reverses; $M1B$ is driven up from B_0 to $+B_s$, its Darlington is on, and $M1A$ is forced down from B_s to B_0. Power Darlington on time is fixed by B_0, the initial starting point on the BH loop, and that is determined by the DC current in the control winding N_c.

Because of the winding polarities, there is no net fundamental AC voltage across N_c. Now N_c is bridged between the DC output voltage and a reference voltage as in Fig. 10.15. The polarity of N_c is such that if the DC output voltage goes up, the gate windings are biased further up toward B_s, time to saturate the core decreases and the Darlington on time decreases, bringing the DC output voltage back down.

Thus the control winding serves as the error voltage sensor. It is referenced to output ground and DC current in it serves to control the Darlington on time on input ground by controlling the gate winding's initial (starting) flux density B_0. It is this last feature which is perhaps the most useful characteristic of the circuit. Resistors $R7$, $R8$ serve to set the control winding error-amplifier gain.

In the circuit of Fig. 10.15, the MA cores were of ¼-mil Square Permalloy wound on bobbins of 0.290 in OD, 0.16 in ID, and 0.175 in height. The gate windings—winding 1–3, which linked core A only, and winding 2–3, which linked core B only, consisted of 40 turns of No. 35 wire. The control winding 4–5, which linked both cores, consisted of 250 turns of No. 37 wire.

References

1. C. Mullett, "Design and Analysis Of High Frequency Saturable Core Magnetic Regulators," *Proceedings Powercon 10*, 1983.
2. C. Mullett, "Design of High Frequency Saturable Reactor Output Regulators," *High Frequency Power Conversion Conference Proceedings*, 1986.
3. Toshiba Corp. Bulletin, *Toshiba Amorphous Magnetics Parts*, Mitsui & Co., New York.
4. C. Jamerson, "Calculation of Magnetic Amplifier Post Regulator Voltage Control Loop Parameters," *High Frequency Power Conversion Conference Proceedings*, 1987.
5. Magnetics, Inc. Bulletin TWC 300S, Butler, PA.
6. Allied Signal Technical Bulletin, *Metglas Amorphous Alloy Cores*, Parsippany, NJ.
7. Toshiba Corp. Bulletin, *Toshiba Amorphous Saturable Cores*, Mitsui & Co., New York.
8. Magnetics Inc. Bulletin, *New Magnetic Amplifier Cores and Materials*, Butler, PA.
9. R. Dulskis, J. Estey, and A. Pressman, "A Magnetic Amplifier Controlled 40 kHz Switching Regulator," *Wescon Proceedings*, San Francisco, CA, 1977.
10. R. Taylor, "Optimizing High Frequency Control Magamp Design," *Proceedings Powercon 10*, 1983.
11. R. Hiramatsu, K. Harada, and T. Ninomiya, "Switchmode Converter Using High Frequency Magnetic Amplifier," *International Telecommunications Energy Conference*, 1979.
12. S. Takeda and K. Hasegawa, "Designing Improved Saturable Reactor Regulators with Amorphous Magnetic Materials," *Proceedings Powercon 9*, 1982.
13. R. Hiramatsu and C. Mullett, "Using Saturable Reactor Control in 500 kHz Converter Design," *Proceedings Powercon 10*, 1983.
14. A. Pressman, "Amorphous Magnetic Parts for High Frequency Power Supplies," *APEC Conference 1990* (Toshiba Seminar), Mitsui & Co., New York.
15. C. Jamerson and D. Chen, "Magamp Post Regulators For Symmetrical Topologies with Emphasis on Half Bridge Configuration," *Applied Power Electronics Conference (APEC)*, 1991.

11

Turnon, Turnoff Switching
Losses and Snubbers

11.1 Introduction

In topologies which have a transformer in series with their power
transistor (all except the buck regulator), switching losses due to the
overlap of falling current and rising voltage across the power transistor during the turnoff interval account for most of the losses. The integral $\int I(t)V(t)dt$ over the turnoff interval, which may last anywhere
from 0.2 to 2 μs (for bipolar transistors), generally has a very high
peak value.

Even averaged by the turnoff duty cycle, it can be two to four times as
large as dissipation during the transistor conduction time. This spike of
AC dissipation coming once per period is, of course, a larger fraction of
the total transistor dissipation at higher frequencies. It is one of the
prime limitations to the use of bipolar transistors above 100 kHz.

Circuits to minimize these overlap losses at turnoff are called turnoff snubbers and are the prime subject of discussion in this chapter.

Switching losses at the instant of turnon are considerably smaller
for topologies with a power transformer because of transformer leakage inductance. At the instant of turnon, the large instantaneous impedance of the leakage inductance forces the voltage across the transistor to drop rapidly to zero while the leakage inductance slows up
current rise time.

Thus, throughout most of the current rise time, voltage across the
transistor is close to zero and switching losses due to voltage-current
overlap are negligible.

In the buck regulator (Fig 1.4), however, there are large voltage-
current overlap losses in the transistor at both turnon and turnoff. In
the buck, the power transistor turns on into the negligibly low imped-

ance of the conducting free-wheeling diode $D1$ and the overlap of rising current and falling voltage amounts to a large spike of instantaneous power dissipation. Such turnon losses in the buck transistor and circuits to minimize them (turnon snubbers) have been discussed in Secs. 1.3.4 and 5.6.6.3 to 5.6.6.8.

Switching losses in the buck transistor at turnoff are minimized by the same turnoff snubber circuit usually used in transformer-loaded topologies.

With MOSFETs, turnoff switching losses are considerably less than those with bipolar transistors. Current fall time with a MOSFET is so rapid that current in it will have fallen almost to zero by the time the voltage across it has risen significantly.

Thus, although turnoff snubbers are used with MOSFETs, their prime function is not to reduce overlap dissipation, which is already low. Rather, the function of the MOSFET turnoff snubber is to reduce the amplitude of the leakage inductance voltage spike. Since leakage inductance voltage spikes are proportional to dI/dt in the transistor, a MOSFET with much faster current turnoff time than a bipolar will have a larger voltage leakage spike. Thus, although a MOSFET also requires a turnoff snubber, it is a more benign one and has less drawbacks than does one for a bipolar transistor.

With MOSFETs, there is considerable dissipation at turnon; this is due not to overlap of simultaneous high voltage and current, but to the relatively high MOSFET output capacity C_o. This capacity is charged (usually to twice the supply voltage) and stores an energy $\frac{1}{2}C_o(2V_{dc})^2$ at turnoff. At the subsequent turnon, this energy is dissipated in the MOSFET and results in a dissipation, averaged over a period T, of $\frac{1}{2}C_o(2V_{dc})^2/T$.

Unfortunately, this dissipation is increased by the small, benign snubber the MOSFET requires for minimizing the leakage inductance voltage spike as it adds capacity at the transistor output.

All this will become more obvious after considering the design of the usual RCD (resister, capacitor, diode) turnoff snubber.

11.2 Transistor Turnoff Losses without a Snubber

Consider the elements of a forward converter shown in Fig. 11.1a. The turnoff snubber consists of $R1$, $C1$, $D1$. Assume that its output power is 150 W and it operates from a nominal DC supply voltage of 160 V (maximum 184, minimum 136 V). These are roughly the rectified DC supply voltages for an off-line power supply operating from a nominal 115-V-AC line.

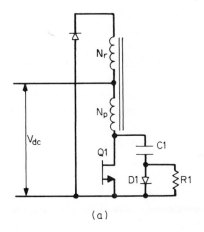

(a)

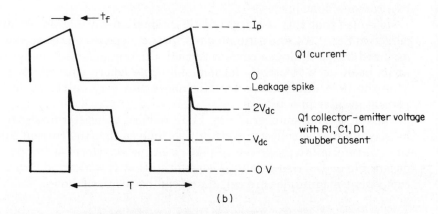

(b)

Figure 11.1 (a) A forward converter with snubber $R1$, $C1$, $D1$. When $Q1$ turns off, collector voltage starts to rise. But immediately $D1$ latches in and $C1$ slows up voltage rise time to minimize the overlap of rising voltage and falling current and thus reduce $Q1$ switching loss. The next time $Q1$ turns off, $C1$ must have lost the $2V_{dc}$ charge it picked up the previous turnoff. It looses that charge in the previous $Q1$ on time. Capacitor $C1$ discharges through $Q1$ and $R1$. (b) With snubber absent, collector voltage rises almost instantaneously; $Q1$ dissipation is $(2V_{dc}I_p/2)(t_f/T)$.

From Eq. 2.28, $Q1$ peak current is $I_p = 3.13P_o/V_{dc} = 3.13 \times 150/136 = 3.45$ A. Assume that $Q1$ is a very fast bipolar transistor such as the third-generation Motorola 2N6836. It has a V_{ceo} rating of 450 V (850 V V_{cev}) and a 15-A collector current rating. Its data sheet shows that collector current fall time from 3.5 A with a 5-V reverse bias is 0.15 μs. This presumably is nominal—assume that the worst case is twice that or 0.3 μs.

Assume that the snubber network $R1$, $C1$, $D1$ is absent. At the instant of turnoff, the collector rises as in any forward converter with equal power and reset winding turns to twice V_{dc}. The force which drives the collector to $2V_{dc}$ is the current that had been stored in the magnetizing inductance and leakage inductances in series. As with any inductor which is carrying a current, when a series switch opens to open that current, the polarity across those inductors reverses and drives the collector toward $2V_{dc}$.

Since collector output capacity is low, assume that this voltage rise is instantaneous. Assuming a maximum V_{dc} of 184 V, the voltage rises instantaneously to 368 V and the current falls linearly from 3.45 A in 0.3 μs as seen in Fig. 11.1b.

This amounts to a dissipation, averaged over the 0.3 μs, of $368 \times 3.45/2 = 635$ W. Further, assuming a 100-kHz switching frequency, power dissipation, averaged over one period, is $635 \times 0.3/10 = 19$ W. This is excessive and would require, in most cases, an unacceptably large heat sink to keep the transistor junction temperature to a reasonable value.

Note also that this is an optimistic dissipation calculation. As discussed in Sec. 1.3.4, the estimated dissipation depends on the scenario assumed in the timing of current turnoff. Current generally hangs on at its peak for a relatively incalculable time before starting to fall. Thus the 19-W dissipation calculated above may very well be about 50 percent greater in actuality.

The $R1$, $C1$, $D1$ snubber of Fig. 11.1a reduces transistor dissipation by slowing up the collector voltage rise time so that the current fall-time waveform intersects the voltage rise-time waveform as low down as feasible on the rising voltage waveform. How it works and how the component magnitudes are calculated can be seen as follows.

11.3 *RCD* Turnoff Snubber Operation

In Fig. 11.1a, when the $Q1$ base receives its turnoff command, the transformer leakage inductance attempts to maintain the peak on current which had been flowing just before the turnoff command. That peak current divides in some way between the off-turning collector and $C1$ through diode $D1$ which has latched in.

The amount of current I_{C1} flowing into $C1$ slows up the collector voltage rise time, and by making $C1$ large enough, the rising collector voltage and falling collector current intersect so low down on the rising collector voltage waveform that transistor dissipation is decreased significantly.

There is a limitation on how large $C1$ can be made, as can be seen in

Fig. 11.2, where it is shown that at the start of any turnoff—say, at
$A1$—$C1$ must have no charge on it. At the end of the turnoff (at B), $C1$
has slowed up the voltage rise time but has accumulated a voltage
$2V_{dc}$ (neglecting for the moment the leakage inductance spike).

At the start of the next turnoff at $A2$, $C1$ must again have no voltage across it. Thus, at some time between B and $A2$, $C1$ must be discharged. It is discharged in the interval C to $A2$ by resistor $R1$. When
$Q1$ turns on at C, the top end of $C1$ goes immediately to ground and $C1$
discharges through $Q1$ and $R1$.

Thus, once $C1$ has been selected large enough to yield a sufficiently
slowed up collector voltage rise time, $R1$ is chosen to discharge $C1$ to
within 5 percent of its full charge in the minimum t_{on}. Or

$$3R1C1 = t_{on(min)} \tag{11.1}$$

But if $C1$ accumulates a voltage $2V_{dc}$ at each turnoff, it stores an energy of $0.5C1(2V_{dc})^2$ joules. If it dissipates that energy in $R1$ during
each on time, power dissipation in $R1$ in watts (for T in seconds) is

$$PD_{R1} = \frac{0.5C1(2V_{dc})^2}{T} \tag{11.2}$$

It will be seen in the following section that power dissipation in $R1$
given by Eq. 11.2 seriously limits how much collector voltage rise time
can be slowed up by increasing $C1$.

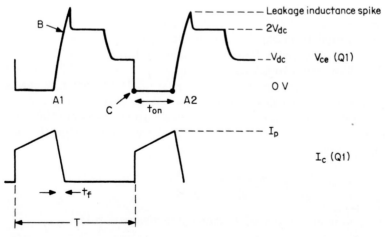

Figure 11.2 Snubber capacitor $C1$ slows up collector voltage rise time from $A1$ to
B at turnoff. At the next turnoff at $A2$, $C1$ must lose the $2V_{dc}$ charge it picked up
at time B. It loses that charge in the on time t_{on} just before a turnoff. With snubber in, $Q1$ dissipation is $(2V_{dc}I_p/12)(t_f/T)$.

11.4   Selection of Capacitor Size in *RCD* Snubber

Equation 11.2 shows that power dissipation in $R1$ is proportional to $C1$. Hence there must be some procedure to select $C1$ large enough to adequately slow up collector voltage rise time and yet not cause excessive dissipation in $R1$.

There is no best way to select $C1$. It is done in different ways by different designers who make different assumptions as to how much of the peak current in $Q1$ is available to charge $C1$, how much the $Q1$ collector voltage rise time is to be slowed up, and how fast the collector current fall time to zero is. The last depends strongly on the turnoff speed of the transistor actually used and the amount of its reverse base drive.

The following has been found to be a satisfactory scheme to select $C1$ for bipolar transistors.

When the $Q1$ base receives its turnoff command, the peak current the collector had been carrying is partly diverted into $C1$ as the voltage across it starts to increase. It is assumed that half the initial peak current I_p is diverted into $C1$ and half remains flowing into the gradually off-turning collector (since the transformer leakage inductance keeps the total current constant at I_p for some time).

Capacitor $C1$ is then selected so that the collector voltage will be permitted to rise to $2V_{dc}$ in the same time t_f that the collector current will fall to zero. This last is read or estimated from data sheets for the specific transistors. Thus

$$C1 = \frac{I_p}{2} \frac{t_f}{2V_{dc}} \qquad (11.3)$$

Now capacitance $C1$ can be calculated from Eq. 11.3, resistance $R1$ can be calculated from Eq. 11.1 from the known minimum on time, and dissipation in resistor $R1$ can be calculated from Eq. 11.2.

Overlap dissipation in $Q1$ can be estimated as in Sec. 1.3.4 on the assumption that during the turnoff interval t_f, $Q1$ current $I_p/2$ starts falling toward zero at the same time its voltage starts rising toward $2V_{dc}$ and that the collector current reaches zero at the same time the collector voltage reaches $2V_{dc}$. In Sec. 1.3.4, it was noted that the collector dissipation during that interval t_f is

$$\frac{I_{max}V_{max}}{6} = \frac{I_p}{2} \frac{2V_{dc}}{6}$$

and averaged over one period T, transistor dissipation is

$$\frac{(I_p/2)(2V_{dc})t_f}{6T} \qquad (11.4)$$

11.5   Design Example—*RCD* Snubber

Design the *RCD* snubber for the forward converter of Sec. 11.2. Recall that the peak current I_p just before turnoff was 3.45 A, transistor fall time was 0.3 µs, and transistor dissipation without a snubber was 19 W. From Eq. 11.3

$$C1 = \frac{(I_p/2)t_f}{2V_{dc}}$$

$$= \frac{(3.45/2)(0.3 \times 10^{-6})}{2 \times 184}$$

$$= 0.0014 \ \mu F$$

and from Eq. 11.1

$$R1 = \frac{t_{on(min)}}{3C1}$$

But recall that a forward converter transformer is designed so that maximum transistor on time is at minimum DC voltage and will be forced to be $0.8T/2$. For a switching frequency of 100 kHz, this is 4 µs. But in Sec. 11.2, maximum and minimum input voltages were 15 percent above and below the nominal value. Then $t_{on(min)}$ is 4/1.3 or 3 µs. Then from Eq. 11.1

$$R1 = \frac{3 \times 10^{-6}}{3 \times 0.0014 \times 10^{-6}}$$

$$= 714 \ \Omega$$

and from Eq. 11.2

$$PD_{R1} = \frac{0.5C1(2V_{dc})^2}{T}$$

$$= \frac{0.5(0.0014 \times 10^{-6})(2 \times 184)^2}{10 \times 10^{-6}}$$

$$= 9.5 \ W$$

and from Eq. 11.4, $Q1$ overlap dissipation is

$$PD_{Q1} = \frac{(I_p/2)(2V_{dc})t_f}{6T}$$

$$= \frac{(3.45/2)(2 \times 184)(0.3 \times 10^{-6})}{6 \times 10 \times 10^{-6}}$$

$$= 3.2 \ W$$

Thus, although 9.5 W has been added in a resistor $R1$, dissipation in the transistor, which is far more failure-prone, has been reduced from 19 to 3.2 W. Actually overlap dissipation in the transistor may be more than the calculated 3.2 W, as a best-case scenario has been assumed for the relative timing of the current fall time and voltage rise time (Sec. 1.3.4).

If temperature measurement on the $Q1$ case indicates that it is running too warm, $C1$ can be increased, but only at the expense of more dissipation in $R1$. But this is far more acceptable than dissipation in $Q1$.

It is sometimes thought that decreasing $R1$ decreases its dissipation. This, of course, is not so, as Eq. 11.2 indicates. Making $R1$ smaller only ensures that $C1$ is totally discharged earlier than needed (earlier than $A2$ in Fig. 11.2). Dissipation is equal to the energy stored on $C1$ (and released through $R1$) per cycle, and energy stored is proportional only to the magnitude of $C1$ and the square of the voltage to which it is charged at turnoff. Dissipation in $R1$ is thus unrelated to its magnitude.

11.5.1 *RCD* snubber returned to positive supply rail

The RCD snubber is often (and preferably) returned to the positive supply rail as shown in Fig. 11.3. It works exactly in the same way as when it is returned to ground as in Fig. 11.1. At turnoff, $D1$ latches in and $C1$ slows up collector voltage rise time with its charging current flowing into V_{dc}. At the following turnon, $C1$ is discharged through $Q1$ and the supply source V_{dc}.

The advantage of returning $R1$, $D1$ to V_{dc} instead of to ground is

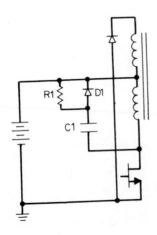

Figure 11.3 When snubber is returned to positive rail, voltage stress on $C1$ is half that when it is returned to ground.

that the maximum voltage stress on $C1$ is now only V_{dc} instead of $2V_{dc}$ when it is returned to ground.

11.6 Nondissipative Snubbers[1-8]

The conventional RCD snubber most often ends up dissipating 10 W or more for off-line switching supplies operating at over 50 kHz. This is troublesome not only for the added dissipation but also because of the size and required location of the snubber resistor. General practice is to derate power resistors by a factor of 2 and thus 10 W of dissipation usually requires the use of a 20-W resistor.

A 20-W resistor is quite large, and finding a location for it is often difficult. Also, in dissipating 10 W, it heats any surrounding nearby components, which further complicates the selection of a satisfactory location for it.

"Dissipationless snubbers," as in Fig. 11.4, although more complex, provide a good solution to this problem. Just as does the conventional RCD dissipative snubber, they use a capacitor to slow up collector voltage rise time. But they do not get rid of the resulting charge on the capacitor by discharging it through a resistor, which would waste power.

Instead, they change the stored electrostatic energy on the capacitor into electromagnetic energy in the form of stored current in an inductor. Then later in time (but before the next cycle when the capacitor must again be discharged), the inductor current is forced to discharge its stored current back into the DC input bus. Thus no energy is wasted—it is first stored on a slow-up capacitor, then returned back with negligible loss to the input bus.

The details can be seen in Fig. 11.4. When $Q1$ turns off, its collector voltage starts rising, $D1$ latches in, and $C1$ slows up the voltage rise time just as in Fig. 11.3. The bottom end of $C1$ is driven up to $2V_{dc}$, and its top end is clamped to V_{dc} through $D1$.

Now when $Q1$ turns on, capacitor $C1$ with a voltage V_{dc} across it is switched across $L1$ and $D2$ in series. An oscillatory current "ring" commences with a frequency $F_r = 1/2\pi\sqrt{L1C1}$.

At the end of a half period of this ring, the electrostatic energy in the form of voltage on $C1$ has been changed into electromagnetic energy in the form of stored current in $L1$. During the next half period of this ring, the voltage at the top end of $L1$ rings positive enough for $D1$ to conduct and the current in $L1$ flows through it back into the supply bus. If $L1$ is a high-Q inductor, all the energy stored in it in the first half cycle of the ring is returned back to V_{dc} in the second half cycle.

Capacitor $C1$ is first chosen large enough to slow up the $Q1$ voltage

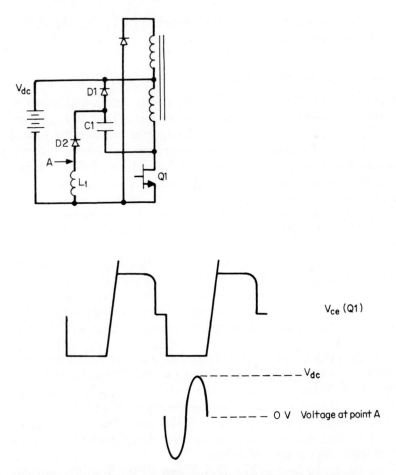

Figure 11.4 A dissipationless snubber. Capacitor $C1$ slows up $Q1$ collector voltage rise time as with RCD snubber. But at $Q1$ turnon, stored energy on $C1$ is transferred to stored magnetic energy in the form of current in $L1$ during the first half cycle of a "ring." During the second half cycle of the ring, point A goes positive and returns this energy to V_{dc} without loss.

rise time as much as required. Then $L1$ is chosen so that the full ring period is somewhat less than the minimum $Q1$ on time.

11.7 Snubber Reduction of Leakage Inductance Spike to Avoid Second Breakdown

The snubber offers a second very important advantage in addition to slowing up voltage rise time and thus decreasing average transistor dissipation. It prevents second breakdown, which occurs if the instantaneous voltage and current cross the reverse-bias safe operating area

(RBSOA) boundary given in the manufacturer's data sheets (Fig. 11.5).

This boundary can be crossed by the omnipresent leakage inductance spike (Fig. 2.10) which occurs at the instant of turnoff. Transistor manufacturers state that if the boundary is crossed even once, second-breakdown failure may occur.

An exact analysis of the sequence of collector voltage changes and their magnitudes at the instant of turnoff is not possible without computer analysis. But the following not-too-exact discussion illustrates the magnitude of the problem and how the snubber capacitor reduces the leakage inductance spike.

When $Q1$ turns off, the transformer leakage inductance keeps the current which had been flowing in it constant for some short time. It was assumed above that, to an approximation, half that current continues to flow into the slowly off-turning transistor and half flows into the snubber capacitor $C1$.

Now in Fig. 11.6, when $Q1$ turns off, the voltage across the magnetizing inductance reverses and this reverses the voltage across the reset winding N_r. The top end of N_r goes immediately negative and is clamped to ground by $D4$. Since $N_p = N_r$, this clamps the voltage across L_m to V_{dc} and the voltage at point A rises to $2V_{dc}$.

But half the original peak current $I_p/2$ flowed into the series combination of the leakage inductance L_l, the snubber capacitor $C1$, and diode $D1$. This causes a sinusoidal ring whose half period is $\pi\sqrt{L_lC_1}$. To a close approximation, the amplitude of the first half cycle is $1/2\pi(\sqrt{L_l/C1})$.

This first half-cycle ring, which is the leakage inductance spike, sits on top of the voltage $2V_{dc}$ at point A. The quantity $\sqrt{L_l/C1}$ is often referred to as the *characteristic impedance* of the LC circuit. Thus increasing $C1$ to slow up collector voltage rise time also decreases the leakage inductance spike.

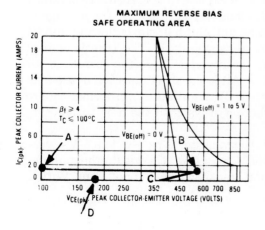

Figure 11.5 Reverse-bias safe operating area (RBSOA) for fast 15 A, 450-V transistor type 2N6836. At turnoff, because leakage inductance in transformer keeps current constant, operation is along A to B at the tip of the leakage inductance spike. If not for the reverse base bias, operation would have crossed the RBSOA boundary and transistor would have failed in second-breakdown mode. The *RCD* snubber, in addition to decreasing overlap dissipation, decreases amplitude of the leakage inductance spike. (*Courtesy Motorola Inc.*)

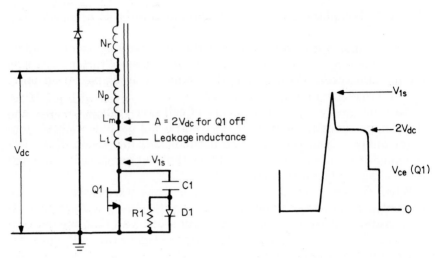

Figure 11.6   The leakage spike is roughly $(I_p/2)(L_1/C1)$ above $2V_{dc}$.

It is of interest to calculate the magnitude of the leakage inductance spike on the basis of these observations. The leakage inductance of a 100-kHz transformer for the design example at the end of Sec. 11.4 is expected to be about 15 μH. Then in the preceding example $\sqrt{L_l/C1} = \sqrt{15 \times 10^{-6}/0.0014 \times 10^{-6}} = 103$ Ω, and for the 3.45-A peak current in $Q1$ just prior to turnoff, the leakage inductance spike amplitude is $(3.45/2)103 = 178$ V. Peak voltage at the top of the leakage inductance spike is then $2V_{dc} + 178 = 547$ V.

Although not too precise an analysis, this yields the amplitude of the leakage inductance spike sufficiently accurately to explain the possibility of second breakdown.

In Fig. 11.5, just prior to turnoff, the location of $Q1$ on its volt-ampere curve is at point A—3.45 A at close to 0 V. As the transistor is turned off, its load-line locus is along the path $ABCD$. The leakage inductance keeps total current constant. But half starts flowing into $C1$, leaving 1.73 flowing into the transistor itself. The transistor itself then moves horizontally along the line AB. At B, the current is still 1.73 A and the voltage is 547 V. After the short duration of the leakage spike, the locus drops down to $2V_{dc}$, until the transformer core resets, and then back to V_{dc}, where it stays until the next turnon (Fig. 2.10.).

Now Fig. 11.5 shows that if the transistor is subject to a 5-V reverse bias at turnoff, the point at 547 V, 1.73 A is still within the manufacturer's RBSOA curve and second breakdown should not occur. With no reverse bias, the transistor is outside the RBSOA curve and second breakdown failure will occur.

Thus, although the initial selection of the snubber capacitor $C1$ (Fig. 11.1) was to slow up collector voltage rise time, it may have to be increased above the value calculated from Eq. 11.3 to reduce the leakage inductance spike. At higher output powers, even with a 5-V reverse base bias at turnoff, the leakage inductance spike may cross the RBSOA curve as the turnoff locus is at a higher current along its horizontal portion. This then would require a larger snubber capacitor.

11.8 Transformer-Aided Snubber

Figure 11.7 shows a scheme which reduces and even totally eliminates the leakage inductance spike for an RCD snubber. It does this without requiring an increase in the snubber capacitor—which would have increased snubber resistor dissipation.

The tradeoff for this is the addition of the very small transformer $T1$. It still requires the conventional RCD snubber, but $C1$ can be considerably less than if the scheme were not used. It works as follows. As shown in Fig. 11.7, $T1$ is a small 1/1 transformer. Its core area and number of turns must be such as to sustain the maximum volt-second product across the $T2$ primary when $Q1$ is off. Since the core size should be as small as possible, this means a small core area and hence a relatively large number of turns. But since the power which $T1$ will be carrying will be quite small, primary and secondary wire size can be small, thus permitting a small core.

Note the dot polarity on the $T1$ primary and secondary. Diode $D1$ does not conduct until the dot end of N_s reaches V_{dc}, and it does not reach V_{dc} until the voltage across the $T1$ primary rises to V_{dc} with its

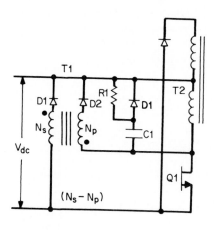

Figure 11.7 A leakage spike clipping aid to an RCD snubber. Transformer $T1$ is a small 1/1 transformer. When $Q1$ collector voltage reaches $2V_{dc}$, $D2$ latches in, forcing $D1$ to latch in and clamp $V_{ce(Q1)}$ to $2V_{dc}$. Thus no leakage spike at the $Q1$ collector above $2V_{dc}$ if $T1$ has very little leakage inductance. This minimizes the size of $C1$.

dot end positive with respect to its no-dot end. But that occurs only when the $Q1$ collector reaches $2V_{dc}$.

Thus, when the $Q1$ collector reaches $2V_{dc}$, $D1$ latches in and clamps the voltage across N_s to V_{dc}. Since the transformer turns ratio is 1/1, the collector voltage is clamped at $2V_{dc}$—i.e., no leakage spike at the collector above $2V_{dc}$. For this to be very effective, the leakage inductance of $T1$ itself must be very small.

When $D1$ has latched in and conducts, the energy stored in the $T2$ leakage inductance is returned with no loss to the V_{dc} supply bus.

References

1. E. Whitcomb, "Designing Non-Dissipative Current Snubbers for Switched Mode Converters," *Proceedings Powercon 6,* 1979.
2. W. Shaunessy, "Modeling and Design of Non-Dissipative *LC* Snubber Networks," *Proceedings Powercon 7,* 1980.
3. L. Meares, "Improved Non-Dissipative Snubbers for Buck Regulators and Current Fed Inverters," *Proceedings Powercon 9,* 1982.
4. M. Domb, R. Redl, and N. Sokal, "Non-Dissipative Turn Off Snubber Alleviates Switching Power Dissipation, Second Breakdown Stress," *PESC Record,* 1982.
5. T. Ninomiya, T. Tanaka, and K. Harada, "Optimum Design of Non-Dissipative Snubber by Evaluation of Transistor's Switching Loss," *PESC Record,* 1985.
6. T. Tanaka, T. Ninomiya, and K. Harada, "Design of a Non Dissipative Snubber in a Forward Converter," *PESC Record,* 1988.

Feedback-Loop Stabilization

12.1 Introduction

Before going into the details of stabilizing a feedback loop, it is of interest to consider in a semiquantitative way, why a feedback loop may oscillate.

Consider the negative-feedback loop for a typical forward converter in Fig. 12.1. The essential error-amplifier and PWM functions are contained in all pulse-width-modulating chip. The chip also provide many other functions, but for understanding the stability problem, only the error amplifier and pulse-width modulator need be considered.

For slow or DC variations of the output voltage V_o, the loop is, of course, stable. A small, slow variation of V_o due to either line input or load changes will be sensed by the inverting input of error amplifier EA via the sampling network $R1$, $R2$ and compared to a reference voltage at the noninverting EA input. This will cause a small change in the DC voltage level V_{ea} at the EA output and at the A input to the pulse-width-modulator PWM.

The PWM, as described heretofore, compares that DC voltage level to a roughly 0- to 3-V triangle V_t at its B input. It generates a rectangular pulse whose width t_{on} is equal to the time from the start of the triangle t_0 until t_1, the time the triangle crosses the DC voltage level at the B input of the PWM. That pulse fixes the on time of the output transistor of the chip and should also fix the on time of the power transistor.

Thus a slow increase (e.g.) in V_{dc} causes a slow increase in V_y and hence a slow increase in V_o since $V_o \cong V_y t_{on}/T$. The increase in V_o causes an increase in V_s and hence a decrease in V_{ea}. Since t_{on} is the time from the start of the triangle to t_1, this causes a decrease in t_{on} and restores V_o to its original value. Similarly, of course, a decrease in V_{dc} causes an increase in t_{on} to maintain V_o constant.

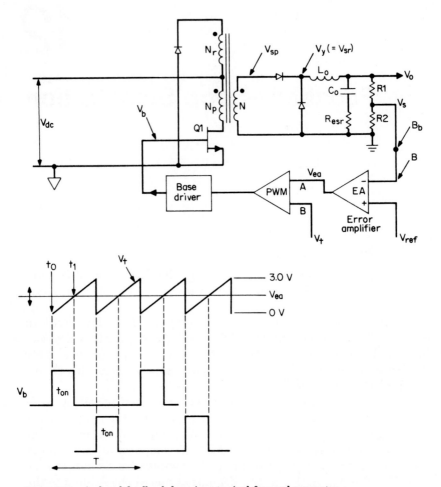

Figure 12.1 A closed feedback loop in a typical forward converter.

Drive to the power transistor may be taken from either the emitter or the collector of the chip's output transistor via a current-amplifying base driver. But from whichever point—emitter or collector—output is taken, it must be ensured that polarities are such that an increase in V_o causes a decrease in t_{on}.

Note that most PWM chips have their output transistors on for the time from t_0 to t_1. With such chips, V_s is fed to the inverting EA input and for an NPN power transistor, its base (or gate if a MOSFET) is driven from the emitter of the chip's output transistor.

In some PWM chips (TL494 family), however, the output transistor is on from the time the triangle at the V_t input to the PWM crosses the V_{ea} level (t_1) until the end of the triangle at t_2. With such chips, if the

NPN power transistor were to be turned on when the chip output transistor was on (drive from the chip transistor's emitter), that would cause the power transistor on time to increase as V_{dc} increased. This, of course, would be positive rather than negative feedback.

Thus, with chips of the TL494 family, V_s is fed to the noninverting input to the EA. This causes the output transistor on time to decrease as V_o increases and permits the power transistor to be driven from the chip transistor's emitter.

The circuit in Fig. 12.1 thus provides negative feedback and a stable circuit at low frequencies. But within the loop, there exist low-level noise voltages or possible voltage transients which have a continuous spectrum of sinusoidal Fourier components. All these Fourier components suffer gain changes and phase shifts in the L_o, C_o output filter, the error amplifier, and the PWM from V_{ea} to V_{sr}. At one of these Fourier components, the gain and phase shifts can result in positive rather than negative feedback and thereby result in oscillation as described below.

12.2   Mechanism of Loop Oscillation

Consider the forward converter feedback loop of Fig. 12.1. Assume for a moment that the loop is broken open at point B, the inverting input to the error amplifier. At any of the Fourier components of the noise, there is gain and phase shift from B to V_{ea}, from V_{ea} to the average voltage at V_{sr}, and from the average voltage at V_{sr} through the L_o, C_o filter around back to B_b (just before the loop break).

Now assume that a signal of some frequency f_1 is injected into the loop at B and comes back around as an echo at B_b. The echo is modified in phase and gain by all the previously mentioned elements in the loop. If the modified echo has returned exactly in phase with and is equal in amplitude to the signal which started the echo, if the loop is now closed (B_b closed to B) and the injected signal is removed, the circuit will continue to oscillate at the frequency f_1. The initial signal which starts the echo and maintains the oscillation is the f_1 Fourier component in the noise spectrum.

12.2.1   Gain criterion for a stable circuit

Thus the first criterion for a stable loop is that at the frequency where the total open-loop gain is unity (the *crossover frequency*), the total open-loop phase shift of all elements involved must be less than 360°. The amount by which the total phase shift is less than 360° (at the frequency where the total open-loop gain is unity) is called the *phase margin*.

To ensure a stable loop under worst-case tolerances of the associated components, the usual practice is to design for at least a 35° to 45° phase margin with nominal components.

12.2.2 Gain slope criteria for a stable circuit

At this point, a universally used jargon expression describing the gain slope is introduced. Gain versus frequency is usually plotted in decibels (dB) on semilog paper as in Fig. 12.2. If the scales are such that a linear distance of 20 dB (numerical gain of 10) is equal to the linear distance of a factor of 10 in frequency, lines representing gain variations of ± 20 dB/decade have slopes of ± 1. Circuit configurations having a gain variation of ± 20 dB per decade are thus described as having " ± 1 gain slopes."

An elementary circuit having a gain slope of -1 (beyond the frequency $f_p = 1/2\pi R1C1$) between output and input is the RC integrator of Fig. 12.2a. The RC differentiator of Fig. 12.2b has a $+1$ gain slope (below the frequency $f_z = 1/2\pi R2C2$) or a gain variation of $+20$ dB/decade between output and input. Such circuits have only 20 dB/decade gain variations because as frequency increases or decreases by a factor of 10, the capacitor impedance decreases or increases by a factor of 10 but the resistor impedance remains constant.

A circuit which has a -2 or -40 dB/decade gain slope (beyond the frequency $F_o = 1/2\pi\sqrt{L_oC_o}$) is the output LC filter (Fig. 12.2c), which has no resistance (ESR) in its output capacitor. This, of course, is because as frequency increases by a factor of 10, the inductor impedance increases and the capacitor impedance decreases by a factor of 10.

Now gain and phase shift versus frequency for an L_oC_o filter are plotted in Fig. 12.3a and 12.3b for various values of output resistance $R_o{}^2$. The gain curves are normalized for various ratios of $k_1 = f/F_o$ where $F_o = 1/2\pi\sqrt{L_oC_o}$ and for various ratios $k_2 = R_o/\sqrt{L_o/C_o}$.

Figure 12.3a shows that whatever the value of k_2, all gain curves, beyond the so-called corner frequency of $F_o = 1/2\pi\sqrt{L_oC_o}$ asymptotically approach a slope of -2 (-40 dB/decade). The circuit for $k_2 = 1.0$ is referred to as the *critically damped* circuit. The critically damped circuit has a very small resonant "bump" in gain and at the corner frequency F_o, starts immediately falling at a -2 slope.

For k_2 greater than 1 the circuit is described as *underdamped*. It is seen that underdamped LC filters can have a very large resonant bump in gain at F_o.

Circuits of k_2 less than 1.0 are *overdamped*. It is seen in Fig. 12.3a that overdamped LC filters also asymptotically approach a gain slope of -2. But for a heavily overdamped ($k_2 = 0.1$) filter, the frequency at

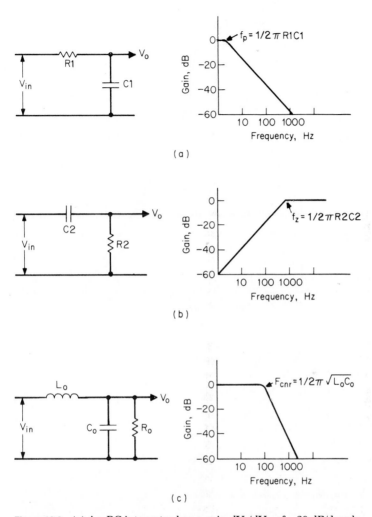

Figure 12.2 (a) An RC integrator has a gain dV_o/dV_{in} of -20 dB/decade beyond $F_p = \frac{1}{2}\pi R1C1$. If the scales are such that 20 dB is the same linear distance as 1 decade in frequency, a gain slope of -20 dB/decade has a -1 slope. Such a circuit is referred to as a -1 *slope* circuit. (b) An RC differentiator has a gain of $+20$ dB/decade. At $F_z = 1/2\pi R2C2$, where $X_{C2} = R_2$, gain asymptotically approaches 0 dB. If scales are such that 20 dB is the same linear distance as 1 decade in frequency, a gain slope of $+20$ dB/decade has a $+1$ slope. Such a circuit is referred to as a $+1$ *slope* circuit. (c) An LC filter has a gain (dV_o/dV_{in}) of unity (0 dB) up to its corner frequency of $F_{cnr} = 1/2\pi\sqrt{L_oC_o}$ when critically damped ($R_o = \sqrt{L_o/C_o}$). Beyond F_{cnr} it commences falling at a rate of -40 dB/decade. This is so because for every decade increase in frequency, X_L increased and X_c decreases in impedance by a factor of 10. If scales are such that 20 dB is the same linear distance as 1 decade in frequency, a gain slope of -40 dB/decade has a -2 slope. Such a circuit is referred to as a -2 *slope* circuit.

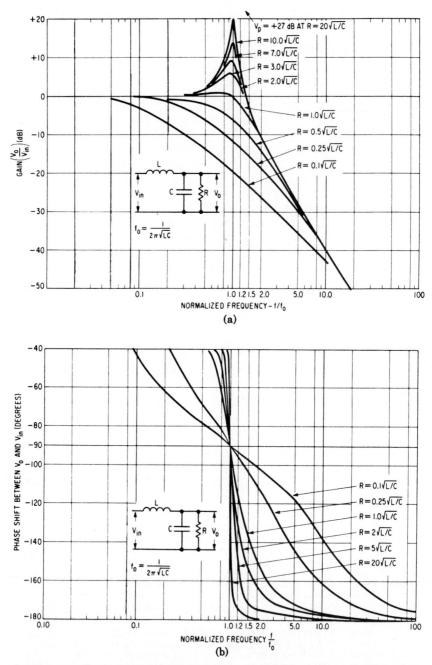

Figure 12.3 (*a*) Gain versus frequency for switching regulator *LC* filter. (*b*) Phase shift versus frequency for switching regulator *LC* filter. (*Courtesy Switchtronix Press*).

which the gain slope has come close to -2 is about 20 times the corner frequency F_o.

Figure 12.3b shows phase shift versus normalized frequency (f/F_o) again for various ratios of $k_2 = R_o/\sqrt{L_o/C_o}$. It is seen for any value of k_2, that the phase shift between output and input is 90° at the corner frequency $(F_o = 1/2\pi\sqrt{L_oC_o})$. And for highly underdamped filters $(R_o$ greater than $\sim 5\sqrt{L_o/C_o})$, phase shift varies very rapidly with frequency. The shift is already 170° at a frequency of 1.5F_o for $R_o = 5\sqrt{L_o/C_o}$.

In contrast, a circuit with a -1 gain slope can never yield more than a 90° phase shift, and its rate of change of phase shift with frequency is far slower than that of a circuit -2 gain slope as exemplified in Fig. 12.3b.

This leads to the second criterion for a stable circuit. The first criterion was that the total phase shift at the crossover frequency (frequency where total open-loop gain is unity or 0 dB) should be short of 360° by the "phase margin," which is usually taken as at least 45°.

This second criterion for a stable circuit is that to prevent rapid changes of phase shift with frequency characteristic of a circuit with a -2 gain slope, the slope of the open-loop gain–frequency curve of the entire circuit (arithmetic sum in decibels of all the gain elements involved) as it passes through crossover frequency should be -1. This is shown in Fig. 12.4.

It is not an absolute requirement that the total open-loop gain curve must come through crossover at a -1 gain slope. But it does provide insurance that if any phase-shift elements have been overlooked, the small phase shift and relatively slow phase-shift–frequency curve characteristic of a -1 gain slope element will still preserve an adequate phase margin.

The third criterion for a stable loop is to provide the desired phase margin, which will be set at 45° herein (Fig. 12.4).

To satisfy all three criteria, it is necessary to know how to calculate gains and phase shifts of all the elements in Fig. 12.1. This is shown below.

12.2.3 Gain characteristic of *LC* output filter with and without equivalent series resistance (ESR) in output capacitor

Aside from the flyback (which has an output capacitor filter only), all topologies discussed herein have an output *LC* filter.[1] The gain-versus-frequency characteristic of this output *LC* filter is of fundamental importance. It must be calculated first as it determines how the gain and phase shift-versus-frequency characteristics of the error amplifier must be shaped to satisfy the three criteria for a stable loop.

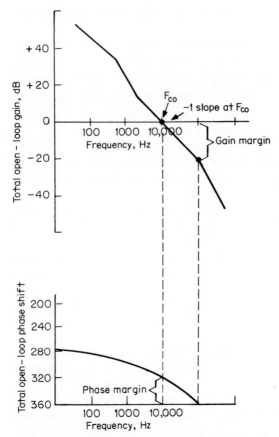

Figure 12.4 Total open-loop gain and phase shift. The frequency at which the total open-loop gain is 0 dB (F_{co}) is forced to be 0 dB is usually chosen one-fourth and one-fifth the switching frequency. For loop to be stable, total open-loop phase shift at F_{co} should be short of 360° by as large a value as possible. The amount by which it is short of 360° is the *phase margin*. A usual phase margin to strive for is 45°. A second criterion for a stable loop is that the total open-loop gain pass through F_{co} at a −1 slope.

The gain characteristic of an output LC filter with various output load resistances is shown in Fig. 12.3*a*. This curve assumes that the output capacitor has zero equivalent series resistance (ESR). For the purpose of this discussion, it is sufficiently accurate to assume that the filter is critically damped, that is, $R_o = 1.0\sqrt{L_o/C_o}$. If the circuit is made stable for the gain curve corresponding to $R_o = 1.0\sqrt{L_o/C_o}$, it will be stable at other loads. Nevertheless, the circuit merits examination for light loads ($R_o \gg 1.0\sqrt{L_o/C_o}$) because of the resonant bump in gain at the LC corner frequency $F_o = 1/2\pi\sqrt{L_oC_o}$. This will be considered below.

Thus the gain characteristic of the output LC filter with zero ESR will be drawn as curve 12345 in Fig. 12.5a. There it is seen that the gain is 0 dB (numerical gain of 1) at DC and low frequencies up to the

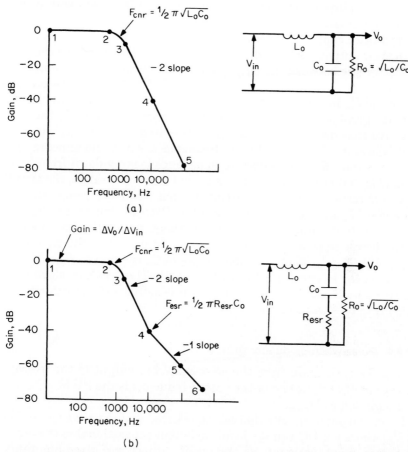

Figure 12.5 (a) Gain versus frequency for a critically damped LC filter in which the output capacitor has zero ESR. (b) Gain versus frequency for a critically damped LC filter in which the output capacitor has an equivalent series resistor (R_{esr}). When C_o has an ESR, the gain slope still breaks from horizontal to a -2 slope at F_{cnr}. But at a frequency $F_{esr} = 1/2\pi(R_{esr}C_o)$, it breaks into a -1 slope. This is because at F_{esr}, $X_{co} = R_{esr}$, the impedance of C_o becomes increasingly small compared to R_{esr}. The circuit is now an LR rather than an LC circuit. An LR circuit falls at a -1 slope because as frequency increases, the impedance of the series L increases, but that of the shunt R remains constant.

corner frequency $F_o = 1/2\pi\sqrt{L_oC_o}$. At DC and frequencies less than F_o, the impedance of C_o is much greater than that of L_o and the output-input gain is unity.

Beyond F_o, the impedance of C_o decreases and that of L_o increases at the rate of 20 dB/decade, making the gain slope fall at the rate of -40 dB/decade or at a -2 slope. Of course, the transition to a -2 slope at F_o is not as abrupt as shown. The actual gain curve leaves 0 dB smoothly just before F_o and asymptotically approaches the -2 slope shortly after F_o. But for the purposes of this discussion, gain will be shown with a relatively abrupt transition as curve 12345 in Fig. 12.5a.

Most filter capacitor types have an internal resistance R_{esr} in series with their output leads as shown in Fig. 12.5b. This modifies the gain characteristic between the output and input terminals in a characteristic way.

Beyond F_o, in the lower frequency range where the impedance of C_o is much greater than R_{esr}, looking down to ground from V_o, the only effective impedance is that of C_o. In this frequency range, the gain still falls at a -2 slope. At higher frequencies, where the impedance of C_o is less than R_{esr}, the effective impedance looking down from V_o to ground is that of R_{esr} alone. Hence in that frequency range, the circuit is an LR rather than an LC circuit. In that frequency range, the impedance of L_o increases at the rate of 20 dB/decade but that of R_{esr} remains constant. Thus in that frequency range, gain falls at a -1 slope.

The break from a -2 to a -1 gain slope occurs at the frequency $F_{esr} = 1/2\pi R_{esr}C_o$, where the impedance of C_o is equal to R_{esr}. This is shown as G_{lc} in curve 123456 in Fig. 12.5b. The break in slope from -2 to -1 is, of course, asymptotic, but it is sufficiently accurate to assume it to be abrupt as shown.

12.2.4 Pulse-width-modulator gain

In Fig. 12.1, the gain from the error-amplifier output to the average voltage at V_{sr} (input end of the output inductor) is the PWM gain and is designated as G_{pwm}.

It may be puzzling how this can be referred to as a *voltage gain*. For at V_{ea}, there are DC voltage level variations proportional to the error-amplifier input at point B, and at V_{sr}, there are fixed-amplitude pulses of adjustable width.

The significance and magnitude of this gain can be seen as follows. In Fig. 12.1, the PWM compares the DC voltage level from V_{ea} to a 3-V triangle at V_t. In all PWM chips which produce two 180° out-of-phase adjustable-width pulses (for driving push-pulls, half or full bridges) these pulses occur once per triangle and have a maximum on or high time of a half period. After the PWM, the pulses are binary-counted and alternately routed to two separate output terminals (see Fig. 5.2a). In a forward converter, only one of these outputs is used.

Now (Fig. 12.1b), when V_{ea} is at the bottom of the 3-V triangle, on time or pulse width at V_{sr} is zero. The average voltage V_{av} at V_{sr} is then zero as $V_{av} = (V_{sp} - 1)(t_{on}/T)$, where V_{sp} is the secondary peak voltage. When V_{ea} has moved up to the top of the 3-V triangle, $t_{on}/T = 0.5$ and $V_{av} = 0.5\ (V_{sp} - 1)$. The modulator DC gain G_m, then, between V_{av} and V_{ea} is

$$G_m = \frac{0.5(V_{sp} - 1)}{3} \qquad (12.1)$$

This gain is independent of frequency.

There is also a loss G_s due to the sampling network R_1, R_2 in Fig. 12.1. Most of the frequently used PWM chips cannot tolerate more than 2.5 V at the reference input to the error amplifier (point A). Thus, when sampling a +5-V output, $R_1 = R_2$ and gain G_s between V_s and V_o in Fig. 12.1 is -6 dB.

12.2.5 Total output *LC* filter plus modulator and sampling network gain

From the above, the total gain G_t (in decibels) of the output *LC* filter gain G_f plus modulator gain G_m plus sampling network gain G_s is plotted as in Fig. 12.6. It is equal to $G_m + G_s$ from DC up to $F_o = 1/2\pi \sqrt{L_o C_o}$. At F_o, it breaks into a -2 slope and remains at that slope up to the frequency F_{esr} where the impedance of C_o equals R_{esr}. At that frequency, it breaks into a -1 slope.

From this curve, the error-amplifier gain and phase-shift-versus-frequency characteristic is established to meet the three criteria for a stable loop as described below.

12.3 Shaping Error-Amplifier Gain-Versus-Frequency Characteristic

Recall that the first criterion for a stable loop is that at the frequency F_{co} where the total open-loop gain is unity (0 dB), total open-loop phase shift must be short of 360° by the desired *phase margin,* which will herein be taken as 45°.

The sequence of steps is then first to establish the crossover frequency F_{co}, where the total open-loop gain should be 0 dB. Then choose the error-amplifier gain so that the total open-loop gain is forced to be 0 dB at that frequency. Next design the error-amplifier gain slope so that the total open-loop gain comes through F_{co} at a -1 slope (Fig. 12.4). Finally, tailor the error-amplifier gain versus frequency so that the desired phase margin is achieved.

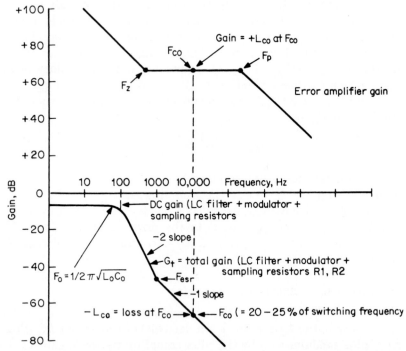

Figure 12.6 Gain G_t = sum of (LC filter + modulator + output voltage sampling resistors) gains determines error-amplifier gain. Error-amplifier gain at F_{co} is made
equal and opposite to loss of G_t. Error-amplifier gain slope at F_{co} is made horizontal
with upward and downward breaks at F_z and F_p. Location of F_z and F_p in frequency
determines total circuit phase margin.

Sampling theory shows that F_{co} must be less than half the switching
frequency for the loop to be stable. But it must be considerably less
than that, or there will be large-amplitude switching frequency ripple
at the output. Thus, the usual practice is to fix F_{co} at one-fourth to
one-fifth the switching frequency.

Thus, refer to Fig. 12.6, which is the open-loop gain of the LC filter
plus the PWM modulator plus the sampling network. The capacitor in
the output filter is assumed in Fig. 12.6 to have an ESR which causes
a break in the slope from -2 to -1 at $F_{esr} = 1/2\pi R_{esr}C_o$. Assume that
F_{co} is one-fifth the switching frequency and read the loss in decibels at
that point.

In most cases, the output capacitor will have an ESR and F_{esr} will
come at a lower frequency than F_{co}. Thus at F_{co} the $G_1 = (G_{lc} +
G_{pwm} + G_s)$ curve will already have a -1 slope.

Now when gains are plotted in decibels, both gains and gain slopes
of gain elements in cascade are additive. Hence, to force crossover frequency to be at the desired one-fifth the switching frequency, choose

the error-amplifier gain at F_{co} to be equal and opposite in decibels to the $G_t = (G_{lc} + G_{pwm} + G_s)$ loss at that frequency.

That forces F_{co} to occur at the desired point. Then, if the error-amplifier gain slope at F_{co} is horizontal, since the G_t curve at F_{co} already has a -1 slope, the sum of the error amplifier plus the G_t curve comes through crossover frequency at the desired -1 slope and the second criterion for a stable loop has been met.

Now the error-amplifier gain has been fixed as equal and opposite to the G_t loss at F_{co} and to have a horizontal slope as it passes through F_{co} (Fig. 12.6). Such a gain characteristic can be achieved with an operational amplifier with a resistor input and resistor feedback as in Fig. 12.7a. Recall that the gain of such an operational amplifier is $G_{ea} = Z2/Z1 = R2/R1$. But how far in frequency to the left and right of F_{co} should it continue to have this constant gain?

Recall that the total open-loop gain is the sum of the error-amplifier gain plus G_1 gain. If the error-amplifier gain remained constant down to DC, the total open-loop gain would not be very large at 120 Hz—the frequency of the AC power line ripple.

Yet it is desired to keep power line ripple attenuated down to a very low level at the output. To degenerate the 120-Hz ripple sufficiently, the open-loop gain at that frequency should be as high as possible. Thus at some frequency to the left of F_{co}, the error-amplifier gain should be permitted to increase rapidly.

This can be done by placing a capacitor $C1$ in series with $R2$ (Fig. 12.7b). This yields the low-frequency gain characteristic shown in Fig. 12.6. In the frequency range where the impedance of $C1$ is small compared to $R2$, the gain is horizontal and simply equal to $R2/R1$. At

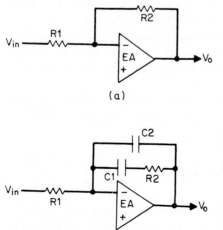

(a)

(b)

Figure 12.7 (a) Error amplifier with resistor feedback $R2$ and resistor input $R1$ arms have a gain equal to $R2/R1$ which is independent of frequency up to the frequency where the open-loop error amplifier inside the loop (EA) commences falling off the gain. (b) Using complex feedback and input arms permits shaping the gain-versus-frequency and phase-shift-versus-frequency curves. The configuration above has the gain-versus-frequency characteristic of Fig. 12.6.

lower frequencies where the impedance of C2 is much higher than $R2$, effectively $R2$ is out of the circuit and the gain is X_{c1}/R_1. This gain increases at the rate of +20 dB/decade (+ 1 slope) toward lower frequencies and yields the higher gain at 120 Hz. Going in the direction of higher frequency, the −1 gain slope breaks and becomes horizontal at a frequency of $F_z = 1/2\pi R2C1$.

Now going to the right of F_{co} toward higher frequency (Fig. 12.6), if the error-amplifier gain curve were permitted to remain horizontal, total open-loop gain would remain relatively high at the high frequencies. But high gain at high frequencies is undesirable as thin, high-frequency noise spikes would be picked up and transmitted at large amplitudes to the output. Thus gain should be permitted to fall off at high frequencies.

This is easily done by placing a capacitor C2 across the series combination of $R2$ and $C1$ (Fig. 12.7b). At F_{co}, X_{c1} is already small compared to $R2$ and $C1$ is effectively out of the circuit.

At higher frequencies where X_{c2} is small compared to $R2$, however, $R2$ is effectively out of the circuit and gain is X_{c2}/R_1. Now the gain characteristic beyond F_{co} is horizontal up to a frequency F_p ($=1/2\pi R2C2$), where it breaks and thereafter falls at a −1 slope as can be seen in Fig. 12.6. This lower gain at high frequency keeps high-frequency noise spikes from coming through to the output.

Now the break frequencies F_z and F_p must be chosen. They will be chosen so that $F_{co}/F_z = F_p/F_{co}$. The farther apart F_z and F_p are, the greater the phase margin at F_{co}. Large phase margins are desirable, but if F_z is chosen too low, low-frequency gain will be lower at 120 Hz than if a higher frequency were chosen (Fig. 12.8). Thus 120-Hz attenuation will be poorer. If F_p is chosen too high, gain at high frequencies is higher than if a lower F_p is chosen (Fig. 12.8). Thus high-frequency noise spikes would come through at a higher amplitude.

Thus a compromise between separating F_z and F_p by a large amount to increase phase margin and decreasing the separation to achieve better 120-Hz attenuation and lower-amplitude high-frequency noise spikes is sought.

This compromise and a more exact analysis of the problem is made easy by introducing the concept of transfer functions, poles, and zeros as shown below.

12.4   Error-Amplifier Transfer Function, Poles, and Zeros

The circuit of an operational amplifier with a complex impedance Z_1 input arm and a complex impedance Z_2 feedback arm is shown in Fig. 12.9. Its gain is Z_2/Z_1. If Z_1 is a pure resistor $R1$ and Z_2 is a pure re-

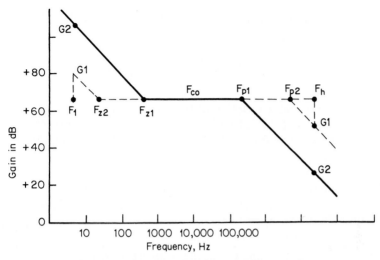

Figure 12.8 Where to locate break frequencies F_z and F_p. The farther apart F_z and F_p are spread, the greater the phase margin. But spreading them further apart reduces low-frequency gain, which reduces the degeneration of low-frequency line ripple. It also increases high gain, which permits high-frequency, thin noise spikes to come through at greater amplitude. If F_z were at F_{z2} instead of F_{z1}, gain at some low frequency F_1 would be G_1 instead G_2. And if F_p were at F_{p2} instead of F_{p1}, gain at some high frequency F_h would be G_1 instead of G_2.

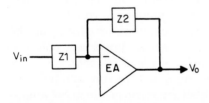

Figure 12.9 If inputs and feedback arms are various combinations of Rs and Cs, various gain-versus-frequency and phase-shift-versus-frequency curves are possible. By expressing impedances Z_1 and Z_2 in terms of an s operator ($= jw$), and performing a number of algebraic manipulations, a simplified expression for the gain arises. From this simplified gain expression (transfer function) the gain-versus-frequency and phase-shift-versus-frequency curves can be drawn at a glance.

sistor $R2$ as in Fig. 12.7a, gain is R_2/R_1 and is independent of frequency. Phase shift between V_o and V_{in} is 180°, as the input is to the inverting terminal.

Now impedances in Z_1, Z_2 are expressed in terms of the complex variable $s = j(2\pi f) = jw$. Thus the impedance of a capacitor $C1$ is then $1/sC1$ and that of a resistor $R1$ and capacitor $C1$ in series is $(R1 + 1/sC1)$.

The impedance of an arm consisting of a capacitor $C2$ in parallel with a series combination of $R1$ and $C1$ is then

$$Z = \frac{(r + 1/sC1)(1/sC2)}{r + 1/sC1 + 1/sC2} \qquad (12.2)$$

Now the gain or transfer function of the operational error amplifier is written in terms of its Z_1, Z_2 impedances, which are expressed in terms of the complex variable s. Thus $G(s) = Z_2(s)/Z_1(s)$, and by algebraic manipulation, $G(s)$ is broken down into a simplified numerator and denominator which are functions of s: $G(s) = N(s)/D(s)$. The numerator and denominator, again by algebraic manipulation, are factored and $N(s)$, $G(s)$ are expressed in terms of these factors. Thus

$$G(s) = \frac{N(s)}{D(s)} = \frac{(1 + sz_1)(1 + sz_2)(1 + sz_3)}{sp_0(1 + sp_1)(1 + sp_2)(1 + sp_3)} \qquad (12.3)$$

These z and p values are RC products and represent frequencies. These frequencies are obtained by setting the factors equal to zero. Thus

$$1 + sz_1 = 1 + s(j\,2\pi f z_1) = 1 + j\,2\pi f R1C1 = 0 \qquad \text{or} \qquad f_1 = 1/2\pi R1C1$$

The frequencies corresponding to the z values are called *zero* frequencies, and those corresponding to the p values are called *pole* frequencies. There is always a factor in the denominator which has the "1" missing (note sp_0 above). This represents an important pole frequency, $F_{po} = 1/2\pi R_o C_o$, which is called *the pole at the origin*.

From the location of the pole at the origin and the zero and pole frequencies, the gain-versus-frequency characteristic of the error amplifier can be drawn as discussed below.

12.5 Rules for Gain Slope Changes Due to Zero and Pole Frequencies

The zero and pole frequencies represent points where the error-amplifier gain slope changes.

A zero represents a $+1$ change in gain slope. Thus (Fig. 12.10a), if a zero appears at a point in frequency where the gain slope is zero, it turns the gain into a $+1$ slope. If it appears where the original gain slope is -1 (Fig. 12.10b), it turns the gain slope to zero. Or if there are two zeros at the same frequency (two factors in the numerator of Eq. 12.3 having the same RC product) where the original gain slope is -1,

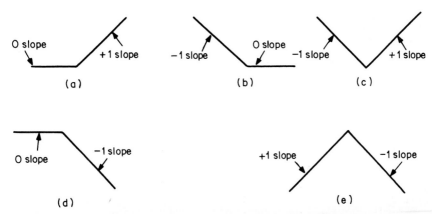

Figure 12.10 (*a*) A zero appearing on a gain curve where the original slope was horizontal turns that gain slope to +1 or +20 dB/decade. (*b*) A zero appearing on a gain curve where the original slope was −1, terms that gain slope horizontal. (*c*) Two zeros at the same frequency appearing on a gain curve where the original slope was −1, turns that slope to +1. The first zero turns the −1 slope horizontal; the second zero at the same frequency turns the horizontal slope to +1. (*d*) A pole appearing on a gain curve where the original slope is horizontal turns that slope to −1 or 20 dB/decade. (*e*) Two poles at the same frequency appearing on a gain curve where the original slope is +1 turns that slope to −1. The first pole turns the original +1 slope horizontal; the second one at the same frequency turns the horizontal slope to −1 or −20 dB/decade.

the first zero turns the gain slope horizontal, and the second zero at the same frequency turns the gain into a +1 slope (Fig. 12.10*c*).

A pole represents a −1 change in gain slope. If it appears in frequency where the original gain slope is horizontal (slope is zero), it turns the gain into a −1 slope (Fig. 12.10*d*). Or if there are two poles at the same frequency at a point where the original gain slope is +1, the first pole turns the slope horizontal and the second at that same frequency turns the slope to −1 (Fig. 12.10*e*).

The pole at the origin, as does any pole, represents a gain slope of −1. It also indicates the frequency at which the gain is 1 or 0 dB. Thus, drawing the total gain curve for the error amplifier starts with the pole at the origin as follows. Go to 0 dB at the frequency of the pole at the origin $F_{po} = 1/2\pi R_o C_o$. At F_{po}, draw a line backward in frequency with a slope of +1 (Fig. 12.11). Now if somewhere on this line, which has a −1 slope in the direction of higher frequency, the transfer function has a zero at a frequency $F_z = 1/2\pi R1C1$, turn the gain slope horizontal at F_z. Extend the horizontal gain indefinitely. But if at some higher frequency there is a pole in the transfer function at a frequency $F_p = 1/2\pi R2C2$, turn the horizontal slope into a −1 slope at F_p (Fig. 12.11).

The gain along the horizontal part of the transfer function is $R2/R1$

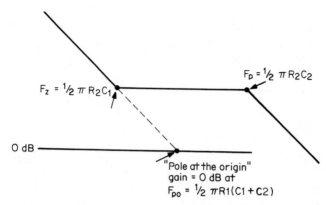

Figure 12.11   Drawing the gain curve of the error amplifier of Fig. 12.7b directly from its transfer function of Eq. 12.3.

and is made (in decibels) equal and opposite to the loss of the G_t curve (Fig. 12.6) at F_{co}.

Thus an error-amplifier gain curve having a single pole at the origin, a single zero, and another single pole has the desired shape shown in Fig. 12.11. It is implemented by the circuit of Fig. 12.7b. It remains only to select the location of the zero and pole frequencies which yield the desired phase margin. This will be discussed below.

12.6   Derivation of Transfer Function of an Error Amplifier with Single Zero and Single Pole from Its Schematic

It has been shown above that if an error amplifier had a single zero, a single pole, and a pole at the origin, its gain-versus-frequency curve would be as in Fig. 12.11.

Now it will be demonstrated how the transfer function of an error amplifier is derived and that the circuit of Fig. 12.7b does truly have a single zero, a single pole, and a pole at the origin. Gain of the circuit in Fig. 12.7b is

$$G = \frac{dV_o}{dV_i}$$

$$= \frac{Z_2}{Z_1}$$

$$= \frac{(R2 + 1/jwC1)(1/jwC2)}{R1(R2 + 1/jwC1 + 1/jwC2)}$$

Now introduce the complex variable $s = jw$. Then

$$G = \frac{(R2 + 1/sC1)(1/sC2)}{R1(R2 + 1/sC1 + 1/sC2)}$$

And by algebraic manipulation

$$G = \frac{1 + sR2C1}{sR1(C1 + C2)(1 + sR2C1C2/C1 + C2)}$$

And since generally $C2 \ll C1$

$$G = \frac{1 + sR2C1}{sR1(C1 + C2)(1 + R2C2)} \qquad (12.4)$$

The error amplifier of Fig. 12.7b, having the transfer function of Eq. 12.4, is commonly referred to as a *Type 2 amplifier* in conformance with the designation introduced by Venable in his classic paper.[1] A Type 2 error amplifier is used when the output filter capacitor has an ESR so that F_{co} lies on a -1 slope of the G_1 curve (Fig. 12.6).

Examination of this transfer function for the circuit of Fig. 12.7b permits immediate drawing of its gain characteristic as follows (Fig. 12.11). Equation 12.4 shows that this circuit (Fig. 12.7b) has a pole at the origin at a frequency of $F_{po} = 1/2\pi R1(C1 + C2)$. Thus, go to 0 dB at that frequency and draw a line backward toward lower frequency with a slope of $+1$.

From Eq. 12.4, the circuit has zero at a frequency of $F_z = 1/2\pi R2C1$. Go to that sloped line and turn it horizontal at F_z. Again from Eq. 12.4, the circuit has a pole at a frequency of $F_p = 1/2\pi R2C2$. Now go out along that horizontal line and turn it into a -1 slope at F_p.

Now that the transfer function of the Type 2 error amplifier can be drawn from its pole and zero frequencies, it remains to be able to locate them (choosing $R1$, $R2$, $C1$, $C2$) so as to achieve the desired phase margin. This is demonstrated below.

12.7 Calculation of Type 2 Error-Amplifier Phase Shift from Its Zero and Pole Locations

Adopting Venable's scheme,[1] the ratio $F_{co}/F_z = K$ will be chosen equal to $F_p/F_{co} = K$.

Now a zero, like an RC differentiator (Fig. 12.2b), causes a phase lead. A pole, like an RC integrator (Fig. 12.2a), causes a phase lag.

The phase lead at a frequency F due to a zero at a frequency F_z is

$$\Theta_{ld} = \tan^{-1}\frac{F}{F_z}$$

But we are interested in the phase lead at F_{co} due to a zero at a frequency F_z. This is

$$\Theta_{ld} \text{ (at } F_{co}) = \tan^{-1} K \qquad (12.5)$$

The phase lag at a frequency F due to a pole at a frequency F_p is

$$\Theta_{lag} = \tan^{-1} \frac{F}{F_p}$$

and we are interested in the lag at F_{co} due to the pole at F_p. This is

$$\Theta_{lag} \text{ (at } F_{co}) = \tan^{-1} \frac{1}{K} \qquad (12.6)$$

The total phase shift at F_{co} due to the lead of the zero at F_z and the lag due to the pole at F_p is the sum of Eqs. 12.5 and 12.6.

These shifts are in addition to the inherent low-frequency phase shift of the error amplifier with its pole at the origin. The error amplifier is an inverter and at low frequency causes a 180° phase shift.

At low frequencies, the pole at the origin causes a 90° phase shift. This is just another way of saying that at low frequencies, the circuit is just an integrator with resistor input and capacitor feedback. This is seen from Fig. 12.7b. At low frequencies, the impedance of $C1$ is much greater than $R2$. The feedback arm is thus only $C1$ and $C2$ in parallel.

Thus the inherent low-frequency phase lag is 180° because of the phase inversion plus 90° due to the pole at the origin or a total lag of 270°. Total phase lag, including the lead due to the zero and lag due to the pole, is then

$$\Theta_{(total\ lag)} = 270° - \tan^{-1} K + \tan^{-1} \frac{1}{K} \qquad (12.7)$$

Note that this is still a net phase lag as when K is a very large number (zero and pole frequencies very far apart), the lead due to the zero is a maximum of 90° and the lag due to the pole is 0°.

Total phase lag through the error amplifier, calculated from Eq. 12.7 is shown in Table 12.1.

12.8   Phase Shift through *LC* Filter Having ESR in Its Output Capacitor

The total open-loop phase shift consists of that through the error amplifier plus that through the output LC filter. Figure 12.3b showed for $R_o = 20\sqrt{L_o/C_o}$ and no ESR in the filter capacitor, the lag through the filter itself is already 175° at $1.2F_o$.

This lag is modified significantly if the output capacitor has an ESR

TABLE 12.1   Phase Lag through a Type 2 Error Amplifier for Various Values of $K(= F_{co}/F_z = F_p/F_{co})$

K	Lag (from Eq. 12.7)
2	233°
3	216°
4	208°
5	202°
6	198°
10	191°

as in Fig. 12.5b. In that figure, the gain slope breaks from a -2 to a -1 slope at the so-called ESR zero frequency of $F_{esr} = 1/2\pi R_{esr}C_o$. Recall that at F_{esr}, the impedance of C_o equals that of R_{esr}. Beyond F_{esr}, the impedance of C_o becomes smaller than R_{esr} and the circuit becomes increasingly like an LR rather than an LC circuit. Moreover, an LR circuit can cause only a 90° phase lag as compared to the possible maximum of 180° for an LC circuit.

Thus the ESR zero creates a boost in phase over a possible maximum of 180°. Phase lag at a frequency F due to an ESR zero at F_{esro} is

$$\Theta_{lc} = 180° - \tan^{-1} \frac{F}{F_{esro}}$$

and since we are interested in the phase lag at F_{co} due to the zero at F_{esro}

$$\Theta_{lc} = 180° - \tan^{-1} \frac{F_{co}}{F_{esro}} \tag{12.8}$$

Phase lags through the LC filter (having an ESR zero) are shown in Table 12.2 for various values of F_{co}/F_{esro} (from Eq. 12.8).

TABLE 12.2   Phase Lag through an LC Filter at F_{co} Due to a Zero at F_{esro}

F_{co}/F_{esro}	Phase lag	F_{co}/F_{esro}	Phase lag
0.25	166°	2.5	112°
0.50	153°	3	108°
0.75	143°	4	104°
1.0	135°	5	101°
1.2	130°	6	99.5°
1.4	126°	7	98.1°
1.6	122°	8	97.1°
1.8	119°	9	96.3°
2.0	116°	10	95.7°

Thus, by setting the error-amplifier gain in the horizontal part of its gain curve (Fig. 12.6) equal and opposite to the G_t (Fig. 12.6) loss at F_{co}, the location of F_{co} is fixed where it is desired. Since F_{co} will in most cases be located on the -1 slope of the G_t curve, the total gain curve will come through F_{co} at a -1 slope. From Tables 12.1 and 12.2, the proper value of K (locations of the zero and pole) is established to yield the desired phase margin.

12.9 Design Example—Stabilizing a Forward Converter Feedback Loop with a Type 2 Error Amplifier

The design example presented below demonstrates how much of the material discussed in all previous chapters is interrelated.

Stabilize the feedback loop for a forward converter with the following specifications:

V_o	5.0 V
$I_{o(nom)}$	10 A
Minimum I_o	1 A
Switching frequency	100 kHz
Minimum output ripple (peak to peak)	50 mV

It is assumed that the filter output capacitor has an ESR and F_{co} will occur on the -1 slope of the LC filter. This permits the use of a Type 2 error amplifier with the gain characteristics of Fig. 12.6. The circuit is shown in Fig. 12.12.

First L_o, C_o will be calculated and the gain characteristic of the output filter will be drawn. From Eq. 2.47

$$L_o = \frac{3V_o T}{I_{on}}$$

$$= \frac{3 \times 5 \times 10^{-6}}{10}$$

$$= 15 \times 10^{-6} \text{ H}$$

and from Eq. 2.48

$$C_o = 65 \times 10^{-6} \frac{dI}{V_{or}}$$

where dI is twice the minimum output current $= 2 \times 1 = 2$ A and V_{or} is the output ripple voltage $= 0.05$ V. Then $C_o = 65 \times 10^{-6} \times 2/0.05 = 2600$ microfarads.

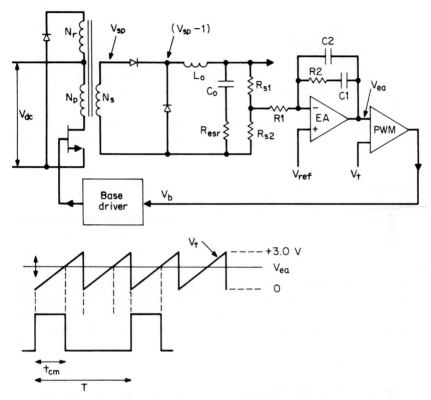

Figure 12.12   Forward converter design example schematic stabilizing the feedback loop.

Corner frequency of the output LC filter, from Sec. 12.2.3, is

$$F_o = 1/2\pi\sqrt{L_oC_o}$$
$$= 1/2\pi\sqrt{15 \times 10^{-6} \times 2600 \times 10^{-6}}$$
$$= 806 \text{ Hz}$$

Again from Sec. 12.2.3, the frequency of the ESR zero (frequency where the gain slope abruptly changes from a -2 to a -1 slope) is

$$F_{esr} = 1/2\pi R_{esr}C_o$$

$= 1/2\pi(65 \times 10{-}6)$ (assuming, as in Sec. 2.3.11.2, that over a large range of aluminum electrolytic capacitor magnitudes and voltage ratings, that $R_{esr}C_o$ is constant and equal to $65 \times 10{-}6$)

$= 2500 \text{ Hz.}$

From Eq. 12.1, the modulator gain G_m is $G_m = 0.5(V_{sp} - 1)/3$, and when the duty cycle is 0.5, for $V_o = 5V$, $V_{sp} = 11$ V since $V_o = (V_{sp} - 1)T_{on}/T$. Then $G_m = 0.5(11 - 1)/3 = 1.67 = +4.5$ dB.

For the usual SG1524-type PWM chip, which can tolerate only 2.5 V at the reference input to the error amplifier, for $V_o = 5$ V, $R_{s1} = R_{s2}$. Sampling network gain (loss) is then $G_s = -6$ dB. Then $G_m + G_s = +4.5 - 6.0 = -1.5$ dB.

The open-loop gain curve of everything but the error amplifier is then $G_t = G_{lc} + G_m + G_s$ and is drawn in Fig. 12.13 as curve $ABCD$. From A to the corner frequency at 806 Hz (B) it has a value of $G_m + G_s = -1.5$ dB. At B, it breaks into a -2 slope and continues at that slope up to the ESR zero at 2500 Hz (C). At point C, it breaks into a -1 slope.

Now crossover frequency is taken at one-fifth the switching frequency or 20 kHz. From the G_t curve, loss at 20 kHz is -40 dB (numerical loss of 1/100). Hence, to make 20 kHz the crossover frequency, the error-amplifier gain at that frequency is made $+40$ dB. Since the total open-loop gain of the error amplifier plus curve $ABCD$) must come through crossover at a -1 slope, the error-amplifier gain curve must have zero slope between points F and G in curve $EFGH$ of Fig. 12.13 since $ABCD$ already has a -1 slope at 20 kHz.

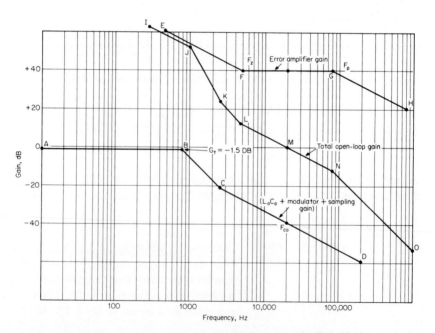

Figure 12.13   Design example stabilizing the feedback loop for Fig. 12.12.

This horizontal gain slope between points F and G is obtained as described above with a Type 2 error amplifier. The gain of the Type 2 error amplifier in the horizontal part of its slope is $R2/R1$. If $R1$ is arbitrarily taken as 1000 Ω, R_2 is 100,000 Ω.

Now a zero is located at F_z to increase low-frequency gain to degenerate 120-Hz line ripple and a pole is located at G to commence decreasing high-frequency gain so as to minimize thin noise spikes at the output. The zero and the pole will be located to give the desired phase margin.

Assume a 45° phase margin. Then total phase shift around the loop at 20 kHz is 360 − 45 = 315°. But the LC filter by itself causes a phase lag given by Eq. 12.7. From that equation, the lag for F_{co} = 20 kHz and F_{esro} = 2500 Hz is 97° (Table 12.2). Thus the error amplifier is permitted only 315 − 97 or 218°. Table 12.1 shows that for an error-amplifier lag of 218°, a K factor of slightly less than 3 would suffice.

To provide somewhat more insurance, assume a K factor of 4 which yields a phase lag of 208°. This, plus the 97° lag of the LC filter, yields a total lag of 305° and a phase margin of 360 − 305° or 55° at F_{co}.

For a K factor of 4, the zero is at F_z = 20/4 = 5 kHz. From Eq. 12.3, $F_z = 1/2\pi R2C1$. For $R2$ determined above as $100K$, $C1 = 1/2\pi$ $(100,000)(5000) = 318 \times 10^{-12}$.

Again for the K factor of 4, the pole is at F_{po} = 20 × 4 = 80 kHz. From Eq. 12.3, $F_{po} = 1/2\pi R2C2$. For $R2 = 100K$, $F_{po} = 80$ kHz, $C2 = 1/2\pi(100,000)(80,000) = 20 \times 10^{-12}$. This completes the design; the final gain curves are shown in Fig. 12.13. Curve $IJKLMO$ is the total open-loop gain. It is the sum of curves $ABCD$ and $EFGH$.

12.10   Type 3 Error Amplifier—When Used and Transfer Function

In Sec. 2.3.11.2, it was pointed out that the output ripple $V_{or} = R_o\, dI$ where R_o is the ESR of the filter output capacitor C_o and dI is twice the minimum DC current. Now most aluminum electrolytic capacitors do have an ESR. Study of many capacitor manufacturers' catalogs indicates that for such capacitors, R_oC_o is constant and equal to an average value of 65×10^{-6}.

Thus, using conventional aluminum electrolytic capacitors, the only way to reduce output ripple is to decrease R_o, which can be done only by increasing C_o. This, of course, increases size of the capacitor, which may be unacceptable.

Within the past few years, capacitor manufacturers have been able (at considerably greater cost) to produce aluminum electrolytic capacitors with essentially zero ESR for those applications where output ripple must be reduced to an absolute minimum.

When such zero ESR capacitors are used, it affects the design of the error amplifier in the feedback loop significantly. When an ESR was present in the output capacitor, F_{co} usually was located on the -1 slope of the output filter. This required a Type 2 error amplifier with a horizontal slope at F_{co} in its gain-versus-frequency characteristic (Fig. 12.6).

With a capacitor with zero ESR, the LC gain-versus-frequency curve continues falling at a -2 slope after the corner frequency $F_o = 1/2\pi\sqrt{L_oC_o}$ (curve $ABCD$ in Fig. 12.14a). Now an error amplifier can be designed to have its gain equal and opposite to the LC loss at the desired F_{co}. But for the total gain to come through F_{co} at a -1 slope, the error-amplifier gain curve must be designed to have a $+1$ slope in its central region at F_{co} (curve $EFGHI$ in Fig. 12.14b).

Now the error-amplifier gain cannot be permitted to fall in the direction of lower frequencies. If it did, it would not provide enough gain at 120 Hz to degenerate line frequency input ripple sufficiently.

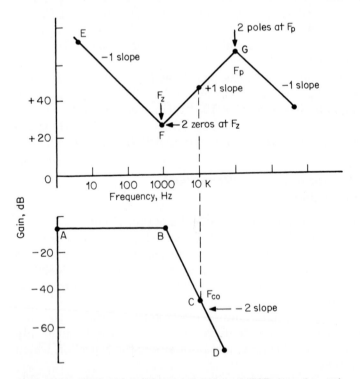

Figure 12.14 When the output capacitor has no ESR, its gain continues to fall at a -2 slope. This requires an error amplifier with a $+1$ slope at F_{co} for the total open-loop gain to come through F_{co} at a -1 slope. To achieve the above error-amplifier gain curve, two zeros are located at F_z and two poles at F_p.

Thus at some point F_z (Fig. 12.14b), the gain curve must be turned around to proceed upward at a $+1$ slope in the direction of lower frequencies. As described in Sec. 12.5, this is done by providing two zeros at the same frequency (F_z) in the error amplifier's transfer function. Below F_z, the gain falls at a -1 slope (in the direction of higher frequencies) because of a pole at the origin which will be provided. At F_z, the first zero turns the gain slope horizontal; the second one turns it to a $+1$ slope.

Now the gain cannot be permitted to continue upward at a $+1$ slope much beyond F_{co}. If it did, gain would be high at high frequencies and thin noise spikes would get through to the output at high amplitudes. Thus, as described in Sec. 12.5, two poles are provided at point H at the frequency F_p. The first pole turns the $+1$ gain slope horizontal; the second pole turns it to a -1 slope.

An error amplifier with the gain-versus-frequency $EFGHI$ in Fig. 12.14 is referred to as a *Type 3 error amplifier* (again following the widely used Venable designation.[1]

As for the Type 2 error amplifier, location of the two zeros at F_z and the two poles at F_p determines the phase lag at F_{co}. The wider the separation between F_p and F_z, the greater the phase margin.

Also with respect to the Type 2 error amplifier, shifting F_z down to too low a frequency reduces low-frequency gain and prevents sufficient degeneration of 120-Hz line ripple. Moving F_p to too high a frequency offers higher gain at high frequencies and permits high-frequency, thin noise spikes to come through at greater amplitude.

Again a K factor is introduced to describe locations of F_z and F_p. This ratio is set equal to $K = F_{co}/F_z$ and $K = F_p/F_{co}$. In the following section, phase boost at F_{co} due to the double zero at F_z and phase lag at F_{co} due to the double pole at F_p will be calculated.

12.11   Phase Lag through a Type 3 Error Amplifier as Function of Zero and Pole Locations

In Sec. 12.7, it was pointed out that the phase boost at a frequency F_{co} due to a zero at a frequency F_z is $\Theta_{zb} = \tan^{-1}(F_{co}/F_z) = \tan^{-1} K$ (Eq. 12.4). If there are two zeros at the frequency F_z, the boosts are additive. Thus boost at F_{co} due to two zeros at the same frequency F_z is $\Theta_{2zb} = 2 \tan^{-1} K$.

Similarly, the lag at F_{co} due to a pole at F_p is $\Theta_{lp} = \tan^{-1}(1/K)$ (Eq. 12.5). The lags due to two poles at F_p are also additive. Thus lag at F_{co} due to two poles at F_p is $\Theta_{12p} = 2 \tan^{-1}(1/K)$. The lag and boost are in addition to the inherent low-frequency 270° lag due to the 180° phase inversion plus the 90° due to the inherent pole at the origin.

Thus total phase lag through a Type 3 error amplifier is

$$\Theta_{tl} = 270° - 2 \tan^{-1} K + 2 \tan^{-1}(1/K) \qquad (12.9)$$

Total phase lag through the Type 3 error amplifier is calculated from Eq. 12.9 for various values of K (see Table 12.3).

Comparing Tables 12.3 and 12.1, it is seen that a Type 3 error amplifier with two zeros and two poles yields considerably less phase lag than does the Type 2 error amplifier, which has only a single zero and a single pole.

However, the Type 3 error amplifier is used with an LC filter which has no ESR zero to decrease the lag down from 180°. Thus the lower lag of the Type 3 error amplifier is essential because of the higher lag of an LC filter with no ESR.

12.12   Type 3 Error Amplifier Schematic, Transfer Function, and Zero and Pole Locations

The schematic of a circuit which has the gain-versus-frequency characteristic of Fig. 12.14b is shown in Fig. 12.15. Its transfer function can be derived in the manner described in Sec. 12.6 for the Type 2 error amplifier. Impedances of the feedback and input arm are expressed in terms of the s operator, and the transfer function is simply $G(s) = Z_2(s)/Z_1(s)$. Algebraic manipulation yields the following expression for the transfer function:

$$G(s) = \frac{dV_o}{dV_{\text{in}}} = \frac{(1 + sR2C1)[1 + s(R1 + R3)C3]}{sR1(C1 + C2)(1 + sR3C3)[1 + sR2(C1C2/(C1 + C2)]} \qquad (12.10)$$

This transfer function is seen to have

(a) A pole at the origin at a frequency of

$$F_{\text{po}} = 1/2\pi R1(C1 + C2) \qquad (12.11)$$

This is the frequency where the impedance of $R1$ is equal to that of $(C1 + C2)$ in parallel.

TABLE 12.3   **Phase Lag through Type 3 Error Amplifier for Various Values of** $K(= F_{co}/F_z = F_p/F_{co})$

K	Lag (from Eq. 12.9)
2	196°
3	164°
4	146°
5	136°
6	128°

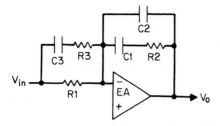

Figure 12.15 A Type 3 error amplifier. It has a pole at the origin, two zeros, and two poles. Its transfer function is

$$G = dV_o/dV_{in}$$

$$= \frac{(1 + sR2C1)[1 + s(R1 + R3)C3]}{sR1(C1 + C2)(1 + sR3C3)[1 + sR2(C1C2/(C1 + C2))]}$$

(b) A first zero at a frequency of

$$F_{z1} = 1/2\pi R2C1 \tag{12.12}$$

This is the frequency where the impedance of $R2$ equals that of $C1$.

(c) A second zero at a frequency of

$$F_{z2} = 1/2\pi(R1 + R3)C3$$
$$\approx 1/2\pi R1C3 \tag{12.13}$$

This is the frequency where the impedance of $(R_1 + R_3)$ equals that of C_3.

(d) A first pole at a frequency of

$$F_{p1} = \frac{1/2\pi R2(C1C2)}{C1 + C2}$$
$$\approx 1/2\pi R2C2 \tag{12.14}$$

This is the frequency where the impedance of $R2$ equals that of the series combination of $C1$ and $C2$ in series.

(e) A second pole at a frequency of

$$F_{p2} = 1/2\pi R3C3 \tag{12.15}$$

This is the frequency where the impedance of $R3$ equals that of $C3$.

To yield the gain-versus-frequency curves of Fig. 12.14b, the RC products will be chosen so that $F_{z1} = F_{z2}$ and $F_{p1} = F_{p2}$. The location of the double-zero and double-pole frequencies will be fixed by the K factor, which yields the desired phase margin. Gain of the error amplifier on the $+1$ slope of Fig. 12.14b will be set equal and opposite to the loss of the LC filter (Fig. 12.14a) at the desired F_{co}.

From Table 12.3 and the transfer function of Eq. 12.10, the RC products which set the zero and pole frequencies at the desired points are determined as in the design example below.

12.13   Design Example—Stabilizing a Forward Converter Feedback Loop with a Type 3 Error Amplifier

Design the feedback loop for a forward converter having the following specifications:

V_o	5.0 V
$I_{o(nom)}$	10 A
$I_{o(min)}$	1.0 A
Switching frequency	50 kHz
Output ripple (peak to peak)	< 20 mV

Assume that the output capacitor is of the type advertised as having zero ESR.

First the output LC filter and its corner frequency are calculated. Refer to Fig. 12.15. From Eq. 2.47

$$L_o = \frac{3V_oT}{I_o}$$
$$= \frac{3 \times 5 \times 20 \times 10^{-6}}{10}$$
$$= 30 \times 10^{-6} \text{ H}$$

Now it was assumed that the output capacitor had zero ESR so that ripple due to ESR should be zero. But there is a small capacitive ripple component (Sec. 1.2.7). This is usually very small, and hence a filter capacitor much smaller than the 2600-μF capacitor used in the Type 2 error-amplifier design example can be used. But to be conservative, for this design assume the same 2600-μF capacitor is used and that it has zero ESR. Then

$$F_o = 1/2\pi\sqrt{L_oC_o}$$
$$= 1/2\pi\sqrt{30 \times 10^{-6} \times 2600 \times 10^{-6}}$$
$$= 570 \text{ Hz}$$

Assume, as for the Type 2 error-amplifier design example, that the modulator plus sampling resistor gain is -1.5 dB. The gain of the LC filter plus modulator plus sampling resistor gain is plotted in Fig. 12.16 as curve ABC. It is horizontal at a level of -1.5 dB up to the corner frequency of 570 Hz at point B. There it changes abruptly to a -2 slope and remains at that slope since the capacitor has no ESR.

Frequency F_{co} is chosen as one-fifth the switching frequency or $50/5 = 10$ kHz. On curve ABC of Fig. 12.16, loss at 10 kHz is -50 dB. Hence to force 10 kHz to be F_{co}, the error-amplifier gain at 10 kHz is set at $+50$ dB (point F in Fig. 12.16). But the error amplifier must have a $+1$ slope at F_{co} to yield a net -1 slope when added to the -2 slope of the LC filter. Thus, at point F draw a line of $+1$ slope. Extend this in the direction of lower frequencies to F_z—the frequency of the double zero. Extend it in the direction of higher frequencies to F_p, the frequency of the double pole. Then determine F_z and F_p from the K factor (Table 12.3) required to yield the desired phase margin.

Assume a phase margin of 45°. Then total phase lag of the error amplifier plus the LC filter is $360 - 45 = 315$°. But the LC filter, not having an ESR zero, has a lag of 180°. This leaves a permissible lag of $315 - 180 = 135$° for the error amplifier.

From Table 12.3, a K factor of 5 yields a lag of 136°, which is close

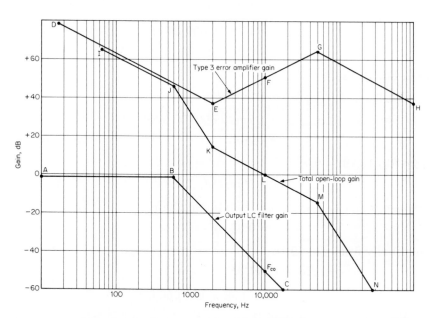

Figure 12.16 Gain curves—design example of Sec. 12.13. Output capacitor with zero ESR and Type 3 error amplifier.

enough. For F_{co} = 10 kHz, K = 5, F_z is 2 kHz and F_p is 50 kHz. Thus in Fig. 12.16, the +1 sloped line is extended down to 2 kHz at E, where it breaks upward to a +1 slope (−1 slope in direction of higher frequencies due to the pole at the origin). It is extended on a +1 slope from F to the double-pole frequency at 50 kHz. There it turns down to a −1 slope because of the two poles.

The curve *IJKLMN* is the total open-loop gain and is the sum of curves *ABC* and *DEFGH*. It is seen to have a gain of 0 dB at 10 kHz (the crossover frequency F_{co}) and to come through F_{co} at a −1 slope. The K factor of 5 yields the required 45° phase margin. Components must now be selected to yield the error-amplifier gain curve *DEFGH* in Fig. 12.16.

12.14   Component Selection to Yield Desired Type 3 Error-Amplifier Gain Curve

There are six components to be selected ($R1$, $R2$, $R3$, $C1$, $C2$, $C3$) and four equations for zero and pole frequencies (Eqs. 12.12 to 12.15).

Arbitrarily choose $R1$ = 1000 Ω. Now the first zero (at 2000 Hz) occurs when $R2 = X_{c1}$ and the impedance of the feedback arm at that frequency is mainly that of $R2$ itself. Thus gain at 2000 Hz is $R2/R1$. From Fig. 12.16, gain of the error amplifier at 2000 Hz is +37 dB or a numerical gain of 70.8. Then for $R1$ = 1K, $R2$ = 70.8K, from Eq. 12.12, we obtain

$$C1 = 1/2\pi R2 F_z$$
$$= 1/2\pi(70,800)2000$$
$$= 0.011 \ \mu F$$

from Eq. 12.14

$$C2 = 1/2\pi R2 F_p$$
$$= 1/2\pi(70,800)(50,000)$$
$$= 45 \ pF$$

from Eq. 12.13

$$C3 = 1/2\pi R1 F_z$$
$$= 1/2\pi(1000)(2000)$$
$$= 0.08 \ \mu F$$

and finally from Eq. 12.15

$$R3 = 1/2\pi C3 F_p$$
$$= 1/2\pi(0.08 \times 10^{-6})(50,000)$$
$$= 40 \ \Omega$$

12.15   Conditional Stability in Feedback Loops

A feedback loop may be stable under normal operating conditions when it is up and running, but can be shocked into continuous oscillation at turnon or by a line input transient. This odd situation, called *conditional stability,* can be understood from Fig. 12.17a and 12.17b.

Figure 12.17a and 12.17b contains plots of total open-loop phase shift and total open-loop gain versus frequency, respectively. Conditional stability may arise if there are two frequencies (points *A* and *C*) at which the total open-loop phase shift reaches 360° as in Fig. 12.17a.

Recall that the criterion for oscillation is that at the frequency where the total open-loop gain is unity or 0 dB, the total open-loop

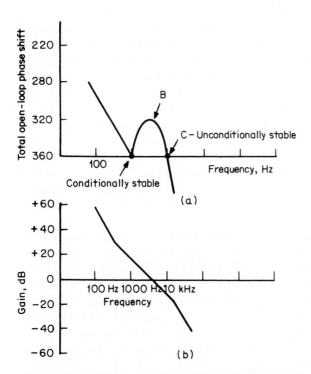

Figure 12.17   A loop may be conditionally stable if there are two frequencies where the total open-loop phase shift is 360°. Loop is conditionally stable at point *A* as a momentary drop in gain to 0 dB such as may occur at initial turnon may result in the conditions for oscillation, i.e., 360° total open-loop phase shift and 0 dB gain. Once oscillation breaks out, it will continue. Circuit is unconditionally stable at *B* as momentary increases in gain are very unlikely.

phase shift is 360°. The loop is still stable if the total open-loop phase shift is 360° at a given frequency but the total open-loop gain at that frequency is greater than 1.

This may be difficult to grasp, as it would appear that if at some frequency the echo of a signal coming around the loop is exactly in phase with the original signal but larger in amplitude, it would grow larger in amplitude each time around the loop. It would thus build up to a level where the losses would be such to limit the oscillation to some high level and remain in oscillation. This does not occur, as can be demonstrated mathematically. But for the purposes herein, it will simply be accepted that oscillations do not occur if the total open-loop gain is greater than unity at the frequency where the total open-loop phase shift is 360°.

Thus in Fig. 12.17a, the loop is unconditionally stable at B as there the open-loop gain is unity but the open-loop phase shift is less than 360° by about 40°—i.e., there is a phase margin at point B. The loop is also stable at point C as there the open-loop phase shift is 360° but gain is less than unity—i.e., there is gain margin at point C. But at point A the loop is conditionally stable. Although the total open-loop phase shift is 360°, the gain is greater than unity (about +16 dB) and, as stated, the loop is stable for those conditions.

However, if under certain conditions—say, at initial turnon when the circuit has not yet come to equilibrium and open-loop gain momentarily drops 16 dB at the frequency of point A—the condition for oscillation exists. Gain is unity and phase shift is 360°. The circuit will break into oscillation and remain oscillatory. Point C is not a likely location for such conditional oscillation as it is not possible for gain to increase momentarily.

If conditional stability exists (most likely at initial turnon), it is likely to occur at the corner frequency of the output LC filter under conditions of light load. It is seen in Fig. 12.3a and 12.3b that a lightly loaded LC filter has a large resonant bump in gain and very fast phase shifts at its corner frequency. The large phase shifts can result in a total of 360° at the LC corner frequency. If total open-loop gain (which is not easily predictable during the turnon transient may be unity or may momentarily be unity—the loop may break into oscillation.

It is rather difficult to calculate whether this may occur. The safest way to avoid this possibility is to provide a phase boost at the LC corner frequency by introducing a zero there to cancel some of the phase lag in the loop. This can be done easily by adding a capacitor in shunt with the upper resistor in the output voltage sampling network (Fig. 12.12).

12.16 Stabilizing a Discontinuous-Mode Flyback Converter

12.16.1 DC gain from error-amplifier output to output voltage node

The essential elements of the loop are shown in Fig. 12.18a. The first step in designing the feedback loop is to calculate its DC or low-frequency gain from the error-amplifier output to the output voltage node. Assume an efficiency of 80 percent. Then from Eq. 4.2a

$$P_o = \frac{0.8(1/2L)(I_p)^2}{T} = \frac{(V_o)^2}{R_o} \qquad (12.16)$$

But $I_p = V_{dc}\overline{T_{on}}L_p$; then

$$P_o = \frac{0.8L_p(V_{dc}\overline{T_{on}}/L_p)^2}{2T} = \frac{(V_o)^2}{R_o} \qquad (12.17)$$

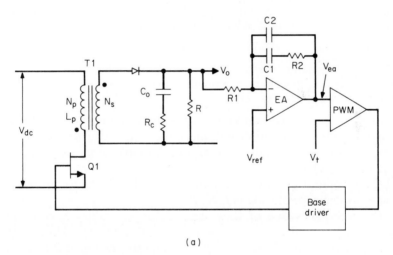

(a)

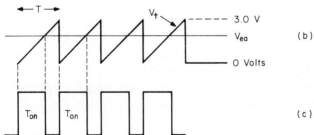

(b)

(c)

Figure 12.18 Discontinuous-mode flyback feedback loop.

Referring to Fig. 12.18b, it is seen that the PWM compares the output of the error amplifier V_{ea} to a 0- to 3-V triangle. It generates a rectangular pulse whose width (T_{on}; Fig. 12.18c) is equal to the time from the start of the triangle to its intersection with DC voltage level V_{ea}. This T_{on} will be the on time of power transistor $Q1$. It is seen in Fig. 12.18b that $V_{ea}/3 = T_{on}/T$ or $T_{on} = V_{ea}T/3$. Putting this into Eq. 12.16, we have

$$P_o = \frac{0.8L_p(V_{dc}/L_p)^2(V_{ea}T/3)^2}{2T} = \frac{(V_o)^2}{R_o}$$

or

$$V_o = \frac{V_{dc}V_{ea}}{3}\sqrt{\frac{0.4R_oT}{L_p}} \qquad (12.18)$$

and the DC or low-frequency gain from the error-amplifier output to the output node is

$$\frac{\Delta V_o}{\Delta V_{ea}} = \frac{V_{dc}}{3}\sqrt{\frac{0.4R_oT}{L_p}} \qquad (12.19)$$

12.16.2   Discontinuous-mode flyback transfer function or AC voltage gain from error-amplifier output to output voltage node

Now assume a small sinusoidal signal of frequency f_n inserted in series at the error-amplifier output point. This will cause a sinusoidal modulation in amplitude of the triangular current pulses (of peak amplitude I_p) in the $T1$ primary. Consequently, there is a sinusoidal amplitude modulation in the triangular secondary current pulses (whose instantaneous amplitude is I_pN_p/N_s).

The average value of these triangular secondary current pulses then is modulated at the same sinusoidal frequency f_n. There is thus a sinusoidal current of frequency f_n flowing into the top of the paralleled combination of R_o and C_o.

But this alternating current flows into the Thevenin equivalent of R_o and C_o in series. It is thus seen that the output voltage across C_o falls off in amplitude at the rate of -20 dB/decade or at a -1 slope starting from the frequency of $F_p = 1/2\pi R_oC_o$.

This is simply another way of saying that the transfer function from the error-amplifier output to the output voltage node has a pole at

$$F_p = 1/2\pi R_oC_o \qquad (12.20)$$

and DC gain below the pole frequency is given by Eq. 12.19.

This is in contrast to topologies which have an *LC* output filter. In such topologies, a sinusoidal voltage inserted at the error-amplifier output node results in a sinusoidal voltage at the input to the *LC* filter. That voltage, coming through the *LC* filter, falls off in amplitude at −40 dB/decade rate or −2 slope. Or to use the common jargon expression, the *LC* filter has a *two-pole rolloff* at the output node.

This −1 slope or *single-pole rolloff* of the flyback topology output circuit, of course, changes the error-amplifier transfer function required to stabilize the feedback loop. The flyback converter output filter capacitor, in most cases, also has an ESR zero at a frequency of

$$F_z = 1/2\pi R_c C_o \tag{12.21}$$

Now, a complete analysis of the stabilization problem should consider maximum and minimum values of both DC input voltage and of R_o. Equation 12.19 shows DC gain as proportional to V_{dc} and to the square root of R_o. Further, the output circuit pole frequency is inversely proportional to R_o.

Thus in the following graphical analysis, all four combinations of V_{dc} and R_o should be considered as the output circuit transfer function may vary significantly with them.

For one output circuit transfer function (one set of line and load conditions), the error-amplifier transfer function is designed to establish F_{co} at a desired frequency and to have the total gain curve come through F_{co} at a −1 slope. Care must be taken, then, that at another output circuit transfer function (different load and line conditions), the total gain curve does not come through F_{co} at a −2 slope and possibly cause oscillation.

For this example, consider that V_{dc} variations are small enough to be neglected. Thus calculate DC gain from Eq. 12.19 and output circuit pole frequency from Eq. 12.20. Assume $R_{o(max)} = 10R_{o(min)}$.

Now in Fig. 12.19, curve *ABCD* is the output circuit transfer function for $R_{o(max)}$. It has a gain given by Eq. 12.19 from *A* to *B*. At *B*, it breaks into a −1 slope because of the output pole given by Eq. 12.20. At *C*, its slope turns horizontal because of the ESR zero of the output capacitor. Frequency at point *C* is given by Eq. 12.21, whereas in Sec. 1.3.7, $R_c C_o$ is 65×10^{-6} for an aluminum electrolytic capacitor over a large range of voltage and capacitance ratings.

Also in Fig. 12.19, curve *EFGH* is the output circuit transfer function for $R_{o(min)} = R_{o(max)}/10$. Its pole frequency is 10 times that for R_o as F_p is inversely proportional to R_o. DC gain at *F* is 10 dB below that for $R_{o(max)}$ as gain is proportional to the square root of R_o (20 log $\sqrt{10} = 10dB$).

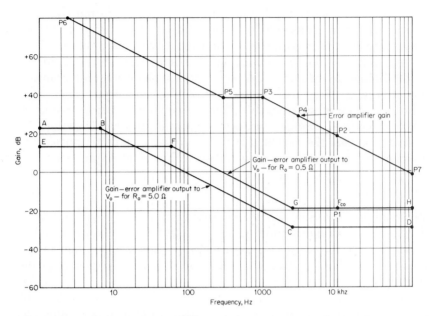

Figure 12.19 Gain curves for stabilizing the feedback loop or the discontinuous-mode flyback of design example in Sec. 12.18.

Thus the output circuit transfer function for $R_{o(\min)}$ is drawn as follows. Go to point F, which is at a frequency 10 times that of point B and 10 dB below point B. Draw a horizontal line back toward DC for the low-frequency gain (line FE). At F, draw a line of -1 slope (-20 dB/decade) and continue it to the ESR zero frequency at G. At G, draw a line of horizontal slope out toward higher frequency.

From output circuit transfer functions $ABCD$ and $EFGH$ of Fig. 12.19, the error-amplifier gain or transfer function curve is drawn as described below (Sec. 12.17).

12.17 Error-Amplifier Transfer Function for Discontinuous-Mode Flyback

In Fig. 12.19, for $R_{o(\min)}$, on curve $EFGH$, F_{co} will be established at one-fifth the switching frequency (point $P1$) as stated in Sec. 12.3. Most often, F_{co} will occur on the horizontal slope of the output circuit transfer function.

To force F_{co} to be at the desired point, the error amplifier will be designed to have a gain at F_{co} (point $P2$) equal and opposite to the output circuit loss at point $P1$. Since the slope of $EFGH$ at F_{co} is horizontal, the error-amplifier gain slope must be -1 (in the direction of higher frequencies) at point $P2$.

Thus, go to point $P2$ and draw a line backward with a slope of $+1$ in the direction of lower frequencies. Extend it to a frequency (point $P3$) somewhat lower than the frequency at C. For at $R_{o(\max)}$, the output circuit transfer function will be $ABCD$. Since the total gain curve must come through the new F_{co} for $R_{o(\max)}$ at a -1 slope, this new F_{co} will occur at the frequency where the loss along the horizontal line CD is equal and opposite (at point $P4$) to the gain of the error amplifier on its -1 slope.

The exact frequency for point $P3$ is not critical. It must be lower than the frequency at C to ensure that for the absolutely maximum R_o, where point C will be depressed to its greatest loss, this maximum loss can be matched by the equal and opposite gain of the error amplifier somewhere along its -1 slope.

Thus a pole is located at the frequency F_p corresponding to the pole at point $P3$. A Type 2 error amplifier is used. The input resistor $R1$ (Fig. 12.18a) is arbitrarily selected sufficiently high so as not to load down the sampling resistor network.

Gain along the horizontal arm (points $P3$–$P5$) is read from the graph and made equal to $R2/R1$ (Fig. 12.18a). This fixes resistor $R2$. From the pole frequency F_p and $R2$, the value of $C2$ in Fig. 12.18a ($= 1/2\pi F_p R2$) is fixed.

Now the gain is extended along the horizontal line $P3$–$P5$ and a zero is introduced at point $P5$ to increase low-frequency gain and offer a phase boost. Frequency of the zero F_z at point $P5$ is not critical; it should be about a decade below F_p. To locate the zero at F_z, $C1$ (Fig. 12.18a) is chosen as $C_1 = 1/2\pi R2 F_z$.

The design example of the following section will clarify all the above.

12.18 Design Example—Stabilizing a Discontinuous-Mode Flyback Converter

Stabilize the feedback loop of the design example in Sec. 4.3.2.7. It is assumed that the output capacitor has an ESR and so a Type 2 error amplifier will be used. The circuit is shown in Fig. 12.18a. Recall its specifications:

V_o	5.0 V
$I_{o(\text{nom})}$	10 A
$I_{o(\text{min})}$	1.0 A
$V_{\text{dc(max)}}$	60 V

$V_{dc(min)}$	38 V
$V_{dc(av)}$	49 V
Switching frequency	50 kHz
L_p (calculated in Sec. 4.3.2.7)	56.6 μH

Recall from Sec. 4.3.2.7 that C_o was calculated as 2000 μF. But it was pointed out there that at the instant of turnoff, the peak secondary current of 66 A would cause a thin spike of 66 × 0.03 = 2 V across the anticipated ESR of 0.03 V for a 2000-μF capacitor. It was noted that either this thin spike could be integrated away with a small LC circuit or C_o could be increased to lower its ESR.

Here, both will be done. Capacitance C_o will be increased to 5000 μF to decrease R_c to (2/5)0.03 or 0.012 Ω (since R_c is inversely proportional to C_o). The initial spike at Q1 turnoff is then 66 × 0.012 or 0.79 V peak. This can easily be integrated down to an acceptable level with a small LC which will be outside the feedback loop.

Now the output circuit gain curve can be drawn—first for $R_{o(min)}$ of 5/10 = 0.5 Ω. The DC gain from Eq. 12.19 is

$$G = \frac{V_{dc}}{3} \sqrt{\frac{0.4 R_o T}{L_p}}$$

$$= \frac{49}{3} \sqrt{\frac{0.4 \times 0.5 \times 20 \times 10^{-6}}{56.6 \times 10^{-6}}}$$

$$= 4.3$$

$$= +12.8 \text{ dB}$$

Pole frequency, from Eq. 12.20, is

$$F_p = 1/2\pi R_o C_o$$

$$= 1/2\pi 0.5 \times 5000 \times 10^{-6}$$

$$= 63.7 \text{ Hz}$$

and ESR zero frequency, from Eq. 12.20, is

$$F_{esro} = 1/2\pi R_o C_o$$

$$= 1/2\pi 65 \times 10^{-6}$$

$$= 2500 \text{ Hz}$$

The output circuit gain curve for $R_o = 0.5$ Ω is then drawn as $EFGH$ in Fig. 12.19. It is horizontal at a level of +12.8 dB up to $F_p = 63.7$ Hz. There it breaks to a −1 slope down to the ESR zero at 2500 Hz. The error-amplifier gain curve can now be drawn.

Then choose F_{co} as one-fifth the switching frequency or as 50/5 = 10 kHz. On *EFGH*, the loss is -19 dB at 10 kHz. Hence make the error-amplifier gain $+19$ dB at 10 kHz. Go to 10 kHz and $+19$ dB (point *P2*) and draw a line backward with a slope of $+1$ ($+20$ dB/decade) in the direction of lower frequency. Now extend that line to a frequency somewhat lower than F_{esro}—say, to point *P3* at 1 kHz, $+39$ dB. At point *P3*, draw a horizontal line back to—say—300 Hz at point *P5* (where a zero will be located).

The location of the zero is not critical. In Sec. 12.17, it was suggested the zero at point *P5* should be one decade below point *P3*. Some designers actually omit the zero at point *P5*.[5] But here it is added to gain some phase boost. Thus, for a zero at point *P5*, at that point turn the gain slope upward to a $+1$ slope (again in the direction of lower frequency).

Now verify that for $R_{o(max)}$ of 5 Ω, the total gain curve (output circuit plus error-amplifier transfer function) comes through F_{co} at a -1 slope.

For $R_o = 5$ Ω, Eq. 12.19 gives a DC gain of 13.8 or $+23$ dB. And Eq. 12.20 gives the pole frequency as 6.4 Hz. The frequency of the ESR zero remains at 2500 Hz. Thus the output circuit transfer function for $R_o = 5$ Ω is *ABCD*.

The new F_{co} is then the frequency where the gain of the error amplifier on *P6–P5–P3–P7* equals the loss on *ABCD*. This is seen to be at point *P4* (3200 Hz), where the output filter loss is -29 dB and the error-amplifier gain is $+29$ dB. The sum of the error-amplifier gain curve and *ABCD* (equal to total gain curve) is seen to have a -1 slope as it passes through F_{co}.

It should be noted, however, that if R_o were somewhat larger, the curve *ABCD* would be depressed to a lower value along its entire length. Then the point at which the previously fixed error-amplifier gain curve is equal and opposite to the output filter loss curve would occur on the -1 slope of each curve.

The total gain curve would then come through the new F_{co} at a -2 slope and oscillations could occur. Thus, as a general rule, discontinuous-mode flybacks should be tested carefully for stability at minimum load current (maximum R_o).

The error-amplifier transfer function of *P6–P5–P3–P7* is implemented as follows. In Fig. 12.18a, arbitrarily choose $R_1 = 1000$ Ω. Gain at point *P3* is seen in Fig. 12.19 to be $+38$ dB or numerical gain of 79. Thus $R_2/R_1 = 79$ or $R_2 = 79{,}000$ Ω. For the pole at point *P3* at 1 kHz, $C_2 = 1/(2\pi F_p R_2)$ or $C_2 = 2000$ pF. For the error-amplifier zero at 300 Hz, $C_1 = 1/(2\pi F_z R_2) = 6700$ pF.

Because of the single-pole rolloff characteristic of the output circuit, its absolute maximum phase lag is 90°. But because of the ESR zero, it is much less and there rarely is a phase-margin problem in the discontinuous-mode flyback.

Thus consider the situation for $R_o = 0.5 \ \Omega$. Lag at F_{co} (10 kHz) due to the pole at 64 Hz and the ESR zero at 2500 Hz is

$$\text{Output circuit lag} = \tan^1\left(\frac{10{,}000}{64}\right) - \tan^1\left(\frac{10{,}000}{25{,}000}\right)$$

$$= 89.6 - 76.0$$

$$= 13.6°$$

and the error-amplifier lag at 10,000 Hz due to the zero at 300 Hz and the pole at 1000 Hz (see Fig. 12.20, curve $P6$–$P5$–$P3$–$P7$) is

$$270 - \tan^{-1}\left(\frac{10{,}000}{300}\right) + \tan^{-1}\left(\frac{10{,}000}{1000}\right) = 270 - 88 + 84 = 266°$$

Total phase lag at 10,000 is then 13.6 + 266 = 280°. This yields a phase margin at F_{co} of 360 − 280 = 80°.

12.19   Transconductance Error Amplifiers

Many of the commonly used PWM chips (1524, 1525, 1526 family) have *transconductance* error amplifiers. Transconductance g_m is the change in output current per unit change in input voltage. Thus

$$g_m = \frac{dI_o}{dV_{\text{in}}}$$

Then for shunt impedance Z_o at the output node to ground

$$dV_o = dI_o Z_o = g_m \, dV_{\text{in}} Z_o$$

or gain G is

$$G = \frac{dV_o}{dV_{\text{in}}} = g_m Z_o$$

The unloaded, open-loop gain characteristic of the 1524, 1525-family amplifiers have a DC gain of nominally +80 dB, have a pole at 300 Hz, and thereafter fall at a −1 or −20 dB/decade slope. This is seen as curve $ABCD$ in Fig. 12.20a.

A pure resistance R_o shunted from output node to ground yields a gain curve which is constant and equal to $g_m R_o$ from DC up to the frequency where it intersects the curve $ABCD$ in Fig. 12.20a. For the 1524, 1525 family, g_m is nominally 2 mA/V. Thus gains for R_o = 500K, 50K, and 30K are respectively 1000, 100, and 60 and are shown as curves $P1$–$P2$, $P3$–$P4$, and $P5$–$P6$ in Fig. 12.20a.

In most cases, Type 2 error-amplifier gain characteristics are re-

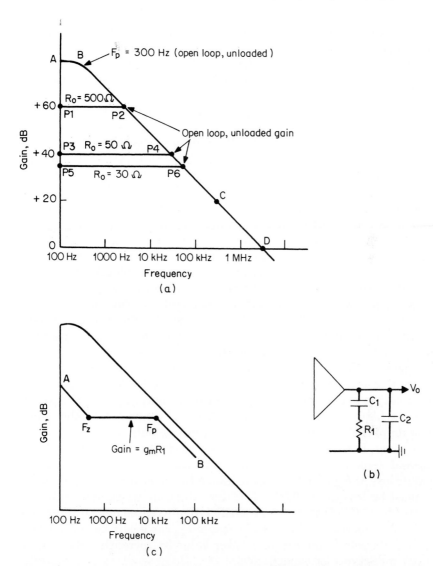

Figure 12.20   (*a*) Open-loop unloaded gain curve for PWM chip 1524, 1525 error amplifiers in *ABCD*. When loaded with indicated shunt resistors to ground, gain is constant at $G = g_m R_o$. (*Courtesy Silicon General*). (*b*) A Type 2 error-amplifier gain curve with shunt network to ground. (*c*) Gain with circuit of Fig. 12.20*b* is *A–F_z–F_p–B*: $F_z = 1/2\pi R1C1$; $F_p = 1/2\pi R1C2$.

quired. This is easily obtained with the network shown in Fig. 12.20*b* shunted to ground.

At low frequencies, X_{C1} is much greater than $R1$ and effectively $C1$ and $C2$ are in parallel with the internal 100 pF to ground which caused the open-loop 300-Hz pole. This shifts the 300-Hz pole to a lower frequency, and after that lower frequency, gain resumes falling at a -1 slope. At a frequency F_z ($= 1/2\pi R1C1$), where $X_{C1} = R_1$, there is a zero and gain slope turns horizontal at a magnitude $g_m R1$. Further on in frequency at $F_p = 1/2\pi R1C2$ where $X_{C2} = R1$, the pole turns the gain slope to -1.

The gain curve with the circuit configuration of Fig. 12.20b is shown in Fig. 12.20c.

Most frequently, in the 1524, 1525 family of PWM chips the error-amplifier gain curves are shaped in the above-mentioned fashion with the network of Fig. 12.20b shunted to ground rather than being used in the conventional operational-amplifier mode.

Whether a network as Fig. 12.20b is shunted to ground or returned around to the inverting input terminal as in a conventional operational amplifier, there is a restriction on the magnitude of $R1$ arising from the following. The internal error amplifiers in the above-mentioned chips cannot emit or absorb more than 100 μA. With a 3-V triangle at the PWM comparator, the error-amplifier output may have to move the 3 V from the bottom to the top of the triangle for sudden line or load changes. Thus for $R1$ less than 30,000 Ω, this 3-V fast swing would demand more than the available 100 μA. Response time to fast load or line changes would then be sluggish.

Because of this 100-μA limit on output current, many designers prefer not to use the error amplifier internal to the PWM chip. Since the chip's output node is brought out to one of the output pins, some prefer to use a better external error amplifier and connect it to the chip's error-amplifier output node at the appropriate output pin.

However, it may be essential from a cost viewpoint to use the chip's internal error amplifier. Calculation of the output filter may show that its loss at F_{co} is so low that to match the error-amplifier gain to it, R_1 must be less than 30,000 Ω. If this situation arises, R_1 can be increased to 30,000 Ω to match an artificially increased output filter loss at F_{co}. This increased output filter loss at F_{co} can easily be achieved by shifting its pole frequency to a lower value by increasing the output filter's inductance or capacitance.

References

1. D. Venable, "The K Factor: A New Mathematical Tool for Stability Analysis and Synthesis," *Proceedings Powercon 10*, 1983.
2. A. Pressman, *Switching and Linear Power Supply, Power Converter Design*, pp. 331–332, Switchtronix Press, Waban, Mass., 1977.
3. K. Billings, *Switchmode Power Supply Handbook*, Chap. 8, McGraw-Hill, New York, 1989.
4. G. Chryssis, *High Frequency Switching Power Supplies*, 2d ed., Chap. 9, McGraw-Hill, New York, 1989.
5. Unitrode Corp., *Power Supply Design Seminar Handbook*, Apps. B, C, Watertown, Mass., 1988.

Chapter

13

Resonant Converters

13.1 Introduction

As newer integrated circuits lead to more electronic functions in smaller packages, it becomes essential for power supplies also to become smaller. The power supplies mainly get smaller by increasing their operating frequency to decrease the size of the power transformer and output LC or capacitive filter. The supplies also get smaller by increasing their efficiency so as to require smaller heat sinks.

Thus the major objective in present-day power supply technology is to operate at switching frequencies higher than the currently commonplace 100 to 200 kHz.

However, going to higher switching frequencies with the conventional square current waveform topologies discussed up to this point increases transistor switching losses at both turnoff and turnon. Turnon losses, due to charging and discharging MOSFET output capacitances (Sec. 11.1), become important only at frequencies over 1 MHz.

As discussed in Chaps. 11 and 1, the overlap of falling current and rising collector voltage at turnoff yields a high spike of dissipation during the turnoff interval. As switching frequency increases, the more frequent the occurrence of high-dissipation spikes results in higher average transistor dissipation.

The higher losses require larger heat sinks to the point where there may be no net size decrease despite the smaller power transformer and output filter.

At sufficiently high frequencies (≥ 1 MHz) transistor switching losses may become so high that even with a sufficiently large heat sink to keep the transistor case temperature at a low value, there still is a problem. The junction-to-case temperature rise with the usual

471

1°C/W junction-to-case thermal resistance may still raise the transistor junction temperature to dangerous levels.

Adding snubbers (Chap. 11) at collector-drain outputs reduces transistor switching losses. But if a dissipative *RCD* snubber (Sec. 11.3) is used, that does not decrease total dissipation—it simply shifts losses from the transistor to the snubber resistor. Nondissipative snubbers (Sec. 11.6) do reduce transistor switching losses but are troublesome at frequencies over 200 kHz.

Thus to operate at higher frequencies which will permit smaller power supplies, transistor switching losses at turnoff and turnon must be decreased.

This is achieved in *resonant converters* by associating a resonating *LC* circuit with the switching transistor, to render its current sinusoidal rather than square wave in shape. It is then arranged to turn the transistor on and off at the zero crossings of the current sine wave. There is thus no overlap of falling current and rising voltage at turnoff or rising current and falling voltage at turnon and hence no switching losses.

Circuits which turn on and off at zero current are referred to as *zero current switching* (ZCS) types.[1] But recall (Sec. 11.1) that switching losses can occur at turnon even though there is no overlap of rising voltage and falling current at the zero crossing of the current sine wave.

Thus in Sec. 11.1 it was pointed out that considerable energy $[0.5C_o(2V_{dc})^2]$ is stored on the relatively large output capacity of a MOSFET. When the MOSFET is turned on once per period T, it dissipates $0.5C_o(2V_{dc})^2/T$ watts in the MOSFET.

Circuits which cope with this are called *zero-voltage-switching* (ZVS) types.[2] They work by ensuring that the transistor output capacity is made the capacitor of a resonant *LC* circuit. Then the voltage or energy stored on it when the transistor is off is changed to stored current or energy in the inductor of the resonant circuit. Then later in the cycle, this energy is returned without loss to the power supply bus. Operation is much like that of the nondissipative snubber of Sec. 11.6.

The intense industry interest in resonant converters started about 10 years ago. In the past decade, there has been a vast army of researchers producing a vast amount of articles on the subject.

Dozens of new resonant converter topologies have been proposed and mathematically analyzed. Some of these have actually been built and have achieved high efficiency (80 to 92 percent) and good power density (some claims of ≤ 50 W/in^3). Such quoted high power densities are presumably for DC/DC converters which do not have the large input filter capacitor required of all off-line converters. Undoubtedly, they also are for cooling by an external "cold plate" whose size and means of cooling are seldom reckoned in calculating power densities.

Coverage of all the (very large number of) resonant converter topologies and their large tree of operating modes is beyond the scope of this text. An overview of only those topologies and their operating modes that are long-lived and not yet cast aside will be presented herein.

It is worth noting here that very frequently in this field, articles on a new approach often end with comments on its restricted usage in line and load variations and excessive component stress. Surely at the next conference the following year, solutions to last year's problems are offered by numerous other investigators, but again with the admonition that there are other restrictions on their usage.

This simply reflects the fact that despite their significant advantage in somewhat restricted areas of application, resonant converters do not yet have the flexibility of PWM converters to cope with large line and load changes, short-circuited or unloaded outputs, and component tolerances. Also, they operate mainly at higher peak transistor currents for the same output power than do conventional PWM square-wave inverters and in some circuit configurations at larger voltage stresses. But this is to be expected in an area where totally new ground is being broken.

13.2   Resonant Forward Converter

First the simplest resonant circuit, the resonant forward converter will be discussed—primarily to see how it is arranged for transistor turnoff to occur at zero current and to see how critical the exact turnoff time may be.

Figure 13.1 shows a simple resonant forward converter[3] operating in the discontinuous mode. *Discontinuous mode* implies that current in the resonant LC circuit is not a continuous sine wave, but a sequence of a burst of one half or one full cycle of sine-wave current separated by a large time interval T_s as in Fig. 13.1.

The resonant frequency of the circuit F_r is $1/2(t_1 - t_0)$ and is fixed by the passive resonant elements L_r and the value of C_r reflected into the primary, $(C_r)(N_s/N_p)^2$. The resonant frequency of the circuit is then

$$F_r = 1/2\pi\sqrt{L_r C_r (N_s/N_p)^2} \qquad (13.1)$$

where L_r is the transformer leakage inductance or that plus some externally added small inductance to make the total L_r relatively independent of production variations in the leakage inductance itself.

Transistor $Q1$ is turned on at a switching frequency rate of $F_s = 1/T_s$. The circuit works as follows. First, L_r and $C_r(N_s/N_p)^2$ form a series resonant circuit with DC secondary current reflected by the transformer turns ratio in shunt across the reflected capacity in the pri-

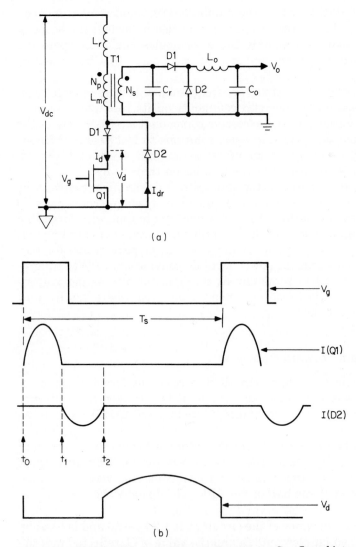

(a)

(b)

Figure 13.1 Resonant forward converter. Capacitance C_r reflected into primary resonates with L_r, the leakage inductance. The MOSFET gate is turned off shortly after the zero crossing of the first positive half cycle of drain current. When the drain rises after $D2$ stops conducting at the end of the first negative half cycle of current in $D2$, a half cycle of resonant ring of the magnetizing inductance L_m with the capacitance C_r reflected into the primary resets the $T1$ core.

mary. In resonant converter jargon, this is a *parallel resonant converter* (PRC) as the load is placed in parallel or shunt with the resonating capacitor. Other circuits, to be discussed later, place the load in series with the series resonating *LC* elements and are called *series resonant converters* (SRCs).

Now just prior to $Q1$ turnon, no current is flowing in the resonant circuit as the circuit is discontinuous—i.e., there is a long time gap between bursts of half sine waves (Fig. 11.1). Thus when $Q1$ does turn on at t_0, a half sine wave of current starts flowing through it. The current amplitude is zero at time t_0 since there has been no current flow in the resonant circuit just prior to turnon.

The current goes through its first positive half sine wave. At t_1, it passes through zero again and reverses, trying to generate the first negative half sine wave. This current is forced to flow by the voltage stored on the resonating capacitor in the primary.

This negative half cycle of current flows up through the anode of $D2$ and completes its loop through the supply source V_{dc}. For the half cycle that current flows through $D2$, the $Q1$ drain remains clamped to about -1 V (the $D2$ forward drop). Now any time after t_1 (between t_1 and t_2) there is no current in $Q1$ and its gate may be turned off.

The $Q1$ on-time duration is thus not at all critical. It must be greater than a half period of the resonant current sine wave and less than a full period. At t_2, the negative half sine wave of current in $D2$ has returned to zero and now current in the $T1$ magnetizing inductance drives the drain up toward $2V_{dc}$ to reset the core.

The magnetizing inductance and the capacitance reflected across it from the secondary form another resonant circuit. When the drain finally rises at t_2, a negative half sine wave of voltage across that resonant circuit resets the core exactly to its starting point on the *BH* loop.

The objective of zero current turnoff has thus been achieved, and there is no turnoff dissipation. The reverse recovery time of diode $D2$ is short enough so that dissipation in it is not significant—especially since current in it is already zero or close to it when the drain rises toward $2V_{dc}$.

For the duration of the first positive half resonant cycle $(t_1 - t_0)$, the primary is delivering a burst of power to the secondary and the output load. The DC output voltage is regulated by varying the spacing between these discontinuous bursts—i.e., varying the switching frequency $F_s C = 1/T_s$. If V_{dc} goes up or the DC output load current goes down, the spacing between bursts must increase (F_s must decrease)—and vice versa, of course; as V_{dc} goes down or load current increases, F_s must increase.

This method of voltage regulation—varying the switching frequency F_s—is a major drawback of resonant converters. In conventional pulse-width-modulated converters, switching frequency remains constant and on-time pulse width is varied. For most resonant topologies, pulse width is constant (the half period of the resonant LC circuit) and its repetition frequency is varied.

Variable-frequency regulation is objectionable in many circumstances. Where a computer is involved, the computer operators often require the power supply switching frequency synchronized to a submultiple of their computer clock. This reduces the probability of any power supply noise spike pickup generating false ones or zeros in the computer logic circuits.

Also where a cathode-ray tube (CRT) screen is involved, it is desirable to have the power supply switching frequency locked in phase with the CRT horizontal line frequency. Unless it is, any power supply switching frequency noise pickup appears running continuously and in a random fashion across the screen. When power supply switching frequency is constant and locked in phase to the CRT horizontal line rate, any noise pickup remains at a fixed location on the screen and is far less disconcerting to an operator.

13.2.1 Measured waveforms in a resonant forward converter

It is of interest to see actual measured waveforms in a resonant forward converter of the type discussed above. The waveforms in Fig. 13.2b are from Ref. 3 and are reproduced with the courtesy of the authors, F. Lee and K. Liu.

The circuit in Fig. 13.2a is a forward converter with an output power of 32 W (5.2 V, 6.2 A). Input voltage V_{dc} is 150 V and the circuit is shown at a switching frequency of 856 kHz. The transformer turns ratio is 10/1.

In Fig. 13.2b, waveform 3, drain current is seen to be a half sine wave whose resonant half period is 0.2 μs (F_r = 2.5 MHz). The secondary capacitor is 0.15 μF, which reflects into the primary as $0.15(0.1)^2 = 0.0015$ μF. Then for F_r = 2.5 MHz, the transformer leakage inductance plus any added discrete inductance must be

$$L_r = 1/4\pi^2(F_r)^2 C = 1/4\pi(2.5)^2(0.0015)10^{-6}$$

$$= 2.7 \ \mu\text{H}$$

It is seen in Fig. 13.2b, waveform 1, that the MOSFET gate is turned off shortly after the first positive half cycle of the current sine wave has passed through zero, thus meeting the objective of zero current turnoff. It is also seen in waveform 4 that the drain voltage has

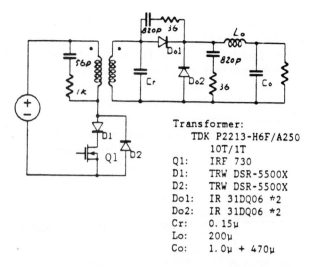

Transformer:
    TDK P2213-H6F/A250
         10T/1T
Q1:   IRF 730
D1:   TRW DSR-5500X
D2:   TRW DSR-5500X
Do1:   IR 31DQ06 *2
Do2:   IR 31DQ06 *2
Cr: 0.15μ
Lo: 200μ
Co: 1.0μ + 470μ

A 800kHz, 30W forward quasi-resonant converter

(a)

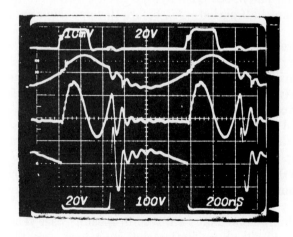

$Vin = 120V$, $Vo = 3.56V$
$fs = 856kHz$, $Io = 4.2A$
1st waveform: $Vgs(20V/Div)$
2nd waveform: $Vcr(20V/Div)$
3rd waveform: Ip $(1A/Div)$
4th waveform: $Vds(100V/Div)$

(b)

Figure 13.2 Measured waveforms on an actual circuit as
Fig. 13.1. (*Courtesy F. Lee and K. Liu*)

started rising shortly after the negative diode current ($D2$) has come back up again to zero as discussed above.

It is also seen that the voltage across the secondary capacitor in waveform 2 (which is a replica of the voltage across the primary magnetizing inductance) has reversed polarity to reset the core as discussed above. That waveform also indicates the maximum switching frequency (F_s). The minimum spacing between $Q1$ turnon pulses must be such as to permit the negative half cycle in waveform 2 to return to zero, as that is an indication that the core has been fully reset.

The foregoing is a small indication of some of the difficulties in making resonant converters work over large line and load variations. Consider the 2.7 µH calculated for the resonant inductor above. This is so small a value that changes in wire lengths and routing to the transformer can result in large percentage changes in the total inductance. For as small a value as 2.7 µH, production spread in the transformer will cause large percentage changes in its leakage inductance. If the inductance increases, the resonant half period increases. Then the MOSFET on time, which should be greater than a resonant half period, may be too short. The MOSFET may find itself turning off before the end of a resonant half period—i.e., before the sine-wave zero crossing.

Then L_r may be increased to make it less susceptible to large percentage changes arising from transformer production spread and wire length and routing. This increases the resonant half period and hence also decreases the maximum switching frequency as that must be sufficiently low to permit complete core resetting.

Now if L_r is increased but C_r is decreased to maintain the same resonant half period, the ratio L_r/C_r is increased. But the peak of the $Q1$ sine-wave current (Fig. 13.2b, waveform 3) is roughly inversely proportional to $\sqrt{L_r/C_r}$. If that is increased, maximum required peak currents may not be obtainable and maximum DC output current may not be obtainable.

Of course, many such problems may be solved in specific cases. The aforesaid is mentioned only as an indication that even such a simple resonant converter has less flexibility to cope with varying specifications, line and load conditions, and manufacturing tolerances.

It is of interest to note that a conventional forward converter operating at a relatively low frequency could yield equal output power at less primary current than shown in Fig. 13.2b. Thus, that figure shows (for full-wave mode) peak current is 1.5 A for V_o = 3.56 V, I_o = 4.2 A or 15.0 W at V_{in} of 120 V.

Equation 2.28 gives the peak primary current for a conventional PWM square-wave forward converter as $I_p = 3.13P_o/V_{dc} = 3.13 \times 15/120 = 0.39$ A. Table 7.2a shows that the next-smaller-sized core than the 2213 pot core used for Fig. 13.2*b* could easily be used, and at a lower frequency. Thus Table 7.2*a* shows that the 1811 core at 150 kHz could put out 19.4 W in a forward converter operating at only 150 kHz.

This is not to put down resonant converters, but only to point out the need to weigh them against conventional, proven topologies.

13.3   Resonant Converter Operating Modes

13.3.1   Discontinuous and continuous;
above resonance and below resonance
operating modes

Operating modes can be discontinuous as in Fig. 13.1. In the discontinuous mode (DCM), as noted, output voltage regulation is accomplished by varying the switching frequency. Power is delivered to the load as sequence of discrete current or power pulses separated by times long compared to their duration.

If the output voltage must be raised because V_{dc} has gone down or DC load current has been increased, the switching frequency or repetition rate of the discrete pulses is increased. Conversely, if output voltage has gone up because input voltage or output load resistance has gone up, the repetition rate of the discrete pulses is decreased.

Silicon controlled rectifier resonant converters, discussed in Chap. 6, have been operating successfully in the discontinuous mode for many years at frequencies in the range of 20 to 30 kHz.

In discontinuous-mode operation, however, large changes in load and line result in large changes in switching frequency. An improvement in this respect is obtained by operating in the continuous-conduction mode (CCM). In CCM, there is no or negligible gap between successive square-wave voltage pulses from the switching transistors or between successive current sinusoids.

The fundamental component of this square wave is a relatively distortionless, continuous sine wave whose frequency is that of the transistor square wave switching frequency. The resonant *LC* circuit has the characteristic Q curve (impedance vs. frequency) shown in Fig. 13.3. The average switching frequency is set either above or below resonance on the side of the Q curve.

Direct-current output voltage in the CCM mode is proportional to either the peak AC voltage on the resonating capacitor or the peak AC current in series in the resonating *LC* circuit.

Now, output voltage regulation is accomplished by moving the switching frequency along the side of the Q curve to change the amplitude of either the voltage output across the resonating capacitor (if

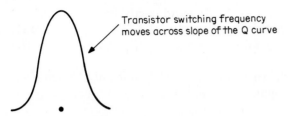

Figure 13.3 Output voltage regulation by shifting switching frequency across the slope of the Q curve of the resonating elements.

output is taken as the voltage across the capacitor) or resonant circuit current (if output is in the form of a resonant circuit current).

When operation is set above the resonant peak of the Q curve, it is referred to as *above-resonance mode* (ARM). Operation below the resonant peak is referred to as *below-resonance mode* (BRM).

In Fig. 13.3, it is seen that with a relatively steep (high Q) Q curve, it requires only small changes in frequency to obtain large changes in output amplitude.

Note that if the average switching frequency is above the resonant peak (ARM mode), to increase the output voltage or current, switching frequency must decrease and that if the average switching frequency is below the resonant peak (BRM mode), to increase the output voltage or current, switching frequency must increase.

This points out one of the problems with resonant converters. Much of the current literature indicates that the CCM is becoming the preferred mode of operation because it results in a smaller frequency range to achieve the usually desired load and line regulation.

If the feedback system has been designed on the assumption that operation is always above the resonant peak (ARM mode), however, a disastrous problem can arise if operation for some reason shifts to the BRM mode. Of course, if in the ARM mode, a decrease in the DC output voltage would be corrected by the variable-frequency oscillator in the control loop decreasing switching frequency to move higher up on the Q curve.

Since the Q curve is relatively steep, small changes in the magnitudes of the resonant L and C due to their production tolerances can shift the resonant peak. If the resonant peak were shifted sufficiently, operation could fall on the other side of the Q curve, and now the feedback loop, sensing a decrease in output voltage, would still try to correct it by decreasing switching frequency. This, of course, would now result in a further decrease in output voltage—i.e., positive rather than negative feedback.

13.4   Resonant Half Bridges in Continuous-Conduction Mode[4]

Much of the current resonant converter development effort seems to be for half-bridge topologies, which will now be considered. The following discussion is based on a classic article by R. Steigerwald.[4]

13.4.1   Parallel resonant converter (PRC) and series resonant converter (SRC)

Output power can be taken from the resonant LC circuit in either of two ways. When the output load (reflected into the power transformer primary) is reflected in parallel with the resonating capacitor, the circuit is referred to as a *parallel resonant converter* (PRC). When the load is reflected in series with the resonating LC circuit, it is referred to as a *series resonant converter* (SRC).

A parallel loaded resonant half bridge is shown in Fig. 13.4b; C_{f1}, C_{f2} are the input filter capacitors used in the scheme for generating a rectified 320 V whether operation is from 120 or 220 V AC (Fig. 5.1). They are large capacitors used only to split the rectified DC and have nothing to do with the resonant LC circuit.

The capacitor C_r is across the power transformer primary and resonates with an external inductor L_r at a frequency $F_r = 1/2\pi\sqrt{L_r C_r}$. The output inductor L_o is large and has a high impedance at F_r so that it does not load down C_r and kill the Q of the resonant LC circuit; L_o is sufficiently large that it runs in the continuous-conduction mode (Sec. 1.3.6). The impedance seen across C_r is the output load resistance multiplied by the turns ratio squared. The $T1$ magnetizing inductance is much larger than this and does not affect circuit operation.

A series-loaded resonant half-bridge converter (SRC) is shown in Fig. 13.4a. Here an external inductor L_r resonates with the equivalent capacity at the junction of the two $C_r/2$ capacitors ($= C_r$). Again the C_f capacitors are large line frequency filter capacitors and have nothing to do with the resonant circuit operation. The load in a SRC is the secondary load resistor reflected by the turns ratio squared in series with the resonating LC elements. In the series resonant circuit, the secondary side inductor is omitted.

The SRC is used for high-voltage supplies as it requires no output inductor. An output inductor for high output voltage would have to support large voltages across themselves and would be bulky. The PRC is used for low-voltage, high-current supplies as the output inductor limits ripple current in the output capacitor.

Both the series and parallel half bridges to be discussed below will operate in the continuous-conduction mode. Since DC voltage will be

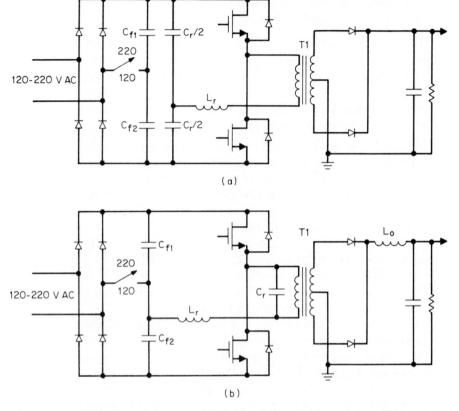

Figure 13.4 (*a*) A series-loaded resonant half bridge. Inductance L_r resonates with capacitance C_r. The load is reflected by $T1$ in series with the resonant circuit. Transistors are turned off directly after the end of the first half cycle of resonant current to achieve zero current switching. In series loading, the output filter is capacitive. (*b*) A parallel-loaded resonant half bridge. Inductance L_r resonates with capacitance C_r. The load is reflected by $T1$ in shunt with the resonating capacitor. In parallel loading, the output filter has a high-impedance inductor input to avoid lowering the Q of the resonant circuit.

regulated by varying the switching frequency, it is necessary to know how AC voltage across the reflected load varies with frequency as operation moves along the side of the resonant circuit's Q curve. The rectified DC output voltage will be proportional to the AC voltage across the reflected resistance.

13.4.2 AC equivalent circuits and gain curves for series- and parallel-loaded half bridges in continuous-conduction mode[4]

Figure 13.5*a* and 13.5*b* shows the equivalent AC circuits for the series- and parallel-loaded half bridges of Fig. 13.4*a* and 13.4*b*, respec-

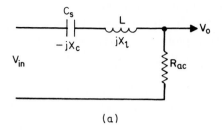

(a)

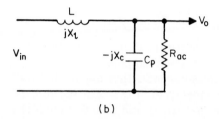

(b)

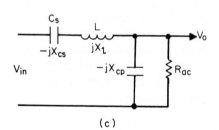

(c)

Figure 13.5 (a) AC equivalent circuit for series-loaded resonant half bridge (Fig. 13.4a). (b) AC equivalent circuit for parallel-loaded resonant half bridge (Fig. 13.4b). (c) AC equivalent circuit for series-parallel-loaded resonant half bridge, often called *LCC circuit*. AC gain between outputs and inputs above fixes the ratio between DC output voltage and half the DC input voltage. (*Courtesy R. Steigerwald*)

tively. Inputs to these circuits are the square waves of amplitude $\pm V_{dc}/2$ generated by the switching transistors. Following the analysis presented by Steigerwald,[4] consider only the fundamental of this square-wave frequency and calculate gain or ratio of output to input voltage as a function of frequency.

From the equivalent circuits of Fig. 13.5, the ratios for series and parallel loaded circuits are

Series-loaded:
$$\frac{V_o}{V_{in}} = \frac{1}{1 + j[(X_l/R_{ac}) - (X_c/R_{ac})]} \tag{13.2}$$

Parallel-loaded:
$$\frac{V_o}{V_{in}} = \frac{1}{1 - (X_l/X_c) + j(X_l/R_{ac})} \tag{13.3}$$

where R_L is the secondary load reflected into the primary and $R_{ac} = 8R_L/\pi^2$ for series loading, $R_{ac} = \pi^2 R_L/8$ for parallel loading.

From these relations, Steigerwald plots the ratio $NV_{odc}/0.5V_{in}$, where N is the power transistor turns ratio, V_{in} is the input supply voltage, and V_{odc} is the DC input voltage.

For the series-loaded case in Fig. 13.6, $Q = w_o L/R_L$ and $w_o = 1/\sqrt{LC_s}$. For the parallel-loaded case in Fig. 13.7, $Q = R_L/w_o L$ and $w_o = 1/\sqrt{LC_p}$.

From Figs. 13.6 and 13.7, some of the problems with resonant converters can be seen.

13.4.3 Regulation with series-loaded half bridge in continuous-conduction mode (CCM)

For a number of reasons, Steigerwald states that operating above the resonant peak (ARM) is preferable to below resonance.

Figure 13.6 shows how the continuous conduction mode SRC half bridge regulates. If initial operation were at A at $Q = 2$ at normalized frequency 1.3, the output/input voltage ratio would be 0.6. Now if the load resistance R_L decreased so as to increase Q to 5, normalized switching frequency would have to be decreased to about 1.15 at point B to yield the same output voltage. If R_L increased to a value which yielded $Q = 1$, for the same output voltage, operation would have to shift to point C, where normalized frequency is about 1.62.

It is obvious that as load R_L increases, Q decreases and the gain curve approaches a horizontal line, making the required frequency change so large as to be impractical. Obviously, regulation at open circuit is impossible as the Q curve has no resonant peak or *selectivity*.

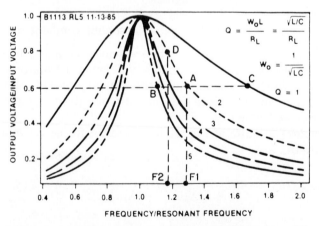

Figure 13.6 Series resonant converter gain curve from AC equivalent circuit of Fig. 13.5a. (*Courtesy R. Steigerwald*)

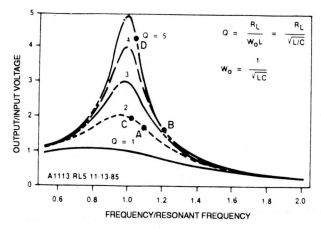

Figure 13.7 Parallel resonant converter gain curve from AC equivalent circuit of Fig. 13.5b. (*Courtesy R. Steigerwald*)

The actual operating point on the Fig. 13.6 gain curve depends on the DC input supply and output voltage. For a given output voltage, if input voltage dropped from A to D, for example, operation would shift out on the same Q curve to a lower normalized frequency at F1 to F2.

Operation is thus very nonlinear over the slopes of the Q curve. Some combinations of line and load may even not be possible. It is also obvious that choosing the exact location to operate on the Q curve is very tricky.

The feedback loop automatically selects the location on the Q curve which yields the correct output voltage. But that location may be too dangerously close to the resonant peak, at a low-Q curve where selectivity or a resonant peak is minimal or on the bottom tail of a high-Q curve where large frequency changes are required.

The scheme is sensitive to tolerances in the resonant components. Operation close to the resonant peak may cause switchover to the opposite side of the peak on load and line transients and result in positive rather than negative feedback.

13.4.4 Regulation with parallel-loaded half bridge in continuous-conduction mode

From Eq. 13.3, Steigerwald plots the gain curve of the parallel-loaded half bridge (Fig. 13.7). Here it is seen that operation at high and even no load is possible. If operation were initially at point A (Q = 2, normalized frequency = 1.1), and R_L increased so that Q ($= R_L/w_oL$) was 5, operation would shift to B at a normalized frequency of about 1.23. Obviously from the shape of the Q curve, even larger values of Q or open-circuit operation could be tolerated.

One problem with the PRC circuit is that if operation is close to the resonant peak at low Q (say, point C) and load momentarily opens or gets much larger to, say, $Q = 5$ before the feedback loop can correct frequency, output voltage could rise dangerously high at point D.

It is sometimes stated that the PRC is naturally short-circuit proof, as even when there is an output short circuit, there is also a short circuit across the transformer primary (Fig. 13.4b) and the resonating inductor limits transistor current.

Further examination indicates that this would not occur. If operation is above resonance, a short circuit at the output would force the feedback loop to move higher up on the Q curve to increase output (Fig. 13.3).

This would move switching frequency lower and eventually over the peak of the Q curve into the positive-feedback region. But the loop would not "know" that; it would continue trying to drive the switching frequency lower, "thinking" that lower frequency would move operation higher up to the top or the resonant peak.

Further, at lower frequency, the resonant inductor would have lower impedance, which would result in increased current drawn from the transistors. A clamp to limit the minimum frequency would not be practical as the resonant peak frequency is subject to large variations because of production spread in the resonant L and C.

13.4.5 Series-parallel resonant converter in continuous-conduction mode

One disadvantage of the PRC is that at light load (large shunt resistor across C_r in Fig. 13.4b), the circulating currents (and currents in the transistor) are no less than those at heavy load. In either case, the effective resistance reflected across C_r must be high so as not to kill the Q of the circuit. If this is true at heavy loads, it is even more true at light loads. This is simply another way of saying that the current in the reflected load resistor across C_r at light load is a small fraction of the current in C_r. Thus power losses in the transistors do not decrease at light load, and efficiency at such loads is poor.

This is not so in the SRC, where, for constant output voltage across the load resistor in series in the resonating LC circuit, as load current decreases, current through the load resistor (which is also current in the transistors) also decreases. Thus efficiency remains high at light load (low output power) in the SRC.

A circuit which takes advantage of the good light-load efficiency of the SRC and the ability to regulate at light or open load of the PRC is the series-parallel continuous-conduction mode converter of Fig. 13.5c. It is also referred to as the *LCC circuit*.[5]

As seen in Fig. 13.5c it has both a series capacitor C_s and a shunt capacitor C_p. For proper selection of C_s and C_p, the advantages of both SRC and PRC can be obtained to an acceptable degree.

It is seen that if C_p is zero, the circuit is that of an SRC. As C_p becomes larger than C_s, it takes on more of the characteristics of a PRC. If it becomes higher than C_s, it develops the poor efficiency at light load characteristic of a PRC.

Again from the Steigerwald article,[4] the AC gain characteristics of the LCC is calculated from its AC equivalent circuit in Fig. 13.5c as

$$\frac{V_o}{V_{\text{in}}} = \frac{1}{1 + (X_{\text{cs}}/X_{\text{cp}}) - (X_l/X_{\text{cp}}) + j[(X_l/R_{\text{ac}}) - (X_{\text{cs}}/R_{\text{ac}})]}$$

and for $Q_s = X_l/R_l$, $R_{\text{ac}} = 8R_l/\pi^2$, $w_o = 1/\sqrt{LC_s}$, and R_l equal to the DC output resistance reflected by the square of the turns ratio into the primary, the gain from half the input supply voltage to the DC output voltage reflected into the primary is

$$\frac{NV_{\text{odc}}}{0.5V_{\text{in}}} = \frac{8/\pi^2}{1 + (C_p/C_s) - (w^2LC_p) + jQ_s[(w/w_s) - (w_s/w)]}$$

This is plotted in Fig. 13.8a and 13.8b for $C_s = C_p$ and $C_s = 2C_p$.

It is seen in Fig. 13.8a and 13.8b, for both cases, for $Q = 1$ and less, that there still remains a resonant bump and some selectivity on the gain curves so that no load operation is possible. This removes one of the drawbacks of the pure SRC circuit—that of no regulation for no-load or light-load conditions (compare to Fig. 13.6 for the pure SRC circuit).

Figure 13.8a and 13.8b illustrates some of the subtleties and complexities of continuous-mode operation. Thus consider that operation is at point A in Fig. 13.8a, DC load resistance and Q are constant, and DC input voltage decreases causing a slight decrease in output voltage.

The feedback loop will attempt to correct this by moving higher up on the same Q curve to get more output. To do this, the switching frequency will be decreased. But if it decreases too much, it will fall over the top of the resonant peak at B and thereafter further frequency decrease will decrease the output.

To avoid this, it must be ensured that at lowest DC input and minimum Q, operation never requires a frequency lower than that corresponding to point B in Fig. 13.8a. A better appreciation of the practical problems in CCM is gained when it is attempted to make the circuit work over all tolerances in the LC product which shift the resonant peak in frequency and amplitude.

Steigerwald concludes that $C_p = C_s$ is a best-compromise design.

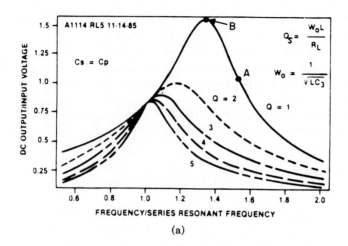

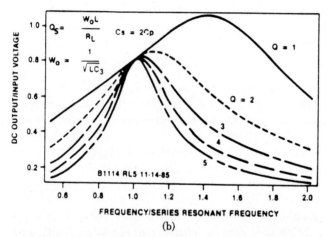

Figure 13.8 (a) Gain curves for series-parallel half-bridge resonant converter (LCC) of Fig. 13.5c for $C_s = C_p$. (b) Gain curves
for series-parallel half-bridge resonant converter (LCC) of Fig.
13.5c for $C_s = 2C_p$. (Courtesy R. Steigerwald)

Additional analyses of the LCC resonant converter, discussed above,
can be found in Refs. 6 to 9.

13.4.6 Zero-voltage-switching
quasi-resonant (CCM) converters[2]

Zero-current-switching (ZCS) converters, discussed above, force the transistor current to be sinusoidal by having the square-wave drive from the
transistor switches drive a resonant LC circuit. Further, by turning the
transistor off as the sine wave of current passes through zero at the end

of the first half period (or shortly after when current has reversed and flows into the antiparallel diode as Fig. 13.1), there is no overlap of high voltage and current and turnoff losses are eliminated.

However, there are turnon losses even though there is no overlap of high voltage and current at turnon because the leakage inductance speeds up drain (or collector) voltage fall time and slows up drain current rise time. These losses occur because the drain capacity stores an energy (at turnoff) of $0.5C(V_{max})^2$ once per cycle and dissipates it in the transistor at the next turnon. This happens once per cycle and results in a dissipation of $0.5C(V_{max})^2/T$. This dissipation becomes significant over 500 kHz to 1 MHz, and as designers move to these higher frequencies to reduce size, this becomes a problem.

A new technique—ZVS—has been proposed to circumvent this problem. It has been proposed for single-ended (flyback or buck) circuits,[10] but its value is mainly for half bridges.

A ZVS half bridge is shown in Fig. 13.9.[2] Its basic principle is that the MOSFET output capacitor is made the capacitor of a resonant LC circuit. It stores a voltage (and hence energy) in one part of the switching cycle. In a following part of the switching cycle, the energy on the capacitor is discharged through the resonant inductor back into the supply bus without dissipation. The following discussion is based on Ref. 2.

Thus in Fig. 13.9, when $Q1$ is on and $Q2$ is off, $C2$ is charged up to V_s. Transistor $Q1$ is first turned off. Transformer $T1$ magnetizing current continues to flow through $C1$, pulling it down. Half way down, there is no voltage across the primary and in the $T1$ secondary, the output inductor tries to maintain a constant current. Both rectifier diodes latch in, which provides a short circuit across the secondary and hence across the primary.

At this point, the energy stored on the top end of $C2$ discharges through the short-circuited primary, through the resonant L, through

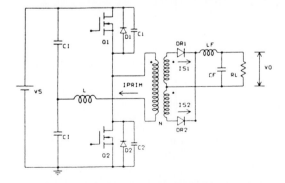

Figure 13.9 A zero-voltage-switching half-bridge resonant converter. (*Courtesy Jovanovic, Tabisz, Lee*)

the bottom filter capacitor C_{r2}, and back into the bottom end of $C2$. Since there are no resistors in this path, the discharge is lossless. The negative resonant voltage impulse on the right hand of L pulls the junction of $C1$, $C2$ down to ground, and now $Q2$ is turned on at zero voltage.

Capacitor $C1$ has slowed up $Q1$ voltage fall time sufficiently, so that there is no simultaneous high voltage and current during its turnoff.

The circuit, a CCM type, operates on the slope of the Q curve of the resonant circuit consisting of L and $C1$, $C2$ in parallel. Jovanovic et al. give the DC voltage conversion curve for the circuit (the equivalent of Figs. 13.5 to 13.8) in Fig. 13.10.[2]

Despite the many articles written on CCM, where regulation is by changing frequency along the steep slope of a resonant Q curve, this author feels it is not a reliable scheme. It will not yield similar results over a large production run of supplies with all the various production spreads in the resonant components and with the limited region of V_{dc} and R_l in the conversion curves such as those in Figs. 13.5 to 13.8 and 13.10.

13.5   Resonant Power Supplies—Conclusion

Despite the enormous number of articles and development work over the past decade or so in many industry and academic circles, there is

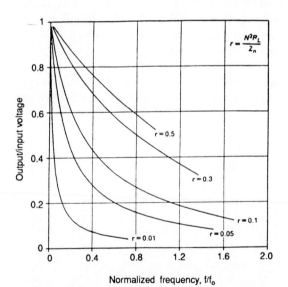

Figure 13.10 Gain curve for the zero-voltage-switching circuit of Fig. 13.9. (*Courtesy Jovanovic, Tabisz, Lee*)

no current industry-wide consensus on the future—or even the present—value of resonant power supplies.

It is of interest to consider the pros and cons on the subject. First, it is interesting to note that to the author's knowledge, resonant power supplies are not listed in any of the major manufacturers' catalogs.

This may indicate that resonant supplies are presently not sufficiently smaller, sufficiently more efficient, and sufficiently flexible in their ability to cope with large line and load changes. It may also indicate that they are not easily and inexpensively manufacturable for a variety of reasons. Possibly they cannot cope with the usual production spread in component values, parasitics in transformers, stray inductances in wiring, and greater susceptibility to problems in wire routing and component layout. It may indicate that it costs more in dollars per watt to produce and sell resonant power supplies.

To the engineer who must decide whether to consider a resonant supply for the next design, the preceding issues are important. The engineer must also ask:

May I do almost as well in watts per cubic inch with a conventional PWM supply operating at 200 to 300 kHz? Are the added complexity, limited line and load capability, and difficulty to design for worst-case conditions worth the extra 3 to 6 percent better efficiency possible with resonant supplies?

Will all units coming off a production line have identical characteristics? Or because of tolerances and production spread in component values, will fine-tuning of each unit or a large fraction of the production run be required?

Do resonant supplies generate less RFI actually because their currents are sinusoidal rather than square wave with their higher di/dt? Considering that most resonant supplies have sine wave currents three to four times the amplitude of PWM square-wave supplies of equal power, may not the RFI problem with resonant supplies be as severe since di/dt at the zero crossing of a sine wave is proportional to its peak value?

How serious is the problem that most resonant supplies regulate by varying frequency? Will users accept this or insist that the switching supply be synchronized to a clock signal which they will supply?

If the decision is to attempt a resonant design, which of the bewildering number of topologies advocated should be the safest approach? Are continuous-mode designs too unpredictable because they require operation on the slippery slope of a narrow resonant Q curve for regulation? There seems to be general agreement that discontinuous-mode operation is more predictable and reproducible. Is the larger frequency range required in discontinuous mode an important drawback?

There is no question that high frequency resonant converters will continue to be studied and improved. But, until circuit configurations are found which lend themselves to simple, worst-case designing and which are as insensitive as PWM circuits to component tolerances, wiring layout, parasitic inductances, and capacitances, high frequently resonant converters will not be widely adopted—certainly not in programs with a large production run. They will occupy only a narrow niche in the power supply field where higher cost, finely tuned component selection, and wiring layout is acceptable.

In summary, in switching power supplies, complexity equals higher cost and unreliability.

References

1. F. Lee, "High Frequency Quasi-Resonant and Multi Resonant Converter Topologies," *Proceedings of the International Conference on Industrial Electronics,* 1988.
2. M. Jovanovic, W. Tabisz, and F. Lee, "Zero Voltage Switching Technique in High Frequency Inverters," Applied Power Electronics Conference, 1988.
3. K. Liu and F. Lee, "Secondary Side Resonance for High Frequency Power Conversion," Applied Power Electronics Conference, 1986.
4. R. Steigerwald, "A Comparison of Half Bridge Resonant Topologies," *IEEE Transactions on Power Electronics,* 1988.
5. R. Severn, "Topologies for Three Element Resonant Converters," Applied Power Electronics Conference, 1990.
6. F. Lee, X. Batarseh, and K. Liu, "Design of the Capacitive Coupled LCC Parallel Resonant Converter," *IEEE IECON Record,* 1988.
7. X. Bhat and X. Dewan, "Analysis and Design of a High Frequency Converter Using LCC Type Commutation," *IEEE IAS Record,* 1986.
8. X. Batarseh, K. Liu, F. Lee, and X. Upadhyay, "150 Watt, 140 kHz Multi Output LCC Type Parallel Resonant Converter," IEEE APEC Conference, 1989.
9. B. Carsten, "A Hybrid Series-Parallel Resonant Converter for High Frequencies And Power Levels," *HFPC Conference Record,* 1987.
10. W. Tabisz, P. Gradski, and F. Lee, "Zero Voltage Switched Quasi-Resonant Buck and Flyback Converters," PESC Conference, 1987.
11. F. Lee, Ed., "High Frequency Resonant Quasi-Resonant and Multi-Resonant Converters," Virginia Power Electronics Center, 1989.
12. Y. Kang, A. Upadhyay, and D. Stephens, "Off Line Resonant Power Supplies," *Powertechnics Magazine,* May 1990.
13. Y. Kang, A. Upadhyay, and D. Stephens, "Designing Parallel Resonant Converters," *Powertechnics Magazine,* June 1990.
14. P. Todd, "Practical Resonant Power Converters—Theory and Application," *Powertechnics Magazine,* April–June 1986.
15. P. Todd, "Resonant Converters: To Use or Not to Use? That Is the Question," *Powertechnics Magazine,* October 1988.

Typical Switching Power Supply Waveforms

Chapter
14

Waveforms

14.1 Introduction

In all previous chapters, voltage and current waveforms have been shown at critical points for the various topologies (e.g., Figs. 2.1, 2.10, 3.1, 4.1 for the major topologies).

These are idealized waveforms, and newcomers to switching power supply design may wonder how idealized these waveforms really are. They may wonder how closely actual waveforms resemble the theoretical ones on which much of the circuit design is based.

Newcomers may question how these waveshapes vary with line voltage and load current variations; whether there are noise spikes on ground buses; whether there is decaying, oscillatory, ringing waveform at sharp transitions in voltage and current; and whether there is time jitter at the leading or trailing edges of the waveforms. Other questions may be as follows: How closely does the on volt-second product equal the reset volt-second product in a transformer or an inductor? What does a leakage inductance spike really look like? Since output inductors and flyback transformers are designed to yield certain current waveshapes, how close are these actual waveshapes to the theoretical ones? Since much of the power transistor dissipation at high frequencies comes from simultaneous high voltage and current at turnoff and turnon, can this be observed on a fast time base? What sort of waveform oddities may be expected?

It is thus felt that it would be very instructive and provide a feeling of confidence, especially to designers seeing high-frequency switching waveforms for the first time, if some actual oscilloscope waveforms at critical points for some of the major topologies were presented.

The topologies selected are the major ones—the forward converter, the push-pull, and the flyback. Some of the critical waveforms for the buck regulator which show the importance of operating output inductors in the continuous mode were shown in the oscilloscope photographs of Figs. 1.6 and 1.7.

The waveforms are taken mostly of points in the so-called power train—the circuitry from the input to the power transistors to the output of the output filters, as that is where most of the energy is handled and where most of the potential failures occur.

The selected circuits operate at switching frequencies above 100 kHz and are powered from telecommunications industry DC supply voltages—nominal 48 V, minimum 38 V, and maximum 60 V. Output powers in all cases are under 100 W as voltage-current waveforms at higher power change only in amplitude but not significantly in shape.

Off-line converters operating from AC voltages of 120 or 220 V will not be considered here. Supplies operating from those rectified voltages have similar waveshapes at corresponding points. But since the rectified DC supply voltages are higher, current amplitudes are lower and voltage waveshape amplitudes are higher than in telecommunications power supplies.

Since the waveshapes to be shown herein are from DC-powered circuits, they have somewhat less time and amplitude jitter than do those on circuits powered from rectified alternating current. The rectified DC in an off-line converter has line frequency ripple which will cause amplitude ripple. The feedback loop, in degenerating the input line ripple, causes time jitter in the pulse widths.

All waveshapes are taken on circuits operating above 100 kHz, use MOSFETs, and thus show no power transistor storage delay.

In all cases, the feedback loop was open and the power transistor(s) was (were) driven with a pulse of the desired frequency. But the pulse width was manually adjusted at each supply voltage input (38, 48, 60 V) so as to maintain the 5-V output within millivolts of 5 V. The slave output voltage was accepted and recorded at the pulse width, which made the 5-V output equal to 5.00 V—just as if the feedback loop were closed.

The power transistor driver for all photos is the UC3525 PWM control chip. Pulse widths were set by feeding the error-amplifier output node (which is available at one of the chip output pins) from a well-regulated DC voltage source adjusted to yield the pulse width required to set the +5-V output at 5.00 V at each DC input voltage.

14.2   Forward Converter Waveshapes

The circuit schematic for these waveshapes is shown in Fig. 14.1. It is a 125-kHz forward converter designed for 100 W, and waveshapes are shown at 80 and 40 percent of full load. Full-load outputs are 5 V at 10 A and 13 V at 3.8 A. Waveshapes are shown for nominal input volt-

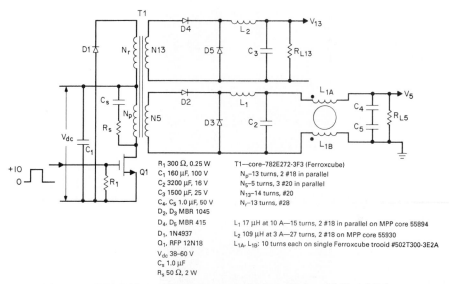

R1 300 Ω, 0.25 W
C1 160 µF, 100 V
C2 3200 µF, 16 V
C3 1500 µF, 25 V
C4, C5 1.0 µF, 50 V
D2, D3 MBR 1045
D4, D5 MBR 415
D1, 1N4937
Q1, RFP 12N18
Vdc 38–60 V
Cs 1.0 µF
Rs 50 Ω, 2 W

T1—core–782E272-3F3 (Ferroxcube)
Np–13 turns, 2 #18 in parallel
N5–5 turns, 3 #20 in parallel
N13–14 turns, #20
Nr–13 turns, #28

L1 17 µH at 10 A—15 turns, 2 #18 in parallel on MPP core 55894
L2 109 µH at 3 A—27 turns, 2 #18 on MPP core 55930
L1A, L1B: 10 turns each on single Ferroxcube trooid #502T300-3E2A

Figure 14.1 The 125-kHz forward converter— + 5.0 V at 10 A, +13 V at 3.8 A.

age of 48 V, minimum of 38 V, and maximum of 60 V. The transformer core was selected from Table 7.2a and the numbers of turns and wire sizes from Secs. 2.3.2 to 2.3.10. The output filters ($L1$, $C2$ and $L2$, $C3$) were chosen from the relations given in Sec. 2.3.11.

14.2.1 V_{ds}, I_d photos at 80 percent of full load

These photographs (photos 1 to 3 in Fig. 14.2) show drain-to-source voltages and drain currents at low, nominal, and maximum DC supply voltages.

Drain currents have the ramp-on-a-step waveshape characteristic of secondaries with output LC filters. Drain current is the sum of the secondary currents reflected by their turns ratios into the primary. Also, since both secondaries have output inductors which yield ramp-on-a-step currents (Sec. 1.3.2), these reflect into the primary as ramp-on-a-step currents.

Drain current amplitude at the center of the ramp should be (from Eq. 2.28) equal to $I_{pft} = 3.12P_o/V_{dc}$. For 80-W output and a minimum DC voltage of 38 V, peak current should be 6.57 A. Photos 1, 2, and 3 (Fig. 14.2) show that to be the current at the center of the ramp as accurately as can be read.

As DC supply voltage is increased, the photos show that pulse width (transistor on time) decreases but peak current and current at the ramp center remain unchanged—as theoretically they should.

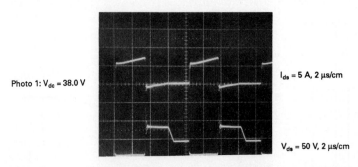

Photo 1: V_{dc} = 38.0 V

I_{ds} = 5 A, 2 μs/cm

V_{ds} = 50 V, 2 μs/cm

V_{dc}, V	I_{dc}, A	P_{in}, W	V_5, V	R_5, Ω	I_5, A	P_5, W	V_{13}, V	R_{13}, Ω	I_{13}, A	P_{13}, W	$P_{(total)}$, W	Efficiency, %
38.0	2.45	93.1	5.000	0.597	8.375	41.9	13.64	5.00	2.728	37.2	79.1	84.9

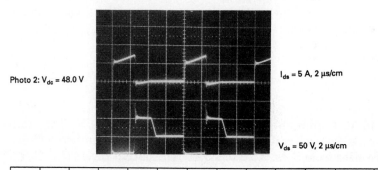

Photo 2: V_{dc} = 48.0 V

I_{ds} = 5 A, 2 μs/cm

V_{ds} = 50 V, 2 μs/cm

V_{dc}, V	I_{dc}, A	P_{in}, W	V_5, V	R_5, Ω	I_5, A	P_5, W	V_{13}, V	R_{13}, Ω	I_{13}, A	P_{13}, W	$P_{(total)}$, W	Efficiency, %
48.0	1.38	87.8	5.003	0.597	8.38	41.9	13.66	5.00	2.73	37.3	79.2	90

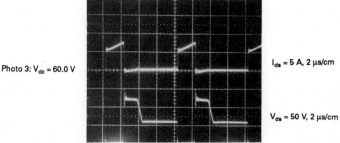

Photo 3: V_{dc} = 60.0 V

I_{ds} = 5 A, 2 μs/cm

V_{ds} = 50 V, 2 μs/cm

V_{dc}, V	I_{dc}, A	P_{in}, W	V_5, V	R_5, Ω	I_5, A	P_5, W	V_{13}, V	R_{13}, Ω	I_{13}, A	P_{13}, W	$P_{(total)}$, W	Efficiency, %
59.5	1.55	92.2	5.004	0.597	8.382	41.9	13.70	5.00	2.74	37.5	79.4	86.1

Figure 14.2   The 125-kHz 100-W forward converter of Fig. 14.1 at 80 percent full load.

Drain-to-source voltages also appear as they should be theoretically. Transistor on time at low line (V_{dc} = 38 V) is seen to be very close to 80 percent of a half period as discussed in Sec. 2.3.2. It is not always exactly that because of the inevitable rounding up or rounding down of fractional secondary turns to the nearest integral number. In this transformer, the calculated 4.5 turns on the secondary were rounded up to 5 turns. This yielded a larger peak secondary voltage and a somewhat shorter on time than called for by Eq. 2.25.

Narrow and barely discernible leakage spikes at the instant of turnoff are seen in photos 1, 2, and 3. At V_{dc} of 60 V, the leakage spike is only about 21 percent above $2V_{dc}$. But at V_{dc} = 38 V, it is about 64 percent above $2V_{dc}$.

The drain-to-source voltage waveshapes also show that V_{ds} at turnoff falls back down to $2V_{ds}$ immediately after the leakage inductance spike and remains there until the on volt-second product equals the reset volt-second product $(V_{dc}t_{on}) = (2V_{dc} - V_{dc})t_{reset}$. After those volt-second areas are equal, the drain voltage drifts back down to V_{dc}.

Figure 14.2 shows the average efficiency from V_{dc} = 38 to 60 V to be 87 percent. This is achieved at a peak flux density of 1600 G with Ferroxcube 3F3 core material. Core temperature rise was under 25°C.

Such high efficiency at 125-kHz and 1600-G peak flux density could not have been achieved with the very widely used, higher-loss core material of only 5 or so years ago—the 3C8. But even with the lower-loss 3F3 material, as discussed in Sec. 7.3.5.1, larger-sized cores could not operate at 1600 G at 125 kHz. Peak flux density would probably have to be reduced to the region of 1400 or possibly 1200 G.

14.2.2 V_{ds}, I_{ds} photos at 40 percent of full load

Photographs 4 to 6 in Fig. 14.3 give much the same information as do photos 1 to 3. At the lower output currents and power, efficiencies average 90 percent over the low, nominal, and maximum DC input voltages.

Leakage inductance spikes are considerably smaller, and transistor on times are slightly shorter as the forward drop in the output rectifier diodes is somewhat less as a result of the lesser output current. This increases the peak square-wave voltage at the cathode of the 5-V rectifier diode and permits a shorter on time to generate the 5 V of output.

14.2.3   Overlap of drain voltage and drain current at turnon/turnoff transitions

The simultaneous high voltage and current at turnon/turnoff transitions result in spikes of high power dissipation. Even though the high-dissipation spikes are very narrow (especially with MOSFETs), when

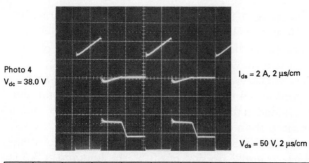

Photo 4
V_{dc} = 38.0 V

I_{ds} = 2 A, 2 μs/cm

V_{ds} = 50 V, 2 μs/cm

V_{dc}, V	I_{dc}, A	P_{in}, W	V_5, V	R_5, Ω	I_5,A	P_5, W	V_{13}, V	R_{13}, Ω	I_{13},A	P_{13}, W	$P_{(total)}$, W	Efficiency, %
38.0	1.15	43.5	4.998	1.18	4.24	21.17	13.3	10.0	1.33	17.69	38.86	89

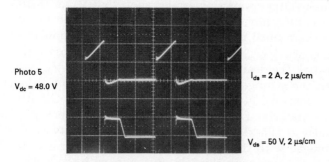

Photo 5
V_{dc} = 48.0 V

I_{ds} = 2 A, 2 μs/cm

V_{ds} = 50 V, 2 μs/cm

V_{dc}, V	I_{dc}, A	P_{in}, W	V_5, V	R_5, Ω	I_5,A	P_5, W	V_{13}, V	R_{13}, Ω	I_{13},A	P_{13}, W	$P_{(total)}$, W	Efficiency, %
48.0	0.853	40.9	5.007	1.18	4.24	21.24	12.88	10.0	1.28	16.46	37.7	92

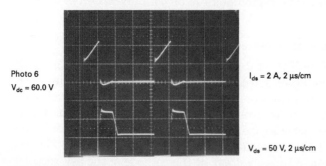

Photo 6
V_{dc} = 60.0 V

I_{ds} = 2 A, 2 μs/cm

V_{ds} = 50 V, 2 μs/cm

V_{dc}, V	I_{dc}, A	P_{in}, W	V_5, V	R_5, Ω	I_5,A	P_5, W	V_{13}, V	R_{13}, Ω	I_{13},A	P_{13}, W	$P_{(total)}$, W	Efficiency, %
59.6	0.736	43.8	5.014	1.18	4.49	22.5	13.2	10.0	1.32	17.5	40.0	91

Figure 14.3 The 125-kHz 100-W forward converter of Fig. 14.1 at 40 percent full load.

they come at a high repetition rate, their average dissipation can be high and can exceed the "conduction" dissipation of $V_{ds}I_{ds}t_{on}/T$.

The overlap dissipation at turnon is not as serious as at turnoff. At turnon, the power transformer leakage inductance presents an infinite impedance for a short time and causes a very fast drain-to-source voltage fall time. The same leakage inductance does not permit a very fast current rise time. Thus the falling V_{ds} intersects the rising I_{ds} quite low on the current waveform and the integral $\int V_{ds}I_{ds} \, dt$ taken over the turnon time is small and dissipation averaged over a full cycle is small. This can be seen on a fast time base of 0.1 μs/cm in photo 7 in Fig. 14.4.

At turnoff (photo 8 in Fig. 14.4), however, the drain current remains constant at its peak for a while (because leakage inductance tends to maintain constant current) as V_{ds} rises to about V_{dc}. Then V_{ds} contin-

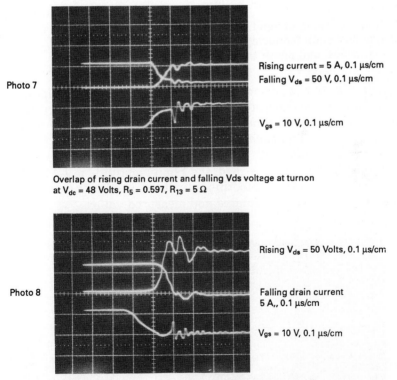

Photo 7

Rising current = 5 A, 0.1 μs/cm
Falling V_{ds} = 50 V, 0.1 μs/cm

V_{gs} = 10 V, 0.1 μs/cm

Overlap of rising drain current and falling Vds voltage at turnon
at V_{dc} = 48 Volts, R_5 = 0.597, R_{13} = 5 Ω

Photo 8

Rising V_{ds} = 50 Volts, 0.1 μs/cm

Falling drain current
5 A,, 0.1 μs/cm

Vgs = 10 V, 0.1 μs/cm

Overlap of falling drain current and rising Vds voltage at turnoff

Figure 14.4   Overlap of rising drain current and falling V_{ds} at turnon and falling drain current and rising V_{ds} at turnoff. Simultaneous high voltage and current during these turnon/turnoff transitions causes the AC switching losses. Losses are greater at the turnoff transition because current falls more slowly and V_{ds} rises more rapidly at turnoff.

ues to rise at a fast rate and reaches $2V_{dc}$ before I_d has fallen significantly below its peak. Thus, as seen in photo 8, the integral $\int V_{ds}I_d \, dt$ over the turnoff time is much greater than the same integral over the turnon time.

Performing an approximate "eyeball" integration of the above two integrals, it is seen that the average dissipation due to the overlap of falling current and rising voltage at turnoff is 2.18 W. At turnon, the average dissipation due to rising current and falling voltage is 1.4 W.

14.2.4   Relative timing of drain current, drain-to-source voltage, and gate-to-source voltage

Photo 9 in Fig. 14.5 is presented to show the negligible delay between the gate input voltage transitions and the drain voltage–drain current transitions at turnon and turnoff.

14.2.5   Relative timing of input voltage to output inductor, output inductor current rise and fall times, and power transistor drain-to-source voltage

Photo 10 in Fig. 14.6 is presented to show the output inductor upramp of current during the transistor on time and the downramp of current during the transistor off time. For $L_1 = 17$ μH, input voltage to the inductor of 16 V and on time of 2.4 μs (last two from Fig. 14.6), the ramp amplitude should be $dI = (16 - 5)2.4/17 = 1.55$ A. As accurately as photo 10 (Fig. 14.6) can be read, the ramp amplitude is 1.4 A. Because of the scales on the photo, this is the best correlation which can be obtained between the calculated and measured values.

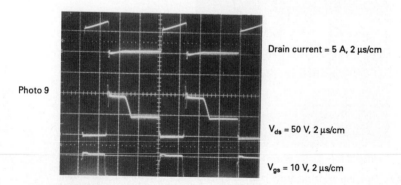

Photo 9

Drain current = 5 A, 2 μs/cm

V_{ds} = 50 V, 2 μs/cm

V_{gs} = 10 V, 2 μs/cm

Figure 14.5   Relative timing of drain current, drain-to-source voltage, and gate-to-source voltage. For 125-kHz forward converter of Fig. 14.1 at $V_{dc} = 48$ V, $R_5 = 0.597$ Ω, $R_{13} = 5$ Ω.

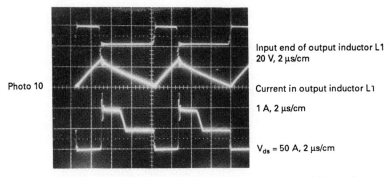

Input end of output inductor L1
20 V, 2 µs/cm

Photo 10

Current in output inductor L1

1 A, 2 µs/cm

$V_{ds} = 50$ A, 2 µs/cm

Figure 14.6 Relative timing input voltage to output inductor and its ripple current and drain-to-source voltage.

14.2.6 Relative timing of critical waveforms in PWM driver chip (UC3525A) for forward converter of Fig. 14.1

This demonstrates how the UC3525A PWM chip generates output pulses whose widths are inversely proportional to the DC supply voltage (see Fig. 14.7).

Internal to the chip, a 3-V peak-to-peak triangle (~0.5 to 3.5 V DC level) is generated and occurs once per half period of the switching frequency. This triangle is compared in a voltage comparator to the DC

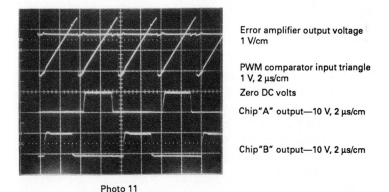

Error amplifier output voltage
1 V/cm

PWM comparator input triangle
1 V, 2 µs/cm
Zero DC volts

Chip"A" output—10 V, 2 µs/cm

Chip"B" output—10 V, 2 µs/cm

Photo 11

Figure 14.7 Significant waveforms in UC3525 pulse-width-modulating control chip. The PWM comparator internal to the chip compares an internally generated 3-V triangle to the DC voltage at its internal error-amplifier output node. The PWM comparator generates two 180° out-of-phase pulses at the chip A and B output pins. The width of these pulses is the time duration between the start of the triangle and the instant the triangle reaches the DC voltage level at the error-amplifier output node. As the error voltage output moves across the 3-V height of the triangle (in response to the difference between an internal reference voltage and a fraction of the output voltage being regulated), the output pulse widths at outputs A and B are varied.

voltage level at the output of the internal error amplifier. The error amplifier compares a fraction of the DC voltage to be regulated (at its inverting input) to a reference voltage.

The voltage comparator generates two 180° out-of-phase rectangular pulses. These pulses commence at the start of the triangle and terminate when the triangle crosses the DC voltage level at the error-amplifier output.

Thus, when the sampled fraction of the voltage to be regulated goes slightly positive, the error-amplifier output goes slightly negative, the triangle crosses the lowered DC voltage level earlier in time, and the PWM comparator output pulse widths decrease. Similarly, a decrease in sampled input to the error amplifier raises the error-amplifier output voltage slightly, the triangle crosses that higher DC voltage level later in time, and the pulse widths increase.

These adjustable-width pulses are alternately routed by a binary counter to two chip output pins for driving the transistors in a push-pull topology. For the forward converter of Fig. 14.1, only one of these pulse outputs was used.

14.3 Push-Pull Topology Waveshapes—Introduction

The next topology for which significant waveforms are presented is a push-pull whose circuit schematic is shown in Fig. 14.8.

The circuit is a 200-kHz DC/DC converter of 85-W maximum output power, and minimum of one-fifth of that. It was designed to operate from standard telecommunications industry supply voltages of 48 V nominal, 60 V maximum, and 38 V minimum. Outputs are +5 V at a maximum of 8 A and +23 V at a maximum of 1.9 A.

Significant waveforms are shown at maximum, nominal, and minimum supply voltages at maximum output currents and also at the same voltages at output currents closely one-fifth of maximum. Some waveforms are also shown at 100-W output power (15 percent above maximum) to demonstrate that at this power level, efficiency is still high, transformer temperature rise is acceptable, and waveshapes remain as expected.

For the design, the transformer core was selected from Table 7.2a and the transformer was designed (peak flux density selection, numbers of turns, wire sizes) from Secs. 2.2.9 and 2.2.10. The output filters were designed from the equations in Sec. 2.2.14.

A 200-kHz operating frequency was chosen arbitrarily as this is close to the currently maximum value of 300 to 400 kHz for square-wave converters. Above 200 kHz, although transformer and output filter sizes still decrease, efficiencies fall more rapidly and transformer

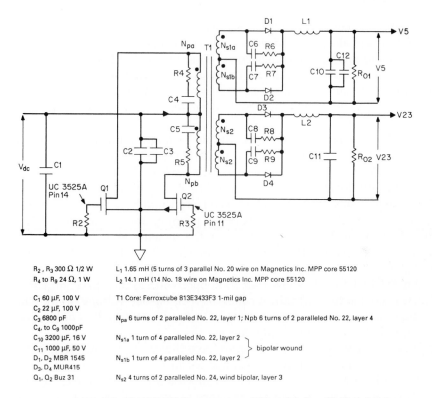

R$_2$, R$_3$ 300 Ω 1/2 W   L$_1$ 1.65 mH (5 turns of 3 parallel No. 20 wire on Magnetics Inc. MPP core 55120
R$_4$ to R$_9$ 24 Ω, 1 W   L$_2$ 14.1 mH (14 No. 18 wire on Magnetics Inc. MPP core 55120

C$_1$ 60 µF, 100 V
C$_2$ 22 µF, 100 V   T1 Core: Ferroxcube 813E3433F3 1-mil gap
C$_3$ 6800 pF
C$_4$, to C$_9$ 1000pF   N$_{pa}$ 6 turns of 2 paralleled No. 22, layer 1; Npb 6 turns of 2 paralleled No. 22, layer 4
C$_{10}$ 3200 µF, 16 V
C$_{11}$ 1000 µF, 50 V   N$_{s1a}$ 1 turn of 4 paralleled No. 22, layer 2 ⎱
D$_1$, D$_2$ MBR 1545   ⎰ bipolar wound
D$_3$, D$_4$ MUR415   N$_{s1b}$ 1 turn of 4 paralleled No. 22, layer 2 ⎰
Q$_1$, Q$_2$ Buz 31   N$_{s2}$ 4 turns of 2 paralleled No. 24, wind bipolar, layer 3

Figure 14.8 A 200-kHz 85-W DC/DC converter: +5 V at 8.0 A, +23 V at 1.9 A.

core and copper losses increase more sharply. Thus, above 200 kHz, it is questionable whether the advantage of a small decrease in size is worth the penalty of increased dissipation and transformer temperature rise.

Here, as for the forward converter of Fig. 14.1, the feedback loop was not closed. At each DC input voltage, the pulse width was manually set (as described in Sec. 14.1) to yield 5.00 V at the 5-V output. The resulting slave secondary voltage was accepted and recorded at the pulse width which yielded 5.00 V at the 5-V output.

14.3.1 Transformer center tap currents and drain-to-source voltages at maximum load currents for maximum, nominal, and minimum supply voltages

Alternate current pulses, as monitored in the transformer center tap, correspond to alternate transistors ($Q1$, $Q2$) turning on.

These waveshapes are shown to demonstrate that with MOSFETs, having no storage times and with equal-width pulses at the two gate inputs, there is no sign of flux imbalance (Sec. 2.2.5). As discussed in Sec. 2.2.5, flux imbalance would show up as an inequality in amplitude of AC pulses monitored in the transformer center tap (as in Fig. 2.4b and 2.4c).

It is seen in photos PP1 to PP3 in Fig. 14.9 that alternate current pulses at any supply voltage are of equal amplitude (as closely as can be read in the photos). No attempt was made to match r_{ds} of MOSFETs $Q1, Q2$.

The V_{ds} waveshapes show negligible leakage inductance spikes at the end of the on times. The largest leakage inductance spike (at V_{dc} = 41 V) is only about 5 V above $2V_{dc}$ (photo PP5).

Negligible leakage inductance spikes result from the fact that at high frequencies, leakage inductance is minimal because the numbers of turns is small and coupling between primary and secondaries is better than would be possible at lower frequencies. Also, sandwiching secondaries between the two half primaries (Fig. 14.8) has helped reduce leakage inductance.

Photos PP1 to PP3 show that as supply voltage increases, on times must decrease to maintain a constant 5.00 output voltage. Peak currents remain constant for constant DC output currents. It is only pulse widths that change as supply voltage changes.

The primary currents are seen to have the characteristic shape of a ramp on a step. They have this shape because they are the sum of the ramp-on-a-step secondary currents, reflected into the primaries by the respective turn ratios, plus the primary magnetizing current which is a triangle (Fig. 2.4e). The secondary currents have ramp-on-a-step waveshape because there are inductors in all outputs.

It should, however, be noted that although the equal current peaks in photos PP1 to PP3 indicate equality of peak currents in $Q1, Q2$ during their on times, those photos give a fictitious picture of the absolute value of the transistor currents (especially during the dead time between turnons). This comes about because of the nature of the magnetically coupled current probe used to monitor currents in the transformer center tap.

Apparently because of the short dead time between alternate transistor turnons, the current probe does not have time to recover to its original starting point on its hysteresis loop and hence gives a false picture of absolute current.

A true measure of absolute current amplitude in each transistor is obtained by monitoring current with the same probe in series with each transistor drain as in photo PP6 in Fig. 14.10. In that photo, it is seen with the longer time between current pulses (more than a half period), the peak current is 4.4 A. This compares to 2.4 A in photo PP2 (in Fig. 14.9), which is taken at the same supply voltage and output load currents.

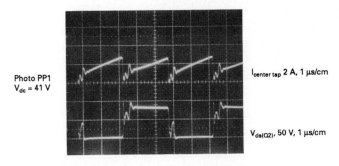

Photo PP1
V_{dc} = 41 V

$I_{center tap}$ 2 A, 1 µs/cm

$V_{ds(Q2)}$, 50 V, 1 µs/cm

V_{dc}, V	I_{dc}, A	P_{in}, W	V_5, V	R_{01}, Ω	I_5, A	P_5, W	V_{23}, V	R_{02}, Ω	I_{23}, A	P_{23}, W	$P_{(total)}$, W	Efficiency, %
41.0	2.46	100.9	5.00	0.615	8.09	40.3	23.55	12.46	1.91	44.9	85.2	84.4

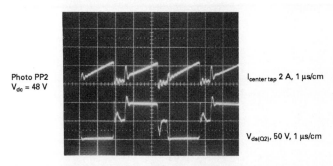

Photo PP2
V_{dc} = 48 V

$I_{center tap}$ 2 A, 1 µs/cm

$V_{ds(Q2)}$, 50 V, 1 µs/cm

V_{dc}, V	I_{dc}, A	P_{in}, W	V_5, V	R_{01}, Ω	I_5, A	P_5, W	V_{23}, V	R_{02}, Ω	I_{23}, A	P_{23}, W	$P_{(total)}$, W	Efficiency, %
48.0	2.16	103.7	5.00	0.615	8.13	40.6	23.74	12.46	1.91	45.2	85.8	82.7

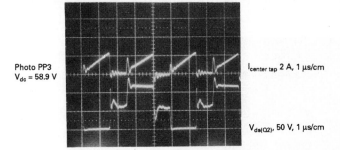

Photo PP3
V_{dc} = 58.9 V

$I_{center tap}$ 2 A, 1 µs/cm

$V_{ds(Q2)}$, 50 V, 1 µs/cm

V_{dc}, V	I_{dc}, A	P_{in}, W	V_5, V	R_{01}, Ω	I_5, A	P_5, W	V_{23}, V	R_{02}, Ω	I_{23}, A	P_{23}, W	$P_{(total)}$, W	Efficiency, %
58.9	1.79	195.4	5.00	0.615	8.13	40.6	23.72	12.46	1.90	45.1	85.7	81.3

Figure 14.9 Transformer center tap current and drain-to-source voltage ($Q2$) at minimum (photo PP1), nominal (photo PP2), and maximum (photo PP3) input voltage for maximum output currents.

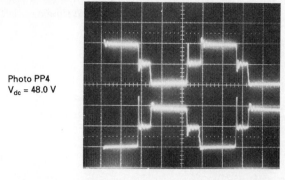

Photo PP4
V_{dc} = 48.0 V

$V_{ds(Q1)}$, 50 V, 1 µs/cm

$V_{ds(Q2)}$, 50 V, 1 µs/cm

V_{dc}, V	I_{dc}, A	P_{in}, W	V_5, V	I_5, A	P_5, W	V_{23}, V	I_{23}, A	P_{23}, W	$P_{o (total)}$, W	Efficiency, %
48.0	2.17	104.1	5.00	8.13	40.6	23.73	1.90	45.1	85.7	82.3

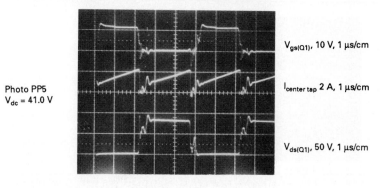

Photo PP5
V_{dc} = 41.0 V

$V_{gs(Q1)}$, 10 V, 1 µs/cm

$I_{center tap}$ 2 A, 1 µs/cm

$V_{ds(Q1)}$, 50 V, 1 µs/cm

V_{dc}, V	I_{dc}, A	P_{in}, W	V_5, V	I_5, A	P_5, W	V_{23}, V	I_{23}, A	P_{23}, W	$P_{o (total)}$, W	Efficiency, %
41.0	2.46	100.9	5.00	8.13	40.6	23.55	1.19	44.9	84.9	84.1

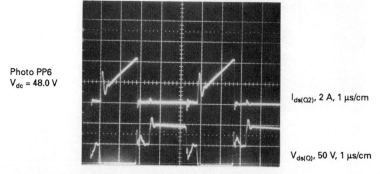

Photo PP6
V_{dc} = 48.0 V

$I_{ds(Q2)}$, 2 A, 1 µs/cm

$V_{ds(Q)}$, 50 V, 1 µs/cm

V_{dc}, V	I_{dc}, A	P_{in}, W	V_5, V	I_5, A	P_5, W	V_{23}, V	I_{23}, A	P_{23}, W	$P_{o (total)}$, W	Efficiency, %
48.0	2.19	105.1	5.00	8.13	40.7	23.79	1.91	45.4	86.1	81.9

Figure 14.10 Significant waveforms in 200-kHz 85-W converter of Fig. 14.8.

The assumption that the amplitude measured with a current probe in the drain as for photo PP6 is more valid than the measurement with the same probe in the transformer center tap (as photos PP1 to PP3) is verified by measuring voltage drop across a small current-monitoring resistor in series in the transistor source. Measurement with a current probe in series in the drain gives exactly the same absolute currents as does measuring the voltage drop across a known resistor in the source lead.

Figure 14.10 shows efficiency to exceed 81.9 percent at any supply voltage for maximum current in the two output nodes. If it were seriously attempted, efficiency could be raised by 3 to 4 percent by going to larger wire size and perhaps decreasing peak flux density. But the efficiency achieved is quite good for an operating frequency of 200 kHz and a peak flux density of 1600 G.

14.3.2 Opposing V_{ds} waveshapes, relative timing, and flux locus during dead time

Photo PP4 (in Fig. 14.10) shows the relative timing of the $Q1$, $Q2$ drain voltages. This is classic and just what would be expected. As one transistor turns on, its drain voltage falls closely to zero and the other drain rises to $2V_{dc}$.

Delays between turnon of one drain and turnoff of the other are seen to be negligible. The highest leakage inductance spike is seen to rise about 20 V above $2V_{dc}$ (Fig. 14.17, photo PP24). Note that for this photo, total output power was increased to 112 W (5 V at 4.85 A and the slave at 21 V, 4.05 A).

Note that at the start of dead time between turnons, after one transistor turns off, there is a leakage inductance spike and immediately thereafter, drain voltage falls back to V_{dc}. It remains at V_{dc} until the opposite transistor turns on, driving it to $2V_{dc}$.

It is important to understand this as it is basic to the operation of a push-pull (also to a half or full bridge, for that matter).

One may ask: What is the transformer core's flux density during the dead time between transistor turnons? At the end of a turnon, the flux density has been driven through a change of $2B_{max}$—say, up from some B_{max} to $+B_{max}$. During the dead time, neither transistor is on. Hence, does the flux density remain at $+B_{max}$ or fall back to remanence (Fig. 2.3) at 0 Oe?

If flux density fell back to remanence (~ 1000 G from Fig. 2.3), at the end of next turnon, an application of the same $2B_{max}$ change would drive the flux density to a peak of $(1000 + 2B_{max})$. This would saturate the core and destroy the transistors.

Thus, obviously, at the end of a transistor turnon, the core flux density, having been driven up to—say— $+ B_{max}$, remains locked there throughout the dead time. At the end of the dead time, the opposite transistor turns on and drives the flux density down from $+B_{\max}$ to $-B_{\max}$ and the cycle repeats.

One may then ask: Since neither transistor is on during the dead time, where is the current coming from to keep the flux density locked at $+B_{\max}$ or $-B_{\max}$? To keep the core there, there must be some oersteds holding it up—and since oersteds are proportional to ampere turns, there must be some current flowing to hold them up during the dead time.

Obviously, since both transistors are off during the dead time, the current holding the core up at $+B_{\max}$ or $-B_{\max}$ must be flowing in the secondaries. This current is the core primary magnetizing current reflected into the secondaries.

During the transistor on time (see Fig. 2.4e), the DC input voltage supplies primary load current (all the secondary currents reflected by their turns ratios into the primary) plus magnetizing current which flows into the primary magnetizing inductance.

However, since current in an inductor cannot change instantaneously, when the on transistor turns off, that stored current or stored energy must continue elsewhere. The magnetizing current then simply continues to flow where it finds a closed path.

That closed path is in the secondaries. As a transistor turns off, the current in each secondary output inductor cannot change. Thus all output inductors reverse polarity at the end of an on time. If there were free-wheeling diodes at the output as for forward converters (see Fig. 2.10), the output inductor current would continue to flow through those diodes.

Since there are no free-wheeling diodes in a push-pull, the output rectifiers serve a similar function (Sec. 2.2.10.3). As the output inductors reverse polarity, when they reach a point one diode drop below ground (or above for a negative output voltage), the rectifier diodes latch in and serve as free-wheeling diodes carrying the output inductor current.

However, the diodes carry more than the output inductor current. By flyback action, the magnetizing current built up in the primary during the on time is reflected by the turns ratio into one of the secondary halves (the one which just previously had not been carrying current). It is this current flowing in one of the secondary halves which keeps the core locked up at $B_{\max}$ during the dead time.

Thus, during the dead time, the output inductor current continues to flow through the half-secondary windings and the rectifier diodes continue acting as free-wheeling diodes. That current divides roughly equally as "ledge" currents (Fig. 2.6d and 2.6e) between the two half secondaries as described in Sec. 2.10.3. But one of those ledge currents is always larger than the other, as can be seen dramatically in photo PP21 (Fig. 14.15).

Thus primary magnetizing current does not result in dissipation. It simply increases in one direction during one transistor on time, is stored (and decreases slightly) in the secondary during the dead time, and reverses direction in the primary during the next transistor on time, repeating the previous half cycle.

As discussed, during the dead time, output inductor current divides roughly equally between the two half secondaries. But since those half secondaries have low impedance, current flowing through them produces no voltage drop across them. Hence there is no voltage drop across either of the two half primaries. Thus voltage at the two off drains during the dead time must equal V_{dc} as seen in photos PP4 and PP1 to PP3.

14.3.3 Relative timing of gate input voltage, drain-to-source voltage, and drain currents

This timing is shown in photo PP5 (Fig. 14.3). It shows negligible delays between gate input voltage rise and fall times and the corresponding drain-current–drain-voltage transitions.

14.3.4 Drain current as measured with a current probe in series in the drain as compared with measurement with a current probe in series in the transformer center tap

As discussed in Sec. 14.3.1, drain current measured with a current probe in series in the drain as for photo PP6 gives a correct measure of absolute drain current.

However, when—as in photo PP1—measured with the current probe in series with the transformer center tap (where both transistor currents are seen), the short transistor dead time between alternate on times does not permit the flux in the current probe transformer to reset. Consequently in such a measurement, the current indicated during the dead time is not zero and absolute values of current cannot be obtained from it.

14.3.5 Output ripple voltage and rectifier cathode voltage

Photo PP7 (in Fig. 14.11) shows a 5-V output ripple voltage and noise. It is seen to be about 80 mV peak to peak. Such measurements are often difficult to make and often fictitious. They are frequently masked by common-mode noise. Common-mode noise voltage is volt-

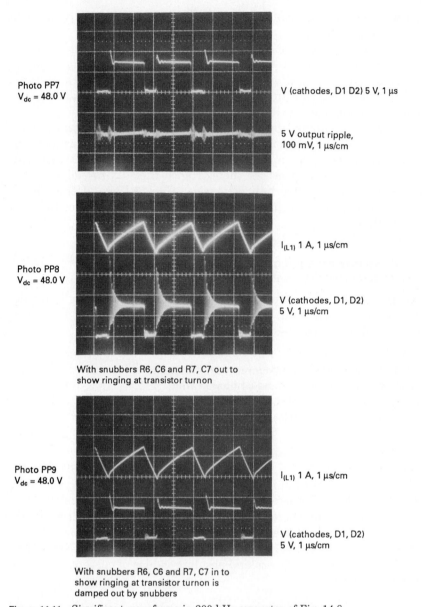

Photo PP7
V_{dc} = 48.0 V

V (cathodes, D1 D2) 5 V, 1 µs

5 V output ripple,
100 mV, 1 µs/cm

$I_{(L1)}$ 1 A, 1 µs/cm

Photo PP8
V_{dc} = 48.0 V

V (cathodes, D1, D2)
5 V, 1 µs/cm

With snubbers R6, C6 and R7, C7 out to
show ringing at transistor turnon

$I_{(L1)}$ 1 A, 1 µs/cm

Photo PP9
V_{dc} = 48.0 V

V (cathodes, D1, D2)
5 V, 1 µs/cm

With snubbers R6, C6 and R7, C7 in to
show ringing at transistor turnon is
damped out by snubbers

Figure 14.11 Significant waveforms in 200-kHz converter of Fig. 14.8.

age simultaneously common to the negative and positive rail across which the measurement is being made.

Such common-mode noise can cause problems at the loads and can be minimized by a common-mode filter or *balun* as shown in Fig. 14.1.

To determine whether noise voltage is truly differential or common-mode, the "hot" end of the voltage probe is short-circuited to its shortest ground lead and those two points are then touched to the return rail of the output voltage.

If the oscilloscope still indicates almost the same large noise voltage (as it most often will), that noise is common-mode noise. It will change in amplitude as oscilloscope ground connections are changed to various points on the power supply ground rail and as grounding lead lengths are changed.

Output ripple voltage measurements should be made with a differential probe which has a good common-mode rejection ratio at high frequencies. With the fast rise and fall times of MOSFETs, the common-mode "ringing" or noise on ground buses can occur at frequencies over 50 MHz.

Photo PP7 also shows the voltage at the 5-V output rectifier cathodes. It is this voltage which is averaged by the output LC filter to yield the desired DC output voltage.

If this waveform has notches, bumps, or odd ledges along its supposedly vertical sides, those contribute area to the voltage being averaged. The feedback loop will then alter the transistor on time so that the averaged volt-second area at the rectifier cathodes yields the desired DC voltage.

Thus the master output voltage will always be correct regardless of whether there are odd bumps, notches, or ledges during the dead time or along the vertical sides of the rectifier cathode waveshapes. But then any slave rectifier cathode voltage may not have the same proportion of extraneous bumps or notches as the master and the slave DC output voltage differ from what would be expected from the relative turns ratio.

For the slave DC output voltages to be what is expected from their turns ratios, the voltages at the rectifier cathodes of the master and all slaves should have steep vertical sides (photos PP7, PP9, Fig. 14.11) and no bumps, notches, or bumps during the dead time which alter their volt-second area. Examples of such aberrations of the rectifier cathode voltages are shown in photos PP11 (in Fig. 14.12) and PP18 (Fig. 14.14). These waveform aberrations will be explained below.

14.3.6   Oscillatory ringing at rectifier cathodes at transistor turnon

This is shown in photos PP8 and PP10 (Figs. 14.11, 14.12) and its elimination in photos PP9 and PP11 (Figs. 14.11, 14.12).

At the instant of transistor turnon, the on-turning rectifier diode (say, diode $D1$ in Fig. 14.8) cancels the free-wheeling current in the opposite diode—say, $D2$. As the $D2$ forward current is canceled and its cathode voltage starts rising, there is an exponentially decaying oscil-

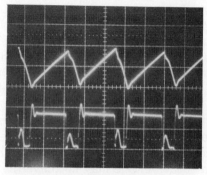

Photo PP10
V_{dc} = 48.0 V

$I_{(L2)}$ 500 mA, 1 μs/cm

V (cathodes, D3 D4)
20 V, 1 μs/cm

With snubbers R8, C8 and R9, C9 out to
show ringing at transistor turnon

Photo PP11
V_{dc} = 48.0 V

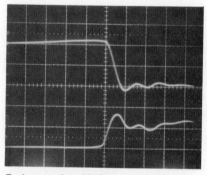

$I_{(L2)}$ 500 mA, 1 μs/cm

V (cathodes, D3, D4)
20 V, 1 μs/cm

With snubbers R8, C8 and R9, C9 in to show
ringing at transistor turn on is damped out
by snubbers

Photo PP12
V_{dc} = 48.0 V

Falling current in Q2 at turnoff
2 A, 50 ns/cm

Rising drain-to-source voltage (Q2)
at turnoff 50 V, 50 ns/cm

To show overlap of falling current and
risingV_{ds} voltage at turnoff; even with the
fast I_{ds} fall time of MOSFETs, this overlap
yields AC switching losses

Figure 14.12 Significant waveforms in 200-kHz converter of Fig. 14.8.

lation or "ring" at the common cathodes as seen in photos PP8 and PP10.

The oscillation is at a frequency determined by the inherent capacity of the off-turning diode $D2$ and the value of the output inductor. The amplitude and duration of the ring are determined by the rectifier diode reverse recovery times and DC output current.

The ring can cause RFI problems, drive the rectifier diodes too close to their maximum reverse voltage rating, and increase their dissipation. The oscillation can easily be eliminated by RC snubbers ($R6$, $C6$; $R7$, $C7$; $R8$, $C8$; and $R9$, $C9$) across the diodes as shown in Fig. 14.8. Cathode waveforms before the snubbers were added are shown in photos PP8 and PP10 and after the snubbers were added, in photos PP9 and PP11.

14.3.7 AC switching loss due to overlap of falling drain current and rising drain voltage at turnoff

This is shown in photo PP12 (Fig. 14.12). Because MOSFETs have negligible storage and very fast current turnoff time, this is close to the best-case scenario described in Sec. 1.3.4.

In that scenario, current starts falling at the very same instant the drain voltage starts rising, and current has fallen to zero at the same instant voltage has risen to its maximum. As mentioned in Sec. 1.3.4, for this case, the AC switching loss averaged over the current fall time is $\int_0^{tf} IV\, dt = I_{max}V_{max}/6 = 4.2 \times 85/6 = 59.5$ W. For a current fall time of about 40 ns at a switching period of 5 μs, the AC switching loss averaged over a full cycle is only $59.5 \times 0.04/5$ or 0.48 W.

14.3.8 Drain currents as measured in the transformer center tap and drain-to-source voltages at one-fifth of maximum output power

Waveshapes for output currents of one-fifth of maximum value (a usual power supply specification for minimum output currents) are shown in photos PP13 to PP15 (in Fig. 14.13).

Efficiencies are still seen in Fig. 14.13 to be close to 80 percent. For the worst efficiency of 78.7 at V_{dc} of 59.8, total internal losses are only 4.3 W—which is quite good.

These last photos and the ones to follow point out an interesting and subtle problem. The problem is not at all a catastrophic failure mode but one which may cause slave voltages to depart significantly from specified values.

The problem arises from too large a transformer primary magnetiz-

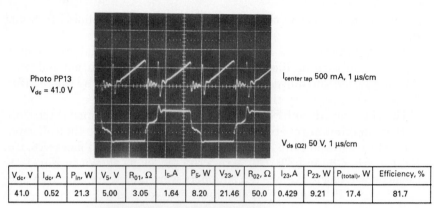

Photo PP13
V_{dc} = 41.0 V

$I_{center tap}$ 500 mA, 1 µs/cm

$V_{ds (Q2)}$ 50 V, 1 µs/cm

V_{dc}, V	I_{dc}, A	P_{in}, W	V_5, V	R_{01}, Ω	I_5,A	P_5, W	V_{23}, V	R_{02}, Ω	I_{23},A	P_{23}, W	$P_{(total)}$, W	Efficiency, %
41.0	0.52	21.3	5.00	3.05	1.64	8.20	21.46	50.0	0.429	9.21	17.4	81.7

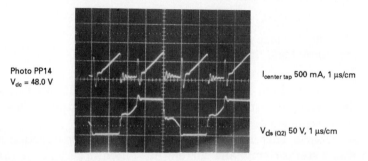

Photo PP14
V_{dc} = 48.0 V

$I_{center tap}$ 500 mA, 1 µs/cm

$V_{ds (Q2)}$ 50 V, 1 µs/cm

V_{dc}, V	I_{dc}, A	P_{in}, W	V_5, V	R_{01}, Ω	I_5,A	P_5, W	V_{23}, V	R_{02}, Ω	I_{23},A	P_{23}, W	$P_{(total)}$, W	Efficiency, %
48.0	0.44	21.1	5.00	3.05	1.64	8.20	21.52	50.0	0.430	9.25	17.5	82.7

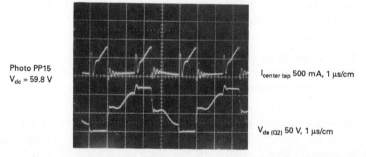

Photo PP15
V_{dc} = 59.8 V

$I_{center tap}$ 500 mA, 1 µs/cm

$V_{ds (Q2)}$ 50 V, 1 µs/cm

V_{dc}, V	I_{dc}, A	P_{in}, W	V_5, V	R_{01}, Ω	I_5,A	P_5, W	V_{23}, V	R_{02}, Ω	I_{23},A	P_{23}, W	$P_{(total)}$, W	Efficiency, %
59.8	0.37	22.1	5.00	3.05	1.64	8.20	21.88	50.0	0.438	9.58	17.8	78.0

Figure 14.13 Transformer center tap current and drain-to-source voltage (Q2) at minimum (photo PP13), nominal (photo PP14), and maximum (photo PP15) input voltage for one-fifth of maximum output currents.

ing current or for a given maximum magnetizing current, from too low a total DC output current. The magnetizing current can become larger than originally specified if the two transformer halves inadvertently separate slightly, thus decreasing the magnetizing inductance and increasing the magnetizing current; or possibly if too large a transformer gap was used to achieve a desired magnetizing inductance; or if the minimum load current is made lower than the value originally specified when the magnetizing inductance was selected.

A clue to the problem can be seen in the DC voltage levels at the drain during the transistor dead times in photos PP13 to PP15. In those photos, the drain voltage during the dead time (which should be firmly at V_{dc} as in photo PP4) starts at V_{dc} but gradually pulls above it before the end of the dead time.

This drain voltage pulling above V_{dc} during the dead time is not the cause of the problem, but only another manifestation of the basic cause. The basic cause is seen in photo PP18 (in Fig. 14.14), which shows the voltage at the cathodes of the 5-V output rectifiers. There it is seen that during the dead time, the rectifier cathodes do not remain clamped to ground as they should be, but gradually pull off ground. This is the bump or ledge discussed in Sec. 14.3.5.

It is this voltage at the rectifier cathodes which is averaged by the output LC filter to yield the 5-V DC output voltage. If that voltage has such a bump in the dead time before the normal transistor turnon time, its volt-second area is increased. Thus the feedback loop (which is forcing the 5-V output to be precisely 5.00 V) will decrease the normal on time. Then, since the slave outputs do not have this increased volt-second area due to a bump at their rectifier cathodes, their DC output voltage will decrease.

This can be seen in a comparison of photos PP9 (Fig. 14.11) and PP18 (Fig. 14.14). For PP9, the rectifier cathodes have no bump during the dead time and the voltage rises vertically from ground at the start of the normal on time. For this case, which is at maximum load current in both outputs, the "23"-V output is 23.74 at V_{dc} of 48.0 V (photo PP2, Fig. 14.1). For photo PP18, at the same V_{dc} of 48 V and at minimum load currents, when the 5-V output is 5.00 V, the "23"-V output is 21.52 V (tabular data for photo PP14 in Fig. 14.13).

The final question to be answered is why this bump during the dead time occurs for too high a magnetizing current or too low a DC output current. This can be understood from the discussion in Sec. 14.3.2 as follows.

As the on transistor turns off, some fraction of the total primary magnetizing current, multiplied by the turns ratio, continues flowing in one of each of the half secondaries. But rectifier diodes of all secondaries are now free-wheeling and carrying about half their associ-

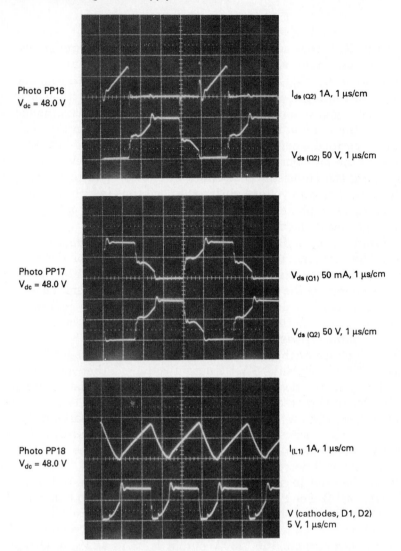

Photo PP16
V_{dc} = 48.0 V

$I_{ds\ (Q2)}$ 1A, 1 µs/cm

$V_{ds\ (Q2)}$ 50 V, 1 µs/cm

Photo PP17
V_{dc} = 48.0 V

$V_{ds\ (Q1)}$ 50 mA, 1 µs/cm

$V_{ds\ (Q2)}$ 50 V, 1 µs/cm

Photo PP18
V_{dc} = 48.0 V

$I_{(L1)}$ 1A, 1 µs/cm

V (cathodes, D1, D2)
5 V, 1 µs/cm

Figure 14.14 Significant waveforms in 200-kHz converter of Fig. 14.8 at minimum (photo PP16), nominal (photo PP17), and maximum (photo PP18) input voltages for one-fifth of maximum output current.

ated output inductor currents. In each secondary, one rectifier diode also carries a portion of the primary magnetizing current which has been reflected into that secondary.

Now in Fig. 14.8, consider the 5-V output rectifiers. Assume that $Q1$ is on. This makes the $D2$ anode positive and $D2$ delivers current to the load via $L1$. When $Q1$ turns off, the dead time starts and the $L1$ current is roughly equally divided between the $D1$ and $D2$ acting as free-wheeling diodes. So long as the sum of the $D1 + D2$ currents is equal to the $L1$ current, their cathodes remain clamped one diode drop below ground.

However, as $T1$ turns off, some fraction of the total primary magnetizing current is transferred by flyback action into N_{s1a} and $D1$ into $L1$. So long as this current is less than the current in $L1$, the $D1$, $D2$ cathodes remain clamped one diode drop below ground and the balance of the $L1$ current is supplied via $D1$, $D2$.

But when the current reflected by flyback action from the primary into N_{s1a} exceeds more than the current in $L1$, the impedance at the input end of $L1$ becomes high and the common cathodes of $D1$, $D2$ pull up from ground before the end of the dead time as seen in photo PP18.

Now with a closed feedback loop, the increased volt-second area due to the bump at the rectifier cathodes during the dead time causes the PWM chip to decrease the on time so that the voltage averaged by the LC filter yields the desired 5.00-V output. This decreased on time then results in a lowered DC voltage for the slave outputs.

14.3.9   Drain current as measured in drain lead and drain voltage at one-fifth of maximum output power

This is shown in photo PP16 (Fig. 14.14). Note that with the current probe in the transistor drain lead, a true measure of drain current is obtained (peak of 1.5 A). When drain current is measured in the transformer center tap as for photo PP14 (Fig. 14.13), a false value of 700 mA is observed. This has been discussed in Secs. 14.3.1 and 14.3.4.

14.3.10   Relative timing of opposing drain voltages at one-fifth of maximum output currents

This is shown in photo PP17 (Fig. 14.14). Nothing new here. It is presented to show relative timings.

14.3.11   5-V output inductor current and rectifier cathode voltage

The inductor current waveform in photo PP18 shows the upslope of inductor current during the transistor on time $[di/dt = (V_{cathode} - V_o)/L_1]$ and the downslope of its current during the dead time $(di/dt = V_o/L_1)$.

It is of interest to calculate $L1$ to verify that the inductor is as designed. Thus as closely as can be read from the cathode voltage waveform, $V_{cathode} = 7.5$ V, and from the inductor current waveform during the upslope di is 1.8 A in 1.45 μs. Then $L_1 = (7.5 - 5)1.45 \times 10^{-6}/1.8 = 2.0$ μH.

The inductor has 5 turns on an MPP 55120 core (see Magnetics Inc. MPP core catalog) which has an A_l of 72 mH/1000 turns at the low-oersted level of PP18. Then a 5-turn winding should have an inductance of $(0.005)^2 \times 72000 = 1.8$ μH. This is as close a correlation as can be expected from reading di/dt from photo PP18.

14.3.12 5-V rectifier cathode voltage at output current higher than minimum

This is shown in photo PP19 (in Fig. 14.15). It is presented to show that when DC output current is increased, the voltage ledge during the dead time shown in photo PP18 vanishes. The voltage remains clamped at ground throughout the dead time and rises steeply to its peak at transistor turnon. As a consequence (as discussed in Sec. 14.3.8, the "23"-V output voltage rises from 21.50 V for photo PP18 to 22.97 V for photo PP19.

14.3.13 Gate input and drain current timing

This is presented (see photo PP20 in Fig. 14.15) to show the relative timing of both gate input voltages and both drain currents. Delays between gate voltage transitions and corresponding drain current rise and fall times are seen to be negligible.

14.3.14 Rectifier diode and transformer secondary currents

This has been discussed in Sec. 14.3.2 (see also photo PP21 in Fig. 14.15). It shows the ledge currents during the transistor dead time. Note that the ledge current immediately after an on time is greater than that before an on time. This is because the previously on diode carries the primary magnetizing current plus half the output inductor current during the dead time immediately after turnoff.

14.3.15 Apparent double turnon per half period arising from too high a magnetizing current or too low DC output currents

This is shown in photo PP22 (in Fig. 14.16). It is an extreme example of the case of photo PP13 (Fig. 14.13). It is seen in photo PP22 that there are apparently two turnons per half period—at $A1$ and $A2$ for $Q1$ and $B1$ and $B2$ for $Q2$.

Actually only at $A2$ and $B2$ do the transistors turn on and bring the

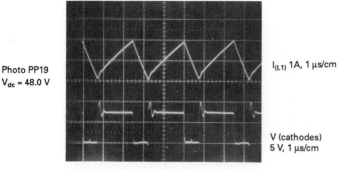

Photo PP19
V_{dc} = 48.0 V

$I_{(L1)}$ 1A, 1 μs/cm

V (cathodes)
5 V, 1 μs/cm

For I_5 = 5 A, I_{23} = 0.425 A
Showing the D1, D2 cathode voltage remaining clamped down to
ground during the transistor off time for larger output currents
because the larger diode free-wheeling current is nit unclamped
by the transformer magnetizing current (compare to photo PP18)

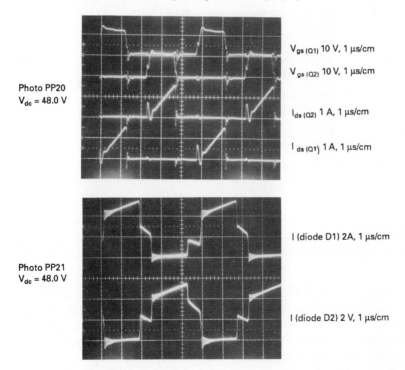

Photo PP20
V_{dc} = 48.0 V

$V_{gs\,(Q1)}$ 10 V, 1 μs/cm

$V_{gs\,(Q2)}$ 10 V, 1 μs/cm

$I_{ds\,(Q2)}$ 1 A, 1 μs/cm

$I_{ds\,(Q1)}$ 1A, 1 μs/cm

Photo PP21
V_{dc} = 48.0 V

I (diode D1) 2A, 1 μs/cm

I (diode D2) 2 V, 1 μs/cm

For I_{dc} (5 V output) of 5 A
Showing "ledge" currents during dead time between transistor on
times (refer to Section 2.2.10.3 and Fig. 2.6

Figure 14.15 Significant waveforms in 200-kHz converter of Fig. 14.8.

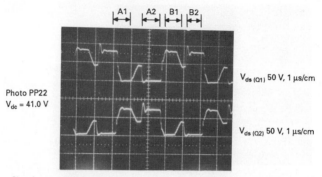

Photo PP22
$V_{dc} = 41.0$ V

$V_{ds (Q1)}$ 50 V, 1 µs/cm

$V_{ds (Q2)}$ 50 V, 1 µs/cm

Showing an apparent failure mode at minimum output current or too high a magnetizing current: each transistor apparently turns on twice per half period (at A1, A2 for Q1 and at B1, B2 for Q2); the drains dropping to zero at A1, B1 are not transistor turnons—they occur for too large a transformer magnetizing current or too low a DC load current, as explained in the accompanying text

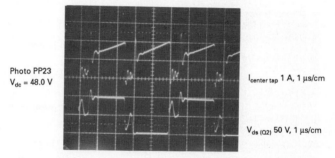

Photo PP23
$V_{dc} = 48.0$ V

$I_{center\ tap}$ 1 A, 1 µs/cm

$V_{ds (Q2)}$ 50 V, 1 µs/cm

Showing critical waveforms on Fig. 14.8 circuit at output power 15% above specified maximum; converter efficiency is still a relatively high 83.8% and transformer temperature rise is only 54°C

V_{dc}, V	I_{dc}, A	P_{in}, W	V_5, V	R_{01}, Ω	I_5, A	P_5, W	V_{23}, V	R_{02}, Ω	I_{23}, A	P_{23}, W	$P_{(total)}$, W	Efficiency, %
48.0	2.51	120.5	5.00	0.339	14.7	73.7	26.12	25.0	1.04	27.3	101.0	83.8

Figure 14.16   Significant waveforms in 200-kHz converter of Fig. 14.8.

drains down to ground. However, $A1$ and $B1$ are fictitious turnons. At those times, the drain is driven down to ground by the positive drain bump after turnoff of the opposite transistor. This phenomenon is an extreme example of the situation seen in photo PP13 obtained by increasing the primary magnetizing current by increasing the transformer gap at low DC output currents.

As discussed in Sec. 14.3.8, this phenomenon occurs for a large magnetizing current reflected into the secondary. When this exceeds the DC load current in the output inductor, the rectifier diodes are unclamped from ground and produce a large positive bump above V_{dc} at the drain.

This, through the transformer coupling, produces a negative dip at the opposite drain. When that negative dip at the opposite drain falls as low as ground, the inherent body diode of that MOSFET clamps in and holds the drain at ground. It appears thus that the MOSFET has turned on.

The circuit may continue to work in this odd mode, but with the feedback loop closed, oscillations may occur. On time will jump erratically from a true $B2$ aided by the fictitious $B1$ to a true on time of $B1 + B2$ at a slightly higher load current or slightly lower primary magnetizing current.

The problem can be avoided by ensuring that there can be no inadvertent increase of the transformer gap which would increase magnetizing current and that the lowest DC load current is always larger than the magnetizing current reflected into the master secondary.

14.3.16   Drain currents and drain-to-source voltage at output power 15 percent above specified maximum

This is presented (see also photo PP23, Fig. 14.16) to show that efficiency is still above 83 percent, transformer temperature rise is still only 54°C, and critical waveforms are still clean at this higher power level. The circuit of Fig. 14.8 has also been run up to 112 W of output power (photo PP24 in Fig. 14.17) with an efficiency of over 86 percent with clean waveforms and transformer temperature rise of only 65°C.

14.3.17   Ringing at drain during transistor dead time

To avoid ringing, RC snubbers ($R4$, $C4$ and $R5$, $C5$) are required across each half primary. Without them, a high-frequency oscillatory ring occurs throughout the transistor dead time (photo PP25 in Fig. 14.17). This worsens the RFI problem and affects slave DC output voltage in the same way as the dead time ledge of photo PP18.

14.4   Flyback Topology Waveshapes

14.4.1   Introduction

Typical significant waveforms will be presented for a relatively low-power discontinuous mode, single-ended flyback.

A discontinuous mode single-ended flyback is selected as it is the simplest for output powers up to about 60 W—the area of greatest usage for flybacks.

About the most serious drawback of the single-ended flyback is that energy stored in the transformer leakage inductance must be ab-

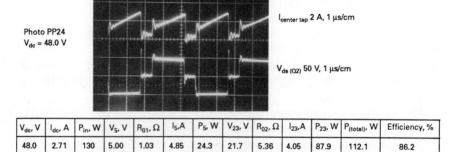

Photo PP24
V_{dc} = 48.0 V

$I_{center\ tap}$ 2 A, 1 µs/cm

$V_{ds\ (Q2)}$ 50 V, 1 µs/cm

V_{dc}, V	I_{dc}, A	P_{in}, W	V_5, V	R_{01}, Ω	I_5,A	P_5, W	V_{23}, V	R_{02}, Ω	I_{23},A	P_{23}, W	$P_{(total)}$, W	Efficiency, %
48.0	2.71	130	5.00	1.03	4.85	24.3	21.7	5.36	4.05	87.9	112.1	86.2

Drain currents and drain-to-source voltage at 30% above maximum specified output power

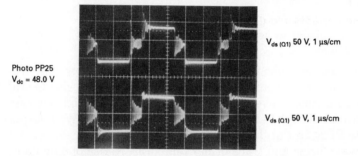

$V_{ds\ (Q1)}$ 50 V, 1 µs/cm

Photo PP25
V_{dc} = 48.0 V

$V_{ds\ (Q1)}$ 50 V, 1 µs/cm

Showing ringing during dead time when RC snubbers (R4, C4 and C5) are removed from primary

Figure 14.17 Ringing at drain during transistor dead time.

sorbed and subsequently dissipated in an *RCD* snubber (Chap. 11). If it is not, the leakage spike amplitude can rise to a voltage high enough to destroy the transistor. But above 60 W (especially for low-input voltage supplies where input currents are high), the high snubber dissipation is a significant drawback.

The double-ended flyback (Sec. 4.6) solves this problem not by storing leakage inductance energy in a snubber capacitor and then dissipating it in a resistor but by returning the leakage inductance energy without dissipation to the input supply bus.

Thus, the double-ended flyback is a desirable and widely used approach for output powers above 60 to 75 W. But significant waveforms in the single-ended flyback are much like those of the superior double-ended flyback, and hence waveshapes of the single-ended circuit only will be shown.

Waveforms shown herein were taken on the circuit of Fig. 14.18. The circuit is a 50-W, 50-kHz supply with one master output and one slave. Here again, the feedback loop was not closed. The transistor in-

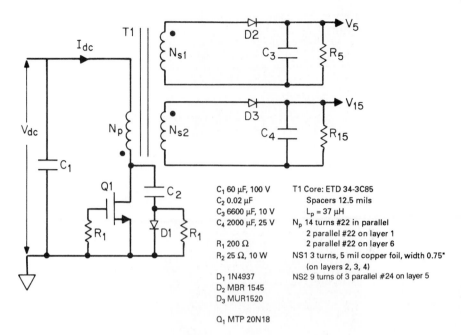

Figure 14.18   A 50-kHz 50-W flyback supply.

C_1 60 µF, 100 V
C_2 0.02 µF
C_3 6600 µF, 10 V
C_4 2000 µF, 25 V

R_1 200 Ω
R_2 25 Ω, 10 W

D_1 1N4937
D_2 MBR 1545
D_3 MUR1520

Q_1 MTP 20N18

T1 Core: ETD 34-3C85
    Spacers 12.5 mils
    L_p = 37 µH
N_p 14 turns #22 in parallel
    2 parallel #22 on layer 1
    2 parallel #22 on layer 6
NS1 3 turns, 5 mil copper foil, width 0.75"
    (on layers 2, 3, 4)
NS2 9 turns of 3 parallel #24 on layer 5

put was driven by a 50 kHz, manually adjustable width, pulse generator (using a 3525A PWM chip).

The pulse width at any input voltage or output load condition was manually set to the value which put the master output exactly at 5.00 V. The voltage of the slave was read and recorded at whatever value it then turned out to be.

The slave turns were chosen to yield 15 V when the master was 5.00 V. As will be noted, the slave output voltage is not entirely determined by the master/slave turns ratio. Due to secondary leakage inductances and interaction between master and slave windings, the slave output voltage is also dependent on the master DC output current.

14.4.2   Drain current/drain to source waveshapes at 90 percent of full load for minimum, nominal, and maximum input voltages

These are shown in Fig. 14.19. They show the characteristic linear ramp of primary current ($di_p/dt = V_{primary}/L_{primary}$) during the transistor on time. At the instant of turnoff, they show the leakage inductance voltage spike at the rising drain. The amplitude of this spike is controlled by the *RCD* snubber capacitor *C2*. That capacitor is chosen

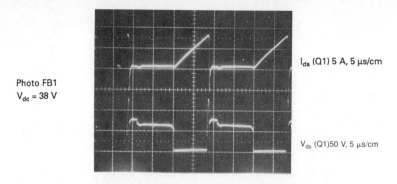

Photo FB1
$V_{dc} = 38$ V

I_{ds} (Q1) 5 A, 5 μs/cm

V_{ds} (Q1)50 V, 5 μs/cm

V_{dc}, V	I_{dc}, A	P_{in}, W	V_5, V	I_5, A	P_5, W	V_{15}, V	I_{15}, A	P_{15}, W	$P_{o\ (total)}$, W	Efficiency, %
38.0	1.67	63	5.002	6.58	32.9	25.3	0.504	12.8	45.7	72.1

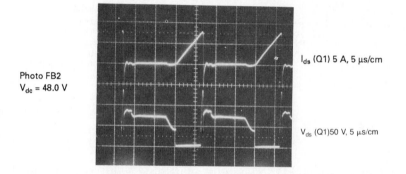

Photo FB2
$V_{dc} = 48.0$ V

I_{ds} (Q1) 5 A, 5 μs/cm

V_{ds} (Q1)50 V, 5 μs/cm

V_{dc}, V	I_{dc}, A	P_{in}, W	V_5, V	I_5, A	P_5, W	V_{15}, V	I_{15}, A	P_{15}, W	$P_{o\ (total)}$, W	Efficiency, %
48.0	1.31	62.6	5.001	6.57	32.9	25.42	0.505	12.8	45.7	72.0

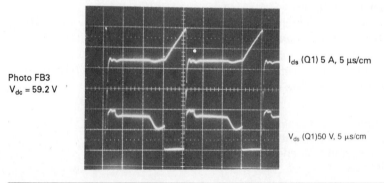

Photo FB3
$V_{dc} = 59.2$ V

I_{ds} (Q1) 5 A, 5 μs/cm

V_{ds} (Q1)50 V, 5 μs/cm

V_{dc}, V	I_{dc}, A	P_{in}, W	V_5, V	I_5, A	P_5, W	V_{15}, V	I_{15}, A	P_{15}, W	$P_{o\ (total)}$, W	Efficiency, %
59.2	1.07	63.1	5.003	6.58	32.9	25.36	0.504	12.8	45.7	72.4

Figure 14.19 Significant waveforms in 50-kHz flyback supply of Fig. 14.18.

large enough to limit the spike to a safe amplitude without causing too much dissipation ($= 0.5C2(V_{peak})^2/T$) in snubber resistor $R1$.

The waveforms show that as V_{dc} increases the pulse width required to maintain a constant master output voltage decreases. This of course is what the feedback loop will do when connected in. It is also seen that the peak-ramp current is constant for all input voltages at constant output power.

It is also seen that after the leakage spike, the drain falls (except for the small pedestal for a short time after the spike) to a level of $V_{dc} + (N_p/N_{s1})$ $(V_5 + V_{D2})$. It remains at that level until the reset volt-second product equals the set volt-second product $[V_{dc}t_{on} = (N_p/N_s)]$ $(V_5 + V_{D2})$ and then falls back to V_{dc}.

Figure 14.20 shows the same waveforms at the three input voltages for a lower total output power (17 W). All on time pulse widths are narrower, and consequently all peak primary currents ($= di = V_{primary}t_{on}/L_p$) are lower. This of course is because less power $[0.5L_p(I_p)^2/T]$ is required from the input bus, and because the peak primary current at the end of the on time is less—so is the leakage inductance spike.

14.4.3 Voltage and currents at output rectifier inputs

These are shown to track down the reason why slave output voltages are not entirely dependent on the master/slave turns ratios, and why they are dependent on the master output current.

When the transistor turns off, all the energy stored in the primary $(0.5L_pI_p)^2$ is delivered to the secondaries (except for some stored in the leakage inductance which is diverted to the snubber capacitor $C2$). That energy is delivered to the master and slave outputs in the form of currents shown in Fig. 14.21. But it can be seen that the currents to the master and slave outputs via their rectifiers are not of equal duration and certainly not of similar waveshapes.

Note that when DC output current of the master is increased from 2.08 A (photo FB8) to 6.58 A (photo FB10), the small voltage pedestal on the slave output rectifier moves up from about 20 to 28 V (photo FB7 and FB9). This occurs because of secondary leakage inductance and mutual coupling between master and slave secondaries, and with the larger voltage at the pedestal at the slave rectifier anode (compare photos FB7 and FB9), the slave DC output voltage is increased.

14.4.4 Snubber capacitor current at transistor turnoff

Figure 14.22 shows that at the instant of transistor turnoff, all the transformer primary current (5 A from photo FB5) is immediately

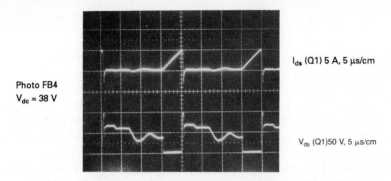

Photo FB4
V_{dc} = 38 V

I_{ds} (Q1) 5 A, 5 µs/cm

V_{ds} (Q1)50 V, 5 µs/cm

V_{dc}, V	I_{dc}, A	P_{in}, W	V_5, V	I_5, A	P_5, W	V_{15}, V	I_{15}, A	P_{15}, W	$P_{o\ (total)}$, W	Efficiency, %
38.0	0.595	22.6	5.003	2.08	10.4	19.1	0.380	7.27	17.7	78.3

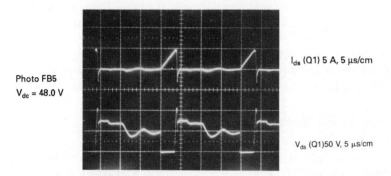

Photo FB5
V_{dc} = 48.0 V

I_{ds} (Q1) 5 A, 5 µs/cm

V_{ds} (Q1)50 V, 5 µs/cm

V_{dc}, V	I_{dc}, A	P_{in}, W	V_5, V	I_5, A	P_5, W	V_{15}, V	I_{15}, A	P_{15}, W	$P_{o\ (total)}$, W	Efficiency, %
48.0	0.481	23.1	5.004	2.09	10.4	19.2	0.381	7.29	17.7	76.6

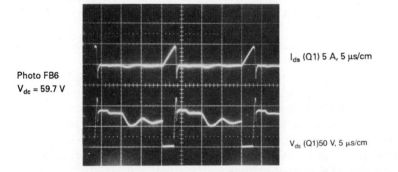

Photo FB6
V_{dc} = 59.7 V

I_{ds} (Q1) 5 A, 5 µs/cm

V_{ds} (Q1)50 V, 5 µs/cm

V_{dc}, V	I_{dc}, A	P_{in}, W	V_5, V	I_5, A	P_5, W	V_{15}, V	I_{15}, A	P_{15}, W	$P_{o\ (total)}$, W	Efficiency, %
59.7	9.397	23.7	5.004	2.08	10.4	19.15	0.381	7.29	17.7	74.7

Figure 14.20 Significant waveforms in 50-kHz flyback supply of Fig. 14.18.

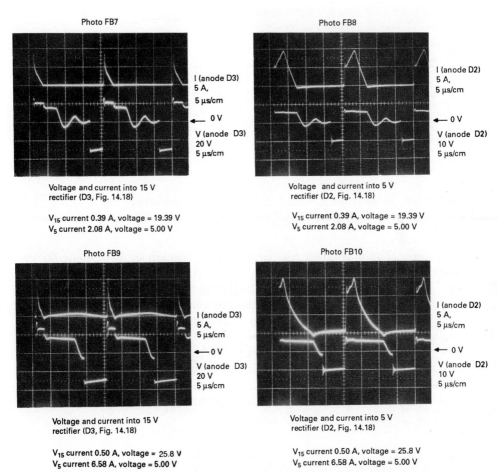

Photo FB7

I (anode D3)
5 A,
5 µs/cm

← 0 V

V (anode D3)
20 V
5 µs/cm

Voltage and current into 15 V
rectifier (D3, Fig. 14.18)

V_{15} current 0.39 A, voltage = 19.39 V
V_5 current 2.08 A, voltage = 5.00 V

Photo FB8

I (anode D2)
5 A,
5 µs/cm

← 0 V

V (anode D2)
10 V
5 µs/cm

Voltage and current into 5 V
rectifier (D2, Fig. 14.18)

V_{15} current 0.39 A, voltage = 19.39 V
V_5 current 2.08 A, voltage = 5.00 V

Photo FB9

I (anode D3)
5 A,
5 µs/cm

← 0 V

V (anode D3)
20 V
5 µs/cm

Voltage and current into 15 V
rectifier (D3, Fig. 14.18)

V_{15} current 0.50 A, voltage = 25.8 V
V_5 current 6.58 A, voltage = 5.00 V

Photo FB10

I (anode D2)
5 A,
5 µs/cm

← 0 V

V (anode D2)
10 V
5 µs/cm

Voltage and current into 5 V
rectifier (D2, Fig. 14.18)

V_{15} current 0.50 A, voltage = 25.8 V
V_5 current 6.58 A, voltage = 5.00 V

Figure 14.21 Showing why slave DC output voltage is not related to master DC output voltage by their respective turns ratio. Master secondary leakage inductance diverts some of its peak secondary current into the slave rectifier anode immediately after turn-off. As long as this diverted current persists, it couples a pedestal voltage into the slave rectifier anode. The slave output capacitor charges up to the pedestal peak which is higher than the induced secondary voltage and is dependent on the master load current. The remedy is to minimize secondary leakage inductances. The effect is minimized by an inductor in series in the slave secondaries.

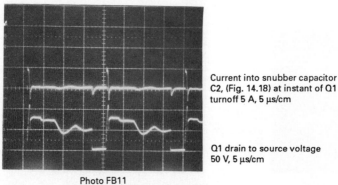

Current into snubber capacitor
C2, (Fig. 14.18) at instant of Q1
turnoff 5 A, 5 μs/cm

Q1 drain to source voltage
50 V, 5 μs/cm

Photo FB11

Figure 14.22 At the instant of turnoff, all the current which had been flowing in series in the transformer magnetizing and leakage inductances is immediately driven into the snubber capacitor of Fig. 14.18c.

transferred to the snubber capacitor $C2$ and through snubber diode $D1$ to ground. That current represents energy stored in the primary leakage inductance $[0.5L_{\text{leakage}}(I_p)^2]$. Until it is transferred to $C2$ as electrostatic energy $[0.5C2(V_p)^2]$, all the current or energy stored in the transformer magnetizing inductance cannot be delivered to the secondaries.

If $C2$ is made too small, the current reflected from the primary at the instant of turnoff may charge it to a dangerously high leakage inductance spike. Thus, $C2$ is selected large enough to limit the leakage spike to a safe value; yet, not so large as to result in excessive dissipation.

Symbols, Units, and Conversion Factors

Symbols Frequently Used in This Book

A_b Winding area of a core bobbin (usually given in square inches)

A_e Effective core area (usually given in square centimeters)

A_l Inductance of core (usually given in millihenries per 1000 turns

B_r Remanence flux density of a core material (flux density at zero oersteds)

B_s Saturation flux density of a core material

D_{cma} Current density in wire (usually expressed in circular mils per rms ampere)

l_m Effective path length of a magnetic core (usually quoted in centimeters)

Φ Flux in a magnetic core (in CGS/EMU units, it is usually given in maxwells and is equal to flux density in gauss × core area in square centimeters)

TABLE A.1   Conversion Table for Frequently Used Magnetic Units

			To convert from	
Quantity	CGS/EMU units	MKS units	CGS/EMU to MKS multiply by	MKS to CGS/EMU multiply by
Flux	maxwell	weber	1×10^{-8}	$1 \times 10^{+8}$
Flux density	gauss	tesla	1×10^{-4}	$1 \times 10^{+4}$
Flux density	gauss	millitesla	1×10^{-1}	$1 \times 10^{+1}$
Flux density	gauss	weber/meter^2	1×10^{-4}	$1 \times 10^{+4}$
Magnetic field intensity	oersted	amprere turns/meter	79.5	1.26×10^{-2}

TABLE A.2   Other Conversion Factors Used in This book

			To convert from	
Quantity	A	B	A to B multiply by	B to A multiply by
Current density	Circular mils	Square inches	7.85×10^{-7}	$1.27 \times 10^{+6}$
Current density	Circular mils	Square centimeters	5.07×10^{-6}	$1.98 \times 10^{+5}$

Bibliography

Bedford, B., and R. Hoft, *Principles of Inverter Circuits*, Wiley, New York, 1964.

Billings, K., *Switchmode Power Supply Handbook*, McGraw-Hill, New York, 1989.

Chryssis, G., *High Frequency Switching Power Supplies—Theory and Design*, 2d ed., McGraw-Hill, New York, 1989.

McLyman, C., *Transformer and Inductor Design Handbook*, Marcel Dekker, New York, 1978.

Middlebrook, D., and S. Cuk, *Advances in Switchmode Power Conversion*, 3 vols., Tesla, Pasadena, Ca., 1981.

Pressman, A., *Switching and Linear Power Supply, Power Converter Design*, Switchtronix Press, Waban, Mass., 1977.

Severns, R., and G. Bloom, *Modern DC-to-DC Switchmode Power Converter Circuits*, Van Nostrand, New York, 1984.

Sum, K., *Switch Mode Power Conversion—Basic Theory and Design*, Marcel Dekker, 1988.

Wood, P., *Switching Power Converters*, Van Nostrand, 1981.

Unitrode Power Supply Design Seminar Handbook, Unitrode Corp., Watertown, Mass., 1988.

Index

ABOUT THE AUTHOR

ABRAHAM I. PRESSMAN is founder and president of
Switchtronix Power, Inc., a company specializing in power
supply design, design review, and consultation. He is well
known as the author of the best-selling book, *Switching
and Linear Power Supply Design, Power Converter Design*
(1978). Mr. Pressman teaches a course on switching power
supply design that has been attended by groups from major
international electronics, communications, and computer
corporations.